PARASITOLOGY

The Biology of Animal Parasites

By

Elmer R. Noble, Ph.D.

*Professor of Zoology, University of California,
Santa Barbara, California*

AND

Glenn A. Noble, Ph.D.

*Head, Biological Sciences Department, California State Polytechnic College,
San Luis Obispo, California*

Second Edition

381 Illustrations and 3 Color Plates

Lea & Febiger

PHILADELPHIA   1964

Library of Congress Catalog Card Number 64:14480
Printed in the United States of America

Preface

THIS second edition constitutes a thorough revision, and, like the first, it "attempts to summarize the biology of animal parasites, but it makes no effort to duplicate the contents of a textbook in clinical parasitology." As before, it "is written primarily for the advanced undergraduate student who has completed at least one year of introductory zoology or biology, and at least one course in elementary chemistry at the collegiate level."

The statements that every species of animal is either a host or a parasite, and that there are many more species and numbers of animal parasites than there are free-living animals, emphasize the relative biomass of parasites as compared with the rest of living things, and the significant position that the study of parasite-host relationships holds in biology. We have continued, therefore, to select examples of parasites and hosts from among all phyla of the animal kingdom, and we have retained our emphasis on the ecology and evolution of parasitism. We offer parasitology as a discipline touching upon all major fields of biology.

In the present edition we have brought the information up to date, expanded the section on Acanthocephala into a separate chapter, eliminated some illustrations and improved others, divided some of the larger chapters into several smaller ones, expanded the introductions and bibliographies for most of the taxonomic chapters, adopted some improved schemes of classification, and expanded the discussion of some of the more commonly known parasites of man— such as the trypanosomes, *Toxoplasma*, schistosomes and *Paragonimus*.

The chapter on Physiology and Biochemistry has been eliminated, and its contents distributed among the descriptive and taxonomic sections. This change was made because, unlike a subject such as "host specificity" which can well be considered separately and from a broad "principle" point of view, the physiology and biochemistry of a parasite or group of parasites is best understood when included with descriptions of behavior, morphology and life histories.

Once again acknowledgement is gratefully extended to all those whose labors and advice have been of material aid and encouragement.

Santa Barbara, California   ELMER R. NOBLE
San Luis Obispo, California   GLENN A. NOBLE

Contents

CHAPTER   PAGE

I.   The Scope of Parasitology 7

II.   Life Cycles 23

III.   Phylum Protozoa, Introduction, Subphylum Mastigophora 32

IV.   Phylum Protozoa, Subphylum Sarcodina 77

V.   Phylum Protozoa, The Sporozoa 97

VI.   Phylum Protozoa, Subphylum Ciliophora . . . 143

VII.   Phylum Platyhelminthes, Introduction, Classes: Turbellaria, Trematoda, Subclasses: Monogenea, Aspidobothria 159

VIII.   Phylum Platyhelminthes, Class Trematoda Subclass Digenea: Introduction 172

IX.   Phylum Platyhelminthes, Class Trematoda Subclass Digenea, Representative Families 195

X.   Phylum Platyhelminthes, Class Cestoidea, Introduction, Subclass Cestodaria 242

XI.   Phylum Platyhelminthes, Subclass Cestoda . . . 259

XII.   Phylum Acanthocephala 288

XIII.   Phylum Nematoda, Introduction, Class Secernentea (= Phasmidia), Orders: Rhabditida, Strongylida . 299

XIV.   Phylum Nematoda, Orders: Ascaridida, Spirurida, Camallanida 335

XV.   Phylum Nematoda, Class Adenophorea (= Aphasmidia) Orders: Dorylaimida, Dioctophymatida . 366

XVI.   Phylum Arthropoda, Introduction, The Crustacea . 384

XVII.   Phylum Arthropoda, Class Insecta I. 419

XVIII.   Phylum Arthropoda, Class Insecta II. Order Diptera 469

XIX.   Phylum Arthropoda, Class Arachnoidea (= Arachnida) 494

6 Contents

CHAPTER   PAGE

XX. Miscellaneous Phyla 521

XXI. Effects of Parasitism on the Host. 530

XXII. Effects of Parasitism on the Parasite 548

XXIII. Ecology of Parasitism. I. General. 566

XXIV. Ecology of Parasitism. II. Distribution and
        Zoogeography 601

XXV. Ecology of Parasitism. III. Parasite-Host Specificity 618

XXVI. The Evolution of Parasitism 648

CHAPTER I

The Scope of Parasitology

ON DEFINITIONS

"He shall be as a god to me, who can rightly divide and define," (Emerson)
"I hate definitions." (Disraeli)

MEN of science frequently become so entangled in various shades of opinion about precise definitions that they lose sight of the facts on which definitions are based. Facts are truth; definitions may vary forever. For every definition of a "parasite" there are many organisms that may or may not fit, depending on interpretation. One of the most common definitions is, "A parasite is an animal or plant that lives at the expense of its host." This statement usually means that the parasite injures the host in some manner. But what do we mean by "injure"? Is the "true" parasite supposed to make its host ill, to retard its growth and development? How can we be sure that a host is *not* "ill"? Perhaps "injure" means something even more vague—like disturbing the normal metabolic balance of the host. Such a meaning is not satisfactory, but it does suggest a direction of investigation that may lead to a solution of our problem.

The original meaning of the word "parasite" was "situated beside," and it referred to being near food, but it had no reference to pathogenicity. We are coming around to the conviction that a parasite is an organism that depends upon its host for the synthesis of one or more nutrients essential for its own metabolism. The synthesis of nutrients requires enzymes. A parasite, then, since it has evolved originally from a free-living ancestor, has lost one or more of its original enzymes, and it is therefore forced to live on or within another organism that possesses these enzymes. In other words, a parasite requires some vital factor which it can obtain only from its host. But this view of a parasite is only half of the picture. All good definitions of parasitism have recognized the mutual relationship between host and parasite. "A parasite lives at the expense of its host, but both are *changed* because of the relationship." When a parasite does physical damage to its host the latter is obviously changed, but let us reflect upon the length of time required for parasites to become changed or evolved. Any genus of plant or animal that has had to live with a "foreign body" (*i.e.* parasite) for millions of years must have had to "adjust" to it, just as changes in

(7)

responses to other environmental factors have taken place. When these adjustments have involved chemical (physiological) alterations at the genetic level, the alterations have become part of the host's normal inherited metabolism.

If the host has changed chemically in response to its parasites, what happens if all the parasites are removed? The result would depend on the extent and nature of the original change, but if the change has been of such a nature that it benefits the host, then the removal of the parasites would remove the benefit, or, in other words, would "harm" the host. We have evidence (see p. 589) that certain intestinal parasites not only depend upon the host for essential nutrients (*e.g.* vitamins), but in turn supply nutrients to the host. If the nutrients supplied by the parasite are essential for the life of the host, and if we accept the definition of "parasite" given above, then true parasitism occurs when host and parasite cannot live without each other.

If true parasitism occurs only when two organisms cannot survive without each other, and if parasitism is dependent upon an exchange of the products of synthesis, then in true parasitism each member of the associating pair is "parasitic" on the other member. It seems absurd to say that man is a parasite of a worm in his intestine, but we must admit that he is if we accept the definitions proposed above (assuming that the worm synthesizes something that man needs and cannot himself synthesize). By the same reasoning we must also acknowledge that man is a parasite on some of his intestinal bacteria. A consideration of the relative sizes of a parasite and its host helps us to solve this problem. But how far should we go with this kind of manipulation of words? A guiding principle should be that of common sense in the use of terms that are commonly understood and universally employed.

The term *symbiosis* was proposed in 1879 by de Bary to mean the "living together" of two species of organisms. This term came to be used in a more restricted sense to connote mutual benefit. Indeed, de Bary used a lichen as the clearest example of symbiosis. O. Hertwig defined symbiosis as "the common life, permanent in character, of organisms that are specifically distinct and have complementary needs." Even a cursory examination of symbiots and their hosts, however, reveals a wide variation in degree in intimacy and shows that one member of the associating pair frequently is "parasitic" on the other. The kind of symbiosis involving mutual benefit, as exemplified by the termite and its gut flagellates, is now commonly called "mutualism."

Now let us go back for a moment to the word *parasitism*. We have seen that its precise meaning is not clear, but we suggested that true parasitism occurs when host and parasite cannot live without each other. But is this definition not symbiosis? It most certainly is. Parasites, then, are symbiots, but we may also consider as parasites those symbiots that take nourishment from the host (*i.e.* live at the expense of the host) whether or not they also provide something that the host needs.

A textbook on parasitology is never restricted to a study of pathogenic parasites. Perhaps most of the organisms studied are not strictly parasites in the usually accepted sense. A "parasitologist" is frequently not concerned with pathogenic parasites at all. Should we not then go back to the original term *symbiosis* to include *all* of our categories of associations, and entitle our text "Animal Symbiosis," and call ourselves "symbiontologists"? Such an attempt to change names would be contrary to our guiding principle of common sense. Everybody knows what "parasitology" means even if we cannot discern its boundaries. While discussing an approach toward a course in the principles of parasitism, Huff *et al.*[11] concluded that "although there is a clear trend to a biology of symbiosis, which would include parasitism, so that the basic course in the subject may eventually be one in symbiosis, present practice seems to call for a course in parasitism. For the present it seems useful to follow this practice, while continually bringing the wider range of relations into the picture."

So we retain the words *parasitology* and *parasite*, and if our concept of *parasitism* cannot easily be distinguished from *symbiosis* we feel even more justified in retaining "parasitism" as a convenient category in which to include all the types of associations normally studied in a course in "parasitology." Let us, therefore, concentrate on the *facts* of associations between organisms of two species, and remember that definitions are only man-made devices designed to help us solve the problems of identifications.

Consistent with the foregoing discussion, we feel that the assignment of a given species to the dignified category of parasite must in many cases be arbitrary. If we were to be fussy we would not include as parasites such animals as mosquitoes, leeches, ticks or lice. We would mention them if they were vectors of parasites, but not treat them in any detail. They are, in a very real sense, small predators on larger prey. However, we shall devote some space to the anatomy, physiology and life histories of some of these animals because they are important in the consideration of parasitic diseases, or because they are commonly studied by parasitologists for their intrinsic interests.

KINDS OF HOSTS IN RELATION TO THE PARASITE CYCLE

The relationship of the parasite life cycle to the host varies considerably and has given rise to the naming of different kinds of hosts. Among these names are *final* (= *definitive*), *intermediate*, *transport*, *paratenic*, *obligatory*, *intermittent*, *reservoir*, *temporary*, and *alternate*. Most of these terms are self explanatory, but the first four require more explanation. The usual definition of "definitive host" is one in which the parasite reaches sexual maturity; the "intermediate host" is the one in which the parasite undergoes larval or juvenile development. Chandler and Read[6] point out that these two terms used in the traditional manner lead to some peculiar inconsistencies among the protozoa. The malarial parasite, *Plasmodium*, for example, reaches sexual maturity in the mosquito, hence the latter is the definitive host and man is the intermediate host. But apparently man is the definitive host for trypanosomes, and the tsetse fly is the intermediate host. Moreover, *Leishmania* has no sexual phase and it therefore confronts us with perplexing problems of identifying the definitive host. The problem is solved by ignoring the location of the sexual phase, if any, and calling the vertebrate host "definitive" and invertebrate arthropod host "intermediate." Normally when two hosts are involved, the intermediate host (usually an invertebrate) is called the *vector*. The transport host merely carries the non-developing parasite to the next host. A potential intermediate host is a "paratenic host."

EXAMPLES OF PARTNERSHIPS

Having presented certain concepts of parasitism, and having become entangled in the meanings of words, we shall attempt a measure of untangling because students are aided by the ability to systematize the parasites which they study. Before proceeding to examples of the various partnerships described above, mention should be made of a much broader relationship of organisms living together, called SYNOECY, involving complicated organic populations. The botanist may call these associations *Formations of Plants*. Such a naturally linked assemblage of species (plants and animals), with a close community of interests, is called a BIOCENOSE (= biocoenose or biocenosis). Various tidepool associations, a coral reef, a community of social insects, comprise communities of this kind, entailing a certain persistent stability among all the organisms living together. A detailed consideration of synoecy, however, is beyond the scope of this book, and can be found in any text on general ecology. See Audy[1] for a consideration of biocenose in relation to disease.

THE THREE CHIEF KINDS OF SYMBIOSIS

1. Commensalism

Commensalism occurs when two species associate in a manner which benefits one but not the other. The relationship, therefore, is not equal, being active on the part of the commensal (usually the smaller of the two) and passive on the part of the host. Van Beneden[24] defined a commensal organism as a messmate that "requires from his neighbor a simple place on board his vessel, and does not partake of his provisions. The messmate does not live at the expense of his host; all he desires is a home or his friend's superfluities." Specialization of the commensal relation began with behavior, as shown by beetles living in birds' nests; and structural modifications probably began with organs of attachment as illustrated by leech-like oligochaetes on gills of crayfishes.

The basis for a commensalistic relationship between two organisms may be space, substrate, shelter, transportation or food. A commensal may be unattached to its host, living in close and direct association with it, as does the fish, *Nomeus gronovii*, which lives among the tentacles of the genus *Physalia* (the coelenterate Portugese-Man-of-War); it may be attached to the body of the host and remain sessile upon it, as does the anemone, *Calliatis parasitica*, which is glued to the shells inhabited by pagurid crabs; or it may live within the body of the host, in the respiratory tract or alimentary canal, as does the fish, *Fierasfer*, which lives within a sea cucumber.

Among unattached commensals the fish, *Amphiprion* (= *Trachichthys*), has attracted especial attention. It swims freely among the tentacles of an anemone (*e.g. Crambactis arabica* in the Red Sea), whereas all other small fish are immediately paralyzed when they come in contact with nematocysts of the anemone. This relationship is not completely one sided because the tentacles do not respond to the *Amphiprion*. Probably some as yet unknown chemical factor elaborated by the fish inhibits the normal response of the anemone. Some commensals exhibit a transitory attachment to their host, as exemplified by the Remora fish (*e.g. Echeneis remora*) which may attach itself by means of a dorsal "adhesive pad" to the skin of a shark. The Remora gets a free ride to the feeding grounds of its host, then detaches itself and darts among the pieces of mangled prey of the shark, and feeds. The shark appears to be unconcerned about the presence of the commensal, and it conveniently catches and serves regular meals to its guest.

External commensals may be called EPIZOOITES, and the relationships to their hosts range from very casual to one verging on pathogenic parasitism. Infusorian protozoa frequently live on the bodies of marine and freshwater animals. *Trichodina* and *Urceolaria* "graze" over the gills of fishes, sometimes damaging their hosts. The Chonotrichida, a cosmopolitian order of ciliates, are attached by stalks to the external surfaces of malacostracan crustaceans, and the associations of chonotrich genera with particular host groups are rigidly restricted. These ciliates always attach themselves to appendages along currents which sweep food particles from the host mouth. Vorticellid ciliates are permanently attached to many kinds of plants and animals, and they utilize currents of water produced by the host (*e.g.* water fleas), and they feed on food particles brought to them. These sedentary epizooites often are highly specific to their hosts, and they become so specialized that host movement is indispensible for their metabolism. If pieces of cuticle with attached vorticellids are moved about in water the ciliates live, but if they are kept motionless the ciliates die. Hydroids become attached to the skin of fish or to the snail shells occupied by hermit crabs, or to the exoskeletons of other arthropods. Barnacles and *Cyamus* (the amphipod whale louse) live permanently on the skin of whales. Coelenterates which are attached to crabs often completely cover their hosts, producing an effective camouflage.

Such associations wherein the relationship between the host and the commensal is limited to the passive transportation of the commensal by the host is termed PHORESY or PHORESIS, from the Greek work meaning "being borne." Phoresy may be permanent as in the case of whale barnacles on whales or vorticellids on crabs, or it may be transitory. A commensalistic association is not phoresy when two species are part of an association in which neither one profits by the presence of the other and each one is capable of living by itself.

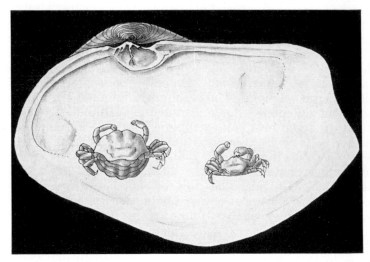

Fig. I–1.—Commensal male (small) and female pea crab, *Pinnixa faba* in shell of gaper clam, *Schizothaerus nuttalii.* × ½. (Original.)

INQUILINISM occurs when one species lives within another but without feeding entirely at its expense. The commensal has a peculiar spatial significance without any physiological relationship involved, but it finds shelter and it diverts for its own use a part of the food collected by its host. The word "inquilinism" comes from the Latin *incolinus* meaning "who lives within." Examples of this kind of association merge almost imperceptibly into examples of pathogenic parasitism. For instance, copepods in ascidians may live in the branchial chambers feeding on food brought in by the respiratory currents of the host; but related copepods may enter the stomach or epicardial tubes and, through a modified buccal apparatus, suck up the liquid food provided by the host.

The fish *Fierasfer* (Family Ammodytidae) lives within sea cucumbers, starfishes and bivalves either in the respiratory tree or in the body cavity. It enters the cloaca of the holothurian, and there it gains shelter, not without some resistance from the host. The commensal apparently feeds on crustacea, not on its host. If the fish takes nothing from its host the relationship is called ENDOPHORE-SIS. If however, the fish feeds partly at the expense of its host the relationship is inquilinism. The *Fierasfer*-holothurian association has been designated by different authors as representing both of these kinds of associations. Crabs which live in the mantle cavities of clams also illustrate this kind of relationship (Fig. I–1).

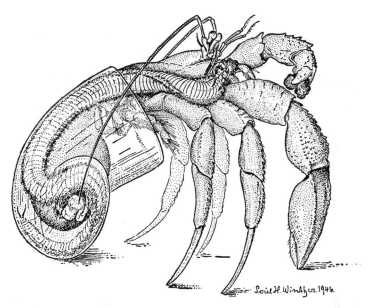

Fig. I–2.—Hermit crab in an artificial glass shell with its commensal *Nereilepas fucata* coming out to take part in a meal of sea urchin ovary. (Caullery, *Parasitism and Symbiosis*, 1952, courtesy, Sidgwick & Jackson, London.)

Another kind of association involves the housing of the commensal, but not within the body of the host. An example is the nereid worm, *Nereilepas fucata*, which resides in the terminal whorls of the shell occupied by the hermit crab, *Eupagurus bernhardus*. The worm crawls out and reaches between the crab mouth parts and seizes pieces of food. The crab tolerates the worm and never attempts to eat it (Fig. I–2). Commensal arthropods frequently share the subterranian dwelling of ants. Among such commensals are mites, dipterous larvae, isopods, spiders, springtails, bugs, crickets, and beetles. But other insects are attacked by ants, whereas still others are sought by ants to be used for the benefit of the ant. An example of the latter kind of association is the well-known use of aphids for the production of "honey dew." This relationship has been called SYMPHILISM. The aphid is called a *symphile*. Some symphiles becomes slaves of the ants, but the partnership is greatly varied in its characteristics and is not usually considered as commensalism.

We have found some protozoan invaders of the gallbladders of California fishes. The invaders appear not to damage their hosts. Are they commensal? A few years ago some fingerling trout were sent to us from the Crystal Lake Hatchery at Mount Shasta, California. The trout had died from the effects of a severe infection of a species of a myxosporidian parasite closely related to those infecting the gallbladders of tide pool fishes. The trout invaders were truly parasitic, if by "true" parasite we mean only those organisms which cause illness or injury to their hosts. But where does true parasitism begin?

"Intermittent parasitism" or, more correctly, "intermittent predatism" deserves mention here before we proceed to "true" parasitism. Nudibranchs and pycnogonids graze on hydroids. Bloodsucking insects take a little of the tissue of the host at regular intervals. Fleas, bugs and leeches likewise intermittently feed at the expense of their hosts. Thus there appears to be a gradual shift to true parasitism as defined below. As has been suggested before, the distinction between a micropredator and a parasite is often impossible to ascertain. There is little or no evidence, moreover, that endophoresis or inquilinism leads ultimately to true parasitism. The student should note that in all of the above kinds of commensalism complex reflexes and physiological behavior are deeply implicated, and for the most part, are not yet well understood. To increase our understanding of these associations studies must be made upon living animals, if possible in their natural habitats.

2. Parasitism

We have already declared our intention of using the word "parasite" for any animal that lives on or in another, larger animal or host. We have also used the words "true parasite" which we define as an organism (symbiote) which is dependent upon its host for one or more essential nutritional factors. In this latter relationship both parasite and host are changed because of the relationship. "Parasitism may therefore be defined as the condition of life which is normal and necessary for an organism nourishing itself at the expense of another, called the host, without destroying it as the predator does its prey. . . . Parasitism is no more than a unilateral deviation from commensalism."[5]

In contrast with a predator, a parasite lives continuously with a single host during at least a part of the parasite life cycle. The parasite obtains successive meals from its host. A predator, on the other hand, generally feeds on animals smaller than itself, usually consuming one or more for a single meal. Predators live apart from their prey and often seek prey in different places for different meals. Many pathogenic parasites (especially the Protozoa) can be cultured in test tubes indefinitely. Such parasites in tubes are not injuring their hosts—they have none; they are living as saprozoites. Cameron[4] has suggested that saprozoites are free-living parasites.

Mosquitoes, hookworms, sucking lice, argasid ticks in nests and other "parasites" are no more than "blood predators," but they have a parasitic relationship to their hosts because of their relatively small size, relatively large numbers and because of other characteristics of parasites. In such considerations the relation to the food organism is the important criterion for identification.

On the matter of confusion in definitions, one should hesitate to use the word "harmful" because immediate harm to an individual or species does not necessarily mean harm from the long-time survival or evolutionary standpoint. Competition can and does increase the rate of natural selection, resulting in favorable adaptations and survival, and "success" of a species.

Parasites usually have a greater reproductive power than do predators. This is another way of saying that parasites have a higher "biotic potential." One large female predator cat may eat many mice and give birth to thirty or forty kittens during its life span, but inside that cat are hundreds of individual parasites which reproduce *continuously* during the life of the cat. Parasites are usually more specialized in structure, life history, and metabolism than are their hosts. Parasitic insects are, in some respects, in an intermediate position between predators and parasites. They often have the host specificity and high biotic potential of parasites and the predator ability of consuming the entire prey. This intermediate kind of relationship, so commonly demonstrated by hymenopteran insects, is known as *parasitoidism*.

Although much study of the biochemistry of parasitism is underway, as yet there has not emerged a distinct "biochemistry of parasites" which sets these organisms distinctly apart from any other living group.

3. Mutualism

Mutualism occurs when two species live together in such a manner that their activities benefit each other. For details on the flagellate-termite and the ciliate-ungulate type of cooperation, see pages 584 to 590. Zoochlorellae (green algae) and zooxanthellae (yellow or brown algae) within cells of certain protozoa and invertebrates are also classic examples of mutualism. The algae find protection, easy access to carbonic acid and other compounds. In turn, they provide oxygen and carbohydrates for the animal cells. As an illustration, radiolaria containing green bodies no longer feed directly, but feed indirectly on the products of the synthesis performed by their symbiotic algae. Radiolaria deprived of their algae can live only with difficulty; thus a new kind of biological unit is constituted, dependent upon both plant and animal nutritional processes, a unit which has been called a PHYTOZOON. The normal functions of coral polyps are absolutely dependent upon their contained zooxanthellae.

parts. Nature consists of an interaction of such wholes which are constantly modified by changes in the environment. According to this concept a zoonoses is a small natural whole, or holoid, unit surrounding and influencing an infectious organism.[9]

Many zoonoses, such as balantidiasis, fascioliasis hepatica and tongue-worm infection, are found almost exclusively in animals and only very rarely in man. Others are common to both man and animals. African sleeping sickness, plague and clonorchiasis fall into the latter category. Well over 100 zoonoses are known, and they can be grouped on the basis of the causative organisms—viruses, rickettsiae, bacteria, fungi, protozoa, nematodes, trematodes, cestodes, and arthropods.

Most of the zoonoses have been known for a long time, but the separation of these particular infections from others is of recent origin. The field of veterinary public health is becoming increasingly important, and it is in this field that the study of the zoonoses especially belongs. The field overlaps the interests and obligations of physicians, and is one in which the M.D.'s and the D.V.M.'s should pool their abilities and activities for the well-being of both animals and man.

PHYSIOLOGY AND BIOCHEMISTRY

The basic biochemical processes of parasites are, of course, those common to all living things. More specialized processes of any one parasite are similar to those to be found in free-living members of the group to which it belongs. Still more specialized processes occur among parasites whose adjustment to their host is so exacting as to involve only particular cells of the host. Thus *Anaplasma marginale*, causing anaplasmosis in cattle, is restricted to the peripheral region of red blood cells. The importance of biochemical differences among parasites is indicated by the fact that anatomically similar parasites may be biologically different, so what is thought to be one species may be a complex of two or more species, thus causing considerable confusion when studies are made concerning host specificity and pathogenicity. One type of *Plasmodium berghei*, for example, causes greater enlargement of the host's spleen and liver than does another type of the same species. The delicate balance between the biochemistry of the host and that of the parasite is often clearly evident. Helminths in migrating birds may vary according to the stage of migration. Some worm species occur only where the birds are nesting, while others can be found only where the birds spend the winter.

Those biochemical events which are the result of a parasitic mode of life are of special interest to parasitologists. The production of histolytic substances, the specific effect of the sex hormones of a host on the sex ratio of its parasites, and specialized phenomena associated with unusual structures or behavior adaptations belong to this group. New techniques are constantly being developed to reveal more of the secrets of parasite physiology.

Physiological and biochemical aspects of the parasitic mode of life are discussed throughout the pages of this book, but the student is urged to consult the following general accounts: von Brand,[2a] Chemical Physiology of Endoparasitic Animals; Cole,[7] Some Physiological Aspects and Consequences of Parasitism; Fairbairn,[8] The Biochemistry of *Ascaris*; Hutner and Lwoff,[13] Biochemistry and Physiology of Protozoa, II; Lwoff,[14] Biochemistry and Physiology of Protozoa, I; Moulder,[15] The Biochemistry of Intracellular Parasitism; Read,[17] The Carbohydrate Metabolism of Worms; Read and Simmons,[17a] Biochemistry and Physiology of Tapeworms; Rogers,[18] The Nature of Parasitism; Stauber,[20] Host Influence on Parasite Physiology; Symposium on Resistance and Immunity to Parasitic Infections (Rice Institute).[22]

MORE DEFINITIONS

SUPERPARASITISM or MULTIPARASITISM occurs when two or more species of parasites inhabit one host. The copepod, *Calanus*, may be infected with a fungus, several species of dinoflagellates, a ciliate, a gregarine, a nematode, a trematode, a tapeworm and an isopod. The likelihood of all of these parasites being present at one time is remote, but several species are commonly to be found together in one host. The larva of the moth, *Plutella*, is parasitized by the ichneumonid fly, *Angitia*, and by larvae of the Braconid wasp, *Apanteles*.[23] An increase in *Apanteles* apparently can occur only if a relative decrease in *Angitia* occurs at the same time. Also, when other parasites in addition to the two just mentioned enter the moth larva and occur in more than their usual numbers, the numbers of *Apanteles* also increase more than usual. These phenomena are not well understood.

Superparasitism has recently been defined as infection with more parasites of one species than the host can bring to maturity. If this definition is accepted it differs from multiparasitism because the latter involves two or more species of parasites.

HYPERPARASITISM occurs when there are parasites of parasites. The oft-repeated ditty: big fleas have little fleas upon their backs to bite them, little fleas have lesser fleas and so on ad infinitum, is more humorous than true, but there are many examples of parasites dwelling on or within other parasites, and when we include bacteria we add another level, and if viruses infect the bacteria we have four levels in succession. Thus many birds are invaded by insect parasites which are infected by bacteria which, in turn, are infected by viruses. Ciliates (Ophryoscolecidae) in cattle are infected by fungus or fungus-like organisms as well as by bacteria-like bodies. The fungi belong to the chytrid group. The parasitic copepod, *Pennella filosa*, which lives on sailfish and on other hosts is occasionally found with clusters of barnacles (*Conchoderma virgatum*) on it, and sometimes the mass of barnacles is many times larger than that of the unfortunate copepod. Even tapeworms may have parasites. The microsporidian, *Nosema helminthorum*, infects the tapeworm, *Moniezia*.

SUPERINFECTION occurs when there is reinfection or reinvasion with a species of parasite which the host already harbors. This phenomenon is sometimes labeled "superparasitism" but the latter term should be restricted to the definition given above. Ordinarily for superinfection to occur the new arrival must be of a different strain or physiological race (see p. 653) from the original inhabitant. This condition for infection is related to the phenomenon called PREMUNITION which is a state of resistance to infection by a parasite after an acute infection by that same species of parasite has become chronic. Premunition normally lasts for as long as the infecting organism remains in the body of the host.

Before leaving the subject of definitions three other terms need to be defined. If the areas of distribution of two species overlap or coincide they are called SYMPATRIC SPECIES. Such species, although occurring together, exhibit a spatial separation caused by biological preference. Examples of sympatric species are the flagellate, *Giardia*, and the tapeworm, *Taenia*, both occupying the intestine of man; or two species of insects living on different parts of the same leaf. If the two species that live together are also closely related, they are called SIBLING SPECIES. *Entamoeba histolytica* and *E. coli* live together in the colon of man, and they are closely related, thus they are sibling species. They are also sympatric species; but non-related species, as indicated above, may also be sympatric. Species with distinct geographical ranges, *i.e.* ranges which do not overlap, are called ALLOPATRIC SPECIES.

AN ECOLOGICAL APPROACH TO THE STUDY OF PARASITOLOGY

The whole assemblage of parasites associated with a host population may be called the PARASITE-MIX. Such an assemblage is a minor biocenose, and it includes all the viruses, bacteria, protozoa, molds, rickettsiae, worms, and arthropods which live on or in a higher organism. The minor biocenose is a biological entity which is constantly changing as it reacts with the environment. A study of symbiosis (parasitology) is thus a study in ecology. Such an approach has been emphasized only in recent years (see Chapter XXIII, p. 566).

When we label morphological or physiological features as specific adaptations to parasitism we must bear in mind the universal need to adapt to the *environment*. Many characteristics which are described as hallmarks of the parasitic habit are also to be found among free-living species. The hallmark is sometimes present in only one or two species, or it may even disappear during a phase in the life cycle of an individual parasite. For example, cyst formation, so characteristic of parasitic protozoa, is common among free-living protozoa and metazoa. The complicated and significant alternation of sexual with an asexual generation during life cycles of sporozoa, trematodes and other parasites, is duplicated in foraminifera, hydroids and many other free-living species. The saprozoic form of nutrition can be illustrated abundantly in soil organisms as well as in parasites.

The above examples are presented to emphasize further the concept that there is nothing about parasitism *per se* that constitutes a special category of broad biological principles. An understanding of the basic principles of ecology, of evolution, of morphogenesis and of physiology is tantamount to an understanding of principles of parasitology. These principles for parasitology, however, should be reformulated and emphasized, and the "minor" principles pertaining more strictly to the state of parasitism must be enunciated.[11]

One of the reasons why we have not been able to describe with great precision the kinds of associations mentioned in this chapter is because we do not yet understand enough of the economics of the various relationships. Such understanding requires precise knowledge of the biochemistry involved—about which relatively little is known. But the precise distinctions among the kinds of associations are not really important. Importance rests upon an understanding of each partnership, and as our knowledge increases, and as details are analyzed, the assumed limits or boundaries of each category of symbiotic association tend to disappear.

BIBLIOGRAPHY

(Including general works not referred to in text.)

1. Audy, J. R., 1958. The Localization of Disease with Special Reference to the Zoonoses. Trans. Roy. Soc. Trop. Med. Hyg., *52*, 308–328.
2. Baer, J. G., 1951. *Ecology of Animal Parasites.* Univ. Illinois Press. 224 pp.
2a. Brand, T. von, 1952. *Chemical Physiology of Endoparasitic Animals.* Academic Press Inc. N.Y. 339 pp.
3. Burrows, R. B. and Swerdlow, M. A., 1956. *Enterobius vermicularis* as a Probable Vector of *Dientamoeba fragilis.* Am. J. Trop. Med. Hyg., *5*, 258–265.
4. Cameron, Thomas W. M., 1956. *Parasites and Parasitism.* John Wiley & Sons, Inc., New York. 322 pages.
5. Caullery, Maurice, 1952. *Parasitism and Symbiosis.* Sidgwick and Jackson Limited, London. 340 pages.
6. Chandler, A. C. and Read, C. P., 1961. *Introduction to Parasitology with Special Reference to the Parasites of Man.* 10th ed. John Wiley & Sons, New York, 822 pp.
7. Cole, W. H. (Editor), 1955. *Some Physiological Aspects and Consequences of Parasitism.* Rutgers Univ. Press. New Brunswick, New Jersey. 90 pp.
8. Fairbairn, D., 1957. The Biochemistry of *Ascaris.* Exp. Parasitol., *6*, 491–554.
9. Heisch, R. B., 1956. Zoonoses as a Study in Ecology. Brit. Med. J., *22*, 669–673.
10. Hoare, C. A., 1962. Reservoir Hosts and Natural Foci of Human Protozoal Infections. Acta Tropica, *19*, 281–317.
11. Huff, C. G., Nolf, L. O., Porter, R. J., Read, C. P., Richards, A. G., Riker, A. J. and Stauber, L. A., 1958. An Approach Toward a Course in the Principles of Parasitism. J. Parasitol., *44*, 28–45.
12. Hunter, G. W., Frye, W. W. and Swartzwelder, J. C., 1960. *A Manual of Tropical Medicine.* W. B. Saunders Co., Philadelphia, 892 pp.

13. HUTNER, S. H. and LWOFF, A., 1955. *Biochemistry and Physiology of Protozoa.* Vol. II. Academic Press, N.Y. 388 pp.
14. LWOFF, A., 1951. *Biochemistry and Physiology of Protozoa.* Vol. I. Academic Press, N.Y. 434 pp.
15. MOULDER, J. W., 1962. *The Biochemistry of Intracellular Parasitism.* The Univ. of Chicago Press. 172 pp.
16. PHILIP, C. B., HADLOW, W. J., and HUGHES, L. E., 1954. Studies on Salmon Poisoning Disease of Canines. I. The Rickettsial Relationships and Pathogenicity of *Neorickettsia helmintheca.* Exptl. Parasitol., *3*, 336–350.
17. READ, C. P., 1961. The Carbohydrate Metabolism of Worms. In Martin, A. W., *Comparative Physiology of Carbohydrate Metabolism in Heterothermic Animals.* Univ. Wash. Press, Seattle. pp. 3–34.
17a. READ, C. P. and SIMMONS, J. E., JR., 1963. Biochemistry and Physiology of Tapeworms. Physiol. Rev., *43*, 263–305.
18. ROGERS, W. P., 1962. *The Nature of Parasitism. The Relationship of Some Metazoan Parasites to Their Hosts.* Academic Press, N.Y. & London. 287 pp.
19. ROTHSCHILD, M. and CLAY, T., 1957. *Fleas, Flukes and Cucoos. A Study of Bird Parasites.* 2nd ed. Collins, London.
20, STAUBER, L. A. (Editor), 1960. *Host Influence on Parasite Physiology.* Rutgers Univ. Press. 96 pp.
21. STEFANSKI, W., 1959. The Role of Helminths in the Transmission of Bacteria and Viruses. Proc. XVth Internat. Cong. Zool., 697–699.
22. Symposium on Resistance and Immunity in Parasitic Infections, 1958. Rice Institute Pamphlet. XLV, April, 208 pp.
23. ULLYETT, G. C., 1943. Some Aspects of Parasitism in Field Populations of *Plutella maculipennis* Curt. J. Entomol. Soc. S. Africa, *6*, 65–80.
24. VAN BENEDEN, J. P., 1876. *Animal Parasites and Messmates.* Appleton-Century Co., New York.
25. YOELI, M., 1960. Animal Infections and Human Disease. Scientific American, May 1960, 161–170.

CHAPTER II

Life Cycles

INTRODUCTION

THE tremendous hazards encountered in reaching maturity are among the most impressive aspects of the life cycles of many parasites. Fantastic numbers of eggs and young usually must develop to ensure the continuous life of the species because enormous numbers of eggs and young die before reaching maturity. The earth is covered with billions of young parasites in their free-living stages. Some of them reach out from the soil, others cling patiently to grasses, while others wander in vast numbers in the sea, all waiting for the host without which they die and which is almost certain never to arrive.

If a young parasite happens to be the "one in a million" which finds the appropriate host, its troubles are not over. It must be able to attach itself to this host, sometimes only during the fleeting moment of passing by. Often a parasite must then be able to enter the body, within which it finds a new world filled with antagonism, so its troubles are still not over. It must also be able to grow, develop and eventually to reproduce. When the host is a vector, the parasite must leave it, only to encounter again the dangers of a free-living life, and to face once more the almost hopeless odds of finding another and different host. Once it is relatively safe within the final host it often must find a mate if the race is to continue.

Most adaptations of a modern parasite to the state of parasitism result in increasing the probability that the next host will be reached. Such adaptations (*e.g.* those leading to the adoption of an intermediate host) might be very different from those that are required for an organism to *become* a parasite. One important adaptation to parasitism is the formation of an infective stage (*e.g.* the eggs of the nematode, *Ascaris*) that is a "resting" stage in which normal processes of development are suspended until the proper host is reached. This "infective stage forms a 'bridge' which enables the parasite to go from one sort of environment to another."[8]

Much interest has arisen concerning the physiology of parasites and a large share of this interest centers on carbohydrate metabolism. Carbohydrate is apparently the most important energy source for parasitic worms. Tapeworms probably require this material in the host diet for normal reproduction and development. Some nematodes may require host carbohydrate. Some trematodes probably digest carbohydrates. As one might expect, phosphorylating glycolysis has been shown to be the major route for the formation of pyruvic acid among the worms, but there are other routes for the catabolism of carbohydrates and lipids and these routes may differ from genus to genus. Aerobic metabolism of carbohydrate also seems to be "standard" in that it follows the tricarboxylic acid cycle, the fixation of carbon dioxide and the cytochrome-cytochrome oxidase system.[5] Any consideration of the significance of life cycles must include a study of the biochemical relationships between parasite and host.

MAJOR TYPES OF LIFE CYCLES

The multitudinous varieties of life histories adopted by parasites can be grouped into a few main types.

1. The first type of life cycle may be complex but the parasitic phase is temporary and limited to the outer surface of the host. The life of a mosquito is a good example. Many other organisms also parasitize man and animals only while feeding or only accidentally. Biting flies, "kissing" bugs (*Triatoma*) and gnats belong to this group as do the larval forms of flukes (flatworms) which attempt to penetrate the wrong host. Organisms grouped into this first type of life cycle are more properly called *micropredators* than *parasites*.

2. In the second type of life cycle the parasite spends only a part of its time with the host, but more than a brief contact. It may be ectoparasitic or endoparasitic. Some ticks, for example, remain on their hosts most of the time, but drop off and lay eggs in the soil. Sometimes a different host is used for each stage in the life cycle. The life of the tick, *Dermacentor andersoni* (p. 503), which carries the causative agent (*Rickettsia*) of Rocky Mountain spotted fever, illustrates a three-host parasite of this type.

Internal parasites may also spend only part of their lives in their hosts. A hookworm egg, for example, hatches in the soil and the larva must develop into an infective stage before it can enter a host—in this case by burrowing through the skin (p. 323). The "threadworm," *Strongyloides stercoralis*, which causes strongyloidiasis in man, sometimes has a life cycle similar to that of the hookworm, but due to little-understood factors, it may live for several generations in the soil as a non-parasitic worm (p. 311).

3. A third type of life cycle includes the many parasites which spend all their lives in or on their hosts except for the period of transmission of the egg, cyst or other stage from one final host to another. The well-known roundworm, *Ascaris lumbricoides*, is not normally found outside of the egg apart from the body of the host. A certain amount of development occurs within the egg before it becomes infective but there is no free-living larval stage similar to that of the hookworm. Protozoan parasites likewise are active only while within the host, the cyst being comparable to the egg of higher organisms in that it is an infective stage.

4. A fourth type of life cycle is similar to 3 but it involves bio-

logical vectors.   The Chinese liver fluke, *Opisthorchis sinensis*, follows this type of cycle.   The adult worm lives in the human liver (also in the dog, cat, and other mammals) and produces eggs which leave the body (by way of the bile duct and intestine) and hatch into free-living larvae which enter snails.   After several changes in form the parasite leaves this intermediate host and enters a third host, a fish.   Man eats the fish and acquires the larval worm which matures in the liver, thus completing the cycle. (For a fuller description see p. 231).

5. A fifth type of life cycle occurs when the parasites need not leave the host even from one generation to the next.   An example is the mange mite, *Sarcoptes scabei* (p. 507).   Autoinfection also illustrates this type.

For a consideration of the life cycles in relation to seasonal changes, host food and other environmental influences, see Chapter XXIII on the general ecology of parasitism.

REPRODUCTION AND DEVELOPMENT

General Considerations

Some general aspects of the reproductive behavior of each major group of parasites are given at the beginnings of appropriate chapters to follow.   Caullery[1] has pointed out that the essential characteristics of reproduction in parasitic worms arise from the fact that the usual possibilities for the meeting of the sexes are restricted because the parasite is living within another animal, and from the fact that the parasite must meet the proper host at the right time.

A major feature which distinguishes cycles of worm parasites from protozoan and other unicellular parasites is the lack of reproductive multiplication of metazoan parasites within the host body. With the exception of such ectoparasites as mites and lice, the eggs or larvae produced within a host must leave that host before they can infect the same or another host.

Each step in the life of a parasite is beset with danger, and the more complicated the life cycle the greater the danger.   This danger is to the entire species, for if the hazards are too great for the completion of the life cycle, the species faces oblivion.   Compensations for the hazards have thus become a necessary part of the lives of parasitic worms.   These compensations include such devices as hermaphroditism, parthenogenesis, increase in numbers of sperm and eggs, and the development of structures for holding the male and female close together to ensure fertilization.

Hermaphroditism is the presence of functional testes and functional ovaries in one individual.   It is a widespread phenomenon among parasites, especially the flatworms.   Figure IX–30, p. 232, illustrates the hermaphroditic liver fluke, *Opisthorchis sinensis*, and Figure XI–13, p. 275 shows this condition (also called *monoecious*) in the tapeworm, *Taenia saginata*.   Self fertilization is a normal occurrence but apparently some worms will indulge in cross fertilization as well. Hermaphroditism favors the continuance of species since it makes of every individual an independent reproductive machine.

Parthenogenesis is the development of the egg without fertilization. Its value to the species is obvious when the chance of a female finding a mate is negligible. The process normally renders the male useless and in some species he passes quietly out of the picture. Curiously enough, however, some females operate parthenogenetically until a male happens to appear. They then carry on in the traditional manner. Occasional bisexual reproduction might save a race from extinction because without the new genetic combinations conferred by cross fertilization a species of parasite tends to become less variable and less able to meet changes in the environment. Parthenogenetic development has been described for some of the blood flukes and has been suggested for the larval stages of other flukes. It also occurs in some of the arthropod parasites. Parthenogenesis among larval flukes is called "**paedogenesis**," a term commonly applied to reproduction by young larvae of any animal.

Increase in numbers of sperm and eggs is an obvious answer to the diminishing chances of these gametes finding each other and the chances of the larval stages of reaching maturity. Many rather startling statistics can be given concerning the productivity of female worms. For example, the fish tapeworm, *Dibothriocephalus latus*, is able to produce up to one million eggs a day!

Gametogenesis

Spermatogenesis in parasitic worms is an open field for research. One of the few studies on this subject is that of Rees[6] on *Parorchis acanthus*, a trematode found in the intestine of the Herring Gull. Each spermatogonium divides three times to form eight primary spermatocytes. The sixteen secondary spermatocytes are formed by a reduction division. A final division produces the thirty-two spermatids which metamorphose into adult spermatozoa. These sperm are formed from extruded chromatic material and the cytoplasm is left behind. In other species of flatworms the cytoplasm is included in the spermatozoa.

Oogenesis in *Parorchis acanthus* is completed after entry of the sperm into the developing egg.[7] Sperm enter just after vitelline cells begin to become attached to the oocytes. In the ootype a shell is deposited and the egg continues to develop into the ootid stage, and it finally matures into the completed ovum. Here one can see both male and female pronuclei, polar bodies and yolk cells all within the developing shell. Each pronucleus contains eleven chromosomes.

Gametogenesis in the blood fluke, *Schistosomatium douthitti*, has been thoroughly worked out by Nez and Short.[3] This fluke normally lives in the veins of meadow mice, and the cercarial stage causes "swimmers itch" in man and apparently in dogs. Oogenesis, fertilization and cleavage in this fluke is, in general, similar to reports for other trematodes, but in this case they differ in that maturation and fertilization are completed after the eggs are deposited in host tissues. The primary spermatogonium divides three times by mitosis and gives rise to eight primary spermatocytes. Thirty-two spermatids arise by two maturation divisions; then by metamorphosis they change into thin bi-flagellated spermatozoa. In oogenesis the developing egg at first shows the appearance of short, thick chromosomes which then become diffuse in the nucleus. At this time the sperm enters the egg and soon afterwards the egg is deposited in host tissue. The sperm apparently just waits until the egg goes through the primary oocyte, secondary oocyte and ootid stages. While the polar bodies are being formed, however, the sperm nucleus gradually loses its filamentous appearance and becomes rounded. It is now the male pronucleus. When the female pronucleus is formed, the egg is mature and the two nuclei unite, thus creating a zygote, the first cell of a new generation.

Oogenesis and fertilization in the typeworm, *Mesocestoides corti*, from the raccoon was described by Ogren.[4] Entry of the sperm occurs before the egg undergoes the first meiotic division. As the egg travels along the uterus it continues to go through the usual stages of oogenesis. Two sperm may enter the egg, but probably only one takes part in fertilization. As in the trematode egg, polar bodies are formed, the male pronucleus enlarges, and when the female pronucleus is mature the two nuclei unite and fertilization is complete.

It can be seen by these examples that the basic processes of gametogenesis are the same in parasitic worms as they are in free-living animals. Lists of parasites with their known chromosome numbers may be found in a paper by Walton.[9]

Early Embryology

The fertilization process in parasites follows the same basic pattern and includes most of the same types of variations as have been described for their free-living relatives. Detailed studies of this important process have not been made with many parasites. For a discussion of fertilization and egg formation in flukes see page 178.

Roundworms, unlike flukes, are almost all dioecious. This separation of the sexes is of only secondary importance in a comparison of the two groups. In *Parascaris* sperm migrate, by ameboid movement, through the uterus to the tubular ovary where they enter primary oocytes. The distal or germinal end of the ovary continues to produce oocytes from oogonia, and the sperm are apparently able to live for a long time in the proximal end. Oogonia are attached to the *rachis*, a central stalk which lies in the ovary and extends from its germinal end almost to the oviduct. During the passage of the elongated oocytes through the ovary from their point of original attachment to the place where the sperm have gathered, the oocytes enlarge by accumulation of carbohydrates, lipoids, and probably of proteins.

After the sperm enters the egg, the latter becomes rounded and the primary layers of the egg shell develop, including a fertilization membrane. The primary oocyte divides to form the secondary oocytes; then the ootids appear by the division of the secondary oocytes. Ootids do not undergo division, but they develop into mature eggs. As the male pronucleus approaches the female pronucleus in the oocyte of *Parascaris*, a sperm protein, ascaridine, is involved in the production of ribonucleic acid which appears between the two pronuclei. Secondary layers of the egg shell develop and the two pronuclei unite with one another. Fertilization is thus completed. These processes occur as the developing egg passes through the uterus. Before the egg gets far, its shell is completed from uterine secretions. Finally, perivitelline fluid appears and the zygote is ready for cleavage.

The Egg Shell

Exhaustive studies of the egg shells of parasitic worms in general have not been made. Most work has been done on the egg shells of ascaroids, especially *Ascaris lumbricoides*. One cannot assume that all roundworm eggs are identical in structure with those of *Ascaris* but probably there is a general similarity.

Ascaris eggs are well-known for their surprising resistance to desiccation and to attack by chemicals. The main layers of the shell can be grouped into an outer, somewhat sticky, coat; a hard, middle layer; and an inner, vitelline membrane. The outer coat is rough and mammilated. It is composed of protein containing a mucopolysaccharide. The middle coat consists of alternating layers of chitin and protein. Chitin seems to be limited to a few groups of nematodes and the acanthocephala. The inner membrane is usually described as primarily lipoidal in nature. A number of amino acids however, have been found in this membrane which is chiefly responsible for the resistance of the egg shell to adverse environmental conditions. For a summary of studies on the structure and function of nematode egg shells see Rogers[8] p. 201–212. *Ascaris* eggs have remained viable after being immersed for various periods of time in such solutions as: 10 per cent formalin (for several weeks), 10 per cent potassium bichromate, 9 per cent sulfuric acid, 14 per cent hydrochloric acid, 2 to 5 per cent antiform, saturated solutions of copper sulfate, iron sulfate and copper acetate.

Some flatworm eggs are already embryonated when they leave the parent worm. An example is *Taenia*, to which genus belong common tapeworms of man and of animals. The embryo is called an *oncosphere*. The shell around the oncosphere possesses a thin outer capsule which is sometimes called the chorionic membrane. Beneath this capsule lie yolk granules under which lies the thick middle layer or shell proper. In this genus of worms the radial striations of the middle layer are characteristic. The middle layer is the remnant of the embryophore, a cluster of cells situated around the developing egg nucleus. Below the middle layer lies the basement membrane, and immediately surrounding the oncosphere is the inner two-layered oncospheral membrane. The yolk cells contain a phenol and protein. Formation of the capsule involves the quinone tanning of a protein.

Segmentation within the fluke egg produces two types of cells: ectoderm and propagatory. The ectoderm cells give rise to the body of the first embryo (miracidium) whereas the propagatory cells remain as germinative elements and, by polyembryony, give rise to the sporocyst, rediae, cercariae and metacercariae. The latter may even become sexually mature and produce viable eggs, a phenomenon known as *progenesis*. In the tapeworms, *Hymenolepis* and *Mesocestoides*, one of the first two cells (blastomeres) which develop goes to form an embryophore which surrounds the other blastomeres.

The embryonic development of the oncosphere of the tapeworm, *Mesocestoides corti*, has been well worked out by Ogren.[4] The zygote divides to form a two-cell embryo. Cleavage continues until a ball of cells, the *morula*, is formed. The morula is surrounded by a few large cells called macromeres. These cells develop a protective layer or membrane, called the embryophore, around the embryo. The inner cell mass, or early embryo, rapidly undergoes differentiation of cells. These cells soon form hooks, muscle fibers, parenchyma and germinative or plastin cells. The penetration gland cells typical of *Hymenolepis* and of other tapeworm larvae are absent.

Organogenesis in parasitic roundworms is not remarkably different from that of free-living worms. The chemistry of early development, however, is intimately related to parasitism, and thus may differ from that of other worms. Segmentation of *Ascaris* eggs is optimum at $31°$ C, and of *Parascaris* eggs at $37°$ C. Under optimum conditions of temperature and of oxygen availability the embryo of *Ascaris* becomes infective in about nineteen days. Development is obligatively aerobic. Unembryonated eggs will survive indefinitely at near freezing temperatures.

PERIODICITY

Periodicity of behavior is one of the intriguing mysteries in the life cycles of many parasites. Reproductive cycles are common in all animals, and have been known for a long time, but the regular appearance of large numbers of offspring never fails to excite the wonder of anyone who discovers it anew.

Regular fluctuations of numbers of amebic cysts to be found in the feces of infected animals or of man is an example of periodicity in parasitic protozoa. A ten-to-fourteen-day period occurs between maximum numbers of *Entamoeba coli* cysts in human hosts. *E. histolytica* also has its cycle of cyst formation, and laboratory technicians soon learn that a single examination for parasitic amebas may lead to inaccurate conclusions, since on one day a stool examination may disclose no amebic cysts whereas on the next day many cysts may appear.

The coccidian, *Isospora lacazii*, in the English house sparrow undergoes a diurnal periodicity in oocyst production. (See p. 110 for life cycles of coccidia). The numbers of oocysts eliminated by the birds reach a peak daily between 3 P.M. and 8 P.M. and they occur in much fewer numbers preceding and subsequent to these hours. Again one is at a loss to explain this type of occurrence. A logical assumption would be that it is associated with enhanced opportunity for the oocysts to be taken up by another host. Perhaps crowding together of birds in preparation for the night has a bearing on the problem.

Malarial organisms offer one of the best-known examples of cyclical behavior among protozoan parasites. The causative agent in benign tertian malaria is a typical example. *Plasmodium vivax* has a minimal prepatent period of eight days. What the parasite is doing in the body during these eight days immediately after the bite of a mosquito is discussed on page 117. A "clinical periodicity" of forty-eight hours follows this period. An event which occurs every forty-eight hours falls on every third calendar day; thus the name *tertiary malaria* is given to the disease caused by *P. vivax*. Every forty-eight hours many red blood cells of a man infected with this type of parasite rupture due to the completion of a parasite division process called *schizogony*. The rupture of millions of these cells, all approximately at the same time, with the liberation of their contents into the blood stream, produces the chills and fever characteristic of malaria. The same type of cycle occurs in bird plasmodia. *P. gallinaceum* in ducks has a cycle of thirty-six hours, and it often starts in such a manner that rupture of red blood cells occurs at noon and at midnight alternately.

Periodicity among the multicellular parasites is as common as that among the protozoa. Cercariae, representing one of the larval stages in the life cycle of flukes, probably emerge from snails at times related to the light of day. Under laboratory conditions some cercariae leave their snail hosts only during the early evening. The student should never assume that behavior in the laboratory is exactly similar to behavior under normal conditions in the native habitat of an organism, but periodic activity related to certain daylight hours is so widespread among parasites that one is probably safe in concluding that the laboratory behavior of these cercariae is a reflection of normal periodicity.

Microfilariae in man are involved in one of the most interesting of all examples of periodicity among parasites. *Wuchereria bancrofti* is a worm which causes "elephantiasis." Adult worms live in blood and lymphatic vessels deep in the body where females produce living young. These larval worms, or microfilariae, may remain in the deeper vessels or they may come to the body surface between the hours of 10 P.M. and 4 A.M. The fact that the worm is transmitted by the bite of a mosquito leads to the conclusion that there is some relation between this behavior of the young worms and the visits of mosquitoes while the host is sleeping. The conclusion is problematical. In some of the islands of the Pacific the worms come to peripheral blood vessels during the day instead of the night, but in these areas the mosquito vector is a day-biting instead of a night-biting variety! In other places (*e.g.* the Philippines) both types of behavior can be found. In areas where the nocturnal periodicity exists, a man may change his working hours from daytime to night-time and sleep during the day. If he is infected with *W. bancrofti*, the microfilariae respond to this change by remaining deep in the body at night and coming to the surface during the day.

No single factor has yet been proven to be the cause of larval periodicity. The following suggestions, however, have been made. (1) Periodicity is associated with and perhaps controlled by the metabolic processes accompanying periods of rest and of activity on the part of the host. (2) Simultaneous development of the larvae within most of the adult female worms leads to a periodic mass delivery of young worms, this batch of microfilariae being destroyed by the reticuloendothelial system of the host before a new batch arrives. (3) A totally unexplained adjustment of the migrations of the young worms to the feeding habits of the insect vector occurs. (4) Periodicity is caused by the location of the adult worms in the body. In man if they are in the lower part of the body, the young parasites find ascent through the thoracic duct easier when the host is reclining, usually at night, than when the host is upright. If the adult worms are in the head or neck, the young parasites more readily get into the general circulation during the day when the host is active. One should not overlook the possibility of some intrinsic factor which lies at the basis of the cyclic behavior of the parasite.

BIBLIOGRAPHY

(Including general works not referred to in the text)

1. CAULLERY, M., 1952. *Parasitism and Symbiosis.* London, Sidgewick and Jackson. 340 pp.
2. DOGIEL, V. A., PETRUSHEVSKI, G. K. and POLYANSKI, YU. I., 1958. *Parasitology of Fishes.* Leningrad Univ. Press. First English Ed., 1961. Oliver and Boyd, Great Britain. 384 pp.
3. NEZ, M. M., and SHORT, R. B., 1957. Gametogenesis in *Schistosomatium douthitti* (Cort) (Schistosomatidae: Trematoda). J. Parasitol., *43*, 167–182.
4. OGREN, R. E., 1956. Development and Morphology of the Onchosphere of *Mesocestoides corti*, a Tapeworm of Mammals. J. Parasitol., *42*, 414–424.
5. READ, C. P. in MARTIN, A. W., 1961. *Comparative Physiology of Carbohydrate Metabolism in Heterothermic Animals.* Univ. Washington Press. Seattle. 144 pp.
6. REES, F. G., 1939. Studies on the Germ-Cell Cycle of the Digenetic Trematode *Parorchis acanthus* Nicoll. Part I. Anatomy of the Genitalia and Gametogenesis in the Adult. Parasitology, *31*, 417–433.
7. REES, F. C., 1940. Studies on the Germ-Cell Cycle of the Digenetic Trematode *Parorchis acanthus* Nicoll. Part II. Structure of the Miracidium and Germinal Development in the Larval Stages. Parasitology, *32*, 372–391.
8. ROGERS, W. P., 1962. *The Nature of Parasitism. The Relationship of Some Metazoan Parasites to Their Hosts.* Academic Press, N.Y. & London, 287 pp.
9. WALTON, A. C., 1959. Some Parasites and Their Chromosomes. J. Parasitol., *45*, 1–20.

membrane. This type may be combined with one of the other two mentioned below. **Holozoic** nutrition is the ingestion of particulate food through the cytostome or directly into the body wall through a temporary opening. Food vacuoles in which digestion occurs are formed in the cytoplasm, and undigested matter is eliminated through a pore called a "cytopyge" or through a temporary opening in the body wall. **Holophytic** nutrition (typical of green plants) is the synthesis of carbohydrates by means of chlorophyll. This type occurs in all of the unicellular species containing chloroplasts, such as *Euglena*. Since these species are plants they are generally placed in a separate phylum, but some of them may lose their chloroplasts and behave exactly like animals. The boundary line between plants and animals is thin indeed, and there are sound and logical grounds for using Ernst Haeckel's term "Protista" for all single-celled organisms.

Excretion in the protozoa is accomplished either by diffusion through the cell membrane, or by the formation of "contractile vacuoles" in the cytoplasm. These vacuoles are often complex organelles consisting of radiating and pulsating canals. They empty their contents through the body wall, and they probably function more as osmoregulatory devices than as excretory structures. They are common in freshwater species, but rare in marine and parasitic species.

Respiration in parasitic species may be aerobic (*e.g.* the malarial parasite, *Plasmodium*; some of the trypanosomes) or anaerobic (*e.g.* the amebic dysentery parasite, *Entamoeba histolytica*; *Trichomonas*). The host intestine, however, is not completely devoid of oxygen. The oxygen tension in the intestinal gases of a pig has been estimated to average about 30 mm. Hg, or about one-fifth that of air. It should not be assumed that the oxygen tension of any one habitat is a uniform phenomenon. It varies considerably. There is apparently an oxygen gradient in the intestines, evidenced by the gathering of some protozoa on the periphery of the fecal mass. This distribution of parasites might, of course, be due to other factors. The common flagellate, *Giardia muris*, in the intestine of mice is often found massed concentrically. The phenomenon may be due to differences in the pH values of the different areas. A similar gradient exists in tissues near small blood vessels. Also, bacteria may alter the conditions near a parasite by using the available oxygen themselves.

Reproduction and Life Cycles

Protozoan life cycles may consist of a simple series of binary fissions, or multiple fissions called "schizogony" (see below); or they may be elaborate and precise integrations of sexual and asexual reproductions. Parasitic species employ either one host, and are thus called *monoxenous* (or *monoecious*), or two or more hosts and are called *heteroxenous*. If a parasite has a narrow host range it is called *stenoxenous*; if the host range is broad the parasite is *euryxenous*. There are all gradations, however, between these two extremes of host preference (see chapter XXV on host specificity). If there is no alternation of generations the parasite is called *monogenetic*, and when alternations of generations occur the parasite is called *heterogenetic*.

Sometimes the events of mitosis take place entirely within the nucleus and involve a connecting strand, the *paradesmose*, between the poles of the separating elements. Amitotic division is characteristic of the macronucleus of parasitic ciliates. This organelle may divide by constriction and it may undergo a change in form before constriction. The macronucleus is derived from the micronucleus and it contains a mass of duplicated sets of chromosomes, thus being highly polyploid. It functions in the normal differentiation of the protozoan body, and even a small fragment of it is able to control regeneration.

Schizogony is a form of asexual multiplication. Since no gametes are involved, the process is sometimes called *agamogony* in contrast with gamete production which may be called *gamogony*. In schizogony the nucleus undergoes repeated division after which process each nucleus becomes surrounded by a separate bit of cytoplasm, and the original cell membrane ruptures liberating as many daughter cells as there were nuclei. These daughter cells are *merozoites*. While the parent cell is undergoing nuclear division it is called a *schizont*. These processes are part of the life cycle of *Plasmodium* (p. 117). If the multinucleate cell divides into portions which are still multinucleate, the process is called *plasmotomy* (as in some Myxosporida). When a syncytium (many nuclei within one cell membrane) is produced (as in the Myxosporida), the process is *nucleogony*.

Budding is another method employed by some unicellular parasites. Essentially, the process is simply mitosis with unequal cellular division. *Tritrichomonas augusta*, a flagellate parasite, occasionally becomes rounded and then develops into several new individuals. This exogenous budding is also common among the Myxosporida and Telosporida. Endogenous budding within the cell membrane occurs in other sporozoa, in the flagellate, *Crithidia euryophthalmi*, which inhabits the bug, *Euryophthalmus convivus*, and in other protozoan parasites.

Sexual reproduction in parasitic protozoa exists in various forms and its description involves several new terms. If two cells come together and exchange nuclear material, the process is *conjugation* (common in ciliates). When they separate, each cell may be called an *exconjugant*. If sex cells (gametes) are produced, they unite by *syngamy*. These cells may be identical in appearance or they may be similar to eggs and sperm of higher organisms. If they are identical they are known as *isogametes*, and if dissimilar they are *anisogametes*. In the body of a mosquito the *Plasmodium* of malaria occurs, first as gametes of markedly different size and shape. The large variety (female) is a *macrogamete*, whereas the smaller one is the *microgamete*. The cell (in vertebrate blood) which gives rise to the macrogamete is a *macrogametocyte* and the cell producing the microgamete is the *microgametocyte.* The life cycle of *Babesia bigemina*, the causative agent of cattle tick fever, demonstrates the union of isogametes. In either instance, a zygote is produced and it is the first cell of a new individual.

In *Trichonympha* (Fig. III–27) and other flagellates which live in the woodroach sexual reproduction is common, as it is in a ciliate, *Nyctotherus cordiformis*, in the intestine of a metamorphosing tree frog, *Hyla versicolor*. In the ciliate, *Anoplophrya orchestii*, a parasite of the blood vascular system of the sandhopper. *Orchestia agilis*, the micronucleus elongates and divides mitotically exhibiting a spindle and numerous small chromosomes. The macronucleus elongates and divides by constriction. Two individuals come together in conjugation and the micronuclei undergo three maturation divisions which produce two pronuclei. During this time a protoplasmic bridge connects the conjugating animals and an exchange of pronuclei takes place through the bridge. The two complimentary nuclei fuse together. Halves of each macronucleus also are exchanged through the bridge; then the conjugants separate. A reorganization in each ciliate completes the process.

Coprophilic Protozoa

Coprophilic protozoa are those which live in feces outside of the body. The group does not include the usual intestinal protozoa. Often, however, cysts of coprophilic protozoa get into the gut of animals or man and are mistaken for true parasites. Thirty or more species of such soil, sewage and fecal forms have been reported from various animals. They include flagellates, amebas and ciliates. The name *coprozoic* is also used to describe these organisms but it should be restricted to those organisms which can be cultured in feces.

Coprophilic protozoa normally do not excyst in the vertebrate body but motile stages are often abundant in feces which has been left standing for some time. If feces from any mammal remains at room temperature or even in a refrigerator for a few days, normal motile parasitic protozoa disappear but abundant motile amebas, flagellates and ciliates of the coprophilic varieties may be found. Motile coprophilic amebas can be distinguished from parasitic species by the presence in the former of a contractile vacuole and, usually, a large endosome in the nucleus, although much variation exists. The ciliates are usually clearly freshwater species. The cyst stage of the protozoa is the one which causes most of the confusion in identification.

A gradual increase in numbers of the coprophilic protozoa (Fig. III–2) normally occurs in stored feces at room temperature or in a refrigerator at 4° C. The numbers of protozoa and bacteria fluctuate but the fluctuation of one species is not necessarily in unison with that of another. There is a direct correlation between numbers of protozoa and numbers of bacteria. Either the conditions which favor bacterial growth also favor protozoan development or

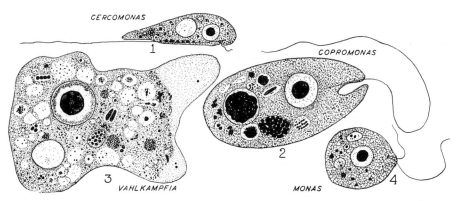

FIG. III–2.—Coprophilic protozoa from cattles feces. *1, Cercomonas* sp.   × 5000, *2, Copromonas* sp. × 6000, *3, Vahlkampfia* sp. × 1600. *4, Monas communis* × 5000. (Noble, courtesy of J. Parasitol.)

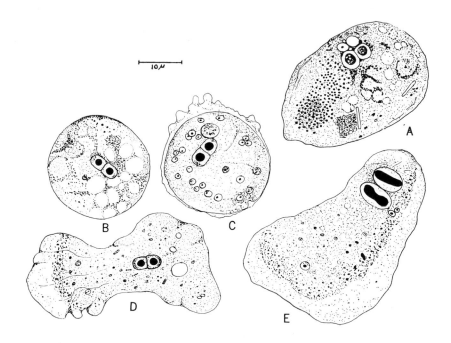

FIG. III–3.—*Sappinia diploidea*, a binucleate coprophilic ameba found in feces of large mammals.

A, Motile *Sappinia diploidea* without pseudopodia. The two adjacent nuclei are clearly evident. The mass of black cytoplasmic dots may be metachromatic granules. *B*, Probably a cyst of *S. diploidea*. *C*, A motile form entering the precystic stage. Note the parasites in the cytoplasm. *D*, Typical motile *S. diploidea* with a large, almost clear pseudopodium, a contractile vacuole, and ectoplasmic lines. There is a crescent-shaped mass of granules between each endosome and the nuclear membrane. *E*, A dividing *S. diploidea*. (Noble, courtesy of J. Protozool.)

the bacteria produce a substance or substances necessary for the normal life of the protozoa, or both.   It is well known that in prepared cultures of protozoa the presence of at least one species of bacterium is usually essential.

The first motile coprophilic flagellate to appear in stored feces of large mammals is often a member of the genus *Cercomonas*, a small protozoan flagellate averaging 2.5 × 5.4 microns. It is shaped somewhat like a tadpole with a flexible "tail", an extremely short anterior flagellum, and a long trailing flagellum. Another common flagellate, and one which remains viable for the longest period of time in stored feces, is *Copromonas ruminantium*. This species, with a single anterior flagellum, is generally oval in shape and it averages 5 × 12 microns in size. Frequently a very small flagellate, *Monas communis*, possessing one flagellum, appears after a few days.

Amebas of the coprophilic variety also excyst in old feces. They usually appear after the flagellates have become established and after a rich culture of motile bacteria develops. *Vahlkampfia* sp. is common, and the peculiar binucleate *Sappinia diploidea* (Fig. III–3) often becomes abundant. The motile form of *Vahlkampfia* sp. usually measures between 20 to 40 microns in diameter, and the mononucleate cysts range from 8 to 15 microns. *Sappinia diploidea* averages about 45 microns in diameter but it may reach 60 microns. The two nuclei of this species are closely associated and the cytoplasm is highly granular.

Ciliates of many types may appear in old feces if the material is kept for several weeks. Some of them are large holotrichs, and they tend to appear after the other protozoa have flared up in numbers and then died down.

This sequence of events in mammal feces occurs in much the same manner in material left at room temperatures, but at the higher temperatures there is increased likelihood of drying and of the development of mold. Although these organisms are not true parasites, the presence of many protozoan cysts in the digestive tracts of animals indicates one of the ways in which parasitism probably originated. The student has only to imagine that some of the cysts excysted in the gut and managed to remain there, eventually to live at the expense of their hosts. See chapter XXVI for a full discussion of the evolution of parasites.

For general references to the protozoa see: Grell,[18] Hall,[19] Hyman,[21] Jahn and Jahn,[22] Kudo,[23] Levine,[25] Lwoff,[26] MacKinnin and Hawes,[27] Manwell,[28] and Wenyon.[33]

CLASSIFICATION

The classification of the Protozoa is constantly being revised and improved. The system used here is a combination of several published systems, and modified on the basis of relationships revealed by recent studies with the electron microscope. Only those taxa that contain parasites are listed, and the representative families are those that are mentioned on the following pages of this book. For details on classification see Ainsworth and Sneath,[1] Cain,[6] Corliss,[8,9] Fallis and Bennett,[12] and Levine.[25]

CLASSIFICATION OF THE PHYLUM PROTOZOA

Subphylum Mastigophora
  Order Dinoflagellida
  Order Rhizomastigida
  Order Kinetoplastida
    Families include: Trypanosomatidae, Cryptobiidae
  Order Retortamonadida
    Family Retortamonadidae
  Order Diplomonadida
    Family Hexamitidae
  Order Trichomonadida
    Families include: Monocercomonidae, Trichomonadidae, Devescovinidae,
               Calonymphidae
  Order Hypermastigida
    Families include: Hoplonymphidae, Trichonymphidae
Subphylum Sarcodina
  Class Rhizopodea
    Order Amoebida
      Families include: Dimastigamoebidae, Amoebidae, Entamoebidae
  Class Actinopodea
    Order Proteomyxida
      Families include: Labyrinthulidae, Pseudosporidae
Subphylum Euspora
  Class Telosporea
    Subclass Gregarinia
      Order Eugregarinida
        Suborder Cephalina
        Suborder Acephalina
      Order Schizogregarinida
    Subclass Coccidia
      Order Eucoccidiida
        Suborder Adeleina
          Families include: Adeleidae, Haemogregarinidae, Hepatozoidae
        Suborder Eimeriina
          Families include: Aggregatidae, Lankesterellidae, Eimeriidae
        Suborder Haemosporina
          Family Plasmodiidae
  Class Piroplasmea
    Order Piroplasmida
      Families: Babesiidae, Theileriidae
  Class Toxoplasmea
    Order Toxoplasmida
      Families: Sarcocystidae, Toxoplasmatidae
Subphylum Cnidospora
  Class Cnidosporidea
    Order Myxosporida
    Order Microsporida

Order Helicosporida
Order Actinomyxida
Subphylum Ciliophora
  Class Ciliatea
    Subclass Holotrichia
      Order Gymnostomatida
        Families include: Bütschliidae, Entorhipidiidae, Isotrichidae
      Order Hymenostomatida
        Families include: Tetrahymenidae, Ophryoglenidae
      Order Thigmotrichida
        Family Ancistrocomidae
      Order Apostomatida
        Family Foettingeriidae
      Order Astomatida
      Order Trichostomatida
        Family Balantidiidae*
      Order Peritrichida*
        Families include: Scyphidiidae, Urceolariidae
      Order Chonotrichida*
      Order Suctorida*
    Subclass Spirotrichia
      Order Heterotrichida
        Family Plagiotomidae
      Order Entodiniomorphida
    Incertae Sedis
      Order Opalinida

* The family Balantidiidae, the peritrichs and the chonotrichs have generally been considered as spirotrichs (see below); while the suctoria are usually considered as a separate class. See Corliss.[8,9]

Since this book went to press the following proposals have been adopted by the Committee on Taxonomy and Taxonomic Problems of the Society of Protozoologists, or they have been submitted by committee members. See abstracts numbered 85, 86, 87, and 88 in the J. Protzool., *10*, Supplement, Aug., 1963.

A new Subphylum Sarcomastigophora which includes Class Mastigophora and Class Sarcodina. Under the latter class is placed the new subclasses Labyrinthulia and Proteomyxidia. The new Superclass Opalinata which belongs between the flagellates and the ciliates. The new Class Microsporidea to parallel the Class Myxosporidea. These two classes represent the two groups of the subphylum Cnidospora.

SUBPHYLUM MASTIGOPHORA

The Mastigophora are known as flagellates because of the presence of one or more long whip-like flagella or "tails" used for locomotion. The term "tail" is not always appropriate, however, because in some species this structure is anterior in position and pulls the animal along rather than pushes it (*e.g. Copromonas ruminantium* in cattle feces). Many orders of Mastigophora contain parasitic genera. Members of the subphylum are solitary or colonial; asexual reproduction is typically by binary fission; sexual reproduction occurs in some groups; nutrition may be saprozoic, holozoic, or holophytic.

ORDER DINOFLAGELLIDA

These free-swimming organisms, a few of which are parasitic, produce food reserves of starch and lipids and they contain chromatophores. The flagellates are abundant in all oceans. The body possesses two grooves, one longitudinal (girdle) and one transverse (sulcus). A flagellum usually lies in each groove (Fig. III–4).

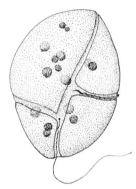

Fig. III–4.—A generalized dinoflagellate showing the body grooves containing two flagella. (Original.)

Members of the Dinoflagellida can be found in numerous invertebrates. *Blastodinium* lives in the gut of the crustacean, *Cyclops*. A parasite of corresponding size in man would cause a lump in his body as large as his liver. Parasitic dinoflagellates may also be found on other crustacea, in annelids and salpids (ascidians), and on the gills of some freshwater and marine fishes. These protista can even be found within cells of Siphonophora (colonial coelenterates) and in protozoa (tintinnioid ciliates and Radiolaria). *Coccodinium*, for example, parasitizes other dinoflagellates and *Duboscqella tintinnicola* occurs as a large (100 microns) parasite in a tintinnioid ciliate. *Paradinium poucheti* lives in the body cavity of copepods, whereas copepod eggs may be inhabited by *Chytriodinium parasiticum* and by *Trypanodinium ovicola*. The latter parasite occurs as biflagellated swarmers measuring fifteen microns long.

ORDER RHIZOMASTIGIDA

The order Rhizomastigida shows affinities with the amebas by possessing ameboid bodies which often produce pseudopodia. They possess one to four flagella, and are mostly free-living. *Rhizomastix gracilis* is a species found in crane-fly larvae and in the salamander known as *axolotl*. *Mastigina hylae* occurs in the intestines of many species of frogs; its nucleus is situated at the extreme anterior end of the body.

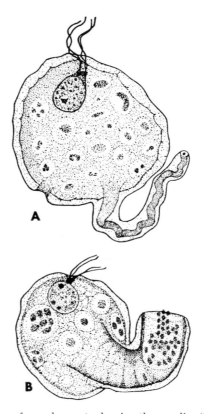

Fig. III–5.—*Histomonas* from pheasants showing the peculiar "tube" which is characteristic of these flagellates. × 1300.

A, Relatively narrow "tube" with many bends and kinks; slight internal component. *B*, Very thick "tube," with cluster of bacteria in outer concavity. The "tube" represents about one-third the bulk of the cell. (Wenrich, courtesy of Jour. Morphol.)

The best-known parasitic member of the Rhizomastigida is *Histomonas meleagridis* (Figs. III-5 and 6). This flagellate uses another parasite, the cecal nematode worm, as an intermediate host. *H. meleagridis* is often rounded but it varies in size and shape. It ranges in diameter from 4 to 30 microns and it may possess up to four flagella or none. The parasite usually lives in the liver of poultry, causing infectious enterohepatitis, but it may also infect the ceca, kidney, or spleen. The bird's head characteristically turns a dark, almost black color—hence the common name of the disease is "blackhead," but the darkening does not always occur.

This coloring may also be the result of some other disease. No protective cyst is formed, so when the parasite is eliminated from the host's body with feces, it soon dies. The protozoa, however, may become enclosed within the egg shell of the poultry cecal worm, *Heterakis gallinae*. This worm seems to cause little, if any, harm to its host, but when the embryonated eggs of the worm are eaten by poultry, the enclosed *Histomonas* is liberated.

Blackhead is one of the most serious diseases of turkeys, and it costs the American poultry farmer approximately three and a half million dollars a year. The disease is not as serious for chickens, which usually recover after a mild reaction. About half the losses

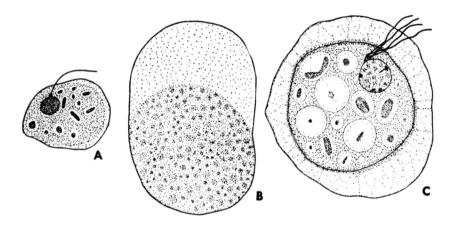

Fig. III–6.—*Histomonas* from chickens and pheasants. × 1300.
A, Small specimen from chicken caecum. B, Copy of free-hand sketch of living specimen. Note clear ectosarc and granular endosarc; no flagella seen. C, Individual showing relatively thick ectosarc, and sharp boundary between ectosarc and endosarc. Figures A and C are from smears fixed with Schaudinn's sublimate-alcohol-acetic fluid and stained with iron-alum hematoxylin. (Wenrich, courtesy of Jour. Morphol.)

are due to death and half to delayed marketing because of weight loss and down-grading of carcasses. Further losses are due to lowered resistance which renders the birds more susceptible to other diseases.

Resistant chickens and turkeys may harbor both the protozoon, *Histomonas meleagridis*, and the worm, *Heterakis gallinae*, at the same time. Such birds are reservoirs of infection for all new chicks. Chickens and turkeys obviously should not be raised together. Even raising young turkeys with older turkeys is apt to expose the young ones to serious protozoan and worm diseases.

Symptoms of histomoniasis are similar to those of many other types of diseases of poultry. The birds become listless, their wings droop and their eyes are partly or completely closed much of the time. With turkeys especially, the head may become darkened. Young birds may die within two or three days and older birds may last a week or two before death, or they may recover after a few days. Cleanliness and isolation are the keys to prevention. The drug of choice against the worm infection is phenothiazine, whereas Enheptin T (a nitrothiazole) is effective against the protozoa.

ORDER KINETOPLASTIDA

Family Trypanosomatidae. This family consists of elongated, leaf-like, or sometimes rounded protozoa each possessing a single flagellum at the anterior end. The flagellum arises from a granule called a *blepharoplast* situated posterior to an elongated blind pouch or reservoir (not seen with an ordinary direct light microscope). The group is relatively unspecialized and, associated with its various habitats, has developed a variety of body forms[7] (Fig. III-7). These forms or stages may all appear in the life cycle of a single species of parasite, or some of the forms may be lacking. They may not only represent polymorphism in the life cycle of one species, but, in other

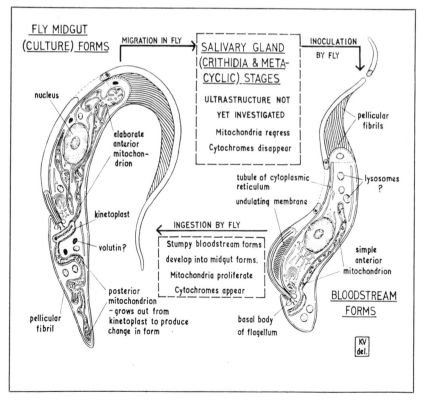

Fig. III–6A.—Diagram showing schematic change in ultrastructure of a trypanosome during its life-cycle. The trypanosomes are shown partly in sagittal section. (Vickerman, courtesy of Transactions of the Royal Society of Tropical Medicine and Hygiene, London.)

members of the group, they may represent different genera. Vickerman[32] has recently proposed a logical theory of development based on the fine structures as revealed by the electron microscope (Fig. III-6A). His suggestions refer to the *Trypanosoma-brucei* group, but they may well be applicable to the family Trypanosomatidae because apparently in each member the *kinetoplast* (Fig. III-6A) is a part of a giant mitochondrion. Vickerman states that, "It is thought possible that the physiological and morphological changes in cyclical development of trypanosomes of the *T. brucei* sub-group will prove intelligible in terms of the mitochondrial proliferation and regression demanded by the environment."

Six main genera occur in animals, and one genus, *Phytomonas*, is found in the latex of certain plants. Those genera parasitic in animals are: *Leptomonas, Blastocrithidia, Crithidia, Herpetomonas, Trypanosoma*, and *Leishmania*. The first six genera range from 12 microns to 130 microns in length; *Leishmania* reaches about 3 microns in diameter. See figure III-8 for a comparison of four genera.

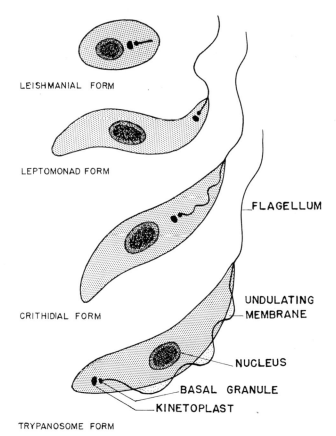

LEISHMANIAL FORM

LEPTOMONAD FORM

FLAGELLUM

CRITHIDIAL FORM

UNDULATING
MEMBRANE

NUCLEUS

BASAL GRANULE

KINETOPLAST

TRYPANOSOME FORM

FIG. III-7.—The four body forms occurring in the family Trypanosomatidae.
(Original.)

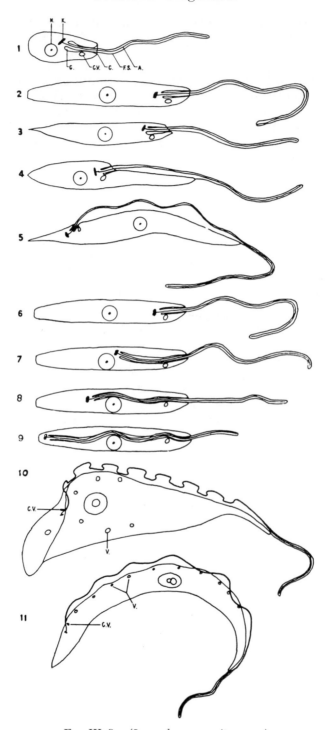

Fig. III–8.—(*Legend on opposite page.*)

Phytomonas is a heteroxenous genus that lives in the fluid or latex of plants (*e.g.* the fig, *Fucus scabra*). Undoubtedly a careful search for flagellates in other latex-containing-plants would be rewarding.

Leptomonas looks like a "typical" flagellate with a relatively short flagellum. The flagellum arises from a basal granule called a *blepharoplast* located near the anterior tip of the body. Close to the blepharoplast and connected to it by a short thread, is a slightly larger organelle, the *kinetoplast*. Most leptomonads are parasites of invertebrates. For example, *L. ctenocephali* occurs in the dog flea and *L. bütschlii* lives in the gut of the nematode worm, *Trilobus gracilis*. The parasites pass as cysts from host to host in contaminated feces. Only leptomonad and leishmanial stages occur in the life cycle.

Crithidia has a leptomonad form with the flagellum extending from an anterior depression. The body is short and truncated. There is no undulating membrane. Species of the genus are monoxenous in arthropods, and they pass through the leishmanial stage. For example, *C. fasciculata* lives in the gut of the mosquito, *Anopheles maculipennis*; and *C. leptocoridis* occurs in the nymph of the box-elder bug, *Leptocoris*.

Blastocrithidia has the typical crithidial appearance with its kinetoplast and basal granule situated just anterior to the nucleus; and a short undulating membrane. This body type was at first erroneously ascribed to the genus *Crithidia*, hence the transference of the term "crithidial" to another genus.[24] The life cycle of *Blastocrithidia* involves the leishmanial, leptomonad and crithidial stages. Members of the genus live in invertebrates.

Herpetomonas is elongated and usually pointed at both ends. It appears similar to *Trypanosoma* and is found in invertebrates. The blepharoplast lies in the posterior end of the body and the undulating membrane lies in a long reservoir which extends the length of the body. The free anterior flagellum may be considerably longer than the body. Leishmanial, leptomonad, crithidial and trypanosome stages occur in the life cycle. *H. drosophilae* is a parasite of the fly, *Drosophila confusa*, and *H. muscae-domesticae* (= *H. muscarum*) inhabits the intestine of flies belonging to *Musca*, *Calliphora*, *Sarcophaga*, *Lucilia*, *Phormia*, and to other genera. Most of the

---

Fig. III–8.—1, Stubby, membraneless type as exemplified by *Crithidia fasciculata*. *N*,–nucleus, *K*,–kinetoplast, *G*,–bullet or reservoir, *C.V.*–contractile vacuole, *C*,–cytosome or mouth of reservoir, *F.S.*,–flagellar sheath, *A*,–axoneme. *2*, Morphological type exemplified by *Herpetomonas muscarum*. *3*, Morphological type exemplified by *Leishmania tropica*. *4*, Short-membraned type exemplified by culture form of *Trypanosoma cruzi*. *5*, Blood stream form of genus *Trypanosoma* as exemplified by *Trypanosoma lewisi*. *6–9*, *Herpetomonas muscarum*, showing some of the forms seen in culture. *10*, *Trypanosoma ranarum*. Drawn with the aid of a camera lucida. *C.V.*,–contractile vacuole, *V*,–vacuole. *11*, *Trypanosoma diemyctyli*. Drawn with the aid of a camera lucida. (Clark, courtesy of Jour. Protozoology.)

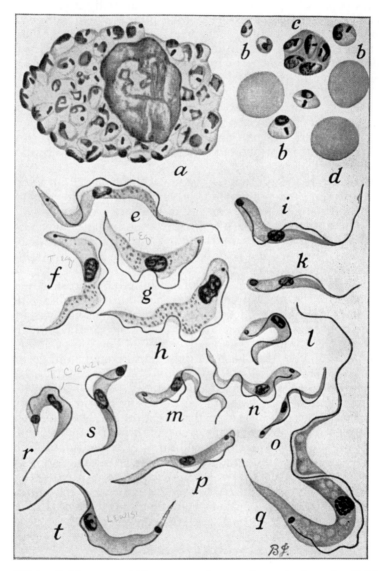

Fig. III–9.—*Leishmania* and *Trypanosoma* from various animals. *a,b,c, Leishmania* in tissue smears. *a*, Macrophage packed with parasites. *b*, Parasites scattered by rupture of host-cells. *c*, Detached portion of host-cell with parasites. *d*, Erythrocytes. *e–t*, Trypanosomes. *e–h, T. brucei.* *e*, Slender; *f*. Intermediate; *g*, Stumpy. *h*, Posterior-nuclear forms. *e,f, T. evansi* and/or *T. equiperdum.* *i, T. vivax.* *k, T. uniforme.* *l,p, T. congolense.* *l,m,n,o, T. simiae.* *q, T. theileri.* *r.s, T. cruzi.* *t, T. lewisi.* (Richardson and Kendall, *Veterinary Protozoology*, courtesy Oliver and Boyd, 1957.)

herpetomonads live in the gut of insects but one species, *Trypanophis sagittae*, can be found in the intestine of the arrow worm, *Sagitta*. In this host the flagellate loses its undulating membrane and flagellum and attaches itself to the intestinal lining where it might be mistaken for a gregarine.

Trypanosoma is similar in general appearance to *Herpetomonas* but the reservoir, near the posterior end, is very short, and the undulating membrane is thus exposed along most of its length along the side of the body. A cytostome has been described for some species (e.g. *T. muris*). Species of the genus pass through all of the four body stages.

Leishmania (Fig. III–9) is a small, rounded or slightly elongate parasite which does not possess a free flagellum. It has, however, a kinetoplast and a blepharoplast from which a fiber passes to the cell membrane. *Leishmania* may develop into a leptomonad stage by elongation and the production of a flagellum. The leptomonad stage occurs in insects and the leishmania stage occurs as an intracellular parasite of the reticuloendothelium of vertebrates. All three leishmanias of man (p. 57) are morphologically indistinguishable.

TRYPANOSOMA

Trypanosomes (Fig. III–10 and 11) are usually found in body fluids of vertebrates, especially in the blood plasma, and in the digestive system of arthropod or leech vectors. Trypanosomes, however, may occur in any body organ, and some have a "preference" for certain organs such as the heart. The numbers of these parasites in one host may be enormous. For example, twenty million to four billion of them can be recovered from the blood of an animal one hundred hours after infection. Some species, especially *Trypanosoma congolense*, occur in practically all domestic animals; others, like *T. lewisi* in rats, are found almost exclusively in one type of host. See page 661 for an account of their evolution. The trypanosomes of man are *T. cruzi* and *T. rangeli*, both of South and Central America; and *T. gambiense* and *T. rhodesiense*, both of Africa. Reproduction occurs by longitudinal division. See Noble[30] for a detailed account of morphology and life cycles. For a recent review of chemotherapy and chemoprophylaxis see Williamson.[34] An antigenic analysis of the Brucei Group (see below) has been made by Cunningham and Vickerman.[10]

Species of *Trypanosoma* are usually grouped according to certain characteristics they have in common.

1. Lewisi Group.—Posterior end pointed; kinetoplast large, not terminal; free flagellum always present; division occurs in leishmanial, crithidial or trypanosome stages; transmission contaminative through feces (*T. rangeli* also inoculative). Examples: *T. lewisi*, in rats; both *T. cruzi* and *T. rangeli* in man, dog, opossum, monkeys; *T. melophagium* in sheep, *T. theileri* in cattle, *T. duttoni* in mice, *T. nabiasi* in rabbits.

4

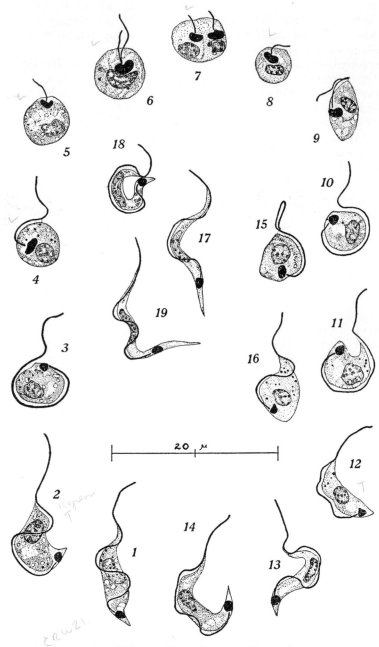

FIG. III–10.—(*Legend on opposite page.*)

2. VIVAX GROUP.—Monomorphic forms, free flagellum always present; rounded posterior end of body; kinetoplast terminal, large; undulating membrane inconspicuous; development in the fly, *Glossina*, in proboscis (*anterior station*) only; *T. vivax* is also transmitted mechanically by tabanid flies. Examples: long forms—*T. vivax*, and short forms—*T. uniforme*, both forms in cattle, sheep, goats, antelope.

3. CONGOLENSE GROUP.—Monomorphic or polymorphic forms; free flagellum may be present or absent; kinetoplast typically marginal, medium in size; development in *Glossina* in midgut and proboscis. Monomorphic forms (free flagellum absent or short, undulating membrane inconspicuous): short forms (means 12.2 to 14.4 microns), *T. congolense* in cattle, horses, swine, sheep, goats, dogs; long forms (means 15.3 to 17.6 microns), *T. dimorphon* in horses, cattle, sheep, goats, dogs. Polymorphic forms, *T. simiae* in swine, cattle, horses, warthogs.

4. BRUCEI GROUP.—Monomorphic or polymorphic forms; free flagellum present or absent; kinetoplast small, subterminal (lacking in *T. equinum*); undulating membrane conspicuous; development in *Glossina* in midgut and salivary glands (except in *evansi* subgroup). Examples: monomorphic forms (stout with short free flagellum)— SUIS SUBGROUP, *T. suis* in swine. Polymorphic forms—BRUCEI SUBGROUP, (stumpy forms always present), *T. brucei* in domestic animals and antelope; *T. rhodesiense* in man and antelope; *T. gambiense* in man. EVANSI SUBGROUP, stumpy forms rare, no cyclic development in insect host, transmission mechanically by insects— *T. evansi* in cattle, camels, horses, dogs; *T. equinum* in horses; transmission by contact (coitus) between mammal hosts—*T. equiperdum* in horses.

5. AVIUM GROUP.[25]—Polymorphic. Examples: both *T. gallinarum* and *T. calmettei* in chickens; *T. hannai* in pigeons; *T. numidae* in guinea fowl; *T. avium* in various birds.

FIG. III–10.—Intramuscular development of Brazilian *Trypanosoma cruzi*. All figures were drawn with the aid of a camera lucida from slides stained with Jenner-Giemsa. The developmental cycle is illustrated by Figures *1* through *14*, exemplifying indirect development (Figures *9*, *10*, *11*, and *12*) of progressive parasites. Less frequently, direct development was observed (Figures *9*, *15*, *16* and *12*).

Description of Figures.—*1* and *2*, Regressive trypanosomes. *3* and *4*, Regressive transition parasites. *5*, Regressive leishmaniform parasite. *6* and *7*, Dividing leishmaniform parasites.

8, Progressive leishmaniform parasite. *9* and *10*, Progressive transition parasites. *11*, Early intermediate size, progressive trypanosome, after formation of V-shaped indentation and separation of extremities. *12* and *13*, Intermediate size, regressive blood and tissue trypanosomes. *14*, Intermediate size, regressive blood trypanosome.

15 and *16*, Developing trypanosomes by direct development or simple elongation. *17*, Metacyclic NIH Brazilian *Trypanosoma cruzi* from *Triatoma protracta*. *18*, Short, slender, progressive blood trypanosome. *19*, Long, slender, progressive blood trypanosome with extended posterior protoplasmic cap. (Wood, courtesy of Am. Jour. Trop. Med. and Hygiene.)

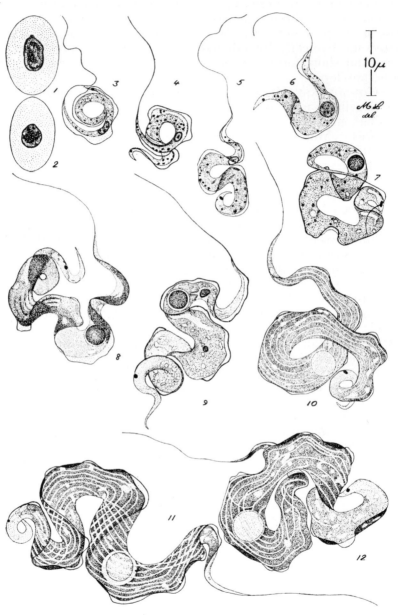

FIG. III–11.—*Trypanosoma caulopsettae* from a New Zealand sand flounder. (Laird, courtesy of Proc. Zool. Soc. London.)

Trypanosoma rangeli (= *T. ariarii*) has been reported from man, monkeys (*Cebas fatuellus*), dogs, and possibly opossums, in Venezuela, Brazil, Colombia, Guatemala, Chile, and French Guiana. The insect vector is the triatomid bug, *Rhodnius prolixus*, which transmits the flagellate during the act of biting the host. To get into the salivary glands of the insect, the parasite must penetrate the midgut, pass through the hemocoel and migrate to the head region where it leaves the vector through the hypopharynx. The infective stage develops in the hindgut as well as in the salivary glands of the bug which can thus transmit the infection both by fecal contamination and through the bite. In the vertebrate host the parasite multiplies only in the trypanosome stage. This trypanosome is not pathogenic to man.

Trypanosoma gambiense is one of the causative agents of human sleeping sickness which is endemic in the west and central portions of Africa. This disease should not be confused with the virus-caused sleeping sickness found in the United States and elsewhere. *T. gambiense* in the blood of man may be long and slender, measuring about 25 by 2 microns, with a flagellum; or short and broad without a flagellum; or intermediate in shape. The usual range in length is 15 to 30 microns. The parasite multiplies by longitudinal splitting and it migrates through the body via the blood stream. The normal habitat is the blood plasma, cerebrospinal fluid, lymph nodes and spleen.

The vector host of this flagellate is the tsetse fly, *Glossina palpalis*, which bites man and feeds on his blood. In the intestine of the fly the parasite reproduces to form both crithidia and trypanosoma stages. After two weeks or more in the gut of the fly, the flagellates migrate to the salivary glands (*anterior station*) where they become attached to the epithelium and develop into the crithidia stage. The crithidia change into infective forms similar in appearance to the trypanosome stage in the blood, and they are now called *metacyclic* trypanosomes. They get into the new vertebrate host, which may be man or domestic or wild animals, by the bite of the fly.

The Gambian or chronic form of sleeping sickness primarily involves the nervous system and the lymphatic system of man. After an incubation period of one or two weeks there are usually fever, chills, headache, and loss of appetite, especially in non-natives. As time goes on, enlargement of the spleen, liver, and lymph nodes occurs, accompanied by weakness, skin eruptions, disturbed vision and a reduced pulse rate. As the nervous system is invaded by the parasites, the symptoms include weakness, apathy, headache, and definite signs of "sleeping sickness". A patient readily falls asleep at almost any time. Coma, emaciation and often death complete the course of the disease which may last for several years. The mortality rate is high. Tryparsamide, suramin, pentamidine, protamidine, and diamidine compounds are effective in treatment, especially during the early stages of the disease. For a consideration of the ecology of African trypanosomiasis see May.[29]

Trypanosoma rhodesiense is closely related to *T. gambiense*. It is identical in appearance and has the same type of life cycle, but it also occurs in the antelope. The insect vectors are the tsetse flies. *Glossina morsitans* and *G. pallidipes*. *T. rhodesiense* causes the Rhodesian or acute and more rapid type of human sleeping sickness which usually results in death within a year. The incidence of infection is less than that with *T. gambiense* and the parasite is restricted to a much more limited area, being almost confined to the high tablelands of south east Africa. Tryparsamide is not useful against *T. rhodesiense* but suramin works well if treatment is begun early in the disease. See Apted *et al.*[3] for a discussion of epidemiology.

Trypanosoma brucei, which causes "nagana" in livestock, is morphologically identical with *T. gambiense* and *T. rhodesiense* but is unquestionably a different species.[10] It is also transmitted by the tsetse fly. *T. brucei* is widely distributed in Africa in dogs, sheep, goats, horses, mules, donkeys, and camels. Cattle and pigs are mildly infected, whereas laboratory animals may be severely infected. The parasites range from 25 to 35 microns in length by 2 to 3 microns in width. Long, short and intermediate forms may appear in the blood stream at the same time. As the parasites spread throughout the body, host reaction is shown by edema, anemia, fever, nervous symptoms, conjunctivitis, keratitis, blindness, paralysis and, especially in horses, death. *T. brucei* is present as a natural infection of many wild mammals in Africa. A related species, *T. suis*, is highly pathogenic to pigs.

Trypanosoma (= *Schizotrypanum*) *cruzi* causes South American trypanosomiasis (Chagas' disease) which is found mainly in Central and South America. A recent World Health Organization report estimates that at least seven million people have the disease. The incidence of infection may be as high as 50 per cent, especially in children. The adult flagellate is similar to *T. gambiense* and it lives in the blood and reticuloendothelial tissues of man and of dogs, cats, rats, monkeys, armadillos, opossums, and other mammals. Within the mammalian host *T. cruzi* enters tissue cells and changes to the leishmania form which multiplies rapidly. The leishmania develop into leptomonad and crithidial stages and finally to trypanosome forms which reenter the blood and lymphatic vessels.

A common insect vector of *Trypanosoma cruzi* is the "kissing bug," *Triatoma infestans*, or other members of the insect family Reduviidae such as *Rhodnius prolixus*, the chief transmitter of the flagellate in Venezuela, and the genera *Eratyrus*, *Eutriatoma* and *Dypetalogastea*. With a meal of blood the trypanosomes are taken to the posterior part of the insect gut (*posterior station*) where they develop into the crithidial stage and multiply. The crithidial forms develop into small trypanosomes. These *metacyclic* individuals occur in the rectum and they are the infective stage. The cycle in the insect requires about two weeks but it varies with the temperature and with other factors. When man is bitten by the bug the insect usually defecates while feeding and thus deposits infective trypanosomes on the skin. The bitten area is often rubbed by the irritated host, so there is considerable opportunity for the parasites to be rubbed into the wound made by the bug. Animals are sometimes infected by eating bugs or by eating other infected animals. The insect is apparently infective for life.

Symptoms of Chagas' disease are so varied that a clear diagnostic picture is difficult to present. Often, however, the bug bites the area of the eye, especially in children, and when the eye is rubbed some insect feces gets on the mucous membranes. This contact causes a characteristic swelling of the area around the eye. Both eyes and even the whole face may become involved. As the parasites invade various organs of the body, enlargements of the spleen, lymph nodes, and liver occur, with headaches, fever, anemia, and prostration. The "mega" condition of enlargement of the esophagus or colon appears to be related to this disease.[13] The heart, striated muscles, and central nervous system may also be affected. Intramuscular forms (Fig. III-10) are somewhat different in appearance than are blood forms. Diagnosis is confirmed by finding the flagellates in the blood. Treatment is of little value and the mortality rate is high, especially in children.

In some parts of the southwest United States, wood rat nests are inhabited by triatomid bugs which are parasitized with *Trypanosoma cruzi*, and the disease in man has been reported a few times from this country. A baby died of Chagas' disease in Texas in 1955. The flagellate has been found in racoons and in other mammals in the United States, and it has been successfully established, experimentally, in sheep, goats, and pigs. Obviously there exists a potential source of considerable danger to man in North America.

Trypanosoma evansi (Fig. III-9) is another serious parasite of horses and camels in which it causes the disease known as "surra". The parasite seldom exhibits the polymorphic stages in vertebrate blood, all forms usually being much like the long stage of *T. brucei*. A small percentage of this species, as well as species of the "Brucei group", develops without a kinetoplast. The organism can be found in dogs, in which host the disease is often fatal, and in donkeys, cattle, and elephants. It is wide-spread throughout Asia and occurs in parts of Africa and certain areas of Central and South America. The principal vector is the horse fly (*Tabanus*) but other flies also mechanically transmit the flagellate. Ticks (*Ornithodoros*) and even the vampire bat have been implicated. The pathology of the disease is similar to that of *T. brucei*.

Trypanosoma equinum in South and Central America attacks horses, causing a disease known as "Mal de Caderas". The parasite may also infect elephants, laboratory animals and a South American rodent called a "capybara". The flagellate resembles *T. evansi* but lacks the kinetoplast. It is transmitted mechanically by flies (*Tabanus* and *Stomoxys*).

Trypanosoma equiperdum (Fig. III–9) causes a disease in horses

known as "dourine". It is transmitted during the mating activity
of horses, and thus is a venereal disease. The flagellate is morphologically identical with *T. evansi* and it ranges in length from
25 to 28 microns. It is a typical trypanosome but it does not exhibit
the usual changes in morphology during its life cycle. The parasite
first affects the sexual organs of male and female horses causing
swelling and ulcers. In these ulcers enormous numbers of the
parasite can be found. The nervous system may become involved,
as evidenced by paralysis of the legs or parts of the face. The
mortality rate is high and there is no effective treatment. Dogs,
mice, rats, and rabbits may become infected with *T. equiperdum*
but in these hosts the parasite remains largely in the blood. A
complement fixation test has been developed for the disease in
horses.

Trypanosoma lewisi (Fig. III–9) is a common blood parasite of
rats throughout the world. It is a slender flagellate, pointed at
both ends and averaging about 25 microns long. The life cycle of
this non-pathogenic organism is similar to that of *T. cruzi* (p. 54),
but the intermediate host is the rat flea, *Ceratophyllus fasciatus*.
T. lewisi has commanded considerable attention in recent years
because it has been the subject of numerous physiological studies.
For example, rats can be immunized against *T. lewisi* infections
by injections of metabolic products of the flagellate. A substance
called *ablastin* is produced by the rat. This substance apparently
inhibits reproduction of the trypanosome and causes the organisms
to become agglutinated, thereby making easier the task of the host
white blood cells (see Chapter XXI).

Trypanosoma theileri (Fig. III–9) is a large blood parasite of
cattle. The flagellate may reach 70 microns in length in the ordinary
blood stage and up to 120 microns in length in animals suffering
from the chronic stage of the disease. The lowest limit of human
unaided vision is about 100 microns, so this relatively huge trypanosome can be seen without a microscope. The life cycle is similar
to that of *T. lewisi*, to which group it belongs, and the insect vector
is probably the horsefly (*Tabanus*).

Trypanosoma melophagium is a common blood parasite of sheep
in England. It is transmitted by the sheep ked (*Melophagus ovinus*)
which is a wingless, bloodsucking fly. Probably up to 90 per cent
of British sheep are infected with this flagellate. A similar parasite,
T. theodori, occurs in goats.

Trypanosoma vivax is an active blood parasite of practically all
domestic animals of Africa, the West Indies and parts of Central and
South America. Dogs and pigs are not easily infected. In Africa
the insect vector is the tsetse fly but in the other countries transmission is by mechanical means (there are no tsetse flies to carry
the flagellates), indicating that the parasites have been introduced
to these countries and have been able to maintain themselves in
spite of the lack of a suitable intermediate host (see p. 662). The
parasites average 22 microns in length with a range of 20 to 26

microns. The posterior end of the body is characteristically wider than is the anterior end. Unlike the life cycle of the Brucei group in tsetse flies, *T. vivax* does not have a stomach phase in the insect vector; it develops only in the proboscis.

Trypanosoma congolense is a short flagellate without a free anterior flagellum. It averages about 13 microns in length with a range of 9 to 18 microns. It is carried by the tsetse fly, in which there is no invasion of the salivary glands. A wide variance in degree of virulence suggests the existence of several strains of *T. congolense*. Usually the infection is serious in cattle in which it causes anemia and other symptoms common to other forms of trypanosomiasis and, with some strains, is almost always fatal. The parasite may also be found in horses, sheep, goats, and camels.

Trypanosoma simiae is similar to *T. congolense* but is longer, averaging 14 to 24 microns. It is a common and virulent parasite of African monkeys, and is also found in sheep, goats, pigs, and camels. It apparently does not affect horses, cattle, or dogs.

Trypanosomes of birds have been reported primarily from domestic species but undoubtedly many wild birds harbor as yet undescribed forms. *Trypanosoma avium* occurs in the blood of various species of birds, *T. gallinarum* is a parasite of chickens and *T. hannai* may be found in pigeons. The names of other bird forms may be found in texts on protozoology.

Trypanosomes of fishes are transmitted by leeches, especially leeches belonging to the genera *Piscidola*, *Pontobdella*, and *Hemiclepsis*. Many fish trypanosomes such as *Trypanosoma giganteum* in the ray and *T. percae* in perch are unusually large (*e.g.* a body up to 130 microns long). *T. caulopsettae*, found in the blood of a sand flounder and in a "witch" in New Zealand, is illustrated in Fig. III–11.

LEISHMANIA

The first description of the ultra-structure of *Leishmania* (*L. mexicana*) was made by Garnham and Bird in 1962.[16] The general features are similar to those of other flagellates belonging to the family Trypanosomatidae. "The flagellum arises from a short blepharoplast or cylinder containing nine peripheral, double fibrils, and ending in a plate from which the axoneme itself begins and by which it leaves the body in an invagination of the cytoplasm." The kinetoplast lies inside an enormous body which occupies a large part of the cytoplasm of *Leishmania*. This body is a single, giant mitochondrion. The outer wall of the leishmanial cell is a double membrane which overlies a layer of hollow fibrils. The nucleus has no obvious membrane.

The nomenclature of the different forms of *Leishmania* is in a state of uncertainty. All of them might be lumped into one species (*L. donovani*) with justification because neither the leptomonad nor mature stage shows any significant differences among the several forms. Important criteria in distinguishing species are serological responses, vertebrate responses, the kind of host, and cultural characteristics.[16] We shall recognize several species as listed below. See de Azevedo[11] for a discussion of species differences as well as their pathology, and Amran[2] for a consideration of the ecology of leishmaniasis.

Leishmania tropica (Fig. III–7 and Fig. III–9) causes a serious cutaneous and mucocutaneous disease of man in the warmer countries of the old world.[4] The name of the commonest variety of lesion is "oriental sore", although the technical name for all types of pathogenic effects caused by leishmania is *leishmaniasis*. The parasites live in the reticuloendothelial cells of the skin. As they increase in numbers these cells are ruptured and some of the leishmania get into the blood stream. Sandflies (*e.g. Phlebotomus papatasii*) bite man and thus pick up the parasites. In the insect the leishmania develop into enormous numbers of the leptomonad forms. When the sandfly then bites man, parasites enter the blood stream, change into the leishmania body type and are engulfed by macrophages in the reticuloendothelial system. Dogs and other animals may become infected. In dogs the species is *L. tropica var. canis*.

Oriental sore may occur as the "moist" type which, according to Soviet workers, is particularly prevalent in isolated rural settlements adjoining open deserts.[20] Visitors to these areas sometimes become infected with *Leishmania tropica* after being bitten by the sandfly which lives in the burrows of ground squirrels. Even the ground squirrels may suffer typical sores on their noses and ears. Ground squirrels thus may serve as host reservoirs of infection.

In towns of Soviet middle Asia, where the ground squirrels have been driven away, the "dry" type of oriental sore occurs. Apparently the sandflies have changed their habits and now are "domiciliated", since they bite only man. A somewhat intermediate condition occurs between the desert areas with ground squirrels and "wet" sores, and the urban areas and "dry" sores.

Skin sores may vary from a small pimple to large ulcerated areas. Treatment for oriental sore is usually successful with various antimony compounds such as stibophen and neostam.

Garnham[15] has recently clarified certain aspects of cutaneous leishmaniasis in the New World. The disease is closely associated with sylvatic conditions from Mexico through South America. All varieties are transmitted by the bite of the sandfly, *Phlebotomus*. The four main varieties are (*a*) the classic "espundia" caused by *Leishmania brasiliensis* in Brasil, Peru, Ecuador and Chile; (*b*) "uta" caused by *L. donovani* in Peru; (*c*) "pian-bois" caused by *L. guyanensis* in Guiana, Venezuela and Panama; and (*d*) "chiclero's ulcer" caused by *L. mexicana* in Guatemala, British Honduras and Mexico

Leishmania donovani (= *L. infantum*) which causes "uta" in Peru (see preceeding paragraph) is responsible for a human visceral leishmaniasis known as "kala-azar" or "dum dum fever" in many regions of Africa, Europe and Asia. It infects reticuloendothelial cells of the liver, spleen and other organs, and its symptoms are numerous. Usually the spleen is enormously enlarged in advanced cases, and headache, fever, weakness and high mortality often accompany the infection.[31] This disease occurs as three types or varieties, separated geographically. The first two types, the Indian and Sudanese, are found mainly in human adults, but not in dogs. The third type, the Mediterranean, is much more widespread, and occurs in southern Europe, middle Asia, China, Central and South America. In this type, dogs are important reservoir hosts, and jackals and a few other mammals have been found to be infected.

About two years after the acute stage of kala-azar (in India), or as the visceral disease subsides (in the Sudan), there may appear a post kala-azar leishmaniasis. The manifestations range from depigmented areas of the skin to pronounced nodular lesions (Fig. III–12).

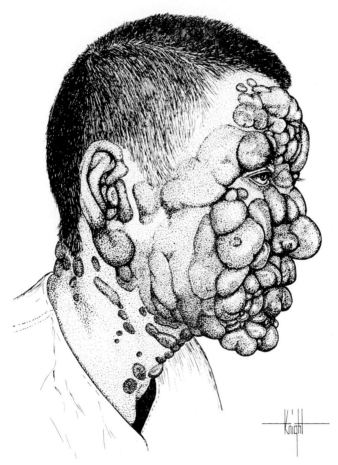

Fig. III–12.—A severe dermal, post-visceral case of "kala-azar" infection caused by *Leishmania donovani*. (Original.)

Loss of hair on dogs is characteristic of a severe case of visceral leishmaniasis, and ulcers on the lips and eyelids frequently occur. Anemia, weakness and enlargement of the liver are common symptoms. Positive diagnosis relies on discovery of the parasite in infected organs, in skin lesions or in peripheral blood. Stray dogs should be eliminated and insecticides used to control the sandflies. Antimony compounds such as sodium stibogluconate and various aromatic diamidines are usually effective in treatment.

L*eishmania denticis* infects the blood, liver, spleen, and kidney of the silver fish, *Dentex argyrozona*. Probably leishmanias infect many other fish and many other non-mammals but little research has been done in this field.

Family Cryptobiidae. Many members of this family of flagellates appear superficially like trypanosomes but they all possess two anterior flagella instead of one. One of these flagella is usually trailing while the other extends anteriorly. The trailing one is the outer

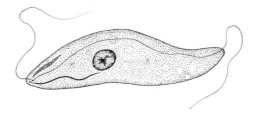

Fɪɢ. III–13.—*Cryptobia helicis* from the reproductive organs of the snail *Helix*. (Original.)

margin of an undulating membrane in those forms called *Trypanoplasma* from the blood of fishes. The parabasal body is usually elongated. *Cryptobia helicis* (Fig. III–13) lives in the reproductive organs of the snail, *Helix*, in which host it may reach a length of 20 microns, but it is often only half that long. *C. borreli*, a somewhat longer species, lives in the blood of several types of freshwater fishes. *C. cyprini* is a blood parasite of carp and goldfish. Other cryptobias inhabit the stomachs of fishes, the gut of the arrow worm, *Sagitta*, and spermatophores of invertebrates. Transmission is presumably accomplished by ingestion of flagellates which escape from a host intestine or through copulation of hosts. Other generic names which are probably synonyms are *Heteromita* and *Diplomastix*.

ORDER RETORTAMONADIDA

Family Retortamonadidae. *Chilomastix mesnili* (Fig. III–14) is perhaps the best-known species of this family. It is probably a harmless flagellate which lives in the cecum and colon of man and other primates and the pig. The trophozoite, or motile form, is usually pear-shaped and averages about 12 microns in length. The spiral (cytostomal) groove in the body is frequently not seen in the usual hematoxylin-stained preparations, and the three anterior flagella are also difficult to see. Probably the most diagnostic feature is the location of the large nucleus very near the anterior end of the body. The cyst is about 9 microns long, oval in shape, with a broad extension of cyst wall at one end to form a spade-like or cone-shaped projection. The large nucleus, large cytostome, and various filaments can usually be seen in stained cysts. *Chilomastix* spp. also occurs in the rectum of amphibians, fishes, and many mammals.

Retortamonas intestinalis (Fig. III–15) is another harmless small flagellate of man. It measures about 6 microns in length by about 4 microns in width. Like *Chilomastix* it possesses a cytostomal groove but has only two anterior flagella, one extending anteriorly and the

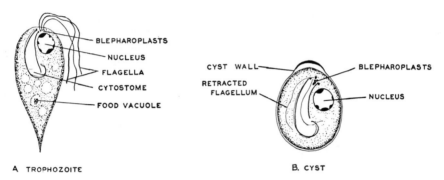

Fig. III–14.—*Chilomastix mesnili.* Motile or trophozoite form and cyst. (Cable, *Illustrated Laboratory Manual of Parasitology,* courtesy of Burgess Publishing Company.)

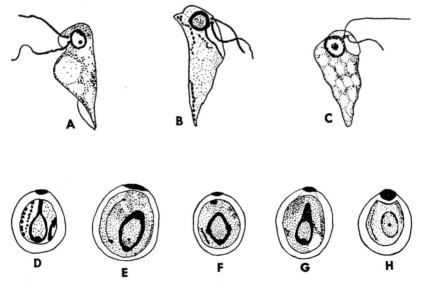

Fig. III–15.—*Retortamonas intestinalis* from man showing three motile forms and five variations of the cyst. (Hogue, courtesy of Jour. Hygiene.)

other passing backward through the cytostome and then trailing from the body. Other members of the genus have been found in insects (e.g. *Embadomonas* [= *Retortamonas*] *gryllotalpae* in the mole cricket).

ORDER DIPLOMONADIDA

Family Hexamitidae. *Giardia lamblia* (Fig. III–16 and 17), a universal and common inhabitant of the upper small intestine of man, monkeys and pigs, is probably the best-known member of this family. It is present in at least 10 per cent of the people of the United States and is usually harmless, but in rare instances it is pathogenic. Motile *Giardia* average about 7 by 14 microns and they seem to have arisen from a fusion of two mononuclear ancestors (or from the failure of an ancestor to divide properly). These protozoa possess two nuclei and four pairs of flagella. The body is unusual for a protozoan cell because it possesses a suction disc on its ventral

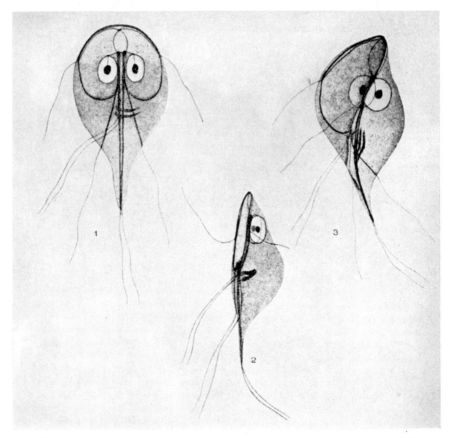

Fɪɢ. III–16.—*Giardia lamblia*, motile form in various aspects. (Kofoid and Swezy, courtesy of University of California Publications in Zoology.)

surface. The mature cyst is usually 8 by 11 microns in size and possesses four nuclei. A comma-shaped parabasal body and deeply-stainable strands, often in pairs, give the cyst its distinctive appearance.

Transmission of the parasite from host to host occurs by the ingestion of cysts in contaminated food or drinking water, or from an infected person who may have cysts on his hands, body or clothes. When the parasite is pathogenic it causes diarrhea, abdominal pain and loss of weight. Apparently it interferes with normal fat absorption in the small intestine. The recommended drugs for treatment are quinacrine (= atabrine), chloroquine, and amodiaquine. Diagnosis is confirmed by finding cysts or motile forms in feces.

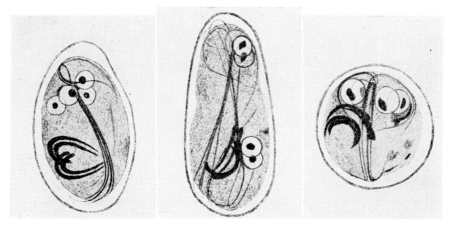

Fig. III–17.—*Giardia lamblia* showing cysts and various stages of division (Kofoid and Swezy, courtesy of University of California Publications in Zoology.)

Similar *Giardia* have been reported from many other animals. Rabbits and dogs may be heavily invaded, and rats can be infected in the laboratory. *G. muris* in mice is distinct from *G. duodenalis* and other species in rats. The pathogenicity of the flagellate to those hosts is in doubt, but, as in man, it is sometimes associated with diarrhea.

Hexamita meleagridis (Fig. III–18) is another well-known member of the family. This parasite, about 9 microns long, is the causative agent of infectious catarrhal enteritis in turkeys. The disease is also known as *hexamitiasis* and is characterized by diarrhea, nervousness, loss of weight and death, especially in younger birds. *H. meleagridis* averages about 9 by 4 microns, is pear-shaped and possesses eight flagella, two of which are attached to the posterior end of the animal while six arise from the anterior end. Aureomycin is used in treatment, with moderate success. Other members of the genus may infect other birds. *Hexamita* (= *Octomitus*) *salmonis* (Fig. III–18) is a species which develops in epithelial cells of the cecum of trout.

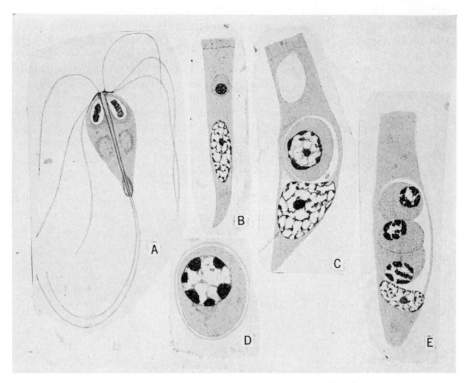

Fig. III–18.—*Hexamita* (= *Octomitus*) *salmonis* a parasitic flagellate of trout. *A*, Typical flagellate. × 2360. *B*, Epithelial cell from cecum of trout containing early stage of parasite. × 1230. *C*, Later stage. × 1230. *D*, Mature intracellular parasite. × 1800. *E*, Schizogony. × 1230. (Davis, Bull. Bureau of Fisheries.)

ORDER TRICHOMONADIDA

Diagnostic features of this order are the *axostyle* (Fig. III–19 and 20), a filament or hyaline rod which passes lengthwise through the body and often projects from the posterior end; and the *parabasal body* which is composed of a granule or one or more elongated bodies often attached by fibrils to the basal granules or *blepharoplasts* of the flagella. There may be a few to many flagella (typically 4–6), and sometimes each flagellum is attached to its own set (mastigont) of cytoplasmic elements, even to its own nucleus. A trailing flagellum is characteristic and there is often an *undulating membrane*. Division occurs by a duplication of organelles and longitudinal splitting. Sexual stages are unknown. In addition to the two families described below there are the Devescovinidae and Calonymphidae, both restricted to termites (see p. 626).

Family Monocercomonidae. In this family are placed many flagellates which live in the digestive tracts of insects and vertebrates. There may be several flagella but usually no undulating membrane. A representative genus is *Monocercomonas* (Fig. III–

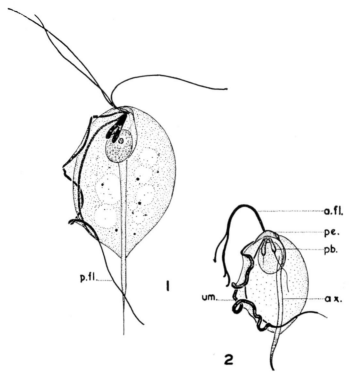

Fig. III–19.—*Tritrichomonas batrachorum* from amphibia showing morphological characters typical of the group. *a.fl.*, anterior flagellum; *ax.*, axostyle, *pb.*, parabasal body; *pe.*, pelta; *p.fl.*, posterior flagellum; *um.*, undulating membrane. (Honigberg, courtesy of J. Parasitol.)

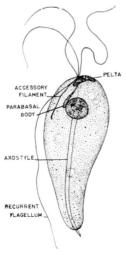

Fig. III–20.—*Monocercomonas*, a trichomonad flagellate. (Original.)

5

20), (also called *Eutrichomastix* and *Trichomastix*) found in both insects and vertebrates (especially fishes).

Family Trichomonadidae. This family is wellknown for its important parasites of man and of animals, both vertebrate and invertebrate. The flagellates are characterized by the presence of several anterior flagella, a *pelta* which stains with silver and lies at the anterior margin of the body, an *undulating membrane*, a deeply staining *costa* which extends along the base of the undulating membrane, and an *axostyle* which extends through the center of the body and often projects as a spike from the posterior end. There is only one nucleus.

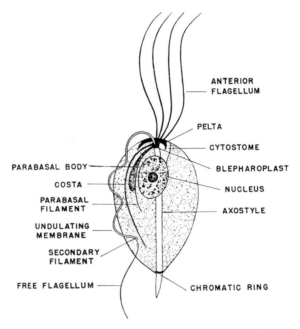

FIG. III–21.—Structures of *Trichomonas*. (Levine, *Protozoan Parasites of Domestic Animals and of Man*, courtesy of Burgess Publishing Company.)

The name *Trichomonas* was first given to a genus which was believed to possess three anterior flagella. Unfortunately, confusion has arisen because species have been found with more and with fewer flagella. The original group actually possesses four flagella but the name *Trichomonas* remains. The following genera are now recognized: *Ditrichomonas*, with two anterior flagella (found in the gut of sheep); *Tritrichomonas* with three anterior flagella; *Trichomonas* with four anterior flagella (Fig. III–21); and *Pentatrichomonas* with five anterior flagella.

A common locus of infection is the intestine but other cavities may be parasitized as well as such organs as the liver (*e.g. T. augusta* in frogs). In domestic and wild animals the flagellates are often more

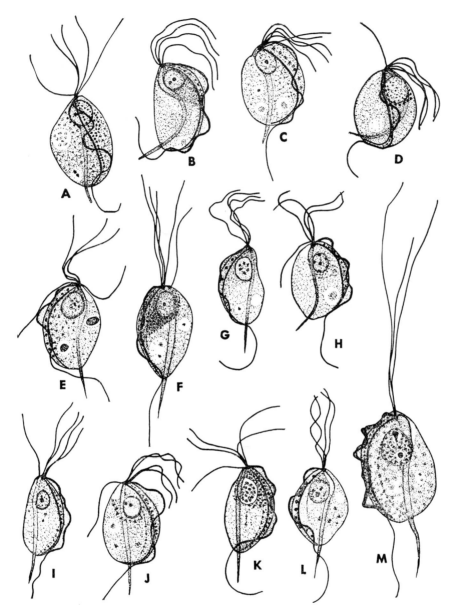

FIG. III–22.—*Pentatrichomonas hominis* from the intestine of man, *A* to *D*, compared with the same species from the monkey, *E* to *G*. *H* is from the cat, *I* from the dog, *J* and *K* from the rat, *L* is *Trichomonas gallinarum* from the pheasant. *M* is *Tritrichomonas fecalis*. (Wenrich, courtesy of J. Morphol.)

abundant in diarrhetic feces than in normal material and, in general, the parasites seem to be more pathogenic in these animals than in man.

Pentatrichomonas hominis, an intestinal form, (Fig. III–22) is one of the three trichomonads that parasitize man, and it is also found in monkeys, cats, dogs and rats. It is oval in shape, measuring about 10 microns by 4 microns, with 5 anterior flagella (4 of which are grouped together at their bases), and a free posterior flagellum extending from the end of a long undulating membrane. At its anterior end it has a costa and a parabasal apparatus composed of a filament and one or more granules. No cysts have been found. The geographic distribution is worldwide but the incidence of infection is heaviest in the warmer countries. Although it is frequently associated with pathogenic conditions, there is no evidence that the organisms actually are responsible for the conditions.

Trichomonas tenax is somewhat smaller than *Pentatrichomonas hominis*, averaging about 7 microns in length. It is similar to *P. hominis* in general appearance but the undulating membrane extends about two-thirds the length of the body and there is no trailing flagellum. The parabasal body is elongated and prominent. This flagellate lives in the human mouth and is a harmless commensal. Its habitat provides the basis for the name *T. buccalis* by which it is sometimes called (see Figs. III–23, *7–10*.)

Trichomonas vaginalis (Fig. III–23) is the largest of the three trichomonads of man. It averages about 13 microns in length but the range is from 10 to 20 microns. The undulating membrane usually reaches to the middle of the body but it may be shorter. There is no trailing flagellum. The parabasal body, with a parabasal filament, is large but it is usually difficult to see. The axostyle characteristically curves slightly around the nucleus. The most significant difference between this species and the other two is its habitat. It lives in the vagina, urethra, or in the prostate gland. The parasite undoubtedly is transferred from one host to another through sexual intercourse.

Trichomonas vaginalis is worldwide in distribution and the incidence of infection in women usually varies from 20 to 40 per cent, whereas in men it varies from 4 to 15 per cent. In women with abnormal vaginal secretions (usually a white discharge) the incidence of infection may be as high as 70 per cent. In this leukorrheic discharge the flagellates can be found in abundance. As with the other species, no cysts are produced.

Truly pathogenic strains exist.[14] *T. vaginalis* and *T. gallinae* (see below) have been found within the cytoplasm of host cells such as macrophages and epithelial cells.[20a] An antiprotozoal antibiotic (PA-128) is said to be effective against this flagellate. Other drugs in use are chiniofon, diodoquin, viofon, carbarsone and oxytetracycline.

Trichomonas gallinarum (Fig. III–22) causes avian trichomoniasis in chickens, turkeys, and other domestic birds. The parasite is pear-shaped, like other members of the genus, and averages about

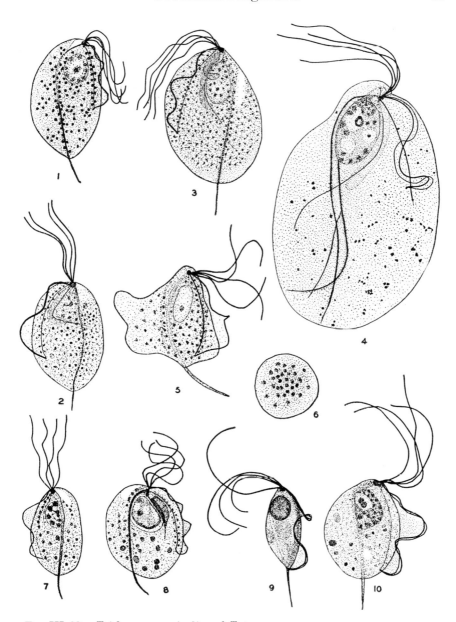

Fig. III–23.—*Trichomonas vaginalis* and *T. tenax.*

1–6, T. vaginalis. 1, Shows 4 flagella, and chromatic granules in cytoplasm. *2,* Shows parabasal body with bend. *3,* Shows extra parabasal body. *4,* Large flattened specimen. Note parabasal apparatus, double margin of undulating membrane, axostyle split into fibrils. *5,* Shows broad pseudopodium. *6,* Detached blob of cytoplasm produced by autotomy. *7–10, T. tenax,* all from cultures. *7,* Shows paracostal granules, cytostome. *8,* Shows parabasal apparatus and paracostal granules. *9,* Deeply stained, undulating membrane full-length. *10,* Flattened individual showing double marginal filament. (Wenrich, courtesy of Am. J. Trop. Med.)

7 by 10 microns in size. A cytostome is prominent. The flagellate lives in the lower intestine of the birds and is the cause of diarrhea, loss of appetite and weight, ruffled feathers and lesions in the intestinal wall. Cysts are not produced, and the method of transmission from bird to bird is unknown. Treatment with 2-amino-5-nitrothiazole is recommended. *Trichomonas gallinae* (Fig. III–24) is a similar parasite which infects the upper intestinal tract of poultry, especially of pigeons.

Tritrichomonas foetus (Fig. III–25) possesses three anterior flagella. It reaches a length of 24 microns. There is a long undulating membrane bordered on its outer margin by a flagellum which be-

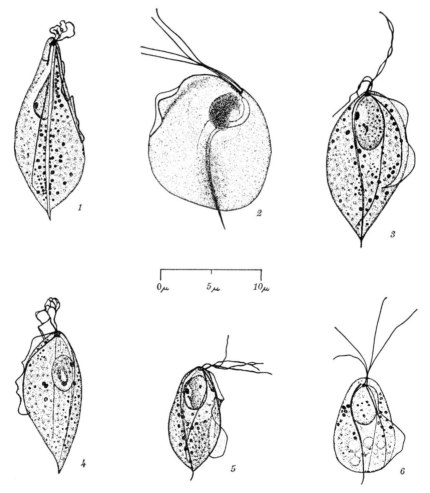

FIG. III–24.—*Trichomonas gallinae* from the intestine of poultry and other birds.

1, Domestic pigeon. Note concentration of granules in axial area. *2*, Domestic turkey. Dried smear, stained with Giemsa; courtesy Dr. Hawn. Note double marginal filament. *3*, Red-tailed hawk. *4*, Golden eagle. *5*, Sparrow hawk. *6*, Red-shouldered hawk. (Stabler, courtesy of Jour. Morphol.)

comes free posteriorly. The axostyle is unusually wide and it projects a short distance from the posterior end of the animal, and the parabasal body is large and the cytosome is prominent. The parasites live in the sheath (preputial cavity) of bulls and are thus readily transferred to the vagina of cows during coitus. In the vagina the flagellates multiply for about three weeks. After the cow is in heat again, the parasites become reduced in numbers or disappear completely. This cycle continues for three to four months, after which time the infection usually is lost. The flagellate may invade other reproductive organs and is apparently able to carry on its metabolic activities both aerobically and anaerobically.

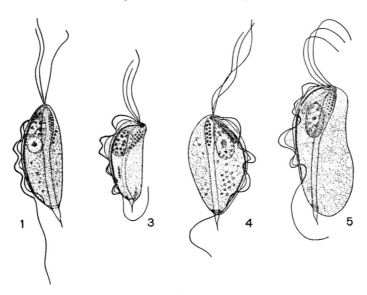

Fig. III 25. *Tritrichomonas foetus*, a parasite which may cause serious disease in cattle.

1, Typical individuals. Figures *1* and *3*, side views. *4* and *5*, Left side and right side views, respectively, showing parabasal body. × 4000. (Wenrich and Emmerson, courtesy of Jour. Morphol.)

If the trichomonads get into the uterus, as they easily do, they cause temporary infertility or abortion. They may even get into the unborn young, appearing in the fetal membranes, the amniotic and allantoic fluids and often in the stomach of the fetus. The parasites seem to have little effect on the bulls. Some bulls apparently have a natural resistance to infection and cows are able to develop some degree of immunity.

Purulent mucus is the best material for demonstrating the presence of the flagellates but other material and preputial washings are often used; care, however, must be taken not to confuse *Tritrichomonas* with other protozoan parasites. A blood agglutination test is useful in diagnosis. Drugs used in treatment have been disappointing, but 3 per cent hydrogen peroxide is said to be partially effective. Other species of trichomonads are common in the intestines of amphibians, fishes, reptiles, birds, mammals and even invertebrates.

ORDER HYPERMASTIGIDA

These protozoa possess many flagella as the name indicates, and they may also possess many parabasal bodies and axostyles. There is a single nucleus and no cytostome. All the species are found in the alimentary tracts of termites, cockroaches and wood roaches. Only two out of at least eight families will be mentioned here.

Family Hoplonymphidae. The members of this family are found in termites and wood roaches. *Hoplonympha natator*, in the intestine of *Kalotermes simplicicornis*, is a narrow, spindle-shaped

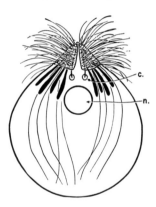

Fig. III–26.—*Barbulanympha ufalula*, resting organism prior to division. (Cleveland, courtesy of J. Protozool.)

organism with two tufts of flagella on its anterior end. The nucleus is near the anterior end and spiral grooves occur on the pellicle. *Barbulanympha ufalula* (Fig. III–26) is an irregularly rounded flagellate with two anterior groups of flagella, below which extends a ring of elongated parabasal bodies surrounding the nucleus. The axostyle consists of a group of filaments which extend into the cytoplasm from the nuclear area. *Rhynchonympha* and *Urinympha talca* are other examples of this family in the roach.

Family Trichonymphidae. Members of this family possess a projection at the anterior end of the body. This "rostrum", which may be cone-shaped, is covered with long flagella except for its tip, while other flagella cover much of the rest of the body in longitudinal rows. The base, or more, of the body may be bare.

Trichonympha corbula is typical of the genus. It possesses circular bands of flagella, each band of a different length. The nucleus is surrounded by the narrow rods of the parabasal body, and the cytoplasm usually contains bits of wood which the animal has ingested. Several other species of this genus live in the intestines of termites and in wood roaches. The sexual cycle of *Trichonympha* has been thoroughly investigated and is partially illustrated in Fig. III–27. *Pseudotrichonympha grassii* in the termite, *Coptotermes formosanus*; and *Mixotricha*, *Deltotrichonympha*, and *Eucomonympha imla* (Fig. III–1), from the wood roach are other examples of the family.

SEXUAL CYCLES OF FLAGELLATES OF *Cryptocercus*

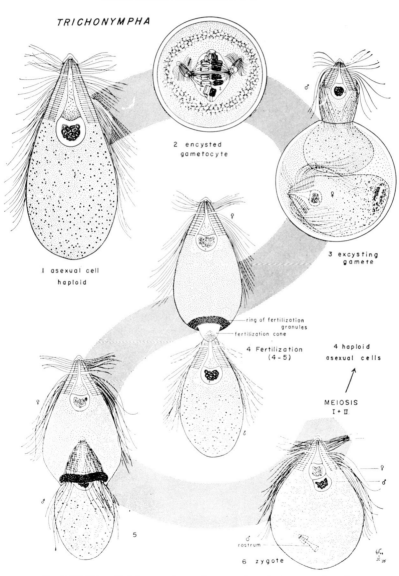

FIG. III–27.—*Trichonympha* and some steps in its sexual cycle. (Cleveland, courtesy of J. Protozool.)

FLAGELLATES OF UNCERTAIN AFFINITIES

Until further morphological and life history studies are made, we will follow Grassé's[17] suggestion to consider the following two genera of flagellates as *incertae sedis*. Both are characterized by a cytostome and four flagella.

Costia, (Fig. III–28) with two short anterior flagella and two trailing flagella (all arising within a slightly spiral longitudinal groove)

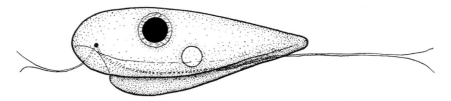

Fɪɢ. III–28.—*Costia necatrix*, showing ventral body groove, basal granule, flagella, nucleus, and contractile vacuole. × 7,500. (Tavolga and Nigrelli, courtesy of Trans. Amer. Micro. Soc.)

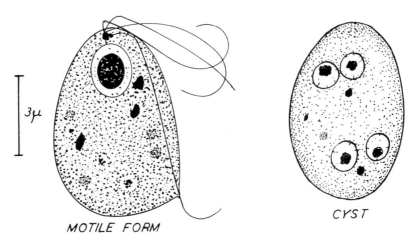

MOTILE FORM   CYST

Fɪɢ. III–29.—*Enteromonas hominis* from the intestine of man. (Original.)

occurs attached to the skin of fishes. *C. necatrix* causes serious damage and often a high rate of mortality in salmon, trout, and pond fishes. *Enteromonas hominis* (Fig. III–29) is a tiny flagellate about 7 microns long by about 4 microns wide. It has been reported from the intestine of man in the warmer countries of the world but it is not pathogenic. There are three anterior flagella and one which arises anteriorly but adheres to the body as it passes backwards, then emerges as a free flagellum posteriorly. The cyst possesses four nuclei, two at each pole.

BIBLIOGRAPHY

1. AINSWORTH, G. C. and SNEATH, P. H. A., (ed.), 1962. *Microbial Classification*. Cambridge Univ. Press, London and New York.
2. AMRAN, A. R., 1961. *The Ecology of Leishmaniasis*. In: MAY, J. M. (ed.), *Studies in Disease Ecology*, Chapter 11. Hafner Publ. Co., N. Y. 613 pp.
3. APTED, F. I. C., ORMEROD, W. E., SMYLY, D. P., STRONACH, B. W., and SZLAMP, E. L., 1963. A Comparative Study of the Epidemiology of Endemic Rhodesian Sleeping Sickness in Different Parts of Africa. J. Trop. Med. Hyg., *66*, 1–16.
4. BIAGI, F. F., 1953. Algunos Comentarios Sobre las Leishmaniasis y sus Agentes Etiológicos. *Leishmania tropica mexicana*, Neuva Subespecie. Medicina, Méx., *33*, 401–406.
5. BOYDEN, A., 1957. Are There Any "Acellular Animals"? Science, *125*, 155–156.
6. CAIN, A. J., 1962. *Evolution of Taxonomic Principles*. In: AINSWORTH AND SNEATH, (ed.), *Microbial Classification*. Cambridge Univ. Press, London and New York, 1–13.
7. CLARK, T. B., 1959. Comparative Morphology of Four Genera of Trypanosomatidae. J. Protozool., *6*, 227–232.
8. CORLISS, J. O., 1961. *The Ciliated Protozoa: Characterization, Classification, and Guide to the Literature*. Permagon Press, New York. 310 pp.
9. CORLISS, J. O., 1962. Taxonomic Procedures in Classification of Protozoa. In: AINSWORTH and SNEATH, (ed.), *Microbial Classification*. Cambridge Univ. Press, London and New York, 37–67.
10. CUNNINGHAM, M. P. and VICKERMAN, K., 1962. Antigenic Analysis in the *Trypanosoma brucei* Group, Using the Agglutination Reaction. Trans. Roy. Soc. Trop. Med. Hyg., *56*, 48–59.
11. DE AZEVEDO, J. F., 1962. Biología da *Leishmania donovani* em Relacão com a sua Accão Patogénica e a Epidemiollgía do Kala-Azar. Rev. Ibérica Parasitol., *22*, 3–48.
12. FALLIS, A. M. and BENNETT, G. F., 1961. Sporogony of *Leucocytozoon* and *Haemoproteus* in Simuliids and Ceratopogonids and a Revised Classification of the Haemosporidiida. Can. J. Zool., *39*, 215–228.
13. FERREIRA-SANTOS, R., 1961. Aperistalsis of the Esophagus and Colon (Megaesophagus and Megacolon) Etiologically related to Chagas' Disease. Symposium by South American Authors. I. Amer. J. Digest. Dis., *6*, 700–726.
14. FROST, J. K., 1961. *Trichomonas vaginalis* and Cervical Epithelial Changes. In: The Cervix, 1961. Ann. New York Acad. Sci., *97*, 792–799.
15. GARNHAM, P. C. C., 1962. Cutaneous Leishmaniasis in the New World with Special Reference to *Leishmania mexicana*. Sci. Repts. Ist. Super. Sanita, *2*, 76–82.
16. GARNHAM, P. C. C. and BIRD, R. G., 1962. A Preliminary Study of the Fine Structure of *Leishmania Mexicana* as seen under the Electron Microscope. Sci. Repts. Ist. Super. Sanita, *2*, 83–88.
17. GRASSÉ, P., 1953. *Traité de Zoologie*. Vol. I, Parts 1–2. Masson et Cie, Paris.
18. GRELL, K. G., 1956. *Protozoologie*. Springer-Verlag, Heidelberg. 284 pp.
19. HALL, R. P., 1953. *Protozoology*. Prentice-Hall, Inc., New York. 682 pp.
20. HOARE, C. A., 1955. The Epidemiological Role of Animal Reservoirs in Human Leishmaniasis and Trypanosomiasis. Vet. Rev. and Ann. 1 Part II, 62–68.
20a. HONIGBERG, B. M., 1961. Comparative Pathogenicity of *Trichomonas vaginalis* and *Trichomonas gallinae* to Mice. I. Gross Pathology, Quantitative Evaluation of Virulence and Some Factors Affecting Pathogenicity. J. Parasitol., *47*, 545–571.
21. HYMAN, L. H., 1940. *The Invertebrates I. Protozoa Through Ctenophora*. McGraw-Hill Book Co., New York. 726 pp.
22. JAHN, T. L. and JAHN, F. F., 1949. *How to Know the Protozoa*. William C. Brown, Dubuque, Iowa. 234 pp.
23. KUDO, R. R., 1954. *Protozoology*, 4th ed. Charles C Thomas, Springfield, Illinois. 966 pp.
24. LAIRD, M., 1959. *Blastocrithidia* n.g. (Mastigophora: Protomonadina) for *Crithidia* (in part), With a Subarctic Record for *B. gerridis* (Patton). Can. J. Zool., *37*, 749–752.
25. LEVINE, N. D., 1961. *Protozoan Parasites of Domestic Animals and of Man*. Burgess Pub. Co. 412 pp.

26. Lwoff, A. (ed.), 1951–1955. *Biochemistry and Physiology of Protozoa*. Vols. I and II. Academic Press, New York.
27. Mackinnon, D. L. and Hawes, R. S. J., 1961. *An Introduction to the Study of Protozoa*. Oxford at the Clarendon Press. 506 pp.
28. Manwell, R. D., 1961. *Introduction to Protozoology*. St. Martin's Press, New York. 642 pp.
29. May, J. M., 1961. The Ecology of African Trypanosomiases. In: May, J. M. (ed.), *Studies in Disease Ecology*, Chapter 9. Hafner Publ. Co., N. Y., 613 pp.
30. Noble, E. R., 1955. The Morphology and Life Cycles of Trypanosomes. Quart. Rev. Biol., *30*, 1–28.
31. Rodrigues Da Silva, J., 1957. Leishmaniose visceral (Calazar). Publ. by the author. Rua Sousa, Lima. 185 Copacabana, Rio de Janeiro, Brazil. 497 pp.
31a.Scholtyseck, E., 1963. Vergleichende Untersuchungen über die Kernverhältnisse und das Wachstum bei Coccidiomorphen unter besonderer Berücksichtigung von *Eimeria maxima*. Zeit. f. Parasitend., *22*, 428–474.
32. Vickerman, Keith., 1962. The Mechanism of Cyclical Development in Trypanosomes of the *Trypanosoma brucei* sub-group: an Hypothesis Based on Ultrastructural Observations. Trans. Roy. Soc. Trop. Med. & Hyg., *56*, 487–495.
33. Wenyon, C. M., 1926. *Protozoology*. 2 vols. Bailliere, Tindall & Cox, London.
34. Williamson, J., 1962. Chemotherapy and Chemoprophylaxsis of African Trypanosomiasis. Exper. Parasitol., *12*, 323–367.

CHAPTER IV

Phylum Protozoa, Subphylum Sarcodina

THESE protozoa are usually microscopic, floating or creeping in fresh or salt water, or occasionally they are sessile. Locomotion is characteristically accomplished by means of "false feet" or *pseudopodia*. These organelles are cytoplasmic extensions which may be broad or filamentous or variable in shape, and they may move rapidly or sluggishly. Pseudopodia usually are thrust out and withdrawn in an unpredictable fashion. The cytoplasm may contain contractile vacuoles (in freshwater species); fluid-filled vacuoles which do not contract; and food vacuoles filled with bacteria, with other microorganisms or with other organic material. There may or may not be a distinct ectoplasm and endoplasm. The nucleus contains an endosome which may be large, small, or it may consist of a group of granules. It may be centrally located or be eccentric in position. Sometimes there is a nucleolus. Chromatin material may easily be seen as clumps or minute granules on the inner nuclear membrane, and thus they may appear as a distinct ring in optical section. Chromatin material may also be scattered in the nucleus or it may form a ring or "halo" around the *endosome*. Reproduction usually occurs by binary fission or by multiple fission, plasmotomy or budding, but sexual processes are involved in some species. Cysts are common among many of the parasitic forms. The motile organism (vegetative or trophic stage) becomes rounded, and secretes a resistant cyst wall around itself. Within this cyst the nucleus may divide several times. Food is stored as a glycogen vacuole in some species and the cytoplasm may contain structures of obscure function, the *chromatoidal* (or *chromatoid*) *bodies*. These structures are deeply stained with certain dyes, are present in young cysts and are convenient objects for taxonomic purposes. They may serve as protein reserves.

There are two classes of Sarcodina, the **Actinopodea** and the **Rhizopodea.** The former class possesses spine-like pseudopodia and is free-living. The latter comprises many parasitic and free-living forms, but we will consider only the parasitic species.

CLASS RHIZOPODEA

ORDER AMOEBIDA

The student whose only familiarity with this group is based upon classroom studies of the free-living *Amoeba proteus* would hardly recognize the parasitic forms. These parasites are usually much smaller than *A. proteus*, many averaging about 10 microns in diameter, and many of them usually seen only in the cyst stage. The motile stage, or *trophozoite*, moves by means of relatively broad pseudopodia, and most of the species possess only one nucleus. The cyst stage, however, often possesses more than one nucleus. Most species live in the digestive tracts of vertebrates and of invertebrates.

Family Dimastigamoebidae. This family is of interest because it clearly shows affinities between flagellates and amebas. The protozoa possess an ameboid phase as well as a flagellated phase (usually bi-flagellated). Common genera are *Dimastigamoeba*, *Naegleria* and *Trimastigamoeba*. They are sometimes found in old feces of insects and of vertebrates, and therefore may be coprophilic (see p. 36).

Family Amoebidae. These amebas are usually free-living or coprophilic and do not possess a flagellate phase. *Vahlkampfia patuxent* is a uninucleate ameba which lives in the gut of the oyster. It possesses a large, broad pseudopodium and it may reach a diameter of 140 microns when cultured *in vitro*. Its usual diameter in the host is about 20 microns. The nucleus contains a large central body known as the *endosome*. This body is also called the *karyosome* or *centriole*. Reproduction is by fission and cyst formation. *Vahlkampfia* (Fig. III–2) is commonly found in the intestines of mammals as a coprophilic protozoon (p. 36). *Acanthamoeba*, which resorbs its endosome during division, and *Hartmanella*, are small forms similar to *Vahlkampfia*, and they may also be found as coprophilic species. *Acanthamoeba* is seriously pathogenic to mice and monkeys if inoculated into these animals. It has been isolated as a contaminant from trypsinized monkey kidney cells.[10] All of these amebas, including the well-known genus *Amoeba*, possess large endosomes in the nucleus, and all may be found in the soil. *Sappinia diploidea* (Fig. III–3), sometimes found in great numbers in old feces, possesses two nuclei.

Family Entamoebidae. Most students are well aware that man may harbor intestinal amebas. Not so well known, however, is the fact that many other animals may play host to these parasites. Even invertebrates have their share, and, surprisingly enough, some protozoa are themselves infected with parasitic amebas. Our whole concept of the relationships between amebas and their hosts is undergoing significant changes. Amebas of monkeys have been found to be infective to dogs; some presumably soil amebas may be pathogenic to monkeys; and some amebas of man have shown themselves able to grow in cultures at room temperatures. We are entering a period of extremely active research on these organisms and soon we will have to revise some of the concepts which have guided our thinking for many years.

The genus *Entamoeba* is usually found in the intestines of invertebrates and vertebrates. The vesicular nucleus possesses an endosome which is usually small and located at or near the center of the nucleus. Granules may occur on the inner wall of the nuclear membrane or around the endosome. The nuclei of the cysts are similar but may number from one to eight. Chromatoidal bodies are often present in young cysts.

The genus *Endamoeba* was originally created for *E. blattae* in cockroaches (see below). There is no endosome but numerous granules are located near the thick nuclear membrane. Cysts may contain many nuclei. Species of this genus are restricted to invertebrates.

AMEBAS IN INVERTEBRATES

Entamoeba sp.,[22] which is morphologically similar to *E. ranarum* in frogs, lives in the opalinid ciliates which themselves are parasitic in toads and frogs. The motile or trophozoite stage of the ameba averages 8 microns in diameter. It lives in pockets in the ciliates, sometimes in such large numbers that there is little room for any-

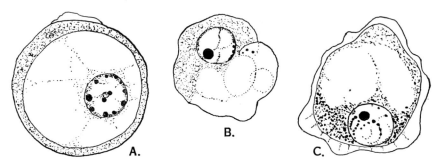

FIG. IV–1.—*Entamoeba phallusae,* an ameba from the intestine of an ascidian at Plymouth, England. (Mackinnon and Ray, courtesy of Jour. Marine Biol. Assn. of the United Kingdom.)

thing else (Fig. VI–3). Cysts averaging 9.4 microns (7.7–10.8 microns) occur in the ciliate host. Some of the amebas are parasitized by dot-like organisms which are probably *Sphaerita* (see p. 140). Thus the frog gut contains ciliates (*Zelleriella*), which harbor amebas which are host to *Sphaerita*.

Endamoeba blattae has been found in the intestines of cockroaches and termites. The parasite varies from 10 to 150 microns in diameter and it forms multinucleate cysts. Pseudopodia are usually broad, and striations often appear to exist in the body. The organism is probably harmless to the insects.

Entamoeba phallusae (Fig. IV–1) has been found in the intestine of the ascidian, *Phallusia mamillata*, at Plymouth, England.[12] It measures 15 to 30 microns by 10 to 15 microns in the motile stage. Cysts average 21 by 19 microns. The nucleus is prominent and eccentric. Small, unidentified amebas have also been found in the ascidian, *Clavellina lepadiformis*.

Entamoeba aulastomi lives in the gut of a horseleech, *Haemopsis sanguisugae*. The cysts contain four nuclei. *Endamoeba philippinensi* and *Endamoeba javanica* both may be found in the intestine of the wood-feeding roach, *Panesthia javanica*. The bee, *Apis mellifica* is the host of *Endamoeba apis*; and crane fly larvae have been found to harbor *End. minchini*.

Hydramoeba hydroxena is a pathogenic parasite of the coelenterate, *Hydra*, on which it lives. The ameba ranges in size from 60 to 380 microns in diameter and it may kill a hydra in a few days by eating the host's epithelial cells.

AMEBAS IN AMPHIBIA

Entamoeba ranarum is a parasite (possibly pathogenic) of the large intestine of frogs. The motile stages usually vary in size from 10 to 50 microns in diameter. There is a small endosome in the nucleus, and the cysts usually possess four nuclei, although as many as sixteen have been reported. Similar amebas have been found in the salamander, *Triton palmatus*, and in *T. taeniatus*.

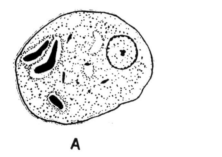 

A   **B**

FIG. IV–2 —*Entamoeba invadens* found in the gut of turtles and snakes. The parasite is pathogenic in snakes. *A*, motile form; *B*, cyst. (Hill and Neal, courtesy of Proc. Zool. Soc., London.)

AMEBAS IN REPTILES

Entamoeba invadens (Fig. IV–2) is the best-known form from these hosts. It lives in the intestine, is similar in many respects to *E. histolytica* of man (see below), and it may be highly pathogenic. This ameba has become a favorite for *in vitro* studies of metabolism. One of the prerequisites for mass encystation of *E. invadens* within its host is the ingestion by the protozoon of minute particles of carbohydrate. The amebas apparently are not able to absorb dissolved food, as do the tapeworms. A comparison of this species of ameba in experimental snakes with those in turtles shows that in herbivorous turtles the ameba is harmless. This difference is probably related to the abundance of particulate carbohydrate in the turtle's intestine, and the absence of it in the gut of the snake.[13] *E. invadens* has been found to be pathogenic to chicks. See Balamuth[1] for a consideration of the effects of some environmental factors upon growth and excystation.

Endolimax clevelandi (Fig. IV–3) was found in the intestine of the turtle, *Pseudemys floridana mobilensis*. The small trophic stage measures 4.7 to 14 microns in diameter, averaging about 7 microns.

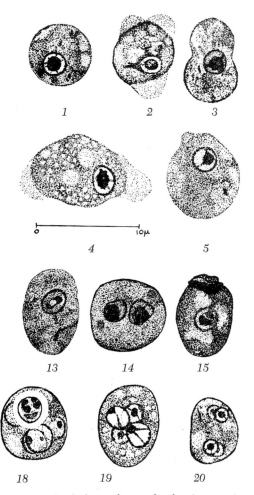

Fig. IV–3.—*Endolimax clevelandi* from the turtle showing motile stages and cysts. *1* to *5* are motile stages, *13* to *15* precystic, *18* to *20* cysts. (Gutierrez-Ballesteros and Wenrich, courtesy of J. Parasitol.)

A finely granular ectoplasm encloses a coarser endoplasm. Vacuoles may or may not be present and some of them may contain bacteria or other food. The nucleus is vesicular in appearance with a large endosome. Cysts are often elliptical (an *Endolimax* trait), and they range from 4.5 to 10 microns in diameter. The mature cyst contains four nuclei which are similar to those in the motile stage.

6

AMEBAS IN BIRDS

The freedom from amebas enjoyed by birds as compared with their burden of other parasites is difficult to explain. Probably a more thorough search of birds for intestinal amebas would be productive. The few amebic parasites reported from birds include *Entamoeba lagopodis* (=*E. gallinarum?*) and *Endolimax gregariniformis* (= *E. janisae*) in the cecum of the grouse, *Lagopus scoticus*; *Entamoeba anatis* in the duck; and *E. gallinarum* in various fowl.

AMEBAS IN MAMMALS

In cattle, *Entamoeba bovis* (Fig. IV–4), from the intestine, has been described. The motile form averages 5.3 by 7.5 microns with

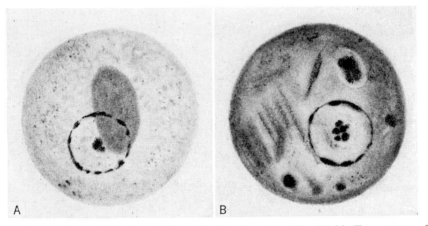

Fig. IV–4.—*Entamoeba bovis* cysts from the intestine of cattle. (Noble E., courtesy of Univ. Calif. Pub. Zool.)

smoothly granular cytoplasm filled with vacuoles. The large nucleus has conspicuous peripheral chromatin and a large central endosome made up of compact granules. Cysts average 8.8 microns (4 to 15), possess a single nucleus and, in young forms, irregular chromatoidal bodies which stain deeply with hematoxylin. Glycogen vacuoles are common in the cysts. *E. histolytica* has been reported from the intestine of cattle.

Sheep are host to *Entamoeba ovis* in the intestine. Examination of host feces rarely discloses motile forms. Cysts average 7.2 microns (4 to 13) in diameter and they contain chromatoidal bodies of irregular shapes. The nucleus is often eccentric in position and is occasionally surrounded by a clear area. Peripheral chromatin is moderate in amount and the endosome is composed of a relatively large compact mass of granules. Many variations of these characteristics exist. *E. caprae* has been reported from the stomach.

Goats and pigs play host to the intestinal ameba, *Entamoeba debliecki* (= *E. polecki*). The motile stage averages 13 by 16 microns and it possesses finely granular ectoplasm and coarser endoplasm. The nucleus is large, usually pale, and the peripheral chromatin appears to be a homogeneous ring. The central endosome is large (2.7 microns) and often indistinct. Cysts average 8 microns (4 to 17) in diameter. Highly variable chromatoidal bodies occur in large cysts. The endosome varies from a very large mass to a small one surrounded by a "halo" of granules. Three other species have been recorded from the goat intestine. They are *E. wenyoni*, *E. dilimani*, and *E. caprae*. The latter has also been found in the stomach.

Pigs have in the large intestine, in addition to *Entamoeba debliecki* (=*E. suis* or *E. polecki*?), *E. histolytica*, *E. coli*, *Endolimax nana* and *Iodamoeba bütschlii* (= *I. suis*).

Considerable confusion exists with regard to the correct names for these entamoebas of domestic animals. They all possess essentially the same morphological features. See Noble and Noble[17] and Hoare[8] for discussions of the problem and a review of the literature. Hoare stated that, "there are definite indications that clinical amoebiasis caused by *Entamoeba histolytica*—both acquired from human sources and spontaneous—does occur in certain mammals, and it is conceivable that they might serve as reservoirs of human infection. Furthermore, the possibility of other species of amoebae being pathogenic cannot be excluded."

Entamoeba intestinalis is said to be a parasite in the intestines of horses, pigs, cats, turkeys, and probably of other animals in Holland. The amebas have certainly been found in the cecum and colon of horses. Trophic forms are common whereas the cysts are rare or absent. The nuclei are of the *E. coli* type (see below) and the eccentric endosome is surrounded by a ring of granules. *E. gedoelsti* has been suggested as a better name for this ameba. *E. equi* (= *intestinalis* ?) has also been found in the feces of horses. Another horse ameba, *E. gingivalis* var. *equi* (= *E. equibuccalis*) may occur around the teeth.

Dogs may harbor amebas but the identification of species is uncertain. *Entamoeba venaticum* (= *E. histolytica* ?, *E. caudata* ?) has been described from the large intestine, and *E. gingivalis* (= *E. canibuccalis*?) has been reported from the mouth. *E. histolytica* was identified in 8.4 per cent of the dogs in Memphis, Tennessee. *E. coli* and *Endolimax nana* have also been reported from the intestine of the dog.

Cats apparently do not have their own amebas, but they can easily be infected with *Entamoeba histolytica* from man. For this reason kittens are often used in experiments with this important human parasite.

Rabbits may harbor *Entamoeba cuniculi* (= *E. muris*) which is similar to *E. coli* of man. Also in the cecum is *Endolimax* sp.

Guinea pigs are host to *Entamoeba cobayae* (= *E. caviae* and *E.*

muris?) also similar to *E. coli* of man. This species occurs in the cecum, but the intestine harbors *Endolimax caviae.*

Rats and mice, like the two hosts above, possess an intestinal ameba which resembles *Entamoeba coli.* It is named *E. muris* (Fig. IV–5). Naturally infected rats with *E. histolytica* have been reported from England, Iraq, Indonesia and the United States. *Endolimax ratti* occurs in the rat colon. It is indistinguishable morphologically from human *E. nana.*

Macaque monkeys may harbor several amebas which are identical with those of man. Those species reported from the large intestine are: *Entamoeba histolytica* (= *E. nuttalli, E. duboscqi, E. cynomolgi*); *E. coli* (= *E. legeri*); *E. chattoni; Endolimax nana* (= *cynomolgi*); *Iodamoeba bütschlii* (= *I. kueneni*).

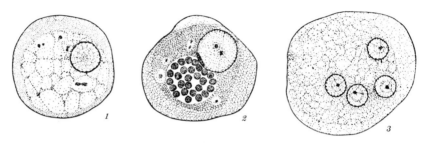

Fig. IV–5.—*Entamoeba muris*, found in rats and mice. The figures show nuclear structure.

1, Ameba with highly vacuolated endoplasm and endosome unstained (hemalum). *2*, With included parasite, *Sphaerita. 3*, With four nuclei. (Wenrich, courtesy of Jour. Morph.)

AMEBAS OF MAN

The genera and species of amebas in man are *Entamoeba histolytica* (sometimes separated into two species—see below), *E. coli, E. gingivalis, Endolimax nana, Iodamoeba bütschlii* and *Dientamoeba fragilis.* As with the amebas of animals, the trophozoites of these species are usually uninucleate, and the cysts are commonly multinucleate. Most of the amebas of man are not pathogenic, but *E. histolytica* causes one of the more serious parasitic diseases (*amebiasis*) of tropical and temperate countries.

Entamoeba moshkovskii deserves mention here since it is similar to *E. histolytica* in appearance and could be confused with the latter if sewage is examined for protozoa. *E. moshkovskii* has been found in sewage in several countries and it is used in laboratory cultures for studies on the biochemistry of amebas.

Entamoeba Histolytica

This amoeba is common in man, apes, monkeys, and may also be found in pigs, dogs, cats and rats. According to a widely held view there is only one species of the *Entamoeba histolytica* complex, with a large and a small race. The large race, according to this theory, has two phases. The common, commensal phase has small trophozoites (the "minuta" form); and the much rarer, virulent phase has large trophozoites (the "magna" form). Both kinds of trophozoites produce spores whose mean diameter is about 12 microns. Brumpt[2], however, recognized three species: a small, non-pathogenic *E. hartmanni*; a large, non-pathogenic *E. dispar*; and the large, virulent *E. dysenteriae*.

We have adopted Hoare's[7,8] theory that there are two species, a small, non-pathogenic *Entamoeba hartmanni*; and a large *E. histolytica*. (For justifications see Sarkisyan;[21] and Goldman and Gleason[5]). *E. histolytica* occurs as two races or strains; one, the nonpathogenic, and the other (less common) virulent strain. Virulence and non-virulence can be distinguished only by the infection of experimental animals. Pathogenicity may be attributed, at least in part, to hereditary factors of the amoeba.[15,16]

About 560 million people (21 per cent of the world's population) are infected with the large strain of *Entamoeba histolytica*, but only a small fraction of this number has any clinical symptoms.[9] Certain aspects of the host-parasite relationship in amebic infections remain obscure in spite of the enormous amount of study that has been carried on for well over eighty years. The role of the host in the *initiation* of pathogenicity is particularly elusive. The intestinal mucosa, host diet, bacterial flora, and concurrent infections with other parasites are factors whose bearing on amebiasis needs intensive investigation.

Mature motile (trophic) *Entamoeba histolytica* (Fig. IV–6) average about 25 microns in diameter but they may be twice that size or even larger. The cytoplasm consists of a clear, outer ectoplasm and a finely granular endoplasm. The endoplasm may include food vacuoles filled with red blood cells in various stages of digestion. Clear vacuoles may also be present. Movement is irregular and is associated with pseudopodia which are usually broad and which may sometimes be finger-like in shape. The type and rapidity of movement is variable depending on the consistency of the surrounding medium, age of the parasite, temperature, variety or race of ameba, stage of treatment of the host, and many other factors. Food for these parasites usually consists of bacteria or other organic material to be found in the intestine. Red blood cells are found only in pathogenic forms. Food vacuoles appear to be formed by invaginations of the plasma membrane, and a different vacuole is generally formed for each kind of food particle.[4]

The vesicular nucleus measures about 3 to 5 microns in diameter and it possesses a centrally located granule, the endosome, or a closely packed cluster of minute granules. Other granules of uniform size lie against the inner wall of the nuclear membrane and they appear as a ring in optical section. Spoke-like lines often radiate

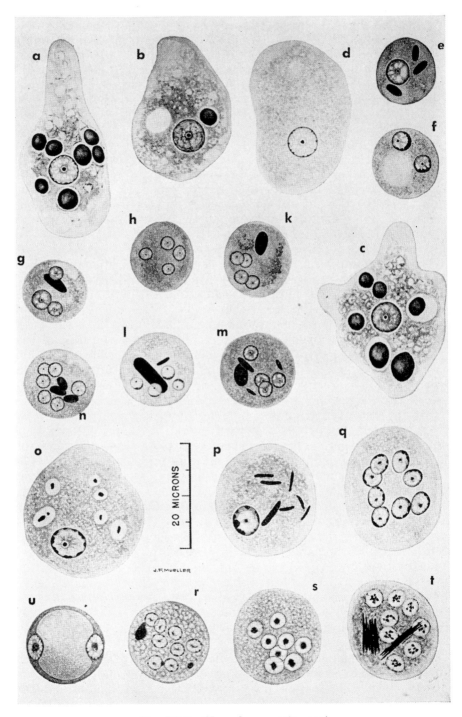

20 MICRONS

J.F.MUELLER

Fig. IV-6.—(*Legend on opposite page.*)

from the endosome to the nuclear membrane. Considerable variation occurs in these morphological features.

Pathogenic forms of this ameba live in lesions of the host's large intestine. They divide by mitotic cell division. The lumen-dwelling forms engulf bacteria, and after a period of feeding and reproduction, vacuoles disappear and the amebas become rounded. Soon a cyst wall begins to form. These uninucleated stages are *precysts*. One or more deeply-staining bar-shaped *chromatoid* bodies characteristically develops in the cytoplasm of the cyst. Cysts, (Fig. IV–6) are about 12 microns in diameter, pass out of the body with feces and become the infective stage. These cysts are killed by drying. Forty-five million cysts may be discharged in the feces of one infected person in one day.

The cyst wall of *Entamoeba histolytica* consists of one layer 0.5 microns in diameter, whereas that of *E. coli*, also common in the human intestine (see below), consists of two layers totaling 1 micron in thickness. Of the two amebas, *E. coli* is far more resistant to drying.

When eaten by a new host, a cyst is carried to the small or large intestine where it escapes the confinement of the cyst wall. The process of escape is called *excystation*. The oxidation-reduction potential possibly acts as a controlling factor in excystation. Once cysts have been formed, they will excyst and produce flourishing cultures in laboratory experiments only if the redox potential is suitably lowered. A rise in potential is accompanied by encystation.

The actual process of excystation starts with increased activity of the ameba within its cyst. Clear ectoplasmic pseudopodia are formed at various points within the cyst and they travel rapidly around the periphery. Frequently they press against the wall at certain spots, as though the imprisoned organism were searching for an exit. Soon a pseudopodium is seen to be applied to one point on the internal surface of the cyst wall. Shortly afterwards the tip of the pseudopodium squeezes through a minute and previously invisible pore at this spot and it appears like a tiny hernia on the outside. Just how the perforation is made is not clearly understood but probably a cytolytic substance is involved.

Metacystic stages involve the division of the quadrinucleate organism into four small uninucleate stages which subsequently

---

Fig. IV–6.—*Entamoeba histolytica. a–c*, Trophozoites from a single case, showing ingested red blood cells. *d*, Trophozoite from another case showing delicate cytoplasm and typical nucleus. *e–n*, Various cysts, with and without chromatoidal bodies, showing 1, 2, 3, 4 and 6 nuclei of varying character. Chromatoidal bodies are commonly present in young cysts, absent in older cysts. In exceptional cases 8 nuclei are present.

Entamoeba coli. o, Trophozoite with ingested bacteria, showing blunt pseudopod, typical nucleus. *p*, Cyst with chromatoidals, single nucleus. *q–t*, Cysts with 8 nuclei, showing varying conditions of cytoplasm, chromatoidals, and nuclear structure. *u*, A common form of coli cyst containing a large central glycogen vacuole and two large nuclei. (Mueller, *The Story of Amebiasis*, courtesy of Winthrop Laboratories.)

grow and divide. The amebas feed on bacteria and on other organic material and, when mature, they usually remain in the lumen of the intestine. The pH near the mucosa is more stable than that of the rest of the lumen contents. Not only the pH, but gases and organic materials in the paramucosal lumen (that portion of the lumen which is immediately adjacent to the mucosa) differ from the condition in the center of the lumen. These physiological strata are obviously of importance in the physiology and distribution of intestinal parasites. They help to explain the differences in ecological niches of such related species as *Entamoeba histolytica* and *E. coli*. The former appears to favor a closer contact with the mucosa.

The mechanism of tissue invasion by *Entamoeba histolytica* is as yet not clearly understood. This ameba can be grown in culture, collected in suspension, and a sterile extract prepared which shows a high proteolytic activity against a casein substrate. This casein-hydrolyzing enzyme is casease. Proteolytic enzymes of this ameba will also dissolve formalin-denatured gelatin, and reduce the viscosity of gelatin solutions.[14] The role of *hyaluronidase* is in the argument stage. That the ameba itself is invasive seems well established. Possibly, however, the parasites merely enter lesions associated with colitis, abrasions, temperature fluctuations, or abnormal diet, or damaged areas produced by other agencies, such as bacteria.

The relationship between bacteria and amebas is an important and little understood one. The presence of living bacteria, or of other living cells, is normally essential not only for the culture of *Entamoeba histolytica* in the laboratory (*in vitro*), but for the life of these protozoa in the intestine of their host. The *pathogenicity* of this ameba is influenced by both pathogenic and non-pathogenic bacteria.[19] Amebas from ameba-trypanosome cultures were found to be unable to establish themselves in germ-free guinea pigs without bacteria, but the addition of either of two species of bacteria (*Aerobacter aerogenes* or *Escherichia coli*) not only permitted the amebas to become established, but promoted invasion of the tissues of the host. Differences in experimental invasiveness and in specific nutritional requirements of *E. histolytica* may be due to bacterial components of the culture rather than to the protozoa. Experiments now in progress with axenic cultures may throw light on this problem.

Since motile amebas are delicate they die quickly when they are outside the body. Transmission is dependent on the cysts which must be kept wet or moist or they, too, will die. If moist, they will live for from a few weeks to a few months depending on the temperature. Cysts normally get into a new host in drinking water or in food. They may be carried mechanically by such insects as flies and cockroaches, or by people with unclean hands. Diagnosis is confirmed by finding cysts or trophozoites in feces.

Entamoeba histolytica may not be confined to the intestine. Once a lesion is made in the intestinal wall, the amebas have an opportunity to travel through the body by way of the blood stream or lymph vessels, and to invade any other tissue. In fact, they have been found in almost all other soft tissue, but the commonest locus of extra-intestinal infection is the liver, particularly the right lobe. Here the infection may be mild, or a large abscess may develop. Abscesses may also occur in the skin, lungs, or brain. Tenderness in the hepatic region is probably due to infection of the hepatic loop of the intestine rather than to pain originating from a liver abscess.[20] Cutaneous amebiasis has also been reported.[11]

The pathology of amebiasis varies a great deal. Among the symptoms are abdominal pains, nausea, vomiting, mild fever, diarrhea, blood and mucus in feces, tenderness over the sigmoidal region of the colon, and hepatitis. Serious infections involve ulceration of the colon, appendicitis, abscess of the liver and, rarely, abscess of the brain. Virulency of *Entamoeba histolytica* can be attenuated by a series of subcultures and it can be increased by repeated passage of the amebas through laboratory animals. Repeated daily stool examinations should be made before proclaiming a negative diagnosis.

Treatment of intestinal amebiasis is usually effective with carbarsone, erythromycin, oxytetracycline, PA-128, triacetyloleandomycin (Tao), paromomycin (Humatin), Entamide or Furamide. E.B.I. (emetine bismuth iodide) and diloxanide furoate have recently been found to be extremely effective. Many other drugs have been used with varying degrees of success. Extraintestinal amebiasis is probably best treated with emetine hydrochloride or with the more recently developed chloroquine phosphate.

Prevention of the disease involves proper disposal of sewage, avoidance of fecal contamination of food, water and eating utensils, and by education. Drugs of preventitive value include bismuth glycoarsanilate and diiodoquin. Immunological techniques have not been proven successful for practical use.

Entamoeba Coli

Another, more common, ameba found in the human intestine is the non-pathogenic *Entamoeba coli* (Fig. IV–6). The organism has a world-wide distribution and the incidence of infection varies greatly. The over-all incidence is probably 28 per cent, making it the commonest species of intestinal ameba of man. Ten to 50 per cent of the population has been reported to be infected in various areas. The type and thoroughness of examination has a great deal to do with the accuracy of the reports.

The life cycle of this parasite differs from that of *Entamoeba histolytica* in that the ameba does not enter tissues. The trophozoite of *E. coli* ranges from 20 to 30 microns in diameter. It is more sluggish than *E. histolytica* and the cytoplasm usually appears much more dense and crowded with food vacuoles. Although there is little clear ectoplasm, a thin clear area is generally to be seen around the nucleus of the trophozoite in stained specimens. The nucleus possesses heavier peripheral chromatin than does *E. histolytica* and the endosome is eccentrically placed. Young cysts are apt to have a large glycogen vacuole and they may possess few nuclei, but mature cysts possess eight nuclei, each being similar to the nucleus of the motile stage. The chromatoidal bodies of the cysts are usually slim with pointed or irregular ends, thus appearing different from the cigar-shaped or bar-shaped bodies in *E. histolytica*. Unlike those of *E. histolytica* the cysts of *E. coli* are not readily killed by drying, which

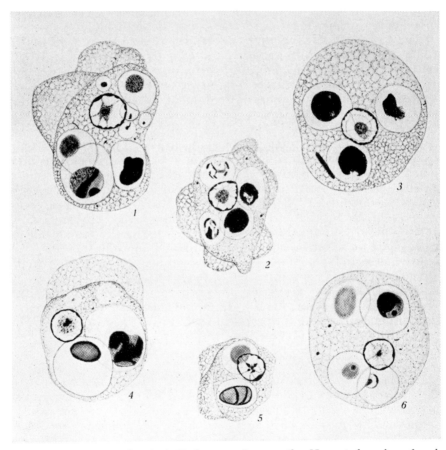

Fig. IV–7.—*Entamoeba gingivalis* from monkey mouth. No cysts have been found.
1, The ameba is thrusting out three pseudopodia. The granules of the halo are spread along the spoke radii. *2,* Many small pseudopodia present, compressed nucleus. The fragmented remains of salivary corpuscles are visible within the vacuoles. *3,* The endoplasm contains one large rod-shaped bacterium. The peripheral chromatin of the nucleus is heavily beaded and the endosome eccentric. *4,* No spoke radii are visible, one large endosomal granule, granular halo sharply defined, one broad pseudopod, and large vacuoles.
5, Six chromosomes within the nucleus, probably a prophase. They are attached by fibers to the peripheral chromatin. Fibers mainly attached to one large peripheral blob. *6,* One small, irregular, central endosomal granule, the granular halo is heavily destained. (Kofoid and Johnstone, courtesy of Univ. Calif. Pub. Zool.)

fact probably accounts for the high incidence of infection. It is possible that they may be air-borne, but this method of infection has not been proved. Monkeys and apes also share with us the honor of this guest; pigs apparently have it but rats seem to be free from it.

Entamoeba Gingivalis

One ameba which is frequently available in a classroom is the mouth form, *Entamoeba gingivalis* (Fig. IV–7). As with *Dientamoeba fragilis* (see p. 94) only the trophozoite stage is known. The ameba lives in the gingival areas of man, other primates, dogs and cats, and can be gathered by gentle probing around the bases of the teeth with a toothpick. The incidence of infection is high, probably around 50 per cent, but the organisms are found more frequently associated with diseased conditions than with healthy mouths. There is no evidence, however, that the amebas cause disease. Related species occur in horses and pigs. Since there are no cysts, and no intermediate hosts are involved, *E. gingivalis* represents the simplest kind of life cycle.

The size of *Entamoeba gingivalis* ranges from 5 to 35 microns in diameter with an average of about 15 microns. In general these amebas appear similar to *E. histolytica* but usually they contain many more large food vacuoles which often enclose remnants of ingested host white blood cells. Chromatin of the nuclei of these host cells takes a deep stain which often gives the cytoplasm of the ameba the appearance of containing several large black nuclei. The nucleus of the ameba is often obscured by the vacuoles. Sometimes a definite ectoplasm may appear to be separated from the endoplasm by a deeply staining ring.

The nucleus is surrounded by beaded peripheral chromatin and it contains an endosome which may consist of a single granule or, more commonly, of several closely grouped granules. Often spoke-like fibrils connect the endosome with the nuclear membrane.

Endolimax Nana

This small intestinal ameba of man, apes, monkeys, and pigs averages about 10 microns in diameter in the motile stage (Fig. IV–8). It lives in the cecum and in the large intestine of 10 to 20 per cent of the population of most countries of the world. Although it is not pathogenic, its presence indicates that the host has been contaminated with fecal material from somebody else. Therefore the presence of *Endolimax nana*, or of any other intestinal parasite whose method of transmission is directly from intestine to mouth, is an indicator that a pathogenic parasite may be present.

Trophozoites of *Endolimax nana* usually appear to be about one-half the size of those of *Entamoeba histolytica* although there may be larger individuals. The cytoplasm often looks rather pale and vacuolated, and the pseudopodia are usually short and broad, with ends showing hyaline ectoplasm.   Food vacuoles are often present.   The single nucleus, usually not readily seen in unstained specimens, contains a large endosome which is often eccentric in position and may even lie against the nuclear membrane.   Sometimes minute threads appear to connect the endosome with this membrane.   Since the nuclear membrane lacks the chromatin clusters or granules common to *E. coli* and to *E. histolytica*, this membrane appears to be an exceedingly fine line and often is barely discernible.

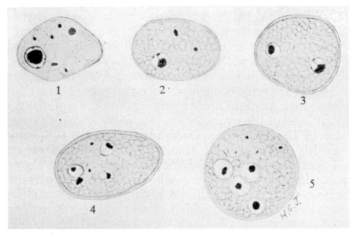

Fig. IV–8.—*Endolimax nana*, a small intestinal ameba of man and monkeys. × 2500.
1, trophozoite with a few endoplasmic inclusions. *2, 3, 4, 5*, one, two and four nucleated cysts. Note the characteristic chromatoid bodies in *2*. *5* may be mistaken for a small cyst of *Entamoeba histolytica*. (Anderson *et al.*, *Amebiasis*, courtesy of Charles C Thomas.)

Cysts of *Endolimax nana* average 9 microns in diameter and are often so pale that they are difficult to see, even in stained material. Four nuclei are usually present and they are similar to those of the motile stage, but only one or two nuclei may be present. In stained material the cysts frequently appear to be no more than indistinct oval bodies containing four tiny, dark dots (the endosomes).

Iodamoeba Bütschlii (=I. Williamsi)

This intestinal ameba (Fig. IV–9) gets its name from its large glycogen vacuole which readily stains brown with iodine.   The organism normally has a diameter of from 9 to 14 microns in the motile state in which the ectoplasm is not clearly differentiated from the endoplasm.[18] The nucleus has little peripheral chromatin and the large endosome is surrounded by a mass of refractile granules.   In stained specimens the endosome is dark but the surrounding granules are usually lighter.

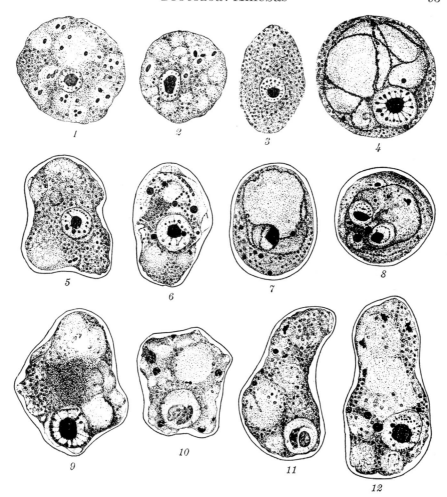

Fig. IV-9.—*Iodamoeba bütschlii* from the intestine of man.

All the figures on this plate were drawn by Mr. R. L. Brown from slides of a single infection (man). *1* to *3*, trophozoites. *1*, Typical individual; nucleus with large deeply-stained endosome surrounded by a row of granules attached to it by radial fibrils. *2*, Small individual with larger nucleus; endosome elongated, granular ring not quite complete. *3*, Probably precystic individual; food bodies mostly absent; endosome of nucleus relatively small; granules more numerous on one side of endosome. *4*, Large early cyst. Large nucleus with granules still in a ring around endosome; apparently several glycogen vacuoles not yet coalesced; dark chromatoidal strands at periphery of glycogen vacuoles. *5*, Cyst of irregular contour; granules of periendosomal ring uneven in size.

6, Normal-sized cyst; note volutin-like granules in cytoplasm; one large intranuclear granule attached to endosome. *7*, Cyst with small nucleus; endosome a lateral plaque against the nuclear membrane, an unusual condition considered to be abnormal. *8*, Round cyst with three and possibly four nuclei; fourth nucleus not clearly distinguishable. *9*, Large cyst with periendosomal granules of nucleus arranged as a peripheral ring as in species of *Entamoeba*. *10* and *11*, Cysts with lightly staining endosomes in nuclei; granules massed into crescents.

12, Large cyst with endosome of nucleus staining more darkly; granules not confined to a lateral crescent. (Wenrich, courtesy of Proc. Amer. Phil. Soc.)

The cyst (about 9 microns long) is unusual because of its rectangular, oval, or varied shape. It, too, normally possesses a large glycogen vacuole. The single nucleus contains a deeply-staining endosome which usually lies against the nuclear membrane, and the granules may be clustered in the shape of a crescent near the endosome. There are many variations in the appearance of these cysts and occasionally two nuclei are present. The ameba is probably nonpathogenic but reports of its pathogenicity exist. It has also been reported from the large intestine of monkeys, apes and pigs, and is probably the same as *Iodamoeba suis*.

Dientamoeba Fragilis

This ameba (Fig. IV–10), as its name indicates, is characterized by the presence of two nuclei. Cysts have never been found. It lives in the intestine of man and is probably present in at least 20 per cent of the population of most countries; an incidence of over 51

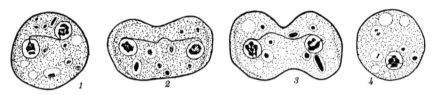

Fig. IV–10.—*Dientamoeba fragilis. 1,* typical binucleate individual, *2* and *3,* stages in division; *4,* uninucleate stage. (Wenrich, courtesy of Jour. Morphol.)

per cent, however, has been reported. The ameba has been found in monkeys and was once reported from sheep. Examination techniques which are especially suited for the identification of cysts would, of course, fail to reveal *Dientamoeba fragilis*. Since the ameba is often difficult to see, most surveys report a very low incidence of infection.

The size of the ameba varies considerably, ranging from 3 to 22 microns with an average of about 8 microns. The cytoplasm, usually pale in appearance even in stained specimens, frequently contains small food vacuoles. Although most specimens possess two nuclei, mononucleate forms are not uncommon and there may even be several of these structures. Each nucleus contains a cluster of closely grouped granules, frequently four, which form the endosome. Frequently a fiber (*paradesmose*) may be seen connecting the two nuclei. There is practically no peripheral chromatin on the nuclear membrane. This ameba resembles a flagellate in some ways.

A tube-like extension can sometimes be seen projecting from the body of *Dientamoeba fragilis*. This organelle seems to be a food-getting apparatus. It is suggestive of a similar structure found on the flagellate, *Histomonas meleagridis*, the causative organism of "blackhead" of turkeys (see p. 42). The mode of transmission is uncertain but a suggestion has been made that the ameba may be carried by an intestinal worm such as *Trichuris* or *Enterobius*.[3]

CLASS ACTINOPODEA

ORDER PROTEOMYXIDA

This group is poorly defined as to its proper taxonomic position and much study is needed to clarify the life cycles of most of the known species. Families of the order include the Labyrinthulidae, Pseudosporidae and Vampyrellidae. Most species attack algae but *Labyrinthula macrocystis* parasitizes eel grass (*Zostera marina*). The labryinthulids are uninucleate but they join to form a network of individuals. The pseudosporids possess ameboid and flagellate stages. In the vampyrellids the mature stage is a plasmodium.

BIBLIOGRAPHY

1. BALAMUTH, W., 1962. Effects of Some Environmental Factors Upon Growth and Encystation of *Entamoeba invadens*. J. Parasitol., *48*, 101–109.
2. BRUMPT, E., 1925. Étude sommaire de l'*Entamoeba dispar* n. sp., amibe à kystes quadrinuclées, parasite de l'homme. Bull. Acad. Méd., *94*, 943–952.
3. BURROWS, R. B. and SWERDLOW, M. A., 1956. *Enterobius vermicularis* as a Probable Vector of *Dientamoeba fragilis*. Am. J. Trop. Med. & Hyg., *5*, 258–265.
4. FLETCHER, K. A., MAEGRAITH, B. G., and JARMILINTA, R., 1962. Electron Microscope Studies of Trophozoites of *Entamoeba histolytica*. Ann. Trop. Med. Parasitol., *56*, 496–499.
5. GOLDMAN, M. and GLEASON, N. N., 1962. Antigenic Analysis of *Entamoeba histolytica* by Means of Fluorescent Antibody. IV. Relationship of Two Strains of *E. histolytica* and One of *E. hartmanni* Demonstrated by Cross-Absorption Techniques. J. Parasitol., *48*, 778–783.
6. HALL, R. P., 1953. *Protozoology*. Prentice-Hall, Inc. N. Y., 682 pp.
7. HOARE, C. A., 1958. The Enigma of Host-parasite Relations in Amebiasis. The Rice Institute Pam., *45*, 23–35.
8. HOARE, C. A., 1959. Amoebic Infections in Animals. Vet. Rev. & Annotations, *5*, 91–102.
9. HOARE, C. A., 1961. Considerations sur l'etiologic de l'amibiase d'apres le rapport hôte-parasite. Bull. Soc. Path. Exot., *54*, 429–441.
10. JAHNES, W. G., FULLMER, H. M., and LI, C. P., 1957. Free Living Amoebae as Contaminants in Monkey Kidney Tissue Culture. Proc. Soc. Exper. Biol. Med., *96*, 484–488.
11. LEÓN, L. A., 1962. Amibiasis Cutánea. Rev. Med. Mex., *42* (899), 375–384.
12. MACKINNON, D. L. and RAY. H. A., 1931. An Amoeba from the Intestine of an Ascidian at Plymouth. Jour. Marine Biol. Ass. of the U.K.XVII (2): 583–586. Fig. 3.
13. MEEROVITCH, E., 1957. On the Relation of the Biology of *Entamoeba invadens* to its Pathogenicity in Snakes. J. Parasitol., *43* (Abstracts), 41.
14. NEAL, R. A., 1956. Proteolytic Enzymes in *Entamoeba histolytica*. Nature, *178*, 599.
15. NEAL, R. A., 1957. Virulence in *Entamoeba histolytica*. Trans. Roy. Soc. Trop. Med. & Hyg., *51*, 313–331.
16. NEAL, R. A., 1958. The Pathogenicity of *Entamoeba histolytica*. Proc. Sixth Internat. Congr. Trop. Med. Malaria, *3*, 5–13.
17. NOBLE, G. A. and NOBLE, E. R., 1952. Entamoebae in Farm Mammals. J. Parasitol. *38*, 571–595.
18. PAN, CHIA-TUNG, 1959. Nuclear Division in the Trophic Stages of *Iodamoeba bütschlii* (Prowazek, 1912) Dobell, 1919. Parasitol., *49*, 543–551.

19. PHILLIPS, B. P., WOLFE, P. A., REES, C. W., GORDON, H. A., WRIGHT, W. H., and REYNIERS, J. A., 1955. Studies on the Ameba-bacteria Relationship of Amoebiasis. Comparative Results of the Intracecal Inoculation of Germfree, Monocontaminated and Conventional Guinea Pigs with *Entamoeba histolytica*. Amer. Jour. Trop. Med. Med. and Hyg., *4*, 675–692.
20. POWELL, S. J., WILMOT, A. J., and ELSDON-DEW, R., 1959. Hepatic Amoebiasis. Trans. Roy. Soc. Trop. Med. and Hyg., *53*, 190–195.
21. SARKISYAN, M. A., 1957. (Observations on *Entamoeba hartmanni*, Prowazek, 1912.) Med. Parasitol. i Parazitarn Bolezni, *26*, 618–623. (Referat. Zhur. Biol., 91033, 1958).
22. STABLER, R. M. and CHEN, T., 1936. Observations on an Endamoeba Parasitizing Opalinid Ciliates. Biol. Bull. LXX (1): 62–71.

CHAPTER V

Phylum Protozoa, the Sporozoa

A WIDE and diversified assemblage of protozoan parasites characterized by the presence of spores has generally been placed, as a
matter of convenience, in a single class or subphylum, Sporozoa, in
spite of the absence of any clear-cut features that bind the assemblage into an obvious taxonomic unit. The complicated spore of the
Myxosporida, with its polar filaments, is totally unlike the *Plasmodium* spore that produces infective sporozoites. The electron
microscope has shown that some forms without spores (*e.g. Toxoplasma*) that are commonly placed as appendages of uncertain affinities, are structurally similar to some of the sporozoan group.

We shall continue to use the term "sporozoa", but only as a well-
known common name for this assemblage, and admit into its embrace
some minute forms that do not produce spores. For our taxonomic
groupings we shall follow the advice of several protozoologists who
published their recommendations in the abstracts of the First International Conference of Protozoologists held at Prague, 1961, and
we shall divide the sporozoa into two subphyla. See Levine,[22] and
Lom and Vávra.[27]

SUBPHYLUM EUSPORA

With few exceptions, spores are produced with one to many motile
sporozoites; no polar filaments or cilia or flagella (except flagellated
microgametes in some species); pseudopodia sometimes present;
complicated life cycle involving sexual, asexual phases; parasitic in
vertebrates and invertebrates.

Locomotion is by gliding or body flexion; pseudopodia, when
present, used for feeding; spores, when present, do not possess a polar
capsule or polar filament; reproduction is by sexual and asexual
methods.

CLASS TELOSPOREA

SUBCLASS GREGARINIA

The gregarines compose a very large group of parasites limited to
invertebrates in which they occupy both tissue cells and body
cavities. Obviously, gregarines within cells are only a few microns
in diameter (from about 10 microns up), but species in body cavities

7   (97)

may be much larger, the maximum being about 10 millimeters in length. In some species the body is divided into two main parts, an anterior *protomerite* and a larger posterior part, the *deutomerite* containing the nucleus. These types are *cephaline* gregarines. In some species the protomerite possesses an anterior anchoring device, the *epimerite* (Fig. V–1), which is left in host tissue when the parasite breaks away. The *acephaline* gregarines lack the septum dividing the body, but sometimes possess an anchoring device known as the *mucron* which remains attached to the parasite when the protozoon becomes free from host tissue. Hosts become infected by swallowing spores.

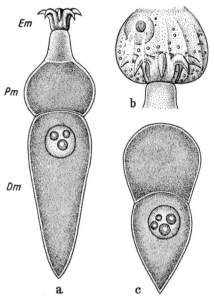

Fig. V–1.—*Corycella armata* a gregarine showing the epimerite, *Em*; protomerite, *Pm*; and deutomerite, *Dm*. *a*, Entire parasite. *b*, Epimerite anchored in host cell. *c*, Gamont detached from epimerite. (Grell, *Protozoologie*, courtesy of Springer-Verlag.)

ORDER SCHIZOGREGARINIDA

The motile stage, or trophozoite, of these gregarines undergoes multiple fission or *schizogony*. The nucleus divides a few or many times without division of the cell itself. Finally the cell divides into as many daughter cells as there are nuclei. This type of trophozoite is called a *schizont*. The daughter cells that appear as the result of schizogony are *merozoites*. Some authors prefer the term *merogony* to indicate the splitting of the schizont into merozoites. Merozoites may repeat the multiplication process but eventually gametocytes are formed. These gametocytes are called *gamonts*. Two gamonts unite in pairs. This union is indicated by the word *syzygy*. After syzygy a cyst develops and the unit is a *gametocyst*.

Within the gametocyst sexual union takes place and the zygote develops into sporozoites which, when liberated, are the infective stages of the parasite. Only one representative of the many genera and species will be mentioned. Most species live in insects.

Schizocystis gregarinoides lives in the intestine of *Helea* (= *Ceratopogon*), a biting midge. The life cycle begins with a zygote, which, with others, lies in a cyst. Each zygote develops into a spore, which germinates into a schizont. Schizogony produces the merozoites, and this cycle—from schizont to merozoites—may be repeated. Eventually some merozoites develop into trophozoites which pair, encyst, and form the zygotes.

ORDER EUGREGARINIDA

Sporozoites enter the host and develop into mature trophozoites without schizogony. The trophozoites become gamonts which unite in pairs, sexual reproduction takes place and the zygote undergoes sporogony. The cephaline gregarines often do not enter host tissue cells, but the acephaline sporozoites usually are intracellular parasites. They often grow large and protrude from the host cells. Finally they leave the gut lining and move freely in the intestinal cavity.

SUBORDER CEPHALINA

Twelve families belong to this suborder found primarily in arthropods and worms. The body of the trophozoite consists of more than one segment or compartment. A typical life cycle is that of *Stylocephalus longicollis* (Fig. V–2), a parasite of the beetle, *Blaps mortisaga*.

Gregarina garnhami (Fig. V–3) is a parasite of the intestinal ceca and mid-gut of the migratory locust, *Schistocerca gregaria*. Sometimes the protozoon destroys considerable areas of the cecal epithelium. The parasites may be present by the hundreds and occur in such masses that there is a barrier between the food material in the lumen of the gut and the gut wall. The gregarines occur in both nymph and adult locusts.

Gregarina blattarum is a common species found in cockroaches (*Blatta orientalis* and others). The sporadins (trophozoites) are enormous, reaching 1100 microns (500 to 1100 × 160 to 400 microns.) The larger ones are easily seen with the naked eye. The cysts open to the outside through eight to ten sporoducts. The life cycle is basically similar to those described above.

SUBORDER ACEPHALINA

This suborder consists of non-septate parasites that live mostly in the coelom of the host. The genus *Monocystis* is well-known because various species are easily found in the seminal vesicles of earth-

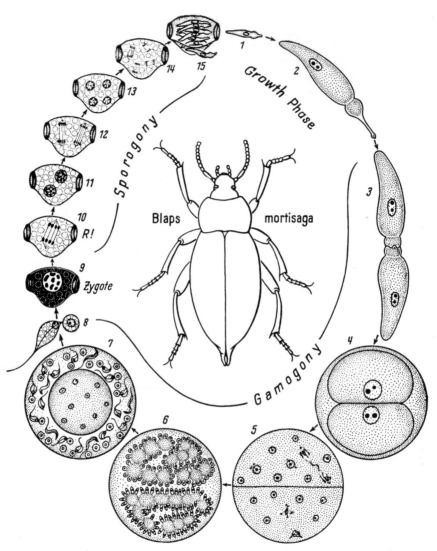

FIG. V–2.—The life cycle of the cephaline gregarine, *Stylocephalus longicollis,* a parasite of the intestine of the beetle, *Blaps mortisaga.* (Grell, *Parasitologie,* courtesy of Springer-Verlag.)

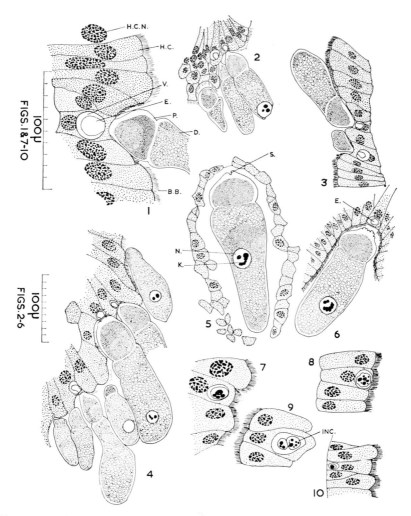

Fig. V–3.—*Gregarina garnhami*, a eugregarine parasite of the intestinal ceca and midgut of the migratory locust, *Schistocerca gregaria*, showing stages in the intestinal ceca. *1* to *4*, Cephalonts (adults) attached to epithelial cells. *5* to *6*, Sporonts (destined to develop into spores) free in the ceca. *7* to *10*, Hyaline inclusions in host cells. (Canning, courtesy of J. Protozool.).

worms and in other oligochaetes. The trophozoites are generally
rounded and do not possess a differentiated anterior end. Spores
produce eight sporozoites.

Monocystis lumbrici (Fig. V–4) lives in the seminal vesicles of
the earthworm, *Lumbricus terrestris*, and in related worms. The
trophozoites, or sporadins, are elongated, measuring about 200 by
65 microns. Infection of the worm occurs by ingestion of mature
spores. In the gut of the worm sporozoites are liberated and they
penetrate the gut wall, migrate through the body and enter the
seminal vesicles. Here the young trophozoites enter tissue cells
and increase in size. The older trophozoites become free from host

Fig. V–4.—*Monocystis lumbrici* from the seminal vesicle of the common earthworm.
(Original.)

tissue and migrate to the sperm funnel where they become attached
again to host cells. Two of them join and secrete a wall around
themselves, becoming a cyst. Within this cyst gametes form and
conjugate, thus producing zygotes (sometimes called sporoblasts).
The sporoblasts become spores and the cycle is complete.

Acephaline gregarines have been found in many oligochaete
worms, sea cucumbers, nemertean worms, insects, and many other
invertebrates. *Lankesteria*, for example, lives in the gut of insects,
planaria and ascidians. A typical life cycle is that of *Lankesteria
culicis*, a parasite of the mosquito, *Aëdes aegypti*. The cycle starts
with the zygote, formed by gametes, occurring in the Malpighian
tubes of the mosquito larva (pupa). Many such zygotes occur in a
large cyst. Each zygote develops into a spore within which eight
sporozoites are formed. When the pupa becomes an adult mosquito
the sporozoites are liberated into the water. Larval mosquitoes eat
the sporozoites which enter cells lining the intestine. Or, if a spore is
eaten, it ruptures in the intestine, liberating the eight sporozoites.
These tiny, motile spindle-shaped organisms enter the gut cells and

develop into the trophozoites. The trophozoites leave the host cells, become gametocytes, and, when the larval mosquito pupates, make their way into the Malpighian tubes. Here the parasites unite in pairs, develop a cyst wall and divide into many gametes which join to produce new zygotes.

SUBCLASS COCCIDIA

These intracellular parasites occur in vertebrates and invertebrates. The protozoa enter epithelial cells and may cause considerable damage. Their distribution is world-wide. Only a few representative families will be described.

The life of a typical coccidian parasite begins with the fertilized *macrogamete* which is the zygote. The parasite at this stage lies imbedded in the intestinal wall, or other epithelial surface, from which it soon breaks and thus lies free in the lumen of the gut. It develops a protective cyst wall and emerges from the host as a unicellular *oocyst*. The cyst wall has two main layers. The exterior one is probably a quinone-tanned protein, whereas the inner one is lipid in nature and is associated with a protein lamella. The viability of an oocyst depends primarily on temperature but it is also influenced by moisture, oxygen, bacteria and fungus action. After a few hours or days, depending on the species, the oocyst undergoes a type of division known as *sporogony*. The nucleus divides into two, then four and finally eight nuclei. Each nucleus, with accompanying cytoplasm, becomes a *sporozoite*. In one genus (*Eimeria*) two sporozoites lie within an enclosing membrane, the *sporocyst*. The sporocyst with its sporozoites is called a *spore*. In another genus (*Isospora*) there are four sporozoites in each of two spores. At this stage the oocyst is infective to another host, and, if it is eaten, the eight sporozoites are liberated in the intestine and each enters a cell of the mucosa. Each sporozoite becomes rounded and forms a *schizont*. There now occurs an asexual process known as *schizogony*, during which process each schizont multiplies into many new cells called *merozoites*. The merozoites break out of the host cells and enter new epithelial tissue. They can develop in the nucleus of host cells as well as in the cytoplasm. Eventually macro- and microgametocytes are formed instead of merozoites. The macrogametocytes enlarge into macrogametes which remain in the host epithelial cells. The microgametocytes develop into motile microgametes which are liberated from the host cells and swim to the cells containing the macrogametes. Fertilization takes place, thus completing the cycle. Characteristically coccidia show a high degree of host specificity. See Becker[2], Levine[23] for a review of the coccidia.

ORDER EUCOCCIDIIDA

The life cycle involves both sexual and asexual phases. Schizogony is present. Parasites of blood cells and epithelial cells of vertebrates and invertebrates.

SUBORDER ADELEINA

Family Adeleidae.   Members of this family are found in the intestinal epithelium and associated glands of invertebrates.   Occasionally they occur in other animals, as in the kidneys of mammals.

Adelina deronis lives in peritoneum cells of the annelid worm, *Dero limnosa*.   The oocyst contains about 12 sporocysts, each of which contains 2 sporozoites.   Oocysts are taken into the digestive tract of the worm where sporozoites are liberated.   The sporozoites make their way to peritoneum cells in which they enter and become trophozoites.

Other genera of the family include *Adelea*, *Karyolysus* (Fig. V–5), *Orcheobius*, *Chagasella*, and *Klossia* (Fig. V–6).   Each varies in the numbers of sporocysts and sporozoites which are produced from the oocysts, and in the host and tissues which are parasitized.

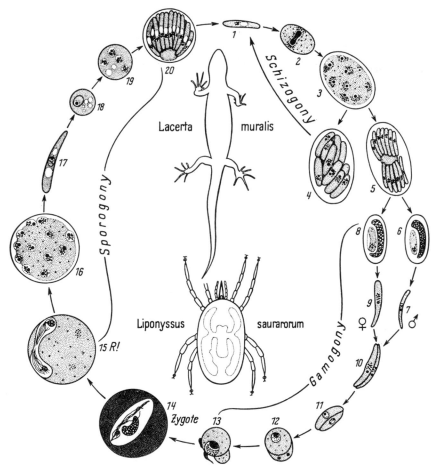

FIG. V–5.—The life cycle of *Karyolysus lacertarum*.   Sporogony occurs in a lizard whereas schizogony and gamogony occur in a mite.   (Grell, *Protozoologie*, courtesy of Springer-Verlag.)

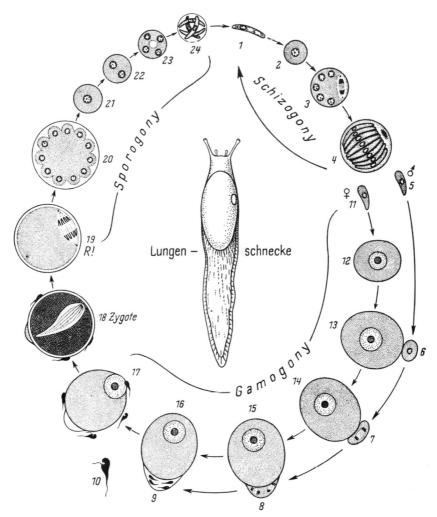

FIG. V–6.—The life cycle of the gregarine *Klossia* which parasitizes a slug. (Grell,
Protozoologie, courtesy of Springer-Verlag.)

Family Haemogregarinidae. This group of coccidia possesses
life cycles involving two hosts: a vertebrate host in which the parasite
lives in the circulatory system, and an invertebrate host involving
the digestive system. Oocysts are small, and there are no sporocysts.
Until more complete life histories are known, the identity and taxonomic position of many described species will remain in doubt. Some
of them may belong to the genus *Hepatozoon*.[18]

Haemogregarina stepanowi (Fig. V–7) begins its life cycle as a
zygote (= ookinete) in the gut of the leech, *Placobdella catenigera*.
The zygote divides three times and forms eight sporozoites. When
an infected leech takes blood from the turtle, *Emys orbicularis*, the

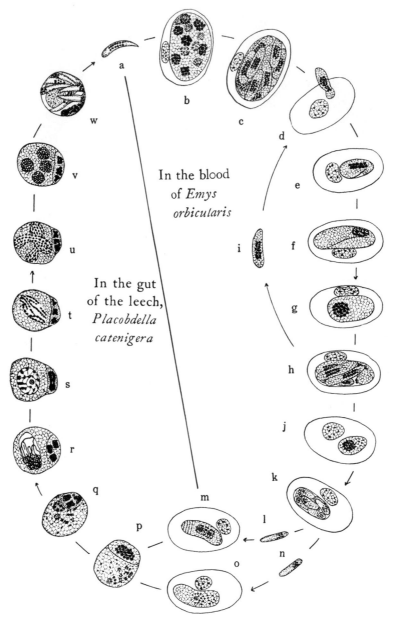

In the blood
of *Emys
orbicularis*

In the gut
of the leech,
*Placobdella
catenigera*

Fig. V–7.—Development of *Haemogregarina stepanowi.* × 1200. (after Reichenow) *a,*
sporozoite; *b* to *i,* schizogony; *j* to *k,* gametocyte-formation; *l, m,* microgametocytes;
n, o, macrogametocytes; *p, q,* association of gametes; *r,* fertilization; *s* to *w,* division of
the zygote nucleus to form eight sporozoites. (Kudo, *Protozoology,* courtesy of Charles
C Thomas.)

sporozoites pass to the vertebrate host and enter red blood cells. Here schizogony occurs and produces merozoites which are liberated from the host cells and infect new red blood corpuscles. Eventually some of the merozoites which enter these host cells develop into gametocytes. If these cells are ingested by a leech, the merozoites are liberated, mature to gametes, and produce zygotes.

Haemogregarines of fish may enter leucocytes as well as erythrocytes, and they can be separated into two broad categories: haemogregarines (without asexual multiplication in red cells) and schizohaemogregarines (with schizogony occurring in red cells.[21] In spite of the large numbers of described species, however, the method of transmission from one fish to another remains a mystery.

Family Hepatozoidae. Many species of *Hepatozoon* occur in the white blood cells of fish, birds and mammals. The oocyst is large and contains numerous sporocysts in which there are numerous sporozoites. The parasite is transmitted by flies, lice, ticks and mites in which the sexual stages occur.

SUBORDER EIMERIINA

In this order there is no syzygy.

Family Aggregatidae. In this family schizogony takes place in the cells of one host, and sporogony in the cells of another host. Marine annelids, crustacea and mollusks serve as hosts. Oocysts typically contain many sporozoites.

Aggregata eberthi (Fig. V–8) undergoes schizogony in the marine crab, *Portunus depurator*, and both sporogony and gamogony in the cuttlefish, *Sepia officinalis*. Sporozoites develop into merozoites in intestinal connective-tissue cells of the crustacean host. When a cuttlefish eats an infected crab, the merozoites develop into gametocytes in the gut wall of the mollusk. Gametes are released, unite, and form zygotes. From the zygotes develop the sporoblasts, spores and finally sporozoites. Crabs eat the spores and the sporozoites enter intestinal cells.

Family Lankesterellidae. The genus *Lankesterella* occurs in amphibia and birds; and the genus *Schellackia* in reptiles. Schizogony, gametogony and sporogony all take place in the tissue cells (*e.g.* macrophage cells of liver, lungs, kidney). Sporozoites enter red blood cells, lymphocytes and monocytes which may be ingested by the intermediate host (leech or mite). The parasites do not develop in the intermediate host. *L. adiei* is common in English sparrows throughout the world.

The genus *Atoxoplasma* has been shown by Lainson to be a synonym of *Lankesterella*. *L. paddae* (Fig. V–9) occurs in passerine birds.

Family Eimeriidae. This family contains a large number of monoxenous genera and species, many of which are of considerable economic importance.[2] Gametes are produced independently and are of two sizes (macro- and micro- gametes). The oocyst (Fig. V–11) usually

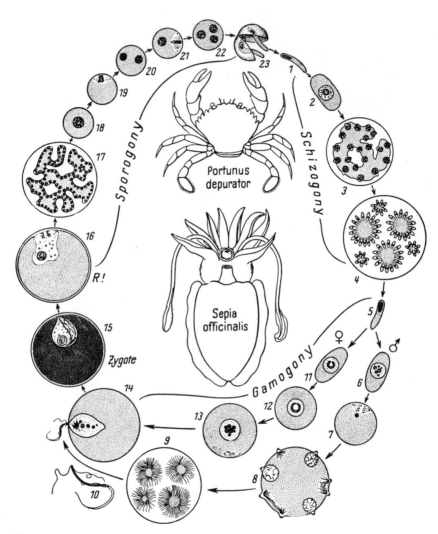

Fig. V–8.—*Aggregata eberthi* showing its life cycle which includes a crab and the cuttlefish. Schizogony occurs in the intestine of the crab whereas sporogony and gamogony occur in the submucosal cells of the intestine of the cuttlefish. (Grell, *Protozoologie,* courtesy of Springer-Verlag.)

contains one to many sporocysts although in a few species sporocysts may be lacking. The number of sporozoites in each sporocyst varies with the species. The oocyst, which is the stage transferred from one host to another, is usually immature when found in fresh feces. A diagram of a generalized life cycle is given in Figure V–10. Note that schizogony and gametogony take place within host cells, and that sporogony occurs outside of the host body.

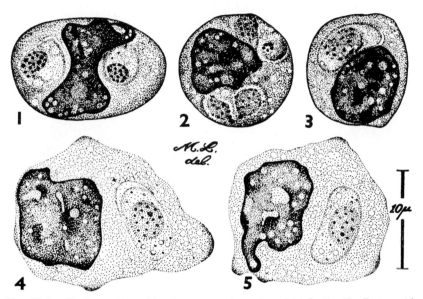

Fig. V–9.—*Lankesterella paddae* from several species of birds (family Zosteropidae, or Silver Eyes) from the South Pacific.
1 and *2*, Division stages, lymphocytes of *Gallirallus australis scotti*, New Zealand. *3*, Non-dividing form, lymphocyte of *Zosterops lateralis lateralis*, New Zealand. *4* and *5*, Non-dividing forms, monocytes of *Zosterops lateralis grisconota*, New Caledonia, and *Z. flavifrons flavifrons*, Futuna, respectively. (Laird, courtesy of J. Parasitol.)

The genus *Eimeria* is characterized by the presence of four spores in each oocyst and two sporozoites in each spore. The many species occur primarily in cells of the gut of vertebrates but may also be found in epithelial cells of the liver, bile duct or other organs. Some species are found in invertebrates. *Eimeria schubergi*, for example, inhabits the intestinal epithelium of the centipede, *Lithobius forficatus*.

The effect of coccidial infection varies widely with the species of host, species of coccidia, age and resistance of host, degree of infection and many other factors. The following description of the effect of coccidiosis in calves, however, gives a general picture of types of symptoms which might be seen in most animals with heavy infections.

"The symptoms of coccidiosis may include rough coat, weakness, listlessness, nervousness, poor appetite, diarrhea, and loss of weight

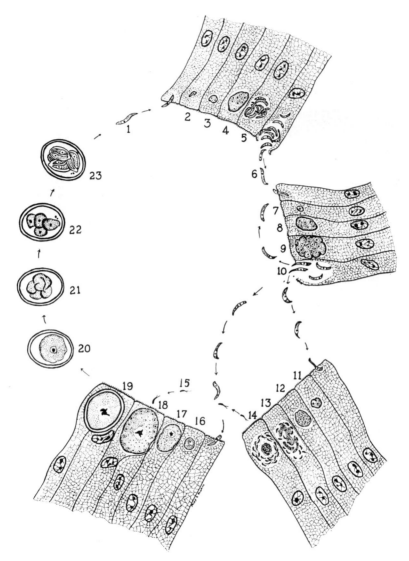

Fig. V–10.—Diagram of a generalized life cycle of a member of the family Eimeriidae.
1, Sporozoite; *2*, Trophozoite; *3* and *4*, Schizonts; *5* and *6*, Merozoites; *7*, Trophozoite; *8* and *9*, Schizonts; *10*, Merozoites; *11* to *13*, Microgametocytes; *14* and *15*, Microgametes; *16* and *17*, Macrogametocytes; *18*, Macrogamete; *19*, Zygote; *20*, Unsporulated oocyst; *23*, Sporulated oocyst.

1 to *5* and *6* to *10*, Schizogony; *11* to *14* and *16* to *19*, Gametogony; *20* to *23*, Sporogony. (Morgan and Hawkins, *Veterinary Protozoology*, courtesy of Burgess Publishing Co.)

or poor gains in weight. The general weakness may cause the calf to defecate without rising, thus soiling its tail, hindquarters and lower part of the body.

When standing the calf may attempt to defecate and not be able to pass feces; the intense straining results in an arched back, raised tail, and a 'pumping' of the sides. The diarrhea may be watery or only slightly liquid, being quite unlike the 'white scours' of calves less than three weeks old. Diarrhea caused by coccidiosis may contain many strands of gelatinous mucus and splotches or streaks of blood. In infections with *Eimeria zurnii* and *E. bovis*, it may be extremely bloody and even include shreds of intestinal tissue or occasionally short lengths of the tubular lining of the damaged intestine."[7a]

Coccidiosis is rare in horses, but cattle are infected by at least twelve species of *Eimeria*. Common ones are *E. zurnii*, *E. bovis* and *E. ellipsoidalis*. Treatment has not been completely successful although the following drugs show promise: sulfaguanidine, sulfaquinoxaline and sulfamethazine. Cleanliness is the best preventative since the disease is carried from animal to animal by oocysts in manure.

At least ten species of *Eimeria* occur in sheep and goats. *E. arloingi*, *E. parva*, *E. faurei* and *E. ninae-kohl-yakimova* are common species. They infect the tissues of the digestive tract, and cause diarrhea, destruction of epithelial tissues, weakness, loss of weight and death. There is no satisfactory treatment although sulfonamides (see above) are of some value. As with calves, clean, dry uncrowded living conditions are strongly recommended.

Hogs may become infected with five species of *Eimeria* and with *Isospora suis*. *E. debliecki* and *E. scabra* (Fig. V–11) are the most pathogenic. Dogs and cats are also host to both genera of coccidia, being infected with *E. canis*, *E. felina* and three species of *Isospora suis*. *E. debliecki* and *E. scabra* (Fig. V–11) are the most pathogenic. Dogs and cats are also host to both genera of coccidia, being infected with *E. canis*, *E. felina* and three species of *Isospora*. Some of the same coccidia occur in foxes. Rabbits may be infected with at least six species of *Eimeria*. A well-known species is *E. stiedae*. Most wild mammals and birds have their own species of coccidia and they are far too numerous even to mention here. Undoubtedly many species are yet to be found and described.

Coccidia are found abundantly in domestic and in wild birds. The parasites cause a serious disease in chickens, geese and turkeys but not, apparently, in ducks. Coccidia which can be found in chickens and turkeys infect mainly the small intestine but they may also be found in other parts of the gut. Twelve or more species infect domestic poultry but those most commonly found in chickens in the United States are *E. necatrix*, *E. acervulina*, *E. maxima*, *E. brunetti*, *E. tenella*, *E. praecox*, *E. mitis* and *E. hagani*. Turkeys are infected with *E. meleagridis*, *E. innocua*, *E. meleagrimitis*, *E. subrotunda*, *E. adenoeides*, *E. dispersa* and *E. gallo-*

pavonis. Young birds are more susceptible than are older ones, and immunity is built up against species harbored. In a bird with heavy infection the intestine may be enlarged and thickened; droppings may be bloody, greenish, brownish or watery. Birds may be obviously ill, and many of them die. One interesting result of infection is a rise in the blood sugar level of the bird. Recent

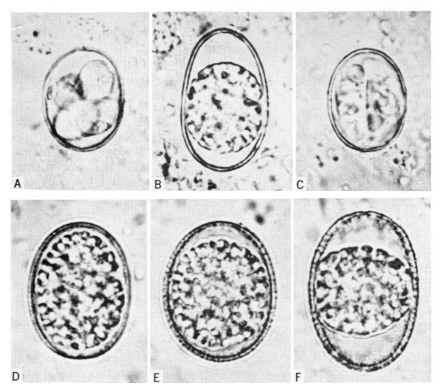

FIG. V–11.—Oocysts of species of *Eimeria* occurring in swine. *A* to *C*, *E. debliecki*, *D* to *F*, *E. scabra.* × 1500.

A, Sporulated cyst of smaller form with polar granule at one side of cyst. *B*, Cyst of larger form with rounded cytoplasm. Clear cyst wall. *C*, Mature cyst.

D to *I*, *Eimeria scabra.* *D*, Immature form with cytoplasm completely filling cyst. *E*, Cyst with cytoplasm beginning to contract. *F*, Cyst with cytoplasm almost entirely contracted, nearly "ball" stage. (Henry, courtesy of Univ. Calif. Pub. Zoo.)

evidence[16] indicates that *Eimeria tenella* within macrophages causes enhanced ribonucleoprotein production by the host cells, and that this new protein is incorporated into the newly formed merozoites. Treatment is reasonably successful with nitrofurazone, sulfaquinoxaline, nicarbazin or nitrophenide. Clean, uncrowded, dry living areas for poultry, as for mammals, are of great importance in prevention and control.

The genus *Isospora* is characterized by the presence of two spores in each oocyst and four sporozoites in each spore. Dogs and cats are parasitized by *Isospora bigemina*, *I. revolta* and *I. felis*. *Isospora suis* has already been mentioned. Frogs may have *I. lieberkühni*. Birds also are parasitized by this genus of coccidia. *Isospora lacazii* is found in the small intestine of sparrows, blackbirds and other passerine birds, and *I. buteonis* occurs in the gut of hawks.

Isospora hominis and *I. belli* (the latter is more common) are found in man. Details of the life cycles have not been worked out but undoubtedly they follow the same general pattern as outlined for all coccidia above. The parasites have been found in man in the Mediterranean area, the Balkan countries, India, the Far East, Hawaii, Mexico, Cuba and South America.

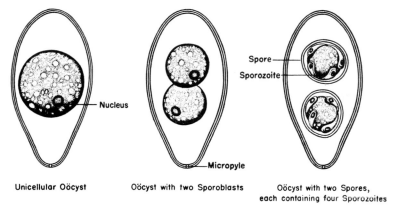

Unicellular Oöcyst | Oöcyst with two Sporoblasts | Oöcyst with two Spores, each containing four Sporozoites

Fig. V–12.—*Isospora hominis*. Oocysts in various stages of development. (Medical Protozoa and Helminth., U.S. Medical School Manual.)

Oocysts of *Isospora hominis* (Fig. V–12) average about 28 by 14 microns in size (20 to 33 microns by 10 to 16 microns). In freshly passed stools the oocysts usually contain undivided zygotes. If the specimen is kept in a covered dish at room temperature for one or two days, the oocysts mature and contain the typical two spores, each enclosing four sporozoites.

Symptoms include abdominal pain, diarrhea, flatulence, digestive disturbances, abdominal cramps, nausea, loss of appetite, lassitude, loss of weight and fever. After the initial infection, the incubation period lasts about a week, then symptoms may or may not appear for about a month. During this time oocysts are discharged. When oocysts are no longer found, the disease has run its course and reinfection apparently does not occur. Coccidiosis, however, is rare in man.

SUBORDER HAEMOSPORINA

The relationships between haemosporina and coccidia are indicated by the general similarity in the asexual cycle, or schizogony, and the sexual cycle, or sporogony. The name "haemosporina" indicates that the parasites live in the blood. Sexual reproduction, which occurs in the blood-sucking invertebrate host, results in naked sporozoites which must be introduced into the vertebrate host by the "bite" of the invertebrate. Schizogony occurs in red blood cells and, in some species, in other cells of the vertebrate body. Microgametes and macrogametes develop independently and the zygote is motile. Pigment (hematin) is usually formed from host hemoglobin. The blood-inhabiting stages are found primarily in birds and reptiles.

Family Plasmodiidae. *Haemoproteus* (= *Halteridium*) is a common parasite of wild birds as well as of domestic ducks and turkeys, and of reptiles. Gametocytes occur in host erythrocytes, and schizogony takes place in endothelial cells of blood vessels. Vectors are midges (Ceratopogonidae) and louse-flies (Hippoboscidae). See figure V–13.

Haemoproteus columbae is a familiar parasite of the red blood cells of the pigeon, *Columba livia*, and of other birds. The sexual phase occurs in the biting (hippoboscid) flies of the genera *Lynchia*, *Pseudolynchia* or *Microlynchia*. Fertilization takes place in the stomach of the fly, and the zygote enters the stomach wall. Asexual reproduction produces a cyst full of sporozoites. The cyst ruptures and the liberated sporozoites enter the bird host with the bite of the fly.

The sporozoites now start the schizogony cycle by entering endothelial cells of blood vessels of various organs, and dividing. Merozoites are produced and are released by the rupture of the infected host cells. These merozoites may enter other endothelial cells or red blood cells. In the latter they become somewhat sausage-shaped. In the erythrocytes they become gametocytes which mature to gametes in the stomach of the fly.

Leucocytozoon (Fig. V–13) is a genus related to *Haemoproteus*.[8] There are relatively few species of this parasite and most, if not all, of them occur in birds. The life cycle lacks erythrocytic schizogony, but schizogony stages occur in the parenchyma cells of the liver or in various other organs, and the schizonts may reach 150 microns in length. As the name indicates, the parasite (gametocytes) may be found in white blood cells, but erythrocytes are also involved. Pigment is not formed in the infected red cells. Dr. Y. C. Pan of the College of Veterinary Medicine, National Taiwan University, finds them only in red blood cells (personal communication). So far as is known, the insect vector is always a blackfly (Simuliidae, p. 477). The zygote in the fly develops into a motile ookinete which eventually forms sporozoites.[10] The two best known species, *Leucocytozoon simondi* and *L. smithi*, of ducklings and turkeys respectively, are seriously pathogenic. The course of the disease in ducklings may be so rapid that the young birds appear in good health one day and are dead the next day. The mortality rate varies a great deal and if a duck recovers it remains a carrier of the disease. There is no ef-

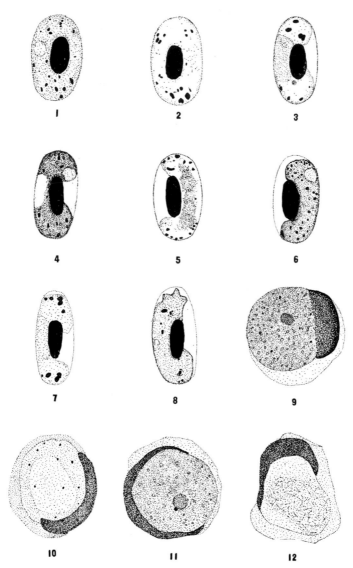

Fig. V–13.—Species of *Haemoproteus* and *Leucocytozoon* from the blood of various birds. *1* to *10*, are × 1942; *11* and *12* are × 1750. *1* and *2*, *Haemoproteus archilochus* from the Ruby-throated Humming bird, showing a macro- and microgametocyte entirely enclosing the host cell nucleus. *3* and *4*, *Haemoproteus quiscalus* from the Bronzed Grackle. A micro- and macrogametocyte. *5* and *6* *Haemoproteus* sp. from the Baltimore Oriole. A micro- and macrogametocyte. *7* and *8*, *Haemoproteus* sp. from the Blue Jay. A micro- and macrogametocyte. *9* and *10*, *Leucocytozoon coccyzus* from the Yellow-billed Cuckoo. A macro- and microgametocyte. *11* and *12*, *Leucocytozoon sakharoffi* from the Eastern Crow. A macro- and microgametocyte. (Coatney and West, courtesy of Amer. Midland Nat.)

fective treatment. The nature of the disease in turkeys parallels that in ducks with minor modifications. Infected birds are weak and nervous and may die in a few hours after symptoms appear. Treatment is of little value, if any. Keeping blackflies away from the bird is a sure preventative but difficult for the average farmer. Screened pens for young birds are recommended. See papers by Fallis et al.,[9,10] and Liu.[25]

Malaria

Plasmodium is of tremendous significance to man because it causes the disease *malaria*, but many other animals also may become infected with *Plasmodium*, among them being monkeys, rats, birds and lizards. Only a general account will be given of the parasites which cause human malaria. Pathogenicity will be mentioned and an outline of the various life cycles will be sketched. The literature on this subject, including vectors, the disease, treatment and control is enormous.

At least two million human beings still die of malaria each year. Why should this be so when we know what causes the disease? We can trace the life cycle of the parasite in detail. We know a great deal about the mosquito that transmits malaria. We even possess drugs that can cure the disease, so why do we permit so many people to die? The answer is because the problem is not primarily a biological one, nor a medical one. The problem is one of economics and sociology. Masses of people in tropical and semitropical countries (such as India) do not have the economic resources with which to combat the mosquito, and to identify and treat the millions of patients, nor, in many areas, do the patients and their families possess enough social awareness of the problem to assist adequately the public health authorities. A community must *want* to be cured before application of scientific knowledge can be effective through cooperation between those ill with malaria and those who know how to eradicate the affliction. But great strides have been made, and large areas of the world once covered by the misery of malaria are now completely free from it. The prospects look bright because the long-sought-for cooperation to wipe out malaria is underway. As Asa Chandler put it, "Malaria today is definitely sick."

The word "malaria" means "bad air", and it was so labeled centuries ago when people thought that night air was bad for the health, especially when one was sleeping. This fear of the unknown, the mystery of the dark, still lingers, and induces some people to close all windows at night. Of course, the night air has nothing to do with malaria, nor with any other disease except that it may bear the organisms which are responsible for the illness. Mosquitoes fly by day as well as by night, but it is during the night when sleep deprives one of his awareness of what is going on about him, that mosquitoes enjoy long hours of freedom for the attack.

Malaria has undoubtedly played a decisive role in the history of civilization. The fall of the Roman empire can be attributed in part to the devastative effect of the illness, to debilitation and death caused by malaria.

In man there are three common species of *Plasmodium: P. vivax, P. malariae* and *P. falciparum.* A fourth species, *P. ovale,* is quite rare. These plasmodia are world-wide in distribution, occurring largely in the warmer countries but they may be found in areas which are freezing cold during the winter, such as North Korea, Manchuria, Southern Russia and a small part of Central United States. Hundreds of millions of people become infected with plasmodia each year.

The Life Cycle of Plasmodium

The life cycle of *Plasmodium* (Fig. V–14) starts with a zygote in the stomach of a female mosquito (many species of *Anopheles* and, for lizard and bird malaria, culicine mosquitoes). The zygote is the result of fertilization; thus the cycle in a mosquito is the sexual phase. The zygote is active and moves through the stomach or mid-gut wall. The parasite at this stage is a "traveling vermicule" and so is called an *ookinete.* Under the lining of the gut the ookinete becomes rounded, forms a cyst, and is called an *oocyst.* The nucleus of the oocyst divides repeatedly to form many nuclei, each of which, with its surrounding cytoplasm, develops into a separate, elongate cell, a *sporozoite*[13]. As a result, the oocyst becomes greatly enlarged and finally bursts, liberating the mass of sporozoites into the body cavity. The development of these sporozoites is known as *sporogony.*

The sporozoites invade the entire mosquito and many of them get into the salivary glands and so are in a favorable position to enter the next host when the mosquito bites man.

When sporozoites are introduced into the blood stream of man by the bite of a mosquito, a series of cycles begins involving different cells and tissues. The blood is non-infective during early stages of infection. The sporozoites mark the end of the sexual cycle. They promptly enter various tissue cells such as liver parenchyma and fixed macrophages. Within these cells the parasite is first known as a *cryptozoite,* because it is not found in the blood smear and thus is hidden from view. Its body enlarges and its nucleus divides several times. The splitting of the nucleus is the basis for another term, the *schizont,* which refers to the asexual form with multiple division of the nucleus but no division of the parasite cell. Division of the schizont nuclei is *schizogony.* Eventually the parasite cell divides into as many units as there are nuclei and the host cell ruptures, liberating the new parasites. These new parasites are *metacryptozoites* (also called *merozoites*) which may enter other tissue cells and repeat the schizogony cycle. This repetition apparently does not occur in the cycle of *Plasmodium falciparum.* To this point the parasites have not entered red blood cells; thus they have been in the *exoerythrocytic* stage.[3]

Metacryptozoites gain access to the blood stream and enter the erythrocytes and start the *erythrocytic phase* of the life cycle. In the red blood cells, in typically-stained smears, a plasmodium soon shows a red nucleus and a ring-shaped blue cytoplasm. This appearance gives rise to the name *signet ring* for the parasite at this stage. The ring configuration is altered as the protozoan cell begins to grow within the blood cell. At this stage the plasmodium may be active, and is called a *trophozoite*. These intracellular parasites engulf portions of the host cytoplasm.

Schizogony occurs again. The schizont is characterized by dividing or segmenting nuclei, so it is sometimes called a *segmenter*. The cytoplasm of the red blood cell may contain various pigment granules (*e.g.* Schüffner's dots). The plasmodium divides into merozoites which are comparable to the metacryptozoites formed earlier in the life cycle. Merozoites break out of the red cells and each may enter other erythrocytes, or even liver parenchyma, and repeat the process of schizogony. It is interesting to note that the stages outside of the red blood cells have a much higher metabolic rate than do those within these host cells. Eventually some of the merozoites in the blood cells develop into the sexual forms starting as small solid bodies and growing into male *microgametocytes* or female *macrogametocytes*. When a mosquito bites man at this stage of the life cycle, the micro- and macrogametocytes are taken

---

LEGEND FOR PLATE I.

Stages of *Plasmodium vivax* in human erythrocytes from thin-film preparation.
1. Normal sized red cell with marginal ring form trophozoite.
2. Young signet ring form trophozoite in a macrocyte.
3. Slightly older ring form trophozoite in red cell showing basophilic stippling.
4. Polychromatophilic red cell containing young tertian parasite with pseudopodia.
5. Ring form trophozoite showing pigment in cytoplasm, in an enlarged cell containing Schüffner's stippling.*
6, 7. Very tenuous medium trophozoite forms.
8. Three ameboid trophozoites with fused cytoplasm.
9, 11, 12, 13. Older ameboid trophozoites in process of development.
10. Two ameboid trophozoites in one cell.
14. Mature trophozoite.
15. Mature trophozoite with chromatin apparently in process of division.
16, 17, 18, 19. Schizonts showing progressive steps in division ("presegmenting schizonts").
20. Mature schizont.
21, 22. Developing gametocytes.
23. Mature microgametocyte.
24. Mature macrogametocyte.

*Schüffner's stippling does not appear in all cells containing the growing and older forms of *P. vivax* as would be indicated by these pictures, but it can be found with any stage from the fairly young ring form onward.

Reproduced with permission from the Manual for the Microscopical Diagnosis of Malaria in Man, National Institutes of Health Bulletin No. 180. (By Aimee Wilcox.)

PLATE I

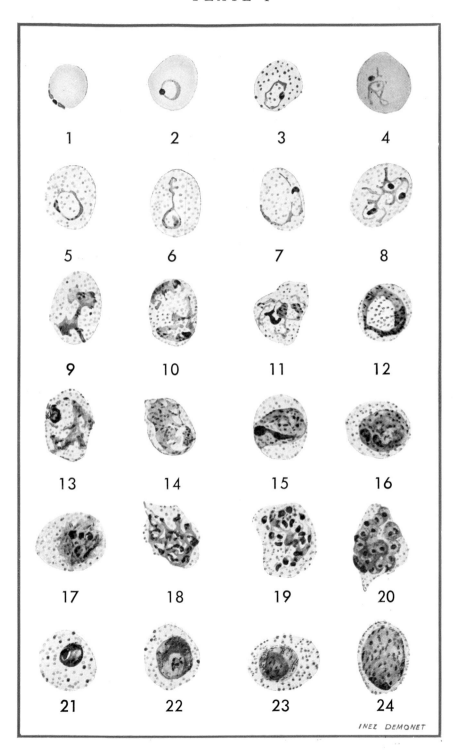

PLATE II

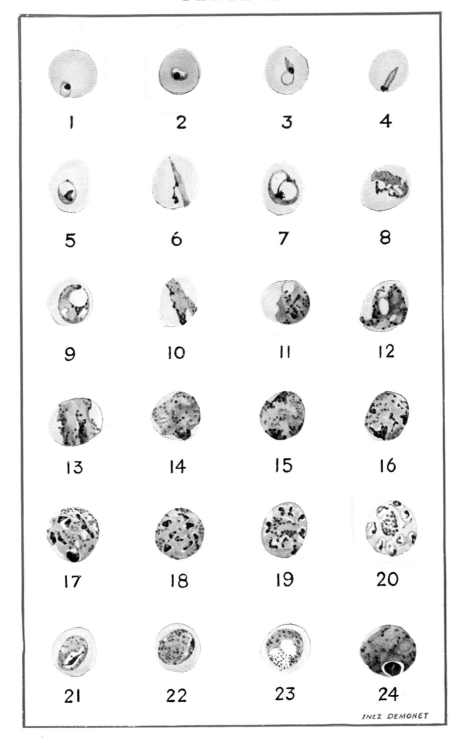

Stages of *Plasmodium falciparum* in human erythrocytes from thin film preparation.

1. Very young ring form trophozoite.
2. Double infection of single cell with young trophozoites, one a "marginal form," the other, "signet ring" form.
3, 4. Young trophozoites showing double chromatin dots.
5, 6, 7. Developing trophozoite forms.
8. Three medium trophozoites in one cell.
9. Trophozoite showing pigment, in a cell containing Maurer's spots.
10, 11. Two trophozoites in each of two cells, showing variation of forms which parasites may assume.
12. Almost mature trophozoite showing haze of pigment throughout cytoplasm Maurer's spots in the cell.
13. Estivo-autumnal "slender forms."
14. Mature trophozoite, showing clumped pigment.
15. Parasite in the process of initial chromatin division.
16, 17, 18, 19. Various phases of the development of the schizont ("presegmenting schizonts").
20. Mature schizont.
21, 22, 23, 24. Successive forms in the development of the gametocyte—usually not found in the peripheral circulation.
25. Immature macrogametocyte.
26. Mature macrogametocyte.
27. Immature microgametocyte.
28. Mature microgametocyte.

Reproduced with permission from the Manual for the Microscopical Diagnosis of Malaria in Man. National Institutes of Health Bulletin No. 180. (By Aimee Wilcox.)

PLATE III

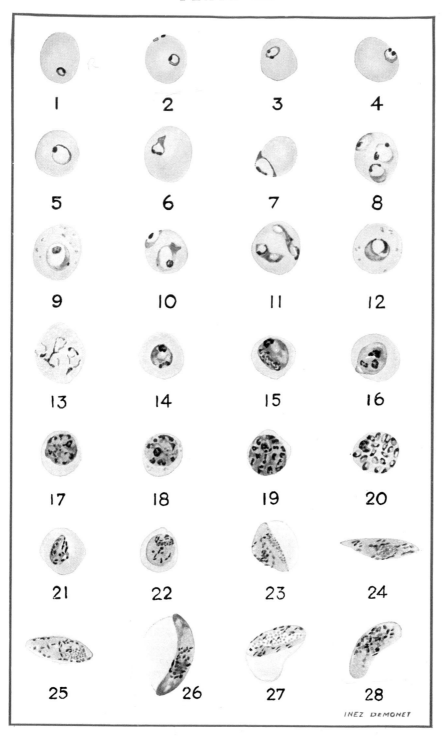

PLATE IV

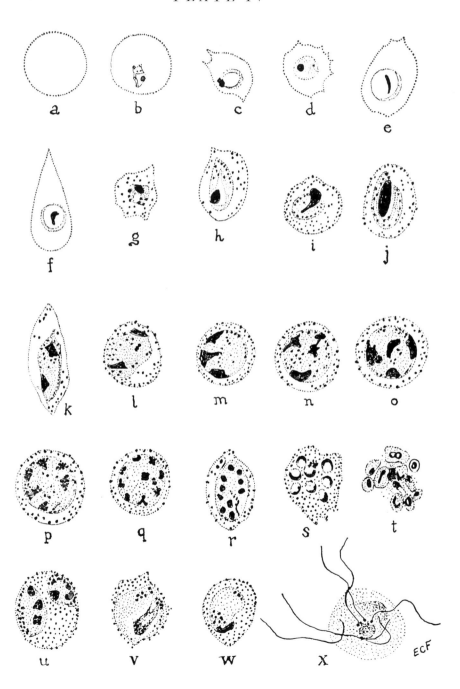

a   b   c   d   e

f   g   h   i   j

k   l   m   n   o

p   q   r   s   t

u   v   w   x

ECF

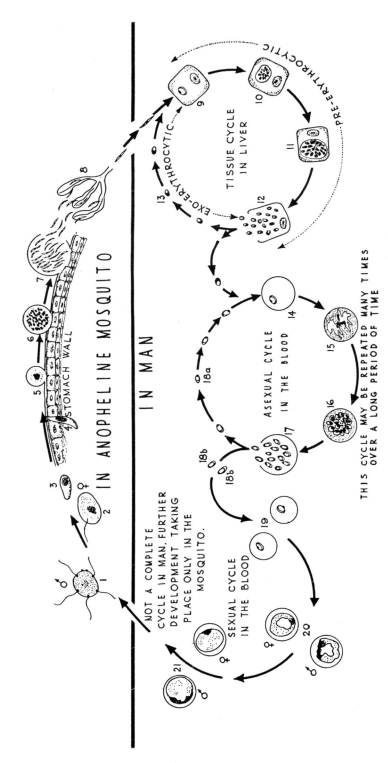

IN ANOPHELINE MOSQUITO

IN MAN

STOMACH WALL

NOT A COMPLETE CYCLE IN MAN, FURTHER DEVELOPMENT TAKING PLACE ONLY IN THE MOSQUITO.

PRE-ERYTHROCYTIC

TISSUE CYCLE IN LIVER

EXO-ERYTHROCYTIC

ASEXUAL CYCLE IN THE BLOOD

THIS CYCLE MAY BE REPEATED MANY TIMES OVER A LONG PERIOD OF TIME

SEXUAL CYCLE IN THE BLOOD

Fig. V-14.—The life cycles of *Plasmodium* in a mosquito and in man. (Blacklock and Southwell, courtesy of H. L. Lewis & Company, London).

(119)

into the insect's stomach and there they mature into the microgametes and macrogametes. The microgametes are flagella-like outgrowths from the microgametocytes. They become detached and
behave like sperm cells in higher animals. Fertilization now takes
place and the zygote thus formed completes the life cycle.

A summary of the reproductive cycles just outlined may be
stated as follows. Once the infection is well started in man schizogony
normally occurs regularly in the liver cells and in the blood cells. At
intervals of from five to twelve days, depending on the species, multiplication takes place in the liver, and each generation produces a
large number of parasites which invade the blood, and a smaller
number which continue the cycle in the liver. Cyclic multiplication in
the blood is manifested in cyclic onset of chills and fever.

"Anoxemia, caused by the destruction of infected and unpara-
sitized red blood cells, and anoxia, with stagnation of blood in
cerebral capillaries and increased permeability of their walls, together with constriction of blood vessels in the liver, constitute the
dynamics of the clinical picture of malaria, especially that produced
by *Plasmodium falciparum.*"[11]

Symptoms. The most characteristic response to malarial infection is the paroxysm. It begins with gradually mounting fever
and chills. The patient's teeth chatter, he gets "goose pimples" and
he tries to cover himself with all the blankets he can find. After
twenty to sixty minutes he ceases shivering and quickly begins to
feel intensely hot. His fever may reach 106° F. with headache and
nausea and his temperature may remain high for one to four hours.
Perspiration then starts, may become profuse, and lasts a few hours
as his temperature subsides. The entire paroxysm lasts from six to
ten hours and occurs every third day (with *P. vivax*) for one to two
weeks.

Treatment. Tremendous advances in the treatment of malaria
have been made during the past few years. Of the newer drugs,
Chloroquine (Aralen, Resochin) is probably the best for general
purposes. It is especially effective against *vivax* malaria. Primaquine
is also excellent and is sometimes used in conjunction with Chloroquine if the patient is having an attack. Daraprim (Pyrimethamine)
is highly effective against both blood and tissue parasites but is not
as effective as Chloroquine during attacks. It is a good suppressive
drug. See any clinical text for a detailed discussion of these and
many other drugs.

Space will not be given for a detailed description of each of the
four species of *Plasmodium* of man. Table V–1 gives their comparative characters in tabular form, while Plates I, II, III, IV show
the stages of each species in human erythrocytes as they appear in
stained blood smears. The mosquito vector is discussed with other
arthropods on page 472.

Intracellular parasites provide an interesting subject for the
study of intracellular protein metabolism. A review of work done
on the protein metabolism of malarial parasites is given by Moulder

(in Cole).[6] The same types of enzyme systems are responsible for the synthesis of both host and parasite protein. The parasites contain both ribo- and deoxyribonucleic acid (RNA and DNA), lipids, polysaccharides, and proteins.

Malaria Today

An analysis[37] of the status of malaria today shows that the disease is finally under control in most areas of the world, or at least the prospects for control are encouraging. In North America and in Europe malaria has been retreating during the past seventy-five years. In the 1930's as many as 6 or 7 million cases occurred annually in the United States, but now there is almost no malaria in the United States or Canada although the two vectors, *Anopheles freeborni* in California and *A. quadrimaculatus* in the Mississippi Valley, are still prevalent. In every malarious country in South America a nationwide mosquito eradication program is in progress. The disease has already been driven out of Chile and has been eradicated from Scandinavia, the United Kingdom, the Balkan countries and Germany. There is practically no malaria or only faint endemicity in the Netherlands, Corsica, Italy, Spain, Portugal, the USSR and Taiwan.

In southern Europe fewer than 10,000 new cases of malaria are reported annually. Before the introduction of the insecticide DDT, however, about 4,000,000 cases were reported annually. Malaria has been eradicated from Cyprus and it is rapidly dwindling in Iran, Lebanon, Turkey, Jordan, Israel and Syria. The disease remains a serious problem in parts of north Africa, and in parts of the middle and far East where nationwide malaria eradication programs are in progress. Malaria has been eradicated from wide areas in Ceylon and Thailand. In April, 1958, the largest malaria eradication program in the world was inaugurated in India where a few years ago one million people each year died from this infection. Malaria is still highly prevalent in New Guinea, New Hebrides, Papua, Solomon Islands and West New Guinea; and in the world as a whole at least 200,000,000 cases occur annually. For a consideration of the ecology of malaria, see May.[34]

Racial differences appear in relation to malarial infection. Africans, for example, often show no symptoms with malarial parasites in their blood, not even an enlarged spleen. Indonesians, however, usually show symptoms even with a few malarial parasites in their blood. It has been suggested that hemoglobin S (a pathological hemoglobin responsible for sickle cell anemia) may be related to the ability of the host to withstand plasmodia. This hemoglobin is present among the Africans. Indonesians possess hemoglobin E, rare in other countries, and this substance may be responsible for the ability of these people to throw off the disease in a day or two. Apparently a premunition occurs in Africa but not in Indonesia.

In spite of the tremendous amount of work that has been done

TABLE V-1.—COMPARATIVE CHARACTERS OF PLASMODIA OF MAN

(STAINED THIN SMEARS.) (Faust and Russell, *Clinical Parasitology*)

Stage or Period	Plasmodium vivax	Plasmodium malariæ	Plasmodium falciparum	Plasmodium ovale
Early trophozoite or ring	Relatively large; usually one chromatin dot, sometimes two; often two rings, sometimes more, in one cell	Compact; one chromatin dot; double cell infections rare	Small, delicate; sometimes two chromatin dots; multiple red cell infection common; appliqué forms frequent	Compact; one chromatin dot; double infection uncommon
Large trophozoite	Large; markedly ameboid; prominent vacuole; pigment in fine rodlets	Small; often band-shaped; not ameboid; vacuole inconspicuous; pigment coarse	Medium size; usually compact, rarely ameboid; vacuole inconspicuous; rare in peripheral blood after half grown; pigment granular	Small; compact; not ameboid; vacuole inconspicuous; pigment coarse
Young schizont or presegmenter	Large; somewhat ameboid; chromatin masses numerous; pigment in fine rodlets	Small; compact; chromatin masses few; pigment coarse	Medium size; compact; chromatin masses numerous; pigment granular; rare in peripheral blood	Medium size; compact; chromatin masses few; pigment coarse
Mature schizont or segmenter	Larger than normal red cells; may have double rosette	Smaller than normal red cells; single rosette	Smaller than normal red cells; single rosette	Larger than *P. malariæ*; irregular rosette
Number of merozoites	8 to 24, usually 12 to 18	6 to 12, usually 8	8 to 26, usually 8 to 18	6 to 12, usually 8
Microgametocytes (usually smaller and less numerous than macrogametocytes)	Spherical; compact; no vacuole; single large nucleus; diffuse coarse pigment; cytoplasm stains light blue	Similar to *P. vivax* but smaller and less numerous	Crescents usually sausage-shaped; chromatin diffuse; pigment scattered large grains; nucleus rather large; cytoplasm stains paler blue	Similar to *P. vivax* but somewhat smaller; never abundant

Macrogametocytes	Spherical; compact; larger then microgametocyte; smaller nucleus; pigment same; cytoplasm stains darker blue	Similar to P. vivax but smaller and less numerous	Crescents often longer and more slender; chromatin central; pigment more compact; nucleus compact; cytoplasm stains darker blue	Similar to P. vivax but somewhat smaller; never abundant
Pigment	Short, rather delicate rodlets irregularly scattered; not much tendency to coalesce	Seen in very young rings; granules rather than rods; tendency toward peripheral scatter	Pigment granular; early tendency to coalesce; typical single solid mass in mature trophozoite; coarse scattered "rice grains" in crescents	Similar to but somewhat coarser than P. vivax; sometimes clumped or in lateral bands
Alterations in the infected red cell	Enlarged and decolorized; Schüffner's dots usually seen	Cell may seem smaller; fine stippling (Ziemann's dots) occasionally seen	Normal size but may have "brassy" appearance; Maurer's dots (or "clefts") may be seen; host cell of crescent barely seen	Enlarged and decolorized; Schüffner's dots appear early and are prominent at all stages; numerous oval-shaped red cells; or crenated margins
Length of asexual phase	48 hours or a little less	72 hours	36–48 hours	48 hours or a little longer
Prepatent period, minimal	8 to 17 days, average 13	14 to 37 days, average 28	5 to 12 days, average 8	8 to 16 days, average 14
Usual incubation period	8 to 31 days, average 14	28 to 37 days, average 30	7 to 27 days, average 12	11 to 16 days, average 14
Interval between parasite patency and gametocyte appearance	3 to 5 days	7 to 14 days; appearance irregular and numbers few	7 to 12 days	12 to 14 days; appearance irregular and numbers few
Developmental period in mosquito	16 to 17 days at 20° C.; 10 days at 25° C.; 8 days at 28° to 30° C.	30 to 35 days at 20° C.; 25 to 28 days at 25° C.	22 to 23 days at 20° C.; 10 to 12 days at 27° C.	16 days at 25° C.

on malaria "there are still mysterious features whose nature continues to elude us. The first concerns host specificity, perhaps the most fundamental question throughout parasitology."[12] Why do only a few of the hundreds of mosquito species act as suitable hosts? After infecting a person with benign tertian malaria in the fall, why do parasites sometimes wait five or six months before appearing in the blood? Why do relapses occur year after year for as long as forty years in cases of quartan malaria? What is the relation of natural tolerance to such hereditary traits as glucose-6-phosphate dehydrogenase deficiency and hemoglobin Barts (both of which appear to protect a person from the worst effects of *falciparum* malaria)? Can man get monkey malaria and do any animal reservoirs for human malaria exist?

Control of Malaria

Detailed descriptions of control measures against mosquitoes, and treatment, can be found in clinical parasitology books. Only one control factor will be discussed here.

Any program of eradication must recognize the existence of a critical level of mosquito density, below which malaria tends to disappear and above which it increases. This level of density depends upon the mosquito reproduction rate. MacDonald[32] has explained the important concept of reproduction rate as follows:

"One may imagine an individual suffering from *falciparum* infection who is infective to all the mosquitoes which feed on him during eighty days (or half of those which feed on him for one-hundred-and-sixty). If ten bite each day he orginally infects 800 mosquitoes. These might have a probability of survival through one day of 0.9; if the temperature were such that the extrinsic cycle lasted twelve days, 28 per cent of these would survive to the development of sporozoites and they would have a subsequent expectation of life of ten days. If the mosquito were entirely anthropophilic, feeding once every two days on man, the survivors would on the average each convey the infection to five people. Through this mechanism 1,120 infections might be distributed in the population from the primary case. In the immediate context it is no matter that a number of these infections would be nullified by overlapping on the same individual. Obviously nothing approaching such a rate of multiplication could go on unchecked for long and there are three brakes on multiplication which eventually restrain it. They are the development of immunity in a population which restricts the duration of infectivity; the existence of previous infections in individuals receiving infective bites which may not therefore apparently produce new cases of the disease; and the occurrence of superinfection in the mosquito which may have previous infections so that subsequent ones do not materially increase its infectivity. These factors together reduce the gross reproduction rate to a new one which may be much lower. Should this fall below one, successive

generations of cases would be smaller than their predecessors and
the disease would disappear; should it be greater than one, successive
generations would increase and the disease would mount in the
population. Obviously the object of all control is to keep the
reproduction rate below one so that successive generations decrease
in size and the disease disappears." In some countries (e.g. India,
Africa) more emphasis perhaps should be placed on control than on
eradication of malaria.[5]

Plasmodium in Animals Other than Man

Plasmodium berghei is a parasite of mice and rats and it has been
useful in laboratory experiments. Bird malarias may not be especially
harmful to the birds, but some infections, particularly those of
domestic birds, have been the basis of a large amount of research on
Plasmodium in general. Much of our knowledge of the life cycles of
plasmodia of man has been derived from studies of bird malarias.

Chickens may be experimentally infected with several species,
such as, *Plasmodium cathemerium* (from English sparrows and
canaries), *P. lophurae* (from ducks), *P. relictum* (from pigeons and
ducks), and, in tropical areas, with the highly pathogenic *P. gallinaceum*. *P. juxtanucleare* causes a serious disease in chickens in
Brazil, Uruguay, Mexico, and Ceylon. *P. durae* is the cause of turkey
malaria. Many plasmodia occur in wild birds, especially in the
passerines. *P. relictum*, *P. elongatum*, and *P. cathemerium* are common examples. Some of the wild birds are hosts to the same species
as are found in domestic poultry. *P. vaughani* in robins and starlings;
P. rouxi in the English sparrow in Algeria; *P. circumflexum* in the
red-winged blackbird; *P. polare* in cliff swallows; *P. nucleophilum*
in the catbird; *P. hexamerium* in the bluebird; and *P. oti* in the Easter
screech owl are other examples of this protozoan parasite in the blood
of birds.

The life cycle of avian plasmodia is basically similar to that of the
human species, but in avian species exoerythrocytic schizogony takes
place in endothelial cells or haemopoietic cells, but not in the liver.
Also, in bird malaria some of the erythrocytic merozoites are able to
develop in tissue cells. Such forms are called "phanerozoites." It
would not occur to many people that birds are bitten by mosquitoes,
but a close examination of any bird will reveal many small exposed
soft areas which invite insects. Avian malaria has a wide range of
mosquito hosts. For example, *P. gallinaceum* can infect *Aëdes*,
Armigeres, *Culex*, *Mansonia*, *Theobaldia*, and *Anopheles*. Exoerythrocytic stages of bird malarias vary with different species of birds
and with different species of *Plasmodium*. It is interesting to note
that there is a six- to eight-fold increase of some amino acids in
erythrocytes during infection of birds by *Plasmodium*.

The nutrition of the avian malarial parasite, *Plasmodium lophurae*,
has received careful study. These organisms, like other intracellular parasites, have lost some of their original synthetic mechan-

isms and depend on certain enzymes of the host cell. This loss makes them exceedingly difficult to cultivate in the laboratory apart from a living host cell. Trager[41] has succeeded in removing *P. lophurae* from its host erythrocyte and in keeping it alive *in vitro* for four days. The technique is complicated and is summarized in his paper referred to above. The culture medium for these organisms contains pyruvate, malate, the coenzymes cozymase, ATP, and Co A, and other substances of unknown nature present in red blood cell extract. All of these materials are essential nutrients of the parasites and are apparently not produced by the parasites *in vitro*.

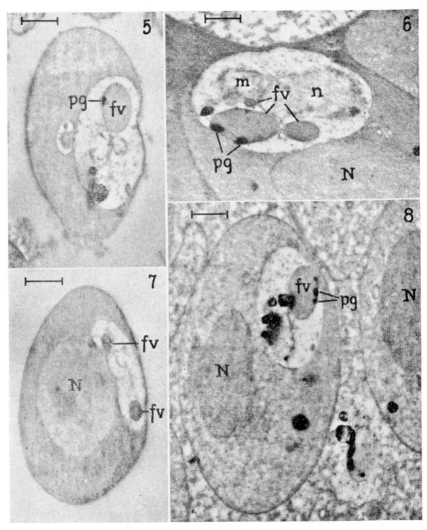

FIG. V–15.—A section of a duck erythrocyte infected with *Plasmodium lophurae* showing the connection between the food vacuole (fv) and cytoplasm of the red cell, *pg*, pigment granules. (Rudzinska and Trager, courtesy of J. Protozool.)

Red cells also synthesize diphosphopyridine nucleotide, a coenzyme required by the parasite. A number of other substances necessary for the protozoan parasite has been found as products of host cell metabolism, but in addition the parasite actually engulfs portions of the cytoplasm of its host, thus proving itself to be an *intracellular phagotroph* (Fig. V–15).

Reptiles may also become infected with plasmodia. *Plasmodium mexicanum* is a species in the lizard, *Sceloporus ferrariperezi*, in Mexico; *P. rhadinurum* occurs in the lizard, *Iguana iguana rhinolopha*, also in Mexico; *P. floridense* may be found in the blood of the Florida lizard, *Sceloporus undulatus*; and *P. lygosomae* occurs in the skink, *Lygosoma moco*, in New Zealand. Undoubtedly a careful examination of the blood of other reptiles would reveal many unreported infections.

Apes and monkeys, as might be expected, also become infected with the malarial parasites. At least 5 species of *Plasmodium* have been found in apes. The species include: *P. reichenowi* and *P. malariae*, both in chimpanzees and gorillas; *P. vivax schwetzi* in chimpanzees; and *P. hylobati* in gibbons. At least 10 species have been reported from monkeys. In the Rhesus monkeys of south east Asia *P. knowlesi* causes a serious and often fatal malaria. Other species in monkeys include: *P. inui* of India and south east Asia, *P. cynomolgi* (very similar to *P. vivax* of man) also of India and south east Asia, *P. gonderi* of Africa, *P. brasilianum* of South America, and *Hepatocystis* spp. of Africa and the Orient. *P. bastianellii*, *P. cynomolgi* and *P. brasilianum* have recently been successfully passed experimentally from monkeys to man by natural (mosquito) transmission. Simian malaria, therefore, should be classified as a true zoonosis. The life cycles of all these plasmodia are essentially similar to those of the malarial organisms in man. Except for *P. knowlesi*, little is known of the pathogenicity of the parasites to their simian hosts.

Experimentation with malarial parasites in the laboratory indicates that the plasmodia form pyruvate by glycolysis and then oxidize it completely via the Krebs tricarboxylic acid cycle just as do many other organisms. It seems likely, also, that the chief source of the parasite protein is the hemoglobin within red blood cells. One evidence of this assumption is the appearance of pigment in plasmodia which undoubtedly comes from hematin, the iron prophyrin component of hemoglobin. An extracellular supply of the amino acid methionine, however, is required for maximum parasite growth.

DNA and RNA have been shown by many investigators to be abundantly present in *Plasmodia* nuclei whether the parasites occupy enucleated or nucleated red blood cells. If the protozoa are in the latter (*e.g. P. gallinaceum* in chicken erythrocytes) the breakdown of the nuclear DNA of the host cell furnishes much of the material for the synthesis of new parasite nucleic acid. Few studies of the lipids of *Plasmodia* have been made. It is known, however, that these parasites have a high lipid content including neutral fat, phospholipid and cholesterol.

Hepatocystis (= *Plasmodium*) *kochi*, a common malarial parasite of African monkeys, is transmitted by the midge, *Culicoides adersi*, and lives in parenchyma cells of the liver where merozoites are formed. Characteristically, only gametocytes appear in monkey blood.[14] In the insect, oocysts develop between the eyes and brain or in thoracic muscles.

CLASS PIROPLASMEA

The relationships of this class to other protozoa are not entirely clear. Although the several species do not produce spores, they possess certain morphological and behavioral characteristics that suggest relationships with the sporozoa group. They are minute, pyriform, rod-shaped or ameboid parasites of erythrocytes and, occasionally, leucocytes or histiocytes of vertebrates. Locomotion is by gliding or body flexion. Reproduction is by binary fission or schizogony.

ORDER PIROPLASMIDA

Family Babesiidae. Members of this family are pyriform, or rounded parasites of erythrocytes of vertebrates. *Babesia* causes considerable damage to livestock and to other animals. Another name for the same organism is *Piroplasma* and thus the disease is known as either *babesiasis* or *piroplasmosis*. The common name for the disease in cattle is *cattle tick fever*. The parasite occurs in the red blood cells of cattle, and it typically divides to form two pear-shaped bodies (trophozoites), hence the species name *bigemina* (Fig. V–16). There may, however, be four such bodies in one red cell. The arthropod vector is the tick (*Boophilus margaropus annulatus*) which feeds on cattle blood. In the tick a sexual phase of the cycle is said to take place, but the occurence of sex in *Babesia* is doubtful. Spores are not formed. The entire cycle resembles that of *Plasmodium*, but there is apparently no cryptozoic phase, although

---

Fig. V–16.—*1*, *Babesia bigemina* in embryonic connective tissue next to the right side of the recently formed esophagus in a seed-tick of *Margaropus annulatus* Say. Note the presence of the extranuclear granule in many of the specimens. Fixed in Bouin's; stained with Delafield's haematoxylin. × 1230.

2, Early trophozoite in erythrocyte. × 4360. *3*, Same as figure 2, following first binary fission. *4,5,6*, Round, amoeboid, and attenuated large early invasion forms.

7,8,9, Pyriform pairs of large early forms. Blepharoplast, rhizoplast, and centrosome associated with vesicular nucleus. *10,11,12*, Duplication of blepharoplast and rhizoplast, with formation and growth of buds.

13, 14, Fission being completed with division of the nucleus. Figure *14* shows the nature of the band, and reorganization of the karyosome. *15*, Pulling away of daughter before plasmotomy has been completed. (Dennis, courtesy of Univ. Calif. Pub. Zool.)

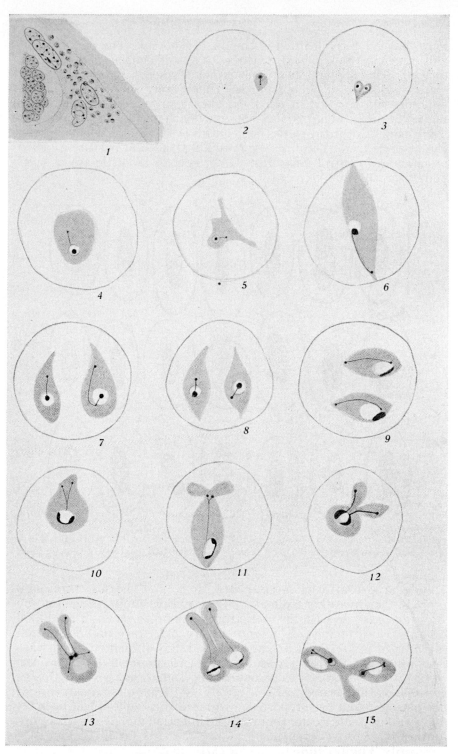

FIG. V–16.—*Legend on opposite page.*

much has yet to be learned of the life of *Babesia*. The parasites engulf large portions of the erythrocyte cytoplasm, as does *Plasmodium*.[36] The pigment hemozoin is not formed. Babesiasis is primarily a disease of older animals. Cattle may suffer fever, loss of appetite, constipation or diarrhea, bloody urine, and anemia. The mortality rate is about 90 per cent, and death may occur in one week. Treatment is of little value, but control is successful when the tick can be destroyed. Dipping cattle, to kill ticks, and pasture rotation are standard control measures. Other species in cattle are *B. bovis* and *B. argentina*.

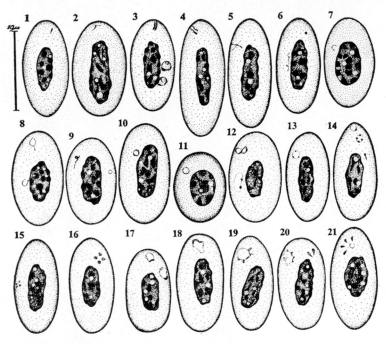

Fig. V–17.—*Babesia moshkovskii* a haematozoan parasite found in the red blood cells of the Indian house crow and in other birds. (Laird and Lari, courtesy of Can. J. Zool.)

Babesia also attacks sheep, goats, dogs, pigs, horses, birds, and probably many other animals. Dog piroplasmosis is caused by *Babesia canis*.[1] As with the cattle form, the protozoa enter red blood cells and cause an increase in temperature, pulse rate, and respiration rate. Dogs become weak and anemic, and they often die. The disease is transmitted by the brown dog tick, *Rhipicephalus sanguineus*. *Babesia moshkovskii*, in the blood of the Indian house crow, *Corvus splevdens*, is illustrated in Figure V–17. At least one human case of piroplasmosis has been reported.[12] A man whose spleen had been removed some years earlier acquired the infection and died with symptoms of blackwater fever.

Family Theileriidae occurs in cattle and other mammals. The life cycle of *Theileria parva* is said to involve a sexual phase in African cattle ticks, *Rhipicephalus evertsi* or *R. appendiculatus*, and schizygony in lymphocytes and in cells of visceral capillaries of the cattle host. After schizogony, minute forms, 1 to 2 microns in diameter, appear in the red blood cells. Since the red blood cells are not normally destroyed, there is no anemia or blood in the urine, but other symptoms are similar to those of babesiasis. Mortality in African cattle may be as high as 95 per cent.

Gonderia is a related genus which infects blood cells of cattle and other ungulates, especially in Africa and Asia.

CLASS TOXOPLASMEA

Spores are absent but cysts or pseudocysts are formed, with naked trophozoites. Reproduction is by binary fission or internal budding. Schizogony has been described but its presence is questionable. Locomotion is by gliding or body flexion. There are no intermediate hosts.

ORDER TOXOPLASMIDA

Family Sarcocystidae. *Sarcocystis* (Fig. V–18) is frequently found in the muscles of animals slaughtered for human consumption, and in wild herbivores. Cattle may be 100 per cent affected. The organisms are also found in birds and reptiles and, rarely, in dogs, cats

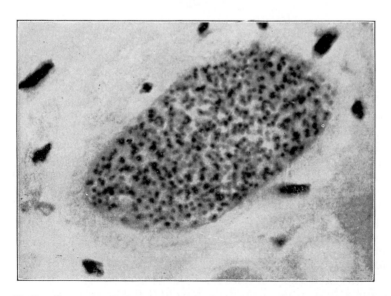

Fig. V–18.—*Sarcocystis lindemanni* in left ventricular wall of a Panamanian child. The cysts contained about 170 cells. Except for enlargement and slight hyaline degeneration of the muscle fibers there were no myocardial lesions. × 1500. (Gilmore, Kean and Posey, Am. J. Trop. Med., courtesy of Williams and Wilkins Co.)

and man. Only 15 human cases have been reported. In striated muscle they occur in elongate compartmented packets, "Miescher's sacs," which may be several millimeters long and thus easily seen with the naked eye.[30] Within the compartments are crowded motile crescent-shaped trophozoites, 6 to 15 microns in length, sometimes called "Rainey's corpuscles." The parasites may also be found in heart muscle. *Sarcocystis* possibly is transmitted by the ingestion of trophozoites from feces or from infected muscles, but there is no clear evidence to substantiate this conjecture. Pathogenicity, if it occurs, is mild. Normally, if meat is found to be infected with *Sarcocystis* it is condemned for human consumption.

The elongated cyst in striated muscles may be so small that it cannot be seen without a lens, or it may be large and appear as a short white streak. Sizes of cysts range from 25 microns to 5 centimeters.

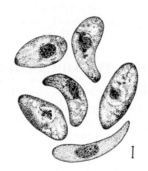

FIG. V–19.—*Toxoplasma gondii.* The line at the lower right represents one micron in length. (Original.)

Species names of some of the many *Sarcosystis* which have been described are *S. miescheriana* in pigs, *S. tenella* in sheep, *S. blanchardi* in cattle, *S. muris* in mice, *S. darlingi* in opossums, *S. kortei* in monkeys, *S. harvathi* in chickens and *S. lindemanni* in man.

Family Toxoplasmatidae. *Besnoitia* forms a pseudocyst which is not compartmented and which possesses a heavy wall. The parasites are found in subcutaneous and connective tissues of domestic and wild mammals in which they may cause disease (*besnoitiosis*).

Encephalitozoon has small rod-shaped trophozoites. A pseudocyst may possibly be formed. The parasite closely resembles *Toxoplasma* but is said to differ significantly in staining reactions. It is found in various organs of mammals.

Toxoplasma gondii (Fig. V–19) is the type species of the genus and is the only generally accepted one. The affinities of the parasite have for a long time been disputed, and it has often been called a fungus, but most workers now agree that it belongs with the protozoa. *Toxoplasma* is monoxenous, produces cysts but no spores, reproduces asexually, and moves by gliding or body flexion. Weinman,[43] Siim,[38] and Levine[23] have given excellent reviews of the organism and its pathogenicity.

Toxoplasma is extremely common in man and in wild and domestic mammals and birds, but the disease, *toxoplasmosis*, is far less common. The parasite invades many kinds of cells and may be found extracellularly in blood or peritoneal fluid. It is crescentic or oval in shape, about 3 by 6 microns in size, although individuals 12 microns long have been reported. The nucleus often is situated in the blunter end of the body. Fibrils from an anterior truncated cone (conoid) extend over the anterior two-thirds of the body. Five to 18 cylindrical or club-shaped *toxonemes* run longitudinally within the body. These details cannot be seen in the slides usually available to students. Papers by Goldman *et al.*[15] and Ludvick[29] are recommended.

Toxoplasma has been reported from man, dogs, cats, chickens, hogs, sheep, frogs, hamsters, pigeons, rabbits, wolves, guinea pigs, rats, mice, sparrows, canaries, monkeys, apes, kangaroos, and from many other homeothermic animals. It is probably the commonest pathogenic parasite of man, infecting 30 to 50 per cent of the human race. From serological evidence 90 per cent of the population of some areas is affected. The Sabin-Feldman dye test and complement fixation test are used as bases for estimates of prevalence, but the isolation of the organism itself by inoculation of experimental animals is more reliable. Human infections are common in veterinarians, slaughter-house workers, rabbit dressers and rabbit trappers. The distribution of this parasite is worldwide.

The life cycle of *Toxoplasma gondii* is not yet completely understood. It enters cells of various tissues, both phagocytic and nonphagocytic. Within these cells it divides repeatedly by binary fission, sometimes forming cyst-like masses of organisms. True cyst walls are formed by the parasites,[33] but sometimes surrounding host tissue forms pseudocysts. When the host cell ruptures, the liberated parasites, within seconds, enter other cells and commence dividing.[31] Goldman *et al.*[15] have presented evidence for a process of internal budding.

Toxoplasma is normally transmitted through the placenta. Other forms of natural transmission are unknown, but infection through mother's milk, cannibalism, and contaminated mouth parts of blood-sucking insects have been suggested. Congenital transmission has been observed through at least 5 successive generations of mice. The parasite has a deleterious affect on mice, shortening their lives and reducing the number of young mice in each litter.

Symptoms of toxoplasmosis depend on the tissues invaded. The parasite may enter cells of the brain or spinal cord, cells of the spleen, liver, lungs, heart, retina, fat cells, reticuloendothelial cells and motile phagocytes; or it may invade the blood plasma and lymph. The central nervous system is usually involved in congenitally infected children.[4]

Lesions caused by this parasite pass through an acute, subacute, and a chronic phase. In both man and animals fever usually ac-

companies the acute stage whose symptoms may involve lympha-
denitis, splenic enlargement, myocarditis, pneumonitis, hepatitis,
hydrocephalus, encephalitis or skin rash. Subacute infection may
involve the eyes and the central nervous system. The chronic phase
is characterized by intracellular cyst-like masses which develop in
the retina, central nervous system, and cardiac and skeletal muscle.
In man the disease may result in abortions, still births, and even
mental defects in children. Mild infections in adults may resemble
mononucleosis. The mortality rate is high. After one infected child
is born, other children are apparently normal.

The incidence of infection varies with host age. Congenital infections are most common in man, and an age immunity develops.
Two or more humoral antibodies are produced against *Toxoplasma*.
Various sulfonamides, especially sulfadiazine, are used in treatment
but without consistent results. The antimalarial pyrimethamine
(Daraprim) is useful, especially in treating ocular toxoplasmosis. In
general, however, there is no satisfactory method of treatment.

SUBPHYLUM CNIDOSPORA

Spores of this subphylum contain polar filaments.

CLASS CNIDOSPORIDEA

(With characters of the subphylum)

ORDER MYXOSPORIDA

The Myxosporida are usually found in the gallbladder, urinary
bladder or in other hollow organs of both salt and fresh-water fishes,
and occasionally these parasites are found in amphibia and reptiles.
In body cavities the parasites may be ameboid. They are also found
in the liver, spleen, kidneys, gills, skin or in other organs in which
they are frequently enveloped by host tissue.

Reproduction occurs by the production of spores which are characterized by the presence of two valves and one or more polar capsules.
Each spore develops into a multinucleate organism. The life cycle
of a myxosporidian parasite is illustrated in Fig. V–20. Infection
seems not to be harmful to the host except occasionally when the
parasites may be so destructive as to produce up to 100 per cent
mortality.

The two nuclei of the sporoplasm of a spore unite when the spore
opens its valves upon being ingested by the host, or when the spore
gains entrance into host tissue by other means. The freed sporoplasm thus becomes a zygote, and the entire life cycle of the large
polysporous species normally occurs within the original zygote
membrane. A budding or plasmotomy may take place. Multiplication in the polysporous species is accomplished largely by nucleo-

gony (= the formation of a syncytium).   The diploid phase of the cycle lasts until the formation of a sporoblast (or pansporoblast) which starts the sporogony part of the cycle.   The sporoblast (or pansporoblast if more than two spores are formed) is derived from a specialized cell which begins as an ordinary vegetative cell or nucleus.   Sporogony may be monosporous, disporous, or polysporous.   Sporoblasts of six to eight nuclei, or pansporoblasts of

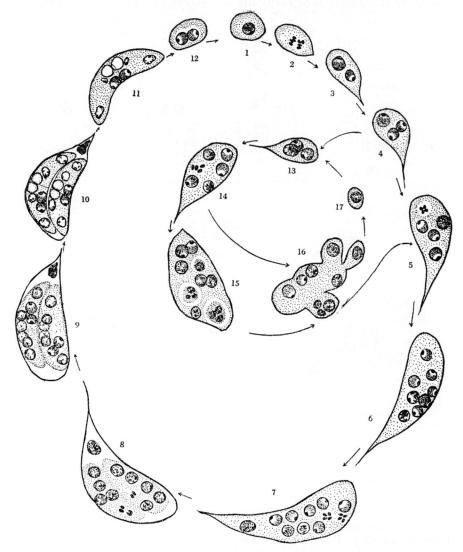

FIG. V–20.—The life cycle of *Ceratomyxa blennius*, a myxosporidian parasite from a tidepool blenny. *1*, zygote; *2* to *11*, sporogony; *8*, two sporoblasts showing reduction division; *9*, young spores; *11*, mature spore; *12*, sporoplasm with gametes; *13* to *17*, nucleogony with cytoplasmic growth and budding; *15*, internal budding; *16*, external budding; *17*, uninucleate bud. (Noble, courtesy of J. Morphol.)

fourteen or more nuclei, may be found. Each sporoblast normally contains six generative and two somatic, residual nuclei. Of the six generative nuclei, two form the thin-walled shell valves, two give rise to the polar capsules, each containing a polar filament, and two, by a reduction division, become the haploid sporoplasm nuclei or gametes. Spores of some species (as well as of some microsporidia) are surrounded by characteristic mucous envelopes that can be revealed by the addition of India ink to material under investigation.[28]

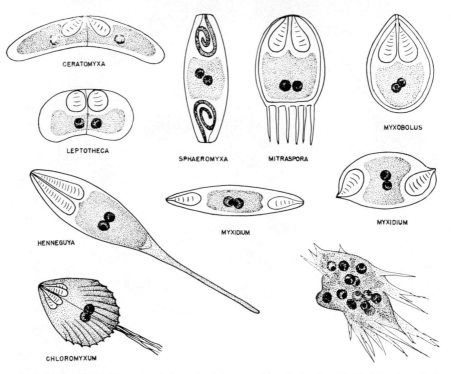

CERATOMYXA

LEPTOTHECA

SPHAEROMYXA

MITRASPORA

MYXOBOLUS

HENNEGUYA

MYXIDIUM

MYXIDIUM

CHLOROMYXUM

FIG. V–21.—Sample spores of the order Myxosporida. Only about half of the described genera are represented. At the lower right corner is a trophic stage with slim, pointed pseudopodia which are typical of several genera. (Original.)

The Order Myxosporida consists of a highly specialized group of protozoan parasites which have become modified so as to possess some basic metazoan characteristics. Common genera of Myxosporida are *Leptotheca, Ceratomyxa, Myxidium, Henneguya, Myxobolus* and *Myxosoma* (Fig. V–21.) *Myxosoma squamalis* is a parasite in rainbow trout, silver salmon, and chum salmon. In the trophozoite stage (= growth stage) the parasite attacks the scales of the fish and makes its way inside the scales and skin where it sporulates. Scales and surrounding tissue may be damaged. For further details on life cycles see Noble.[35]

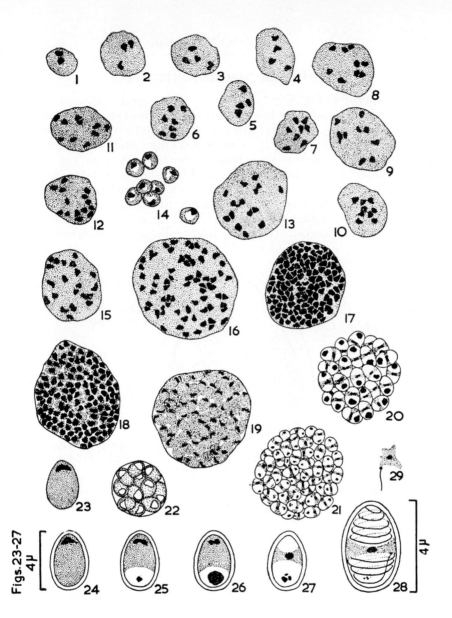

Figs. 1-22,29...10μ =

FIG. V-22.—*Plistophora culicis*, a microsporidian that parasitizes the Malpighian tubules of larvæ of *Culex pipiens* and of the adult mosquito, *Anopheles gambinae*.

1, Bi-nucleate schizont. *2 to 13*, Development of the schizonts. *14*, Merozoites produced by segmentation of 8-nucleate schizont. *15 to 17*, Development of the sporont. *18*, Cytoplasmic cleavage within sporont; nuclei large. *19*, Fully developed sporoblasts within sporont; nuclei compacted.

20, Group of macrospores; sporoplasm binucleate, metachromatic granule large. *21*, Group of microspores at later stage of development. *22*, Fresh preparation of small macrospore cyst. *23 to 27*, Development from sporoblast to mature spore. *28*, Diagrammatic representation of the structure of the mature spore. *29*, Sporoplasm after emergence from spore. (Canning, courtesy of Rivista di Malariologia.)

ORDER MICROSPORIDA

Microsporidia (Fig. V–22 and 23) are intracellular parasites mostly of arthropods (commonly in gut epithelium) and fishes (commonly in skin and muscles), but also found in all invertebrate phyla including Protozoa. Spores (2.0 to 25.0 microns long) each possess a single polar filament. There is no intermediate host. A polar cap (visible when stained with Schiff-periodic acid) at the narrower pole of the spore is considered by Vávra[42] to be a characteristic feature. This parasite enters the host gut epithelium and, via the blood stream or body cavity, makes its way to the skin, muscle or other tissue normal to the species. It enters host cells and undergoes asexual

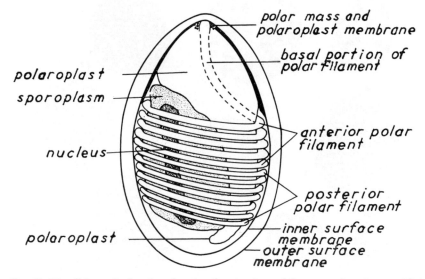

Fig. V–23.—Schematic drawing showing the structure of the spore of a microsporidian, *Thelohania californica*, as revealed by electron microscopy. (Kudo and Daniels, courtesy Jour. Protozool.)

division and sporogony. The smaller of these spores may look like bacteria. If enough host cells are entered, the host dies because of the degeneration of these cells.

Microsporidia are parasites of some animals that are economically important to man. *Nosema bombycis* is a destructive parasite of the silkworm, while *N. apis* causes serious disease in honey bees. *N. stegomyiae* occupies various organs, epecially midgut tissues, of the mosquito, *Anopheles gambiense*. The variety of hosts attacked by microsporidia is indicated by noting that some bryozoa have parasitic microsporidia in their germ cells and body cavity. *Cyclops fuscus* is inhabited by *Nosema cyclopi*, whereas the cytoplasm of the cephaline gregarine, *Frenzelina conformis*, may be parasitized by *Nosema frenzelinae*. Even vertebrates are occasionally infected.

Another interesting case of a parasite within a parasite occurs in the urinary bladder of the fish, *Opsanus tau* and *O. beta*. These fish are parasitized by the myxosporidian, *Sphaerospora polymorpha*. This myxosporidian, in turn, is parasitized by the microsporidian *Nosema notabilis*, which lives in the trophozoite of the protozoan host. The myxosporidian may be killed by its parasite. Another hyperparasite is the microsporidian, *Perezia lankesteriae*, which lives in the cytoplasm of the gregarine, *Lankesteria ascidiae*. This microsporidian also may be found in the intestine of the tunicate, *Ciona intestinalis*. Other genera and species of microsporida inhabit mosquitoes, mice, termites, mayflies, crustaceans, annelids, flies and hemipterans. For detailed descriptions of morphology see Huger,[17] Kudo and Daniels,[20] and Lom and Várva.[26] For a list of microsporidia that infect insects see Thomson.[40]

ORDER HELICOSPORIDA

Helicosporidium parasiticum is the single species belonging to this genus and order. It lives in the body cavity, fat-body and nerve tissue of *Dasyhelea obscura*, a dipteran insect whose larvae are found in the sap in wounds of elm and horse-chestnut trees. Each spore contains three uninucleate sporoplasms and a long spirally coiled filament. Other fly larvae associated with the wounds in these trees may be parasitized.

ORDER ACTINOMYXIDA

The exact taxonomic position of this group of organisms is disputed. Each spore is surrounded by a membrane possessing three valves. There are also three polar capsules, each enclosing a polar filament. In the mature stage eight spores develop within the sporocyst. There are two families: Tetractinomyxidae and Triactinomyxidae. All species occur in marine worms known as sipunculids and in tubificid annelids. *Tetractinomyxon intermedium*, possessing spores 7 to 8 microns in diameter, is found in the coelom in the sipunculid, *Petalostoma minutum*. *Triactinomyxon legeri* lives in the worm, *Tubifex tubifex*. Its spore contains twenty-four uninucleate sporoplasms. These organisms unite in pairs which are liberated as binucleate amoebulae, each of which divides several times and forms a cyst (*pansporocyst*) containing cells of two sizes. These cells are the gametes. Each small cell fuses with a larger one (anisogamy) and forms a zygote which develops into the spores that are transmitted from host to host. For further information and a description of sporogony in *Siedleckiella*, see Janiszewska.[19]

HAPLOSPORIDIA AND OTHER PROTISTA

The affinities of this group are uncertain, and it has often been assigned to the fungi. *Ichthyosporidium*, common in cells, tissues and body cavities of invertebrates and lower vertebrates, exhibits schizogony, without flagella or cilia, but sometimes with pseudopodia.

Other microorganisms sometimes listed as protozoa are *Anaplasma* (probably a rickettsia), *Pneumocystis* (probably a yeast), and *Sphaerita* (Fig. V—24).

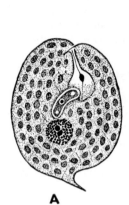
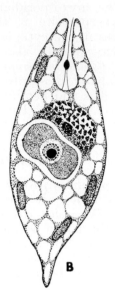

Fig. V–24.—*Sphaerita*, intracellular parasites of protozoa. *A, S. phaci* in *Phacus pleuronectes*. *B, S. dageardi* in *Euglena gracilis* (?). (Jahn, courtesy of Archiv. f. Protist.)

BIBLIOGRAPHY

1. BAYER, M. E., and DENNIG, K. H., 1961.   Elektronenoptische Untersuchungen an *Babesia canis*. Zeitschr. Tropennmed. u. Parasitol., *12*, 28–35.
2. BECKER, E. R., 1934.   *Coccidia and Coccidiosis of Domesticated, Game and Laboratory Animals and of Man*. Iowa State Coll. Press, Ames, Iowa. 147 pp.
3. BRAY, R. S., 1957.   *Studies on the Exoerythrocytic Cycle in the Genus Plasmodium*. Mem. #12, London Sch. Hyg. Trop. Med. Lewis, London, 192 pp.
4. CARMONA, M. D., 1961.   Toxoplasmosis, Parasitologia, Epidemiologia, Clinica, Diagnóstico, Tratamiento (continuación). Rev. Ibérica Parasitol., *21*, 197–220.
5. COLBOURNE, M. J., 1962.   Prospects for Malaria Eradication with Special Reference to the Western Pacific. Trans. Roy. Soc. Trop. Med. Hyg., *56*, 179–201.
6. COLE, W. H., 1955.   *Some Physiological Aspects and Consequences of Parasitism*. Rutgers U. Press, New Brunswick, New Jersey, 90 pp.
7. COVELL, G., RUSSELL, P. F., and SWELLENGREBEL, N. H., 1953.   *Malaria Terminology*. World Health Organization: Monograph Series No. 13. Palais des Nations, Geneva.
7a. DAVIS, L. R. and BOWMAN, G. W., 1956.   Bovine Coccidiosis. *Yearbook of Agriculture*, 1956. pp. 314–317.
8. FALLIS, A. M. and BENNETT, G. F., 1961.   Sporogony of *Leucocytozoon* and *Haemoproteus* in Simuliids and Ceratopogonids and a Revised Classification of the Haemosporidiida. Can. J. Zool., *39*, 215–228.
9. FALLIS, A. M. and BENNETT, G. F., 1962.   Observations on the Sporogony of *Leucocytozoon mirandae, L. bonasae* and *L. fringillinarum*. Can. J. Zool., *40*, 395–400.

10. Fallis, A. M., Davis, D. M., and Vickers, M. A., 1951. Life History of *Leucocytozoon simondi* Mathis and Leger in Natural and Experimental Infections and Blood Changes Produced in the Avian Host. Can. J. Zool., *29*, 305–328.

11. Faust, E. C., 1958. Parasitic Diseases of Man (Recent). Ann. Rev. Microbiol., *12*, 103–126.

12. Garnham, P. C. C., 1962. Parasitological Problems in Tropical Medicine. Radioisotopes in Trop. Med., IAEA, 305–231.

13. Garnham, P. C. C., Bird, R. G., Baker, J. R., and Bray, R. S., 1961. Electron Microscope Studies of Motile Stages of Malaria. II The Fine Structure of the Sporozoite of *Laverania* (= *Plasmodium*) *falcipara*. Trans. Roy. Soc. Trop. Med. Hyg., *55*, 98–102.

14. Garnham, P. C. C., Heisch, R. B., and Minter, D. M., 1961. The Vector of *Hepatocystis* (= *Plasmodium*) *kochi*; the Successful Conclusion of Observations in Many Parts of Tropical Africa. Trans. Roy. Soc. Trop. Med. & Hyg., *55*, 497–502.

15. Goldman, M., Carver, R. K., and Sulzer, A. J., 1958. Reproduction of *Toxoplasma gondii*. J. Parasitol, *44* (2), 161–171.

16. Gresham, G. A. and Cruickshank, J. G., 1959. Protein Synthesis in Macrophages Containing *Eimeria tenella*. Nature, Supplement 15, *184*, 1153.

17. Huger, A., 1960. Electron Microscope Study on the Cytology of a Microsporidian Spore by Means of Ultrathin Sectioning. J. Insect Pathol , *2*, 84–105.

18. Hull, R. W. and Camin, J. H., 1960. Haemogregarines in Snakes: The Incidence and Identity of the Erythrocytic Stages. J. Parasitol , *46*, 515–523.

19. Janiszewska, J., 1955. *Siedleckiella antonii* sp. n. Uwagi nad sporogeneza u. rodzaju *Siedleckiella* i u innych Actinomyxidia. (*Siedleckiella antonii* sp. n. Remarks on the sporogenesis in the genus *Siedleckiella* and in other Actinomyxidia). Zool. Polon., *6*, 88–100.

20. Kudo, R. R. and Daniels, E. W., 1963. An Electron Microscopic Study of the Spore of a Microsporidian, *Thelohania californica*. J. Protozool., *10*, 112–120.

21. Laird, M., 1952. New Haemogregarines From New Zealand Marine Fishes. Trans. Roy Soc. N. Z., *79*, 589–600.

22. Levine, N. D., 1961*a*. Problems in the Systematics of the "Sporozoa". J. Protozool., *8*, 442–451.

23. Levine, N. D., 1961*b*. *Protozoan Parasites of Domestic Animals and of Man*. Burgess Pub. Co. 412 pp.

24. Lewert, R. M., 1952. Changes in Nucleic Acids and Protein in Nucleated Erythrocytes Infected with *Plasmodium gallinaceum* as Shown by Ultraviolet Absorption Measurements. J. Infect. Dis., *91*, 180–183.

25. Liu, S. K., 1958. (The Pathology of Leucocytozoon Disease in Chicks.) (In Chinese with Eng. summ.) Mem. Coll. Nat'l Taiwan Univ., *5*, 74–80.

26. Lom, J. and Vávra, J., 1961. Contribution to the Knowledge of Microsporidian Spore. I. Electron Microscopy. II. The Sporoplasm Extrusion. Abstracts of Papers Presented at the International Conference of Protozoologists, Praha, p. 259–260.

27. Lom, J. and Vávra, J., 1962. A Proposal to the Classification Within the Subphylum Cnidospora. Systematic Zool., *11*, 172–175.

28. Lom, J. and Vávra, J., 1963. Mucous Envelopes of Spores of the Subphylum Cnidospora (Doflein, 1901). Věstnik Českoslov. Spol. Zool. (Acta Soc. Zool. Bohemoslov.), *27*, 4–6.

29. Ludvik, J., 1958. Morphology of *Toxoplasma gondii* in Electron Microscope. Vest. Cesk. Spol. Zool., *22*, 130–136.

30. Ludvik, J., 1960. The Electron Microscopy of *Sarcocystis miescheriana* Kuhn 1865. J. Protozool., *7*, 128–135.

31. Lund, E., Lycke, E., and Sourandea, P., 1961. A Cinematographic Study of *Toxoplasma gondii* in cell cultures. Brit. J. Exptl. Pathol., *42*, 357–362.

32. Macdonald, G., 1957. *The Epidemiology and Control of Malaria*. Oxford Univ. Press, London. 201 pages.

33. Matsubayashi, H., and Akao, S., 1963. Morphological Studies on the Development of the *Toxoplasma* cyst. Amer. J. Trop. Med. Hyg., *12*, 321–333.

34. May, J. M., 1961. The Ecology of Malaria. In: May, J. M. (ed.), Studies in Disease Ecology, Chapt. 8. Hafner Publ. Co., N. Y., 613 pp.

35. NOBLE, E. R., 1944.   Life Cycles in the Myxosporidia.   Quart. Rev. Biol., *19*, 213–235.
36. RUDZINSKA, M. A. and TRAGER, W., 1962.   Intracellular Phagotrophy in *Babesia rodhaini* as Revealed by Electron Microscopy. J. Protozool., *9*, 279–288.
37. RUSSELL, P. F., 1959.   Insects and the Epidemiology of Malaria. Ann. Rev. Entomol., *4*, 415–434.
38. SIIM, J., 1960.   *Human Toxoplasmosis.* Williams & Wilkins, Baltimore.
39. SIMMS, B. T., 1956.   *Treatment of Disease. The Yearbook of Agriculture.* 1956. Animal Diseases, p. 315. U.S. Dept. Agri., U.S. Govt. Printing Office, 591 pp.
40. THOMSON, H. M., 1960.   A List and Brief Description of the Microsporidia Infecting Insects. J. Insect Path., *2*, 346–385.
41. TRAGER, W., 1957.   The Nutrition of an Intracellular Parasite (Avian Malaria). Acta Tropica., *14*, Nr. 4, 21–301.
42. VÁVRA, J., 1959.   Beitrag zur Cytologie einiger Mikrosporidien. Věst. Česk. Spol. Zool., *23*, 347–350.
43. WEINMAN, D., 1952.   Toxoplasma and Toxoplasmosis. Ann. Rev. Microbiol., *6*, 281–298.

CHAPTER VI

Phylum Protozoa, Subphylum Ciliophora

CLASS CILIATEA

THE CILIATES move by means of hair-like projections of the cytoplasm, called *cilia*, each of which is much like a little flagellum in appearance. The cilia are arranged in various ways in the different groups. The Opalinids (see below) are covered with a uniform distribution of cilia in straight or curved rows, while among the others there are many variations. The Holotrichida, as the name indicates, have cilia over their entire bodies, whereas other groups possess cilia in limited areas. Cilia may become specialized in function and be grouped into clumps (*cirri*), membranes or "spines." Zones of cilia around the mouth or cytostome are *oral* in position while zones near the opposite end are *aboral* in position. Organelles formed by modified cilia are known as *membranelles*. The order Heterotrichida consists of ciliates which are usually covered with cilia, but there is a tendency for a reduction in cilia on the dorsal surface, and there usually exists an undulating membrane along the edge of the cytostome. Oligotrichs possess relatively few cilia, but they do have membranelles. The order Peritrichida contains ciliates which are usually attached to some surface, the attachment being either direct or by means of a stalk. Some of the stalked forms are colonial. A sucker-like attachment is common with the parasitic or commensal *Trichodina*, whereas the peculiar *Ellobiophrya donacis* develops slender arms which reach around the gill filaments of its host (a mollusk), thus enabling the ciliate to maintain its position by a clasping mechanism.

Beneath the outer surface of the body in all ciliates there is a system of granules and fibrils which together are known as the *infraciliature*. Two types of nuclei exist: the large *macronucleus* (usually single), and one to many smaller *micronuclei*. Reproduction occurs by both asexual and sexual means. No fusion of independent gametes occurs but two entire protozoa come together temporarily (*conjugation*) and exchange micronuclei. Most groups of ciliates possess at least a few parasitic species, and some groups are entirely parasitic. Only representative families will be selected for discussion.

ORDER OPALINIDS—INCERTAE SEDIS

Members of this group are called *opalinids*. There are about 150 species, mainly in the large intestines of amphibia, and occasionally in fishes, snakes and at least one lizard (*Varanus*). These saprozoic parasites are flattened and are covered with rows of cilia. Usually there are numerous nuclei scattered throughout the cytoplasm, but one form, *Zelleriella*, possesses only two nuclei. Since the opalinids do not have mouths they are called *astomatous* protozoa. There is

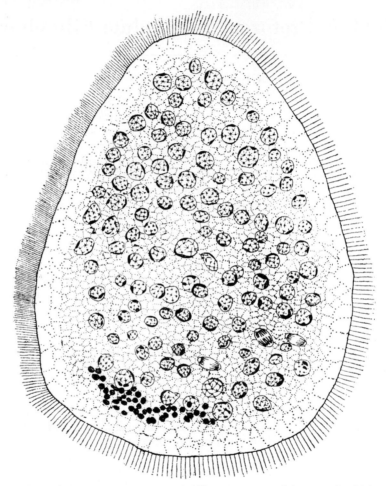

Fig. VI–1.—*Opalina ranarum*. × 460. Shows many nuclei, some of which are in the process of division. Most of the endospherules have been omitted. (Metcalf, courtesy of U.S. Nat. Mus. Bull.)

some justification for placing these protozoa with the flagellates instead of with the ciliates. They might well be considered as a separate class.

The geographical distribution of these protozoa is worldwide but each group has its own special distribution. The largest genus, *Opalina*, for example, can be found in almost any country except Australia and South America.

The life cycles of opalinids are not thoroughly known. In some species the body apparently divides into small ciliates which encyst and pass from the host with feces. These cysts are eaten by new hosts (tadpoles) within which they excyst and develop to maturity. Other opalinids apparently undergo a type of gametogenesis. The

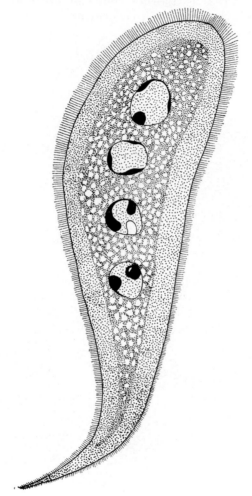

FIG. VI–2.—*Cepedia lanceolata.* × 1707. (Metcalf, after Bezzenberger, U.S. Nat. Mus. Bull.)

gametes unite and the resulting zygote is liberated from the body as a cyst which is eaten by another host.

The genus *Protoopalina* is considered to be primitive. Its members are cylindrical or spindle-shaped and range in size from about 100 to over 300 microns long by about 20 to 70 microns wide. *P. saturnalis* occurs in the marine fish, *Box boops*, while *P. intestinalis* and *P. mitotica* occur in the intestines of amphibia.

Opalina is a genus of flattened, multinucleate forms found in amphibia. They range in size from about 90 to over 500 microns long by about 30 to 180 microns wide, and about 20 to 40 microns thick. Among the several known species are *O. ranarum* (Fig. VI–1), *O. hylaxena, O. oregonensis* and *O. spiralis.*

Cepedia (Fig. VI–2) is another genus of opalinids in amphibia. The ciliates are cylindrical or pyriform and their range in size is

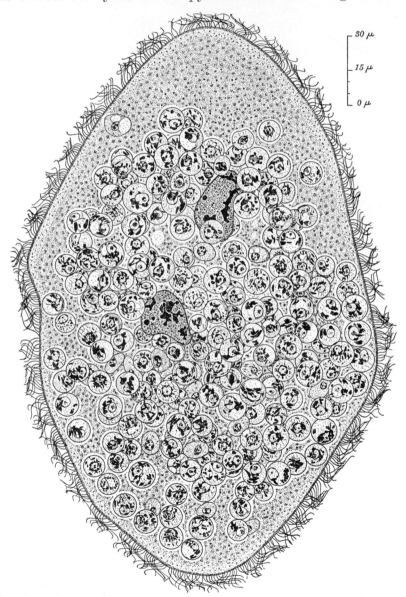

FIG. VI–3.—*Zelleriella opisthocarya*, an opalinid containing over two hundred cysts of *Entamoeba*. (Stabler and Chen, courtesy of Biol. Bull.)

about the same as indicated for the genus *Opalina*. *Cepedia canta-brigensis* is a representative species from the toad, *Bufo lentiginosus*.

Zelleriella is a genus whose members possess only two nuclei, as was mentioned above, and whose bodies are considerably more flattened than are other forms. The parasites live in the intestines of amphibia. *Z. hirsuta* measures about 130 × 60 × 22 microns and inhabits the gut of the toad, *Bufo cognatus*. Another species, *Z. elliptica*, occurs in *Bufo valliceps*. *Z. opisthocarya* is itself para-sitized by an ameba, *Entamoeba* (Fig. VI–3).[4]

SUBCLASS HOLOTRICHIA

Simple cilia cover the entire body surface, or are limited to certain areas; buccal ciliature, if present, inconspicuous.

ORDER GYMNOSTOMATIDA

Family Bütschliidae. These ciliates are of special interest to parasitologists because they live in the alimentary tract of herbivorous mammals. Their size varies considerably but an average size might be about 35 by 55 microns. They are oval, barrel-shaped or pear-shaped, covered with cilia, possess a "mouth" or *cytostome* at the anterior end and an "anus" or *cytopyge* at the posterior end.

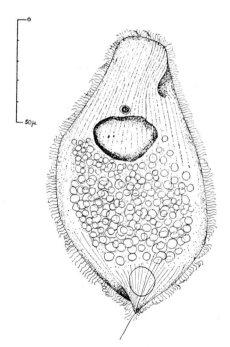

Fig. VI–4.—*Entodiscus borealis* a ciliate from a sea urchin. (Powers, courtesy of Biol. Bull.)

Contractile vacuoles are common. If a drop of fluid from the cecum or colon of horses or from the stomach (rumen) of cattle, camels or other herbivores is placed on a slide and examined immediately through a microscope, one can see swarming masses of these ciliates. For a discussion of the role these organisms play in the digestive tract of their host see p. 587 or Hungate.[2] *Bütschlia* is found in cattle, and among the many genera to be found in horses are: *Blepharoprosthium*, *Didesmis*, *Blepharosphaera*, *Blepharoconus*, *Bundleia*, *Holophyroides*, and *Ampullacula*.

Family Entorhipidiidae. The members of this family are flattened and have a lobe-like anterior end and a tapering or pointed posterior end. They live in the gut of sea urchins. These hosts seem to be especially favored by ciliates. The sea urchins, *Strongylocentrous*. *Echinus*, and *Toxopneustes* and other genera, harbor in their intestines species of *Entodiscus* (Fig. VI–4), *Biggaria*, and *Entorhipidium*.[3]

Among the many ciliates belonging to other families which live in sea urchins are *Colpidium* (Tetrahymenidae), *Anophrys* and *Uronema* (Cohnilembidae), *Plagiopyla* (Plagiopylidae), *Colpoda* (Colpodidae), the hypotrich, *Euplotes*, and the peritrich, *Trichodina*.

Family Isotrichidae. The stomachs of cattle and sheep and of other ungulates contain tremendous numbers of these ciliates. Curiously enough, one species (*Isotricha*) also occurs in the gut of a cockroach. *Isotricha prostoma* and *I. intestinalis*, both about 120 by 65 microns in size, and *Dasytricha ruminantium* occur in the ungulates.

ORDER HYMENOSTOMATIDA

Family Tetrahymenidae. Most of the members of this family are not parasitic. The group has become well-known during the last few years because of studies on protozoan physiology. The genus *Colpidium* has a representative living in sea urchins. Various species of the genus *Tetrahymena* have been experimentally established in larval and adult insects, guppies, tadpoles, and embryo chicks. In the insects the protozoa live as facultative parasites in the hemolymph. *T. corlissi* was established in guppies and tadpoles through artifically produced wounds. In chicks the circulatory system, body cavity and muscle tissue may be invaded by two strains of the parasite, while the yolk sac or allantoic sac may be invaded by six strains.

Tetrahymena limacis is parasitic in the renal organ of the European gray garden slug, *Deroceras reticulatum*. This ciliate can be grown axenically in 1 per cent yeast extract, in tissue infusions and in other particulate media. *Tetrahymena* is also a normal endoparasite of mosquitoes, millipeds, slugs and other animals.

Glaucoma (normally free-living) may occur as a facultative parasite of arthropods and of the central nervous system of fishes and amphibians. This parasite is tolerant of CO_2, which fact suggests one explanation for its ability to be a parasite.

Family Ophryoglenidae. *Ichthyophthirius multifiliis* (Fig. VI–5) lives in the skin of many species of freshwater fishes. The parasites become embedded in the skin and cause serious eruptions which often lead to the death of the fishes. The ciliates leave the lesions, drop to the bottom of the stream, lake, or aquarium, secrete a

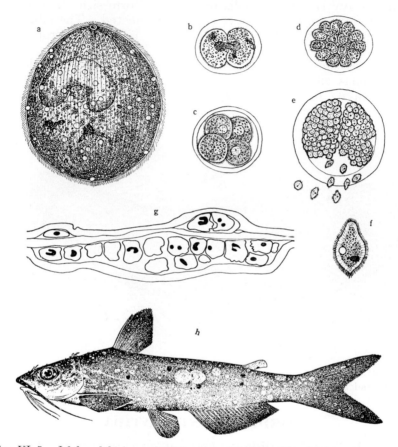

FIG. VI–5.—*Ichthyophthirius multifiliis*, a parasite of the skin of fishes.
a, free-swimming individual. × 75. (Bütschli); *b* to *e*, development within cyst; *f*, a young individual × 400 (Touquet); *g*, section through a fin of infected carp showing numerous parasites, × 10 (Kudo); *h*, a catfish, *Ameuirus albidus* heavily infected with the ciliate (Stiles). (Kudo, *Protozoology*, courtesy of Charles C Thomas.)

gelatinous capsule and reproduce by binary fission. Hundreds of new ciliates are formed in each capsule. When released from the capsule they are ready to attack new fish.

ORDER THIGMOTRICHIDA

Family Ancistrocomidae. The most interesting characteristic of this group is the possession of a tentacle which enables the ciliate to attach itself to the body of its host and ingest its food. The attachment is made more secure by the action of thigmotactic cilia, hence the name of the order. The family Ancistrocomidae has many genera, all species of which may be found attached to the gills and palps of mollusks. The ciliates are, in general, oval to elongate with a heavy covering of cilia of fairly uniform size. The anterior tip of the organism is usually slightly projected. The ciliates are comparatively small, ranging from about 15 to 60 microns in the longest diameter.

Ancistrocoma (= *Parachaenia*) *myae* is a transparent, pale green holotrichous ciliate which lives in the excurrent siphon and pericardial cavity of the clam, *Mya arenaria*. The ciliate is 40 to 100 microns long (Fig. VI–6).

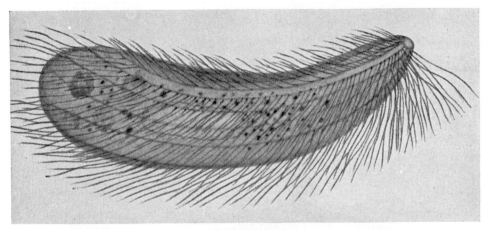

Fig. VI–6.—*Acistrocoma* (= *Parachaenia*) *myae*, a ciliate from the clam, *Mya arenaria*. (Kofoid and Bush, courtesy of Bull. du Musie Royal d'Histori Naturelle de Belgique.)

ORDER APOSTOMATIDA

Family Foettingeriidae. *Foettingeria actiniarum* is a European species which feeds on the material within the gastrovascular cavity of a sea anemone. The ciliate leaves this host and encysts on some object in the sea while undergoing cell division. Products of this division are released and come to rest on crustacea (copepods, ostcracods, and amphipods) as secondary hosts. Here they encyst. Sea anemones receive the ciliate when they feed on infected crustacea.

A complex life cycle has been discovered for this group. It involves special terminology as follows: The coelenterate becomes infected by eating a crustacean or other animal on which the encysted stage, the *phoronte*, is attached. These phorontes then enter the growth stage or *trophont*. After a growth period the *protomonte* stage is reached, which may also become encysted. A period of cytoplasmic reorganization occurs which produces the *tomonte* which is now ready for division. Division results in free-swimming forms, *tomites*, which are released in the water. These free-swimming tomites become attached to the crustacean host where they encyst. The cysts are phoronts, and thus the cycle is complete. *Spirophrya subparasitica* goes through this complete cycle. Twelve other genera of this family have been described.

Another genus, *Chromidina elegans*, lives on the renal epithelium and gonad of squids. It is attached by a papilla and may reach the unusual length of 1500 microns. The macronucleus is also unusual, appearing like the aimless markings a person might make when trying out a new pen.

ORDER ASTOMATIDA

As the name implies, this group is characterized by the absence of a mouth. The ciliates are somewhat larger than some of the other groups, usually being between 250 and 350 microns in maximum length but the range is from 100 to 1200 microns. Transverse fission and budding are common methods of reproduction with the formation of a chain of individuals. They are found in fresh and salt water invertebrates, especially in oligochaete worms.

Six species of astomatous ciliates were found in the alimentary tract of worms from Ochrida Lake, Yugoslavia. Examples are: *Ochridanus ocellatus* in the digestive tract of *Tubifex ochridanus*; *Radiophrya ochridana* in the intestine of *T. oligosetosus*; and *Juxta-radiophrya ochridana* in the gut of *Stylodrilus leukocephalus*.

ORDER TRICHOSTOMATIDA

The cytostome of ciliates in this order is usually situated at the base of an oral groove or pit whose wall bears dense adoral cilia.

Family Balantidiidae. The best-known member of the genus *Balantidium* is *B. coli*, described below. Other species, similar to *B. coli*, are: *B. suis*, in the pig (it is possibly the same species as *B. coli*, any difference being primarily physiological; infection can be fatal); *B. caviae*, in the cecum of the guinea pig; *B. duodeni*, in the gut of the frog; and *B. praenucleatum*, a large species reaching 127 microns in length, in the colon of the cockroach, *Blatta orientalis*.

Balantidium coli is the only ciliate parasite of man, excluding occasional coprophilic species. It is practically worldwide in distribution, lives in the large intestine, and is definitely pathogenic, causing the disease *balantidiasis*. The enzyme hyaluronidase is apparently produced by this ciliate but its function in the life of the parasite is obscure. *B. coli* may also be found in monkeys.

The motile form (Fig. VI–7) is roughly oval in shape and averages about 75 by 50 microns in size. The range in length is from 50 to 100 microns, and in breadth 40 to 70 microns. The body is covered with rows of cilia and there is a peristomal region of slightly longer cilia which guard a cleft leading to the mouth or cytostome. The macronucleus looks like a rather fat sausage while the small dot-like micronucleus lies so close to the macronucleus that it often cannot be seen. The cytoplasm contains many food vacuoles and two contractile vacuoles, one large and one small. Reproduction usually occurs by transverse fission but conjugation also takes place. A host diet rich in starch apparently favors the growth of this parasite.

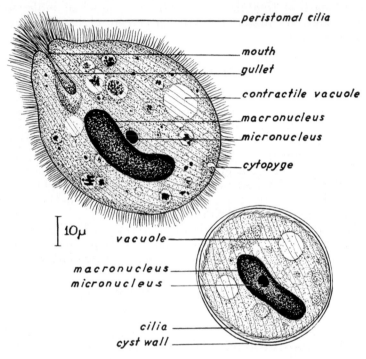

peristomal cilia
mouth
gullet
contractile vacuole
macronucleus
micronucleus
cytopyge
10μ
vacuole
macronucleus
micronucleus
cilia
cyst wall

Fig. VI–7.—*Balantidium coli*, trophozoite and cyst. (Original.)

The cyst is approximately round in outline and measures about 55 microns in diameter. Inside the cyst wall lies the ciliated parasite in which can be seen the large macronucleus and usually a vacuole but often little else. The living cysts are pale yellow or greenish in color but they are rarely seen.

When cysts are eaten in contaminated food they excyst in the host intestine and the released ciliates begin to feed on cell fragments, starch grains, fecal material and other organic matter. Often they invade the mucosa and submucosa of the large intestine or cecum, causing ulceration. Symptoms of infection include diarrhea, abdominal pain, dysentery, nausea, vomiting, weakness and loss of weight. Diagnosis is confirmed by finding the cysts in stool specimens. Treatment is reasonably effective with carbarsone, aureomycin or terramycin.

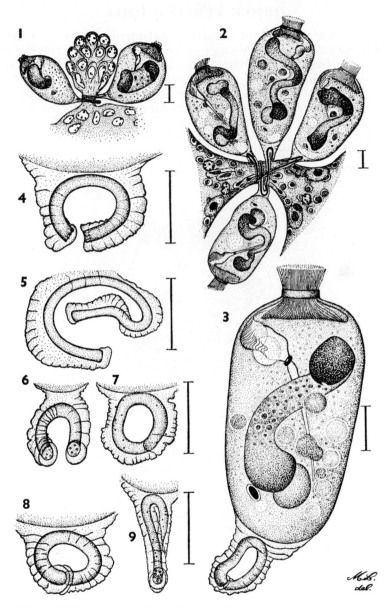

Fig. VI–8.—*Caliperia brevipes* from the gills of the skate, *Raja erinacea*. The scale lines to the right of the figures represent 10 microns taken at the same magnification. *1* and *2*, Habit. × 580. *3*, Whole animal, detached from host. × 1450. *4* to *9*, The attachment organelle. × 2340. (Laird, courtesy of Can. J. Zool.)

ORDER PERITRICHIDA

The oral surface of these ciliates is flattened and forms a disc on which occurs a counter-clockwise spiral of one or more rows of cilia. Many of the free-living species are attached to a substrate by a stalk.

Family Scyphidiidae. *Ellobiophrya donacis* is so modified that it has developed limb-like posterior projections of the cell which join around the trabecula of a molluscan gill and hold the ciliate in place. *Scyphidia* (= *Gerda*) *acanthoclini* similarly attaches itself to the gills of *Acanthoclinus quadridactylus*; and *Caliperia brevipes* (Fig. VI–8) is attached to the gills of the skate.

Family Urceolariidae. *Trichodina* (Fig. VI–9) is a genus which is represented by commensal ciliates on various animals. The aboral

Fig. VI–9.—*Trichodina parabranchicola*, a ciliate from the gills of various intertidal zone fishes × 880. The scale line represents 10 microns at the same magnification. (Laird, courtesy Trans. Royal Soc. of New Zealand.)

end is a flattened disc equipped with rings of cuticular teeth-like skeletal elements; locomotor organelles consist of posterior membranelles; cirri and undulating vellum are present; most species are ectoparasitic. One of the most well-known species is *T. pediculus* which "skates" around on the surface of the coelenterate, *Hydra*. Economically important species live on various fishes, and *T. urinicola* inhabits the urinary bladder of amphibia. Another entozoic species, *Urceolaria urechi*, may be found in the intestine of the echiuroid marine worm, *Urechis caupo*, on the United States Pacific coast. Members of this family often feed on bacteria.

ORDER CHONOTRICHIDA

These peculiar ciliates usually possess the general shape of a vase, and are often stalked. They range in length from about 30 to over 100 microns and may be found attached to various aquatic animals, especially to crustacea. Most of the described species are attached to marine animals, but one species, *Spirachona gemmipara*, occurs on the gill plates of freshwater gammarids (amphipods). Young amphipods are heavily infected. Marine genera include *Stylochona*, *Kentrochona*, *Trichochona*, *Heliochona*, and *Chilodochona*.

ORDER SUCTORIDA

The name of this group indicates one of its major characteristics. The organisms possess suctorial tentacles. Cilia are absent in the adult stages and most of the species are attached to the substrate by a stalk. *Allantosoma intestinalis* (Fig. VI–10), one of the few parasitic species, occurs in the large intestine and cecum of the horse. In this host the suctorea become attached to other ciliates. *A. brevicorniger* may also be found attached to the ciliates in the

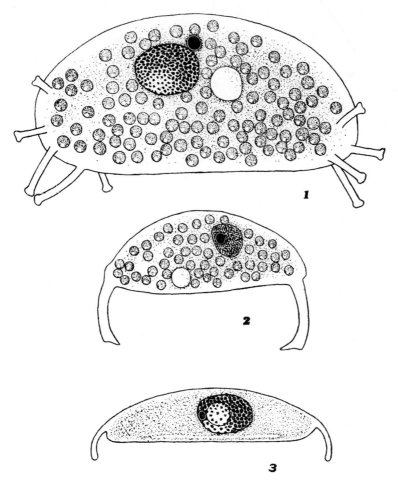

Fig. VI–10.—Three species of *Allantosoma*, parasitic suctorea from the large intestine of the horse. Magnification × 1707. *1, A. intestinalis; 2, A. dicorniger; 3, A. brevicorniger.* (Hsiung, courtesy of Iowa State Coll. J. Sci.)

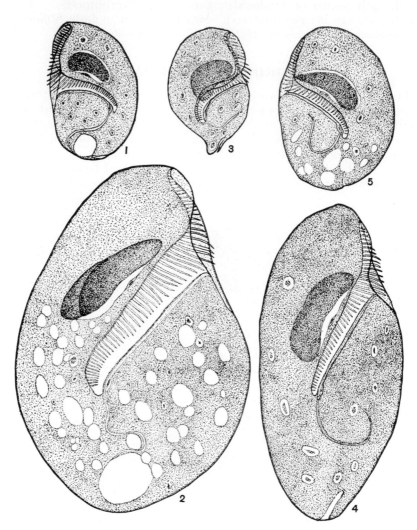

Fig. VI–11.—*Nyctotherus cordiformis*, a ciliate found in frog and toad tadpoles.

1, Typical condition of *Nyctotherus cordiformis* (?) as seen in adult Anuran hosts. Length, 140μ; width, 96μ. *2, Nyctotherus* from tadpole of *Rana clamitans*. Length, 340μ; width, 230μ. Note bilobed nucleus and anterior position of mouth and oblique pharynx. *3, Nyctotherus* from tadpole of *R. catesbeiana*. Length, 132μ; width, 90μ. Note curved pharynx and constricted posterior end.

4, Nyctotherus from tadpole of *R. catesbeiana*. Length, 300μ. Note narrowness, with macronucleus and pharynx almost longitudinal in position. *5, Nyctotherus* from tadpole of *R. clamitans*. Length, 170μ; width, 120μ. Body broadly oval in shape; cytostome forward. (Higgins, courtesy of Trans. Amer. Micros. Soc.)

colon or cecum of the horse while *A. dicorniger* lives unattached in the colon of these hosts. The last two species are about thirty microns long.

SUBCLASS SPIROTRICHIA

The modified cilia around the cytostome (adoral zone of membranelles) of this group is arranged in a spiral fashion, passing from the right side of the peristome into the cytopharynx.

ORDER HETEROTRICHIDA

Family Plagiotomidae. The peristome of these organisms contains an undulating membrane, and the entire body is ciliated. Parasitic forms may be found in many invertebrates and vertebrates. *Nyctotherus* is one of the best-known genera. These ciliates are, in general, kidney shaped; the indentation of the body contains a zone of cilia and leads to a cytostome which opens to a ciliated "esophagus." One species, *N. faba*, has been reported from the intestine of man. It is probably not pathogenic nor are the species which live in animals noticeably harmful. *N. velox* can be

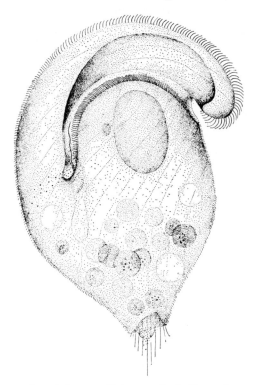

Fig. VI–12.—*Metopus circumlabens*, a ciliate parasite in Bermuda sea urchins. (Biggar, courtesy of J. Parasitol.)

found in the milliped, *Spirobolus marginatus*; *N. ovalis* inhabits the cockroach, *Blatta orientalis*; *N. parvus* and *N. cordiformis* (Fig. VI–11) live in amphibia. The latter ciliate can often be found in large numbers in the colon of frogs, toads, and tadpoles.[1] This ciliate conjugates in the intestine of tadpoles at the time of metamorphosis of the host. *Plagiotoma lumbrici*, a related species, may be found in the coelom of earthworms, and *Metopus circumlabens* (Fig. VI–12) is an inhabitant of Bermuda sea urchins.

ORDER ENTODINIOMORPHIDA

Throughout this survey of parasitic ciliates several groups have been mentioned as being found in the digestive canals of herbivores. The Entodiniomorphida are especially well-known as rumen ciliates in cattle, sheep and related hosts. The family Ophryoscolecidae has many representatives in the rumen of cattle and sheep. The latter host may harbor several species of each of the following genera: *Isotricha* (family Isotrichidae), *Entodinium*, *Diplodinium* and *Ophryoscolex*. Cycloposthiidae are found more often in horses. The elephant, rhinoceros and even gorilla and chimpanzee may play host to members of the latter family. See page 587 for a discussion of these and other ciliates in ruminants.

BIBLIOGRAPHY

1. HIGGINS, H. R., 1929. Variations in the *Nyctotherus* (Protozoa, Ciliata) Found in Frog and Toad Tadpoles and Adults. Trans. Amer. Micros. Soc., *48*, 141–157.
2. HUNGATE, R. E., 1955. Mutualistic Intestinal Protozoa. pp. 159–199 in *Biochemistry and Physiology of Protozoa*. Ed. by S. H. Hutner and André Lwoff-Academic Press Inc. N. Y. 388 pp. 1955.
3. POWERS, P.B.A., 1935. Studies on the Ciliates of Sea Urchins. A General Survey of the Infestations Occurring in Tortugas Echinoids. Pap. Tortugas. Lab., Carnegie Inst. Wash., *29*, 293–326.
4. STABLER, R. M. and CHEN, T., 1936. Observations on an *Endamoeba* Parasitizing Opalinid Ciliates. Biol. Bull., *70*, 56–71.

CHAPTER VII

Phylum Platyhelminthes, Introduction
Classes: Turbellaria, Trematoda
Subclasses: Monogenea, Aspidobothria

INTRODUCTION

MEMBERS of this phylum are usually flattened dorsoventrally without segmentation; are bilaterally symmetrical; possess an incomplete digestive tract (except in Cestoidea); lack a body cavity; are without special skeletal, circulatory, respiratory structures; possess a flame-cell type of excretory system; possess a nervous system consisting of a pair of anterior ganglia with one to three pairs of longitudinal nerve cords connected to transverse commissures; contain both sexes in one individual (few exceptions); and undergo direct or indirect development.

Flatworms are divided into three chief classes: *Turbellaria*, which are almost all free-living; *Trematoda*, all parasitic and known as "flukes"; and *Cestoda*, all parasitic and known as "tapeworms."

CLASS TURBELLARIA

These flatworms are mostly free-living; epidermis usually ciliated; body undivided; life cycle simple. They are grouped into five orders with many suborders, but only order RHABDOCOELA is discussed here because this group contains the few turbellarians which are parasitic.

One flatworm living as a parasite in another flatworm is rather unusual, but the rhabdocoel, *Oekiocolax plagiostomorum*, lives in the mesenchyme of a free-living turbellarian, *Plagiostomum*, and causes degeneration of the ovaries of its host. *Paravortex gamellipara* is parasitic in the clam, *Modiolus*, which may be found on the New England coast. Sea cucumbers, sea lilies, sea urchins, sea stars, sipunculids and marine crustacea are all known to become infected with various species of this type of worm. *Anoplodium, Syndesmis* and *Collastoma* (Fig. VII–1) are representative genera of the parasites. *Syndesmis franciscana* inhabits the oral half of the gut of the sea urchins, *Strongylocentrotus franciscanus* and *S. purpuratus*. It is difficult to understand why so many turbellarians are parasitic in echinoderms, and this relationship could be the basis of some interesting research.

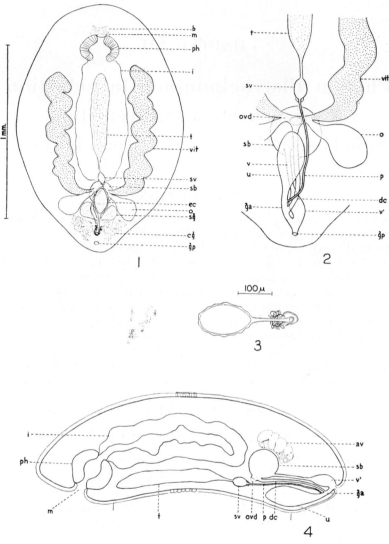

Fig. VII–1.—*Collastoma pacifica*, a rhabdocoel turbellarian which lives in the gut of the sipunculid worm, *Dendrostoma pyroides*. *1*, Entire worm, ventral view. *2*, Reproductive system, ventral view; semidiagrammatic; "cement glands" and "shell glands" omitted. *3*, Outline of egg capsule. *4*, Median sagittal section; semidiagrammatic. Abbreviations: *av*, accessory vesicle dorsal to seminal bursa; *b*, brain; *eg*, "cement glands"; *dc*, ductus communis; *ec*, egg capsule; *ga*, genital atrium; *gp*, genital pore; *i*, intestine; *m*, mouth; *o*, ovary; *ovd*, ovovitelline duct; *p*, chitinized portion of sperm duct ("penis"); *ph*, pharynx; *sb*, seminal bursa; *sg*, "shell glands"; *sv*, seminal vesicle; *t*, testis; *u*, uterus; *v*, vagina; *v*[1] dilated posterior portion of vagina; *vit*, vitellarium. (Kozloff, courtesy of J. Parasitology.)

Temnocephalidia (Fig. VII–2) is a suborder which is composed of small worms with tentacles and sucker-like structures. They live on crustaceans and on a few other animals but feed on free-living organisms. *Fecampia*, a genus of this suborder, is known to be pathogenic to its host, a European marine crustacean. The ciliated immature parasite enters the hemocoel of a crustacean and undergoes profound modification, losing most of its viscera but retaining the intestine. In the crustacean the parasite reaches sexual maturity,

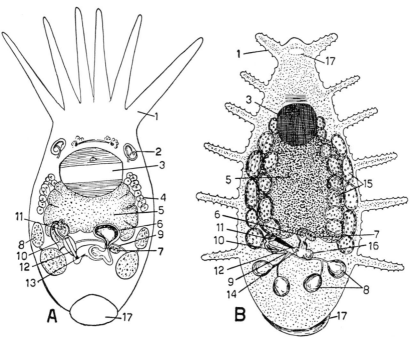

Fig. VII–2.—Two Temnocephalida. *A*, *Temnocephala* (*after Haswell*, 1893). *B*, *Actinodactylella* (*after Haswell*, 1893). *1*, tentacles; *2*, excretory ampulla; *3*, pharynx; *4*, tentacle glands; *5*, intestine; *6*, bursa; *7*, ovary; *8*, testis; *9*, sperm duct; *10*, seminal vesicle; *11*, prostatic vesicle; *12*, penis stylet; *13*, common antrum; *14*, common gonopore; *15*, yolk glands; *16*, uterus; *17*, adhesive disk. (Hyman, *The Invertebrates*, courtesy of McGraw-Hill Book Co.)

then leaves its host, produces eggs, and dies. *Temnocephala brevicornis* in El Salvador has been found attached to freshwater crustaceans, whereas in Brazil the same species becomes attached to turtles where the parasites apparently eat oligochaete worms which are attached to the same turtles.

CLASS TREMATODA

Fishes bear the heaviest burden of fluke parasites. Birds come next with about three times as many kinds as occur in amphibia and reptiles, and also about three times as many as in mammals. In a single host there may be only one species but hundreds of individuals.

The study of trematodes of fishes is a field wide open for investigators, and many of these flukes are yet to be described. Adult flukes of numerous species occur in the intestines or in other organs, and larval forms are commonly imbedded in skin, gills, mesentery, muscles, liver and other organs. In addition, there may be monogenetic species attached to gills or mouth parts. The monogenetic species apparently do little harm while the others may or may not be injurious depending on the numbers of individual worms and the organ infected. Apparently penetration and encystment of at least some cercariae in fish elicit the production of melanophores which surround the parasites. This reaction may be a defense mechanism.

SUBCLASS MONOGENEA

These flukes are usually found as ectoparasites on the lower vertebrates, especially on fishes, but some of them inhabit the gill chambers, mouth cavity, urinary bladder, cloaca, ureter or body cavity. Their life cycles do not involve more than one host. Adult flukes are attached to the host by a modification of the posterior end known as a *haptor* or, more accurately, *opisthaptor* (the haptor at the anterior end is the *prophator*)[3] which normally possesses suckers or hooks or both, and effectively holds the parasite to the skin of the host. In general, an egg hatches into a larva which swims to its host, attaches to the skin, gills or elsewhere and gradually changes by metamorphosis into the adult.

The morphology of monogenetic trematodes is fundamentally similar to that of other flukes but many modifications occur based on their peculiar mode of life (Fig. VII–3). The length of the adult is usually between a few millimeters to 2 or 3 centimeters, and the body outline ranges from spindle-shape to circular. The most striking feature of the body is the haptor. Since this organ is used to cling to the host it usually possesses one or more suckers or cups, and since the Greek name for cup is *cotyl*, we have many generic and other names for members of the group which incorporate this term. The genus *Cyclocotyla*, for example, includes monogenetic trematodes which possess a ring of suckers on the haptor. In the simpler forms of Monogenea there may be no fully-formed sucker but just an expanded posterior end of the body. As the number of suckers increases, the posterior part of the body becomes larger and forms a disc. This disc may be divided radially by septa. The whole organ, including septa and suckers, is activated by muscles and forms a complex haptor. Added to this complexity are hooks. There may be a few hooks, rings of hooks, or hooks of different sizes. These structures are also activated by muscles and can be extended or withdrawn, somewhat like a cat's claw. All this complexity creates an effective holdfast, and the parasite is not readily washed away from a precarious perch on the host.

The anterior end of the parasite also usually possesses one or

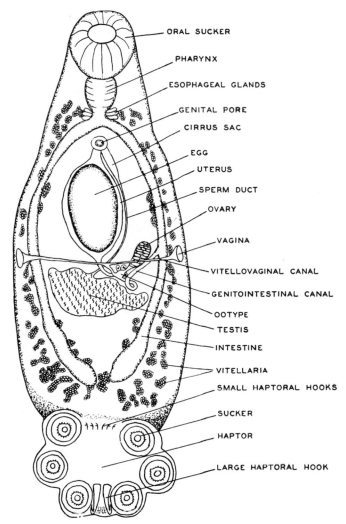

ORAL SUCKER

PHARYNX

ESOPHAGEAL GLANDS

GENITAL PORE

CIRRUS SAC

EGG

UTERUS

SPERM DUCT

OVARY

VAGINA

VITELLOVAGINAL CANAL

GENITOINTESTINAL CANAL

OOTYPE

TESTIS

INTESTINE

VITELLARIA

SMALL HAPTORAL HOOKS

SUCKER

HAPTOR

LARGE HAPTORAL HOOK

Fig. VII–3.—*Polystomoidella oblongum,* a monogenetic trematode from the urinary bladder of turtles. (Cable, *Illustrated Laboratory Manual of Parasitology,* courtesy of Burgess Publishing Co.)

more suckers. These organs are not ordinarily as well developed as is the oral sucker of digenetic trematodes, but there are often two of them. Sometimes, instead of suckers, various other head organs such as lappets, glandular areas, and extensions exist. The function of these organs is primarily adhesive, probably mainly to hold the mouth to the region of feeding.

The mouth is normally at or near the anterior end but it may be near the middle of the body, and the opening ranges from slit-like to circular. It may be in, near or removed from the anterior sucker or suckers. On the basis of histochemical examination, Uspenskaya[7] has shown that monogenes feed principally on host blood. Male and female genital pores may open together or separately, but they usually occur closely associated on the ventral surface toward the anterior end of the animal. The cuticle of the body is generally smooth and is pierced by a few other openings such as the excretory ducts, and ducts from secretory glands.

Inside the parasite (Fig. VII–4) there is no true body cavity, the various organs lying in a sort of packing tissue, the *parenchyma*.

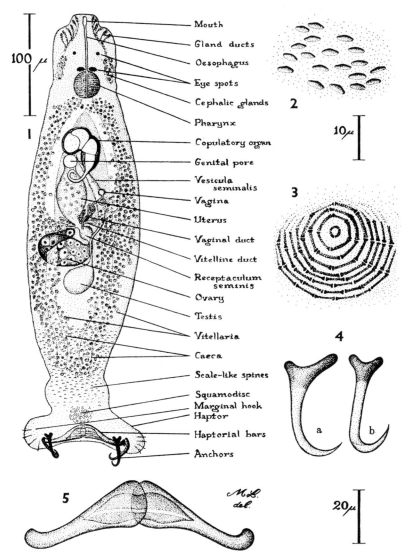

Fig. VII–4.—*Diplectamum melanesiensis* from the serranid fish, *Epinephelus merra.* *1,* Whole animal, ventral view. *2,* Scale-like spines of posterior part of body. *3,* Squamodisc. *4,* (*a*) Dorsal and (*b*) ventral anchors. *5,* Haptorial bars. (Laird, courtesy of Can. J. Zool.)

Like other flukes, the Monogenea carry on excretion with the aid of flame cells, tubules and vesicles. The digestive tract consists of the mouth, pharynx, esophagus, and gut. The gut may be simple or branched, sometimes with innumerable small blind pouches or *ceca*. There is no anus. The worms are hermaphroditic and the reproductive systems are basically the same as those to be described for the digenetic trematodes. There may be a single testis or many testes. Sperm pass through the vasa efferentia to the vas deferens and are assisted from the body by a copulatory organ. Female

MONOGENETIC TREMATODE

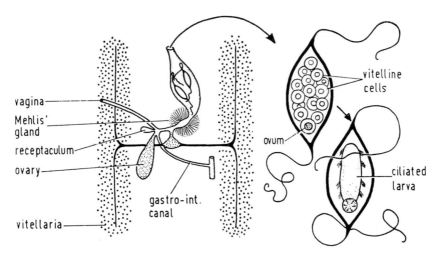

FIG. VII–5.—Diagrammatic representation of genitalia and egg of a monogenetic trematode. (Smyth and Clegg, courtesy of Experimental Parasitology.)

structures are more complicated. The ovary is often branched or folded, and several organs that bring nourishment and shell material to the egg and that ensure its fertilization are present. Figure VII–5 presents a diagrammatic representation of the genitalia and egg of a monogenetic trematode. Egg formation is essentially similar to that described for digenetic trematodes below. The term *oncomiracidia* refers to larvae of all monogenetic trematodes.[5]

For general reference to monogenes see Bychowsky,[2] Baer and Euzet,[1] Sproston,[6] and Yamaguti.[10]

ORDER MONOPISTHOCOTYLEA

An oral sucker is lacking or weakly developed in this group. The anterior end often possesses two or more lobes formed by clusters of adhesive glands. The opisthaptor consists of a prominent disc armed with 1 to 3 pairs of large hooks (anchors) and up to 16 marginal hooklets.

Gyrodactylus (Fig. VII–6) is the generic name of a viviparous member of this group, and it will serve as a representative species. The fluke lives on the surface of freshwater game fish and frogs, and sometimes it causes serious loss in fish hatcheries. The larvae develop within the uterus of the parasite. The "urge" to reproduce must be strong because the larvae themselves contain embryos which, in turn, contain clusters of embryonic cells. The haptor of the adult possesses no suckers but there is a row of sixteen small hooks along its edge. A large pair of hooks occurs in the center.

Marine invertebrates may also be parasitized by monogenetic flukes belonging to this suborder. Squids are host to the genus *Isancistrum* whereas the copepod *Caligus* may have clumps of *Udonella* attached to it. The latter parasite possesses two anterior suckers and a simple haptor. The copepod is itself a parasite on marine fish.

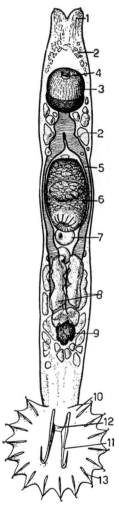

FIG. VII–6.—*Gyrodactylus*. *1*, anterior adhesive organ; *2*, adhesive glands; *3*, pharynx; *4*, mouth; *5*, intestine; *6*, embryo; *7*, uncleaved egg; *8*, ovary; *9*, testis; *10*, opisthaptor; *11*, anchors; *12*, bar; *13*, marginal hooks. (Hyman, *The Invertebrates II*, courtesy of McGraw-Hill Book Co.)

ORDER POLYOPISTHOCOTYLEA

In this group the mouth is surrounded by the prohaptor which consists of 1 or 2 suckers or 2 pits. The opisthaptor may or may not be armed, but always possesses suckers or sucker-like bodies containing clamps.

Endoparasitism is not common among the monogenea but there are some well-known examples. *Polystoma integerrimum*[4,8,9] lives in the urinary bladder of frogs. Fluke eggs pass to the outside with urine. Larval flukes usually attach themselves to the gills of tadpoles and when the tadpoles metamorphose, the larval flukes migrate into the intestine, then into the bladder of the adult frog. In some instances, the larval fluke will attach itself to a very young tadpole and will mature as a *neotenic* (sexually mature larva) ectoparasite. These flukes are smaller than are the endoparasitic ones, and they die when their tadpole hosts metamorphose. This phenomenon of two possible generations, a neotenic one on young tad-

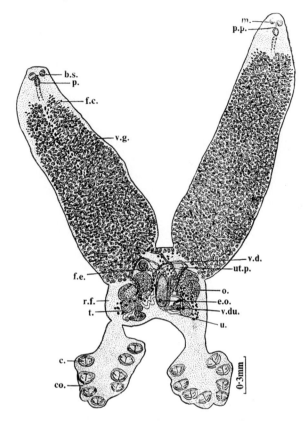

FIG. VII–7.—Two *Diplozoon ghanense* in permanent copulation.

b.s., buccal sucker; *c*, clamp; *co.*, cotylophore; *d.s.*, dorsolateral sclerite; *e.o.*, eggs in ootype; *f.c.*, food contents in intestine, *f.e.*, filament of egg; *m.*, position of mouth; *m.p.*, median U-shaped piece; *o.*, ovary; *p.*, pharynx.

p.p., prepharynx, *r.f.*, region of fusion of copulating pair; *s.d.s.*, spur of dorsal sclerite; *t.*, testis; *u.*, uterus; *ut.p.*, uterine pore; *v.s.*, ventral sclerite; *v.d.*, vas deferens; male duct; *v.du.*, vitelline duct; *v.g.*, vitelline gland. (Thomas, courtesy of J. West. African Sci. Assoc.)

poles and an endoparasitic one in older tadpoles and adult frogs is reminiscent of the two possible life histories of the roundworm, *Strongyloides stercoralis* (p. 311).

Diplozoon ghanense (Fig. VII–7) is a monogenetic fluke which lives on the gills of carp, stickleback and the other freshwater fishes. Its greatest distinction is that, although it is hermaphroditic, a permanent union of the worms occurs. During the larval stage of

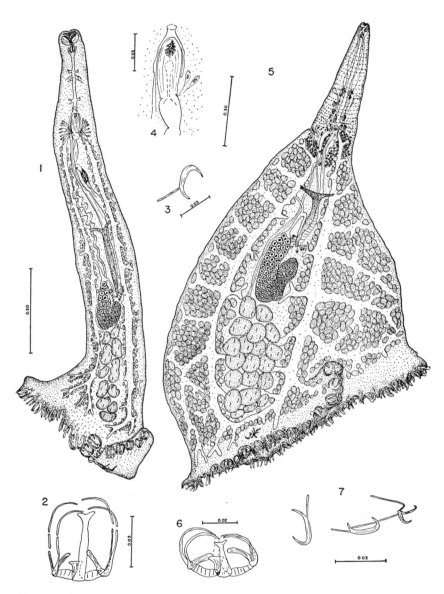

Fig. VII–8.—*Axinoides raphidoma* on the left, *A. truncatus* on the right. Both are monogenetic trematodes from Gulf of Mexico fishes. (Hargis, courtesy of Proc. Helmin. Soc. Wash.)

this fluke a small fleshy knob appears on the dorsal surface. Eventually this knob becomes fitted into a ventral sucker of another larval worm. The two worms become securely fused together and cannot be separated. The gonads then begin to develop, and finally the vagina of one individual opens in the region of the uterus and vas deferens of the other. This arrangement is reciprocal and cross fertilization is made easy.

The family Microcotylidae is represented in Figures VII–8 and VII–9 by three species from the Gulf of Mexico fishes. Peculiarities

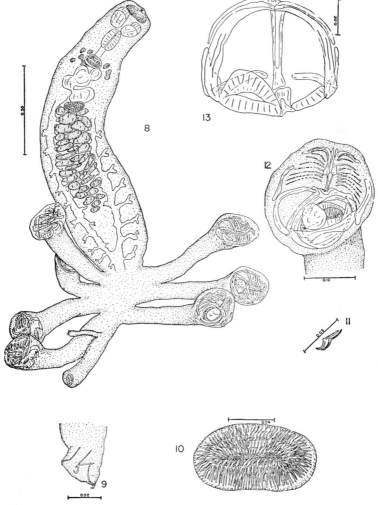

Fig. VII–9.—*Choricotyle louisianensis*, from the gills of Southern Whiting. *8*, Whole mount, ventral view. *9*, Terminal lappet, showing anchor. *10*, Genital atrium armament. *11*, Two genital spines, enlarged. *12*, Sucker-like clamp, ventral view. *13*, Clamp, ventral view, of *Tagia equadori*. Presented for homological comparison of clamp sclerites with those of the more advanced clamps of various *Choricotyle* spp. (Hargis, courtesy of Trans. Amer. Micros. Soc.)

of this group are well illustrated. Sucker-like clamps on the ends of four pairs of lateral peduncles occur in *Choricotyle louisianensis*, a parasite of fishes.

SUBCLASS ASPIDOBOTHRIA

This subclass holds an uncertain position between the monogenetic and the digenetic trematodes, but it is closer to the digenes. The

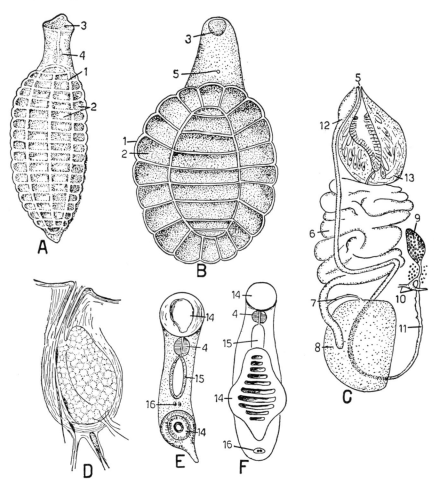

Fig. VII–10.—Types of Aspidobothria. *A, Aspidogaster conchicola (after Monticelli, 1892). B, Cotylaspis (after Osborn, 1903). C,* Reproductive system of *Cotylaspis (after Stunkard, 1917). D,* Longitudinal section of sense organ of sucker margin of *Cotylogaster (after Nickerson, 1902). E, F,* Larval stages of *Aspidogaster (after Voelzow, 1888). E,* Newly hatched larva. *F,* Later stage, definitive sucker developing from larval posterior sucker.

1, sucker; *2,* alveoli; *3,* mouth funnel; *4,* pharynx; *5,* gonopore; *6,* seminal vesicle; *7,* sperm duct; *8,* testis; *9,* ovary; *10,* yolk ducts; *11,* ovovitelline duct; *12,* uterus; *13,* cirrus sac; *14,* larval suckers; *15,* intestine; *16,* nephridiopore. (Hyman, *The Invertebrates,* courtesy of McGraw-Hill Book Company.)

group is divided into two families, Aspidogastridae and Stichocotylidae. The aspidogastrids are characterized by an enormous circular or oval sucker which occupies the greater part of the ventral surface (Fig. VII–10), and they are marine or freshwater parasites of the mantle and pericardial and renal cavities of clams and snails, of the gut of fishes and turtles, and the bile passages of fishes. The stichocotylids, comprising a single genus *Stichocotyle*, are elongate slender worms, about 10 cm. in length, parasitic in the bile passages or spiral valve of skates. The subclass is sometimes called Aspidocotylea or Aspidogastrea. For a discussion of the evolutionary relationships of this group see pages 668 and 669. For a systematic account see Yamaguti.[10]

BIBLIOGRAPHY

1. BAER, J. G. and EUZET, L., 1961. Classe des Monogènes. Monogenoidea Bychowsky. In: Grassé, P. *Traité de Zoologie*. Tome IV. pp. 243–325. Masson et Cie Editeurs Libraires de l'Acad. Méd. Paris.

2. BYCHOWSKY, B. E., 1957. *Monogenetic Trematodes. Their Systematics and Phylogeny*. Edited by W. J. Hargis, Jr., Transl. by P. C. Oustinoff. Amer. Inst. Biol. Sci. Wash., D.C. 627 pp.

3. DAWES, B., 1956. *The Trematoda (With Special Reference to British and Other European Forms)*. Cambridge, at the University Press. 644 pp.

4. KOHLMANN, F. W., 1961. Untersuchungen zur Biologie Anatomie und Histologie von *Polystomum integerrimum* Fröhlich. Zeit. f. Parasitenk., *20*, 495–524.

5. LLEWELLYN, J., 1957. The Larvae of Some Monogenetic Trematode Parasites of Plymouth Fishes. J. Mar. Biol. Assoc. U. K., *36*, 243–259.

6. SPROSTON, N.G., 1946. *A Synopsis of the Monogenetic Trematodes*. Zool. Soc. London. 600 pp.

7. USPENSKAYA, A. V., 1962. (Nutrition of Monogenetic Trematodes.) Dokladi Akademii Nauk SSSR, *142*, 1212–1215. (In Russian).

8. WILLIAMS, J. B., 1960. The Dimorphism of *Polystoma integerrimum* (Frölich) Rudolphi and its Bearing on Relationships Within the Polystomatidae: Parts I and II. J. Helminthol., *34*, 151–192 and 323–346.

9. WILLIAMS, J. B., 1961. The Dimorphism of *Polystoma integerrimum* (Frölich) Rudolphi and its Bearing on Relationships Within the Polystomatidae: Part III. J. Helminthol., *35*, 181–202.

10. YAMAGUTI, S., 1963? *Systema Helminthum*. Vol. IV. Monogenea and Aspidocotylea. Interscience Publ. N.Y. & London. 699 pp.

CHAPTER VIII

Phylum Platyhelminthes, Class Trematoda
Subclass Digenea : Introduction

THIS subclass is characterized by cuplike muscular suckers, usually without hooks or other accessories; by genital pores that normally open on the ventral surface between the suckers; and by a single, posterior excretory pore.

The classic shape of a digenetic trematode, or fluke, is that of a thick, oval leaf. But many variations exist from those which resemble a short piece of pencil, tapered at both ends, to narrow ribbons enormously elongated to 20 feet (7 meters) or more (see Didymozoidae). In contrast, some species (*Euryhelmis*) are wider than they are long. Although two suckers are typical, only one occurs on some flukes and a few species lack both. Normally one sucker surrounds the mouth and is called the "oral sucker" or "anterior sucker." The other one can be called the "posterior sucker," "ventral sucker," or sometimes "acetabulum." *Monostomes* are flukes with one sucker, *distomes* possess two suckers.

All members of digenetic trematodes possess an outer cuticle which is flexible, resistant, protective, and sometimes covered with spines. Under it are muscles, parenchyma and body organs. Proteases of the papain bromelin group may attack the cuticle of parasites, but pepsin and trypsin are usually ineffective, probably because of the presence of acid mucopolysaccharides and polyphenols in the cuticle. This resistance of the cuticle is probably a main factor in protecting the worms from being digested by the host. Paired ganglia in the anterior end of the body serve as a brain, and from it lead various main nerve trunks which, in turn, lead to branches innervating all parts of the body. The mouth leads to a pharynx, esophagus and gut. As in the monogenea, the gut may be simple or highly branched with many blind ceca. There is usually no anus, although in a few species (*Echinostomatidae*) an opening exists between the ceca and the excretory vesicle. Also in a few flukes of fishes one or two anal pores open to the outside. The excretory system is typical of all flatworms, consisting of a system of flame cells connected by tubules which unite to form larger ducts, which either open independently to the outside or join to form a urinary vesicle or bladder, which opens at or near the posterior end of the animal.

The general pattern of fluke anatomy is illustrated in Figure VIII–1 which will serve to identify the organs used in diagnosis.

Excretory ducts begin as flame cells (*flame bulbs*), Figure VIII–2, whose pattern of distribution is of value in species diagnosis (see also Komiya).[12] The flame cells and ducts function not only for excretion but also for water regulation and possibly to keep body fluids in motion.

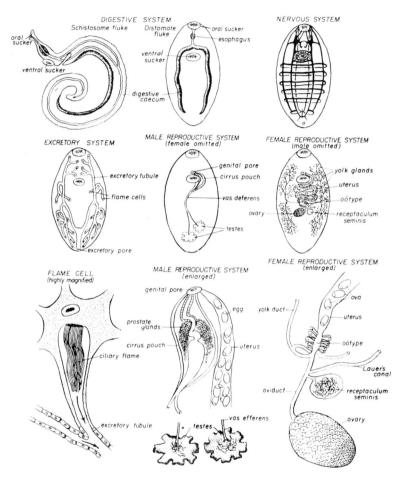

Fig. VIII–1.—Morphology of adult human flukes. (U.S. Navy Medical School Manual.)

The most complicated system is the reproductive apparatus. Testes and ovary may be rounded or branched. Usually there are two testes but in the family Monorchiidae most species possess a single testis. An enlarged detail of the distal end of the male reproductive system (Fig. VIII–3) shows the apparatus used to transfer sperm to the female part of another worm, or perhaps to its own female self. The *cirrus* is analogous to the penis of higher animals. In the female system, Laurer's canal is probably a vestigial duct corresponding to the vaginal canal in the tapeworms. It may function as a sperm-storage organ. On each lateral margin of the body occur bundles of yolk and egg-shell producing cells called *vitellaria* or *vitelline glands* (Fig. VIII–4). The large amount of this gland is probably associated with considerable protein demand for produc-

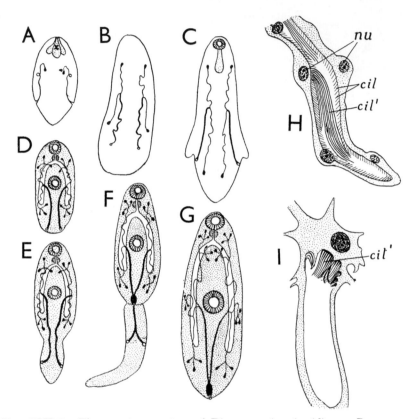

Fig. VIII–2.—The excretory system of Digenea. *A*, miracidium. *B*, sporocyst. *C*, redia. *D,E,F*, stages in development of the cercaria. *G*, metacercaria. *H*, tufts of long cilia and large cells forming the ciliated wall of the canal (not seen in the adult). *I*, young stage flame cell from *Dicrocoelium dendriticum*. (Dawes, *The Trematoda*, courtesy of University Press, Cambridge.)

tion of egg shells. The vitellaria may be dispersed or clumped together but are connected by minute ducts to large vitelline ducts and eventually to main channels from each side which meet near the midline and, as a single tube, connect with other female ducts and form an enlarged tube called the *ootype*. The ootype is surrounded by a mass of minute glands known together as *Mehlis' gland* (Fig. VIII–7). This gland was for a long time considered to be the main contributor to the materials which make up the shell of an egg and therefore was often called the "shell gland." Now, however, there is ample evidence that the gland cannot be directly concerned with the secretion of the bulk of the egg-shell material.[15] It has been suggested that secretions of Mehlis' gland may lubricate the uterus and thus aid the passage of eggs along this tube, and also that the secretions might activate the spermatozoa. A more recent study[8a] showed that the gland (in cestodes) secretes a phospholipid

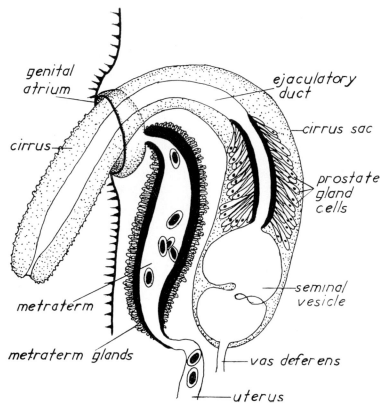

Fig. VIII–3.—Genital opening in a fluke showing the point where eggs emerge from the body and an extended male organ, the cirrus, which transmits sperm to another worm. (Composite from various authors).

which may effect a release of egg-shell precursors from the vitelline cells. Undoubtedly the function of the gland in cestodes is similar to its function in trematodes.

The diagramatic representations of the genitalia of digenetic trematodes (Fig. VIII–6) and of egg shell formation (Fig. VIII–7) are taken from Smyth and Clegg,[15] as is the following description of the method of shell formation. Mature eggs leave the ovary and pass down the short oviduct becoming fertilized by sperm which are stored in the receptaculum or in Laurer's canal. The vitelline reservoir is filled with unusual cells which have been produced by the

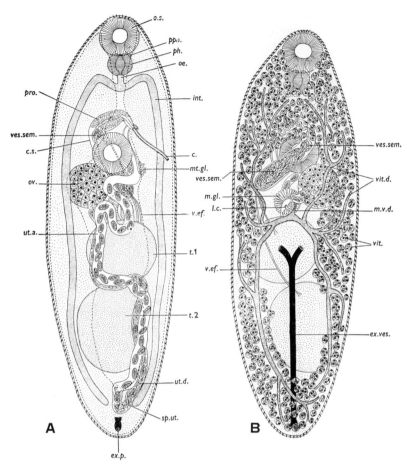

FIG. VIII–4.—*Plagiorchis* (= *Multiglandularis*) *megalorchis* showing the dispersed distribution of the vitellaria and vitelline ducts. *c.* cirrus; *c.s.* cirrus sac; *ex.p.* excretory pore; *ex.ves.* excretory vesicle; *int.* intestine; *l.c.* Laurer's canal; *m.gl.* Mehlis' gland; *m.v.d.* median yolk duct; *mt. gl.* gland cells around metraterm; *o.s.* oral sucker; *oe.* esophagus; *ov.* ovary; *ph.* pharynx; *pph.* prepharynx; *pro.* prostate gland cells; *sp.ut.* sperms in descending uterus; *t.1* anterior testis; *t.2* posterior testis; *ut.s.* ascending limb of uterus; *ut.d.* descending limb of uterus; *v.ef.* vas deferens; *ves.sem.* vesicula seminalis; *vit.* yolk glands; *vit.d.* yolk duct. (Rees, courtesy of Parasitology.)

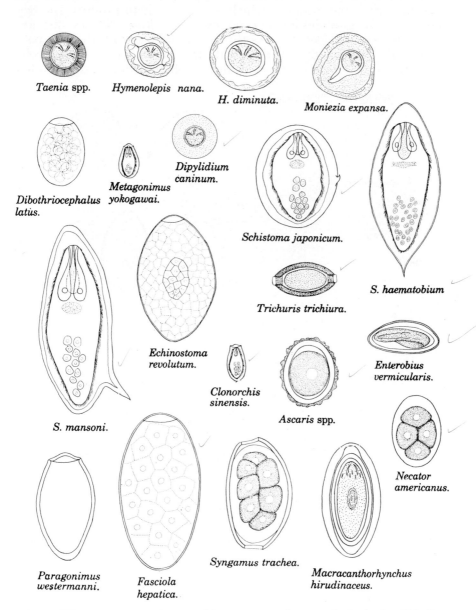

Taenia spp.

Hymenolepis nana.

H. diminuta.

Moniezia expansa.

Dibothriocephalus latus.

Metagonimus yokogawai.

Dipylidium caninum.

Schistoma japonicum.

S. haematobium

Trichuris trichiura.

Echinostoma revolutum.

Clonorchis sinensis.

Ascaris spp.

Enterobius vermicularis.

S. mansoni.

Necator americanus.

Paragonimus westermanni.

Fasciola hepatica.

Syngamus trachea.

Macracanthorhynchus hirudinaceus.

FIG. VIII–5.—Representative parasitic worm eggs of man and of animals. (Schell, *Parasitology* laboratory manual, courtesy of J. Wiley & Sons, N.Y.)

vitelline glands. These vitelline cells possess a nucleus, a mass of yolk material, and granules which are destined to produce the egg shell. These granules have been called *vitelline globules* but are better named *shell globules*. As the egg moves through the ootype a group of vitelline cells surrounds it, the number of vitelline cells being constant for each species of fluke. Shell globules are extruded

DIGENETIC TREMATODES

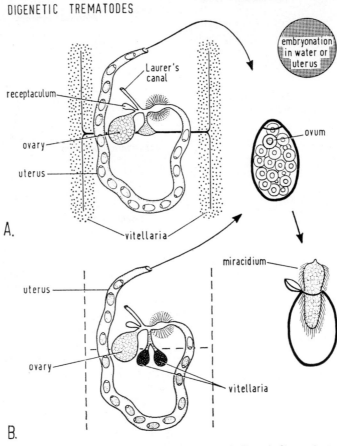

Fig. VIII–6.—Diagrammatic representation of genitalia of digenetic trematodes. *Type A*, with extensive vitellaria; *Type B*, with condensed vitellaria. (Smyth and Clegg, courtesy of Experimental Parasitol.)

from the vitelline cells and coalesce, thus forming a thin membrane. This membrane is the outer portion of the egg shell. More shell globules are released and the egg shell is built up from within. Completion of the shell occurs in the lower part of the oviduct. The egg shell material is protein and it soon becomes brownish in color and hardens. This protein hardening is now believed to be due to quinone-tanning. Compare the schematic diagrams of Smyth and Clegg with the arrangement of the genital organs in *Diplostomum pel-*

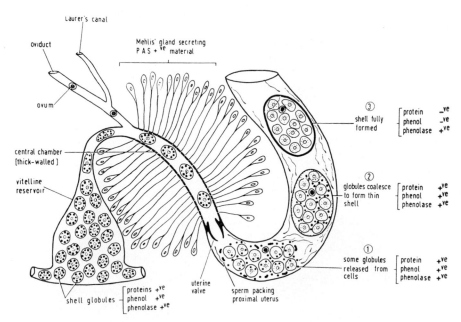

FIG. VIII–7.—Diagrammatic representation of egg shell formation in a trematode. Based on *Fasciola hepatica*. The process is essentially the same in tapeworms. (Smyth and Clegg, courtesy of Experimental Parasitol.)

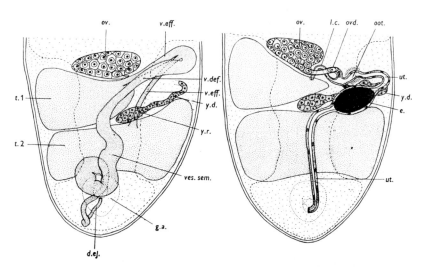

FIG. VIII–8.—*Diplostomum pelmatoides* showing male and female genitalia, ventral view.

t.1, anterior testes; *t.2*, posterior testes; *d.ej.*, ductus ejaculatorius; *ov.*, ovary; *v.eff.*, vas efferens; *v.def.*, vas deferens; *y.d.*, yolk duct; *y.r.*, yolk reservoir; *ves. sem.*, vesicula seminalis, *g.a.*, genital antrum; *l.c.*, Laurer's canal; *ovd.*, oviduct; *oot.*, ootype; *ut.*, uterus; *e.*, egg. (Rees, courtesy of Parasitology.)

matoides (Fig. VIII–8). See figure VIII–5 for eggs of flatworms and nematodes.

Life Cycles. Digenetic trematodes involve two or more hosts in their life cycles and include all the common flukes of man and of domestic animals. The adult parasite in its vertebrate host lives in the intestine, in ducts associated with the alimentary canal, in the gallbladder, urinary bladder, lungs, or in some other cavity of the

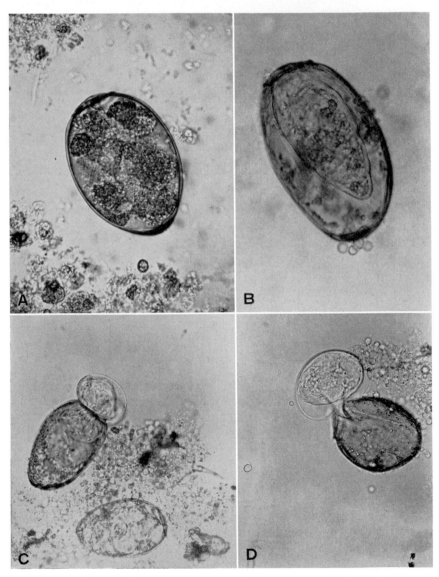

FIG. VIII–9.—Photographs showing hatching of the egg of the lung fluke *Paragonimus westermani*. (Courtesy of Dr. K. J. Lie, University of Indonesia.)

body. Eggs are produced and are eventually discharged from the host. There are many variations of the following brief outline of the life cycle. If an egg gets into water it is either eaten by a snail or hatches (Fig. VIII–9) into a free-swimming ciliated *miracidium*.

Miracidia which are free from their capsules dart about in a "restless", "aimless" fashion. They show great flexibility and continual peristaltic change of form. Their general behavior suggests that they are "seeking something with feverish haste."[2] Whether miracidia find the snail or clam host by chemotactic attraction or by some other means is unknown, but there is good evidence that at least some species perceive and are attracted by the mucus of the snail.[8,11,17] The maintenance of normal environmental characteristics of the habitat, however, seems to be most important.

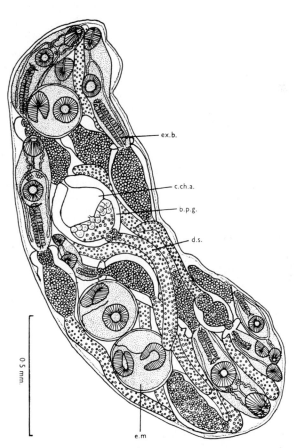

FIG. VIII–10.—Sac-like daughter sporocyst of *Phyllodistomum simile*, a fluke whose adult is found in the urinary bladder of brown trout, *Salmo trutta*. Within the sporocyst can be seen cercariae and metacercariae.

ex.b., excretory bladder. *c.ch.a.*, cercarial chamber. *b.p.g.*, basal portion of tail globe *d.s.*, distal stem. *e.m.*, encysted metacercariae. (Thomas, courtesy of Proc. Zool. Soc., London.)

Miracidia often demonstrate a high degree of selectivity for their hosts. Age of the mollusk, however, is probably a controlling factor in the selection and entry by miracidia.

Entry of miracidia into a snail host is either active or passive. If the egg is small, as is true with members of the fluke families Heterophyidae, Opisthorchiidae, Brachylaimidae and Plagiorchiidae, the miracidium is usually eaten by the snail, whether aquatic or terrestrial, or sometimes by a bivalve mollusk. Since snails readily eat feces, there is considerable opportunity for the passage of fluke eggs into their intestines. Miracidia of medium and large size usually penetrate through the body surface of the snail host, in the region of the mantle, "foot", head or tentacles. According to some investigators, miracidia probe with their anterior end and attempt to bore into almost any object, including various species of unsuitable snails and other animals such as planarians. They may keep on trying to enter an unsuitable host or an unsuitable part of the snail host, such as the shell, until they die of exhaustion. They seem to find the right host by accident, and then succeed in penetrating their host simply because their boring mechanism is adapted to succeed only with that host. Most snails, however, probably secrete a substance which attracts the parasite.

A somewhat different description of the method of entry has recently been given by Dawes.[7] He states that a preliminary attachment of the parasite to the host body occurs by suctorial action. Attachment takes place at an unciliated region of the miracidium. The parasite produces a cytolytic substance which breaks down host tissue and makes a perforation in its skin. The miracidium sheds its cilia and thrusts itself into the snail's body.

Within the snail the miracidium develops into a *sporocyst* (Figs. VIII–10, 11, 12), a sac-like structure which contains germinal cells for the next generation. The sporocyst may be branched or it may resemble a long irregularly coiled tube. At least in some species, temporary contact with the snail is apparently all that is necessary for a miracidium to metamorphose into a sporocyst.[3] Evidence that the snail produces a substance which initiates the body transformation of the parasite is given by the fact that once the process has started it will continue even if the developing sporocyst is removed from the snail. Host regulation is also apparent in the size of the parasites which seem to be fewer and smaller in small snails. Sporocysts contain germinal cells which may be clustered in masses or scattered throughout the body of the parasite. These germinal cells may produce a second sporocyst or several *rediae* (Fig. VIII–12). Small snails harbor fewer numbers of rediae than do large snails. In some species of rediae (*e.g.* amphistomes) there is a cluster of germinal cells in the posterior end of the body. This germinal mass decreases as each cell gives rise to an embryo. In other species of rediae (*e.g.* notocotylids) the germinal mass consists of both unicellular and multicellular elements which probably permit a more extended period of multiplication of germinal cells. In still other groups (psilostomes and echinostomes) the germinal mass is large, more complex, and persistant and probably produces larger numbers of embryos than do the other two types.[5]   Rediae show the beginning of adult characteristics, each having developed a sucker and an embryonic gut.   Most of its internal tissue is germinative and within it develop either another generation of rediae or several *cercariae* (Figs. VIII–13, 14).   All these stages in the life cycle may be considered the result of *polyembryony*.   A cercaria has matured considerably, possessing two suckers, a branched gut and a tail.

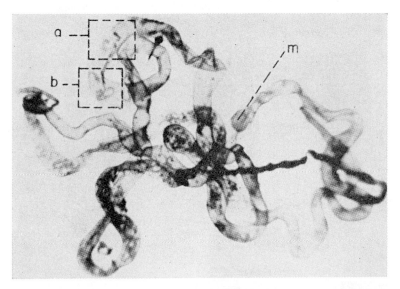

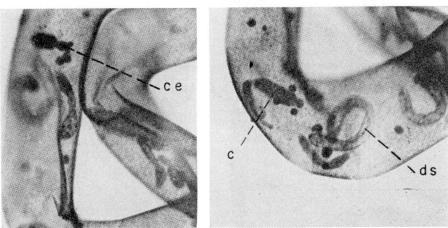

Fig. VIII–11.—Sporocyst of *Cotylurus flabelliformis* in the snail *Lymnea stagnolis appressa*. *1*, Entire mother sporocyst. *2*, Detail from area "a". *3*, Detail of area "b". *c*, cercaria; *ce*, cercarial embrys; *ds*, daughter sporocyst; *m*, metacercaria. (Hussey, Cort and Ameel, courtesy of J. Parasitol.)

Cercariae leave the snail and swim about in the water. They may
enter a new vertebrate host directly by burrowing into the skin,
or they may attach themselves to vegetation or to another transport
host, lose their tails, become rounded and secrete a cyst-like wall.
This cyst form is known as a *metacercaria*. These forms often become
attached to fish (Fig. VIII–15). The final host eats the vegetation
or devours the second transport host and so becomes infected. The
metacercariae are released in the gut and make their way to the site
of preference, mature and soon produce eggs, thus completing the

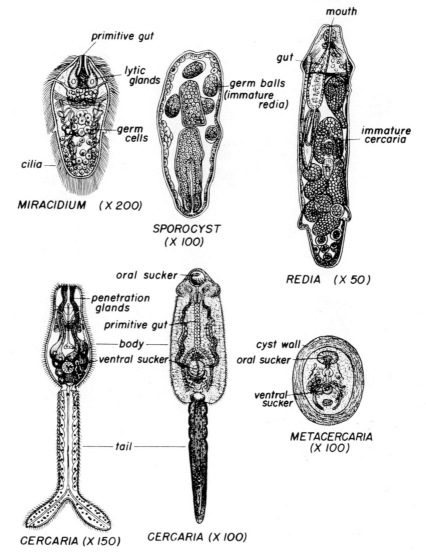

Fig. VIII–12.—Larval types of human flukes. (United States Naval Medical School
Laboratory Manual.) The magnifications indicated should be reduced by 20 per cent.

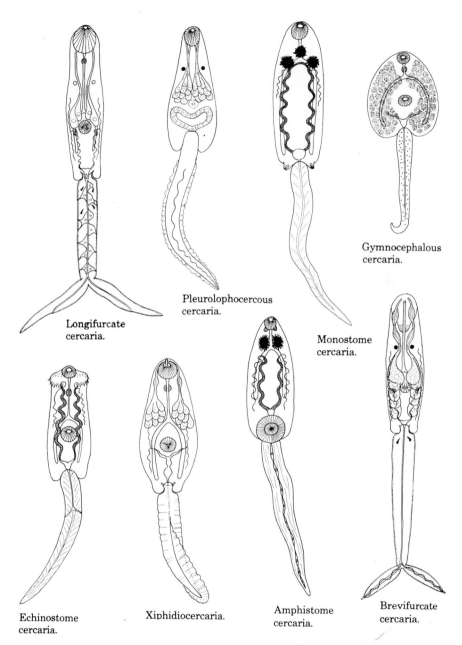

Longifurcate
cercaria.

Pleurolophocercous
cercaria.

Monostome
cercaria.

Gymnocephalous
cercaria.

Echinostome
cercaria.

Xiphidiocercaria.

Amphistome
cercaria.

Brevifurcate
cercaria.

FIG. VIII–13.—Representative types of cercariae. (Schell, *Parasitology* laboratory
manual, courtesy of J. Wiley & Sons, N.Y.)

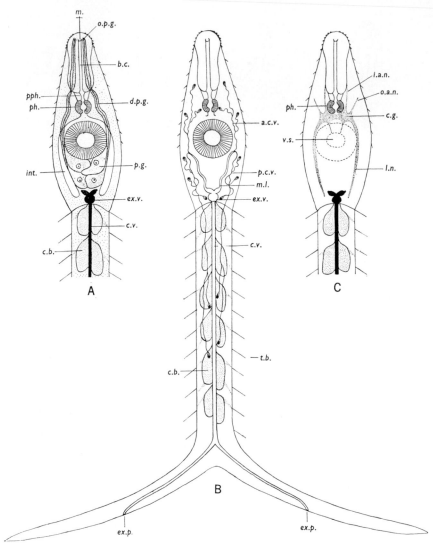

Fig. VIII–14.—*Cercaria diplostomi phoxini*, a furcoceraria which develops into *Diplostomulum phoxini* in the brain of the minnow. *A*, ventral view showing alimentary canal and penetration glands. *B*, Ventral view of complete cercaria showing caudal bodies (*c.b.*) and excretory system. *C*, Dorsal view showing a reconstruction of the nervous system (*c.g.* is the cerebral gangion). *a.c.v.* anterior collecting vessel; *b.c.* buccal cavity; *c.b.* caudal body; *c.g.* cerebral ganglion; *c.v.* caudal excretory vessel; *d.p.g.* ducts of penetration gland; *ex.p.* excretory pore; *ex.v.* excretory vesicle; *i.a.n.* inner anterior nerve; *int.* intestine; *l.n.* lateral nerve; *m.* mouth; *m.l.* main lateral excretory vessel; *o.a.n.* outer anterior nerve; *o.p.g.* openings of ducts of penetration glands; *p.c.v.* posterior collecting vessel; *p.g.* penetration gland; *ph.* pharynx; *pph.* propharynx; *t.b.* tail bristles; *v.s.* ventral sucker. (Rees, courtesy of Parasitol.)

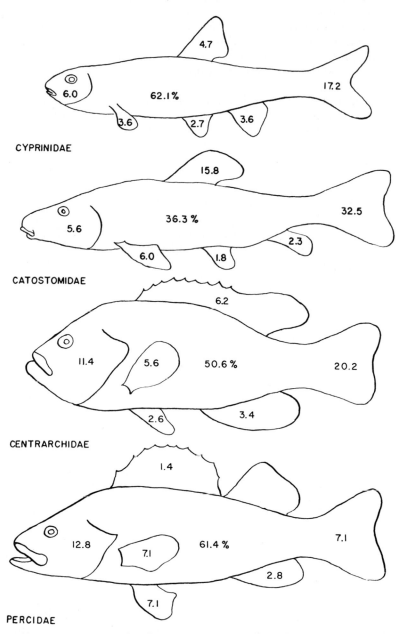

FIG. VIII–15.—Percentage distribution of metacercarial cysts on the left side of some New York fishes. (Evans and Mackiewicz, courtesy of J. Parasitol.)

cycle. Sexual maturity and egg production in metacercarial stages have been described by several authors.[4a] Stunkard[15a] has suggested that this kind of progenesis "appears to be a relict, the survival of an earlier developmental method." A sporocyst of a blood fluke in the snail *Melanoides* may produce miracidia which arise partheno-genetically and develop into second generation sporocysts within the snail.

In several species of flukes the sporocyst-redia-cercaria cycle is repeated in the snail. Both first and second generation rediae may give rise to cercariae. It is possible that all rediae give rise to daughter rediae but that in some species of flukes the second genera-tion rediae have escaped notice because of their minute size. Some genera possess an extra stage in the life cycle. This stage is the *mesocercaria* (see page 197). It develops from the metacercaria after the latter has penetrated a frog or tadpole.

Not all larval stages of flukes demand snail hosts. Certain mem-bers of the family Bucephalidae use a freshwater mussel (*Lampsilis siliquoidea*) instead. *Cercaria tiogoe* inhabits the freshwater unionid clam, *Alasmidonta varicosa*; and a related species, *C. catatonki*, has been seen emerging from the clam, *Strophitus undulatus quadri-plicatus*. *Cercaria milfordensis* is a small, stout-bodied distome which lives in the gonad and digestive gland of the common mussel, *Mytilus edulis* from Long Island, New York. The sporocysts are orange in color and give the mantle lobes of the mussel an orange shade. The annelid worm, *Eupomatus dianthus*, serves as the first intermediate host of the fluke, *Cercaria loossi*, which is probably a fish blood fluke. One might think that in the Antarctic available hosts are few and far between, and the life of the larval trematode, *Cercaria hartmanae*, encourages this assumption because these larvae develop in other species of rediae which occur in the coelom of the marine annelid, *Lanicides vayssierei* at Ross Island. *Allocreadium alloneotenicum* is found as a precociously mature adult fluke in the hemocoel of the caddis fly larvae belonging to the genus *Limne-philus* (Fig. VIII–16). Dead caddis fly larvae liberate fluke eggs which hatch into miracidia which penetrate the bodies of fresh-water clams (*Pisidium abditum*). The life cycle within the clam involves one sporocyst stage, two rediae and the cercariae. The latter leave the clam and penetrate caddis fly larvae to mature in the hemocoel.[16] Cercariae of members of the subfamily Gym-nophallinae are ordinarily found in bivalved mollusks but an unusual one was found in the snail, *Littorina saxatilis*. The parasite was either a cercaria which reproduced like a sporocyst or redia, or it was a sporocyst or redia which looked like a cercaria. Because of this peculiar combination of types it was called a "parthemita." The rounded organism appeared to be a cercaria but was filled with small tailless cercariae.[10]

Larval stages of trematodes, especially the early ones, are defi-nitely host specific. This relationship is in contrast to many of the adults which may occur in several species of vertebrate hosts.

Fasciola hepatica, for example, may inhabit the livers of man, sheep, cattle, pigs, deer, rabbits, and other animals. The effect of parasitism on the intermediate hosts is often not known. With trematodes, however, there is usually an inhibition of the growth of the gonads or even castration. Thus these parasitized snails are unable to reproduce. One study[4] demonstrated that damage to the hepatopancreas often occurs. Rediae may ingest host cells, cause sloughing of tissues, fat accumulation and depletion of glycogen. Heavy infections often destroy the liver of the snail.

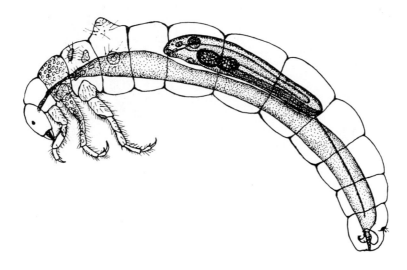

Fig. VIII–16.—The caddis fly larva *Limnéphilus* shown in lateral view with the adult fluke *Allocreadium alloneotenicum* in the haemocoel. Fluke eggs are shown only in the middle thoracic segment. (Wootton, courtesy of Biol. Bull.)

Reproduction of the larval stages of trematodes is best considered to be a process of polyembryony, as was mentioned above. This process is asexual, the germinative cells simply being products of the divisions of other germinative cells. Hence we have a life cycle involving alternation of generations as occurs in many other invertebrates. Some investigators, however, find evidence for sexual reproduction of sporocysts and rediae involving the production of gametes which reproduce by parthenogenesis (progenesis). Sporocysts and rediae produced by this parthenogenic reproduction are called *parthenitae*, the cercariae and metacercariae are called *adolescariae*, and the adult flukes are called *maritae*. Thus when one reads of a *marita* or of the *marital stage*, reference is not made to sexual union with the blessing of the church. We still have much to learn about larval trematodes but it is already clear that a thorough study of these forms would shed considerable light on puzzling taxonomic relations of the adults.

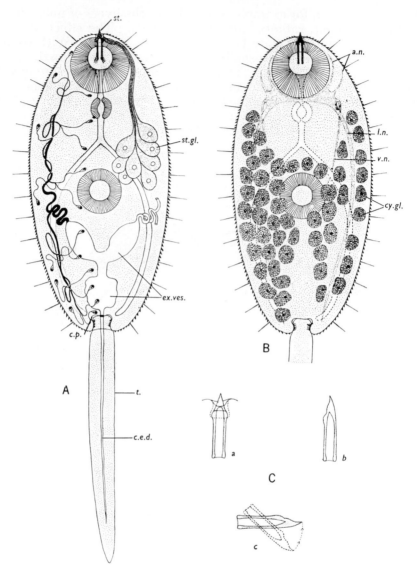

Fig. VIII–17.—Cercaria of *Plagiorchis* (= *Multiglandularis*) *megalorchis* from the turkey.

A, *Cercaria P. (M.) megalorchis*, dorsal view, showing stylet glands on right and excretory system on left.

B, *Cercaria P. (M.) megalorchis* showing distribution of dorsal cystogenous glands and nervous system.

C, (a) Stylet, dorsal view. (b) Stylet, lateral view. (c) Diagram to illustrate arc through which stylet moves during process of penetration. *a.n.* anterior nerves; *c.e.d.* caudal excretory duct; *c.p.* caudal pocket; *cy.gl.* cystogenous gland cell; *ex.ves.* excretory vesicle; *l.n.* lateral nerve; *st.* stylet; *st.gl.* stylet gland cells; *t.* tail; *v.n.* ventral nerve. (Rees, courtesy of Parasitology.)

The position of flame cells in cercariae is indicated by a formula. For example, $2[(3 + 3 + 3) + (3 + 3 + 3)]$ indicates that on each side of the body there are three groups of three flame cells in the anterior portion of the body and a similar triple group of three each posteriorly (Fig. VIII–17).

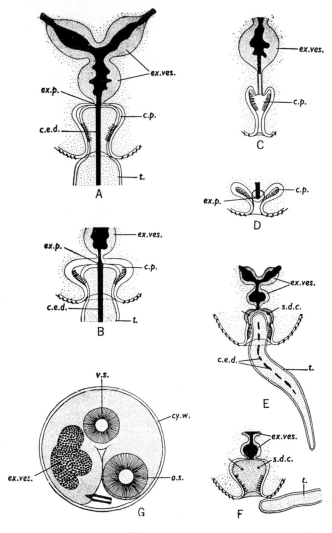

FIG. VIII–18.—The excretory vesicle of *Plagiorchis* (=*Multiglandularis*) *megalorchis* and its relation to the tail in the cercaria.

A, Excretory vesicle, tail root and caudal pockets of cercaria, expanded. *B*, Excretory vesicle (in part), tail root and caudal pockets of cercaria, contracted. *C*, Caudal pockets of cercaria after tail is shed, expanded. *D*, Caudal pockets of cercaria after tail is shed, contracted. *E*, Beginning of shedding of tail. *F*, Completion of shedding of tail. *G*, Fully formed cyst. *c.e.d.* caudal excretory duct; *c.p.* caudal pocket; *cy.w.* cyst wall; *ex.p.* excretory pore; *ex.ves.* excretory vesicle; *o.s.* oral sucker; *s.d.c.* secretion from dorsal glands in caudal pocket; *t.* tail; *v.s.* ventral sucker. (Rees, courtesy of Parasitology.)

Since the development of the excretory system has a significant bearing on correct classification, a brief outline is given here. At first all species follow a fundamental or primitive plan. In the lateral folds of the young cercaria there develop simple, separated flame cells. They are connected to primary collecting tubules which traverse the embryo and open posteriorly through the body wall. As the cercaria matures, the primary collecting tubules meet and fuse along the midline forming the excretory vesicle in the posterior region (Fig. VIII–17). This vesicle opens through a "bladder pore" which possesses a sphincter. There may also be an excretory atrium. In digenetic trematodes the excretory bladder may be the primitive, thin-walled and relatively inefficient type, or the advanced, thick-walled efficient variety; but intermediate types occur. *Schistosoma* and other forked-tailed cercariae possess the simple, thin-walled type of bladder. In other families of trematodes the excretory bladder begins as the thin-walled type and later develops thicker, more muscular walls. In some cercariae the primary excretory tubes enter the tail (Fig. VIII–18) while in others they do not.

Some of the families of digenetic trematodes are listed below with a discussion of important or representative genera and species. For general references to the digenetic trematodes see Baer and Joyeux,[1] Dawes,[6] Hyman,[9] Skrjabin,[14] and Yamaguti.[18]

Classification of the Digenetic Trematodes

La Rue's[13] system is based chiefly on larval life histories and morphology, especially the development of the excretory bladder. It is not a perfect system, but as La Rue himself says, it "may lead eventually to the development of a system which will portray with some degree of accuracy the genetic relationships within the Digenea." We have adopted this system.

Class Trematoda

Subclass Digenea

Superorder Anepitheliocystidia
Cercariae with thin excretory bladder, not epithelial; with forked or single tail.

Order Strigeatoidea (cercariae forked-tailed or modified from that condition; usually distomate; miracidia with 1 or 2 pairs of flame cells).

Families include: Strigeidae, Diplostomatidae, Cyathocotylidae, Clinostomatidae, Spirorchiidae, Aporocotylidae, Schistosomatidae, Azygiidae, Bivesiculidae, Transversotrematidae, Cyclocoelidae, Brachylaimidae, Fellodistomatidae, Bucephalidae.

Order Echinostomida (cercariae develop in collared rediae with stumpy appendages; life cycle usually involves 3 hosts)

Families include: Echinostomatidae, Cathaemasiidae, Fasciolidae, Psilostomatidae, Philophthalmidae, Haplosplanchnidae.

Suborder Paramphistomata (Cercariae without penetration glands; bodies heavily pigmented; no collar in rediae; 2-host life cycle; encyst on substrate). Some authorities believe this should be a separate order.

Families include: Paramphistomatidae, Gastrothylacidae, Cladorchiidae, Diplodiscidae, Brumptidae, Gastrodiscidae, Heronimidae, Notocotylidae, Pronocephalidae.

Order Renicolida (2 to 4 groups of small penetration glands in cercariae anterior to ventral sucker; tail large, often with fins; excretory bladder Y-shaped; develops in sporocyst in marine gastropods; 3-host cycle).

Family: Renicolidae

Superorder Epitheliocystidia
Cercariae with thick-walled epithelial bladder; cercarial tail single, reduced in size or lacking.

Order Plagiorchiida (cercariae without caudal excretory vessels; stylet present or lacking; encystment mostly in invertebrates, rarely in vertebrates).

Families include: Dicrocoeliidae, Eucotylidae, Haplometridae, Lecithodendriidae, Lissorchiidae, Macroderoididae, Microphallidae, Ochetosomatidae, Plagiorchiidae, Acanthocolpidae, Allocreadiidae, Lepocreadiidae, Megaperidae, Monorchiidae, Opecoelidae, Gorgoderidae, Troglotrematidae, Zoogonidae.

Order Opisthorchiida (cercariae with excretory vessels in tail; no stylet).

Families include: Opisthorchiidae, Heterophyidae, Acanthostomatidae, Cryptogonimidae, Hemiuridae. The latter family and the following families belong to the suborder Hemiurata (with non-ciliated miracidia; 2nd intermediate host a copepod). Some authorities believe that this should be a separate order. Some additional families are: Halipegidae, Dinuridae, Didymozoidae.

BIBLIOGRAPHY

1. BAER, J. G. and JOYEUX, C., 1961. Classé des Trématodes (Trematoda Rudolphi). In: Grassé, P., *Traité de Zoologie*. Tome IV. Masson et Cie Editeurs, Libraires de l'Acad. Méd. Paris. 944 pp.
2. BARLOW, C. H., 1925. Life Cycle of *Fasciolopsis buski*. Amer. J. Hyg., Monogr. Ser. 4.
3. CAMPBELL, W. C. and TODD, A. C., 1955. *In vitro* Metamorphosis of the Miracidium of *Fascioloides magna* (Bassi, 1875) Ward, 1917. Trans. Amer. Micros. Soc., *74*, 225–228.
4. CHENG, T. C., and SNYDER, R. W., JR., 1962. Studies on Host-Parasite Relationships Between Larval Trematodes and their Hosts. I. A Review. II. The Utilization of the Host's Glycogen by the Intramolluscan Larvae of *Glypthelmins pennsylvaniensis* Cheng, and Associated Phenomena. Trans. Amer. Micros. Soc., *81*, 209–228.
4a. CHERNOGORENKO-BIDULINA, M. I. and BLIZNYUK, I. D., 1960. The Life-Cycle of the Trematode *Sphaerostoma bramae* Müller, 1776. Doklady Biol. Sci. Sect. (Doklady Akademii Nauk SSSR). Translation—*134*, 780–782.
5. CORT, W. W., AMEEL, D. J., and VAN DER WOUDE, A., 1948. Studies on Germinal Development in Rediae of the Trematode Order Fasciolatoidea Szidat, 1936. J. Parasitol., *34*, 428–451.

13

6. DAWES, B., 1956. *The Trematoda (With Special Reference to British and Other European Forms)*. Cambridge Univ. Press. 644 pp.

7. DAWES, B., 1960. Penetration of *Fasciola gigantica* Cobbold, 1856 Into Snail Hosts. Nature, *185*, 51–53.

8. ETGES, F. J. and DECKER, C. L., 1963. Chemosensitivity of the Miracidium of *Schistosoma mansoni* to *Australorbis glabratus* and Other Snails. J. Parasitol., *49*, 114–116.

8a.HANUMANTHA-RAO, K., 1960. The Problem of Mehlis's Gland in Helminths with Special Reference to *Penetrocephalus ganapatii* (Cestoda: Pseudophyllidea). Parasitol., *50*, 349–350.

9. HYMAN, L. H., 1951. *The Invertebrates: Platyhelminthes and Rhynchocoela*. Vol. II McGraw-Hill Book Co., N. Y., 550 pp.

10. JAMES, B. L., 1960. A New Cercaria of the Subfamily Gymnophallinae (Trematoda: Digenea) Developing in a Unique 'Parthenita' in *Littorina saxatilis* (Olivi). Nature No. 4707, *184*, 181–182.

11. KAWASHIMA, K., TADA, I., and MIYAZAKI, I., 1961. Host Preference of Miracidia of *Paragonimus ohirai* Miyzaki, 1939 Among Three Species of Snails of the Genus Assiminea. Kyushu J. Med. Sci., *12*, 99–106.

12. KOMIYA, Y., 1961. The Excretory System of Digenetic Trematodes. Committee of Jubilee Publ. in Commemoration of 10th Anniversary of Dr. Y. Komiya as Chief of Dept. Parasitol., Nat. Inst. Health, Tokyo, 341 pp.

13. LA RUE, G. R., 1957. The Classification of Digenetic Trematodes: A Review and a New System. Exper. Parasitol., *6*, 306–344.

14. SKRJABIN, K. I., 1947–1962. (*Trematodes of Animals and Man. Elements of Trematodology.*) Akademiia Nauk SSSR, Moscow. (A long continuing series of volumes in Russian)

15. SMYTH, J. D. and CLEGG, J. A., 1959. Egg-Shell Formation in Trematodes and Cestodes. Exp. Parasitol., *8*, 286–323.

15a.STUNKARD, H. W., 1959. Progenetic Maturity and Phylogeny of Digenetic Trematodes. J. Parasitol., *45* (Sect. 2), 15.

16. WOOTTON, D. M., 1957. Studies on the Life-History of *Allocreadium alloneotenicum sp. nov.*, (Allocreadiidae-Trematoda). Biol. Bull., *113*, 302–315.

17. WRIGHT, C. A., 1959. Host-Location by Trematode Miracidia. Ann. Trop. Med. Parasitol., *53*, 288–292.

18. YAMAGUTI, S., 1958. *Systema Helminthum*. Vol. I, Parts 1 & 2, *The Digenetic Trematodes of Vertebrates*. Interscience Pub. Inc. N.Y. & London. 1575 pp.

di
for
the
lar

va
oc
sn
ce
thi
sta
fo

str
en
ce

r
de
sp
em

Fr
co

CHAPTER IX

Phylum Platyhelminthes, Class Trematoda
Subclass Digenea : Representative Families

SUPERORDER ANEPITHELIOCYSTIDIA

THE cercaria possesses a thin, non-epithelial excretory bladder; and a forked or single tail.

ORDER STRIGEATOIDEA

Family Strigeidae. These intestinal flukes are found in reptiles, birds, and mammals. Usually the anterior part of the body is

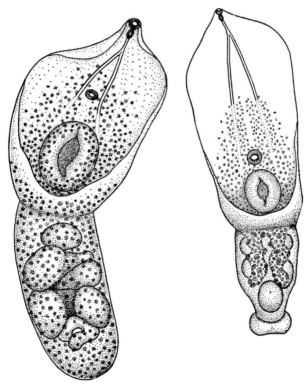

FIG. IX–1.—Left, *Neodiplostomum paraspathula*, ventral view of entire animal. × 40. Right, *Neodiplostomum orchilongum*, ventral view of entire animal, from the intestine of a hawk. (Noble, courtesy of J. Parasitology.)

of other species of trematodes. They do not enter snails containing
C. flabelliformis sporocysts. The strigeid cercariae enter other sporocysts and rediae where they are apparently protected from immune
reactions of the abnormal snail hosts, and where, as hyperparasites,
they are able effectively to utilize the nourishment which the sporocysts and rediae have secured from the snail host. The normal
environment for metacercariae of *C. flabelliformis* is the hermaphroditic gland of lymnaeid snails.

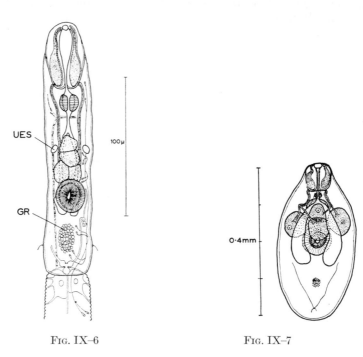

Fɪɢ. IX–6.   Fɪɢ. IX–7

Fɪɢ. IX–6.—*Alaria arisaemoides*. Ventral view of body of cercaria (composite drawing
based on camera lucida outline together with details from living material). *GR*, genital
primordium; *UES*, unpigmented eyespot.

Fɪɢ. IX–7.—*Alaria arisaemoides*. Dorsal view of mesocercaria, showing gut and penetration
glands (camera lucida).

Alaria is another genus which possesses three intermediate hosts.
These flukes occur as adults in the intestines of carnivores such as
the dog, cat, weasel or mink. From the snail, cercariae enter tadpoles, frogs, or other vertebrates, becoming *mesocercariae*. The
infected amphibians are eaten by raccoons, mice, rats, and other
mammals in which the metacercaria stage is reached. The final
host eats the mice, rats, or raccoons. Figures IX–2 to 8 illustrate the
developmental stages of *Alaria arisaemoides* which is found in the
gut of dogs or foxes.

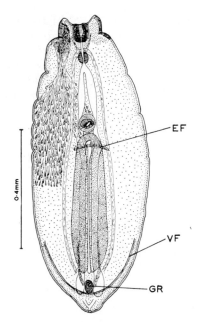

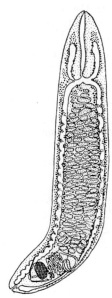

Fig. IX–8.—*Alaria arisaemoides.* Fully developed diplostomulum. Forebody glands and their ducts shown on right side. Note remnants of penetration gland duct in oral sucker and fold over anterior end of holdfast (camera lucida; ventral view). *EF,* edge of fold over anterior end of holdfast organ; *GR,* genital primordium; *VF,* ventral lip of spathiform forebody.

Fig. IX–9.—*Aporocotyle simplex,* from the gills of the flounder and other fishes. About 4 mm long. (Dawes, *The Trematoda,* courtesy of The University Press, Cambridge.)

Family Spirorchiidae. This family is composed of monoecious blood flukes which are distomes or monostomes and which inhabit the heart, larger arteries and sometimes other blood vessels of turtles. The genus *Spirorchis* is characterized by a central row of testes; the genus *Haplorhynchus* contains two testes; and the genus *Vasotrema* has a single testis which is spirally coiled. Eggs make their way from the host's blood vessels to the intestine, pass out of the turtle's body and hatch; the miracidia enter lymnaeid snails, develop into a first generation sporocyst, then another sporocyst, then into the furcocercous (forked-tail) cercariae which leave the snail and penetrate soft tissues of the next turtle host. Other genera are *Haplotrema, Learedium, Neospirorchis* and *Amphiorchis.*

Family Aporocotylidae. This family is composed of blood flukes. They are elongated, worm-like parasites which live in blood vessels of fish. Suckers are weak or absent and the body is covered with minute scales. The flukes are tiny, measuring less than a millimeter long to 5 millimeters, and the sexes are separate. There are four species; one of them, *Aporocotyle simplex,* is illustrated in figure IX–9.

Family Schistosomatidae (= Bilharziidae). Schistosomes are by far the best known of all blood flukes because of the serious disease (schistosomiasis or bilharziasis) which they cause in man. Animals are also hosts to these worms. *Schistosoma bovis* (Fig. IX–22) lives in cattle, sheep, goats and has even been found in horses, antelopes and baboons. It occurs in Africa, southern Asia and southern Europe and possesses essentially the same life cycle as that described below for the species in man. *S. bovis* is probably the same

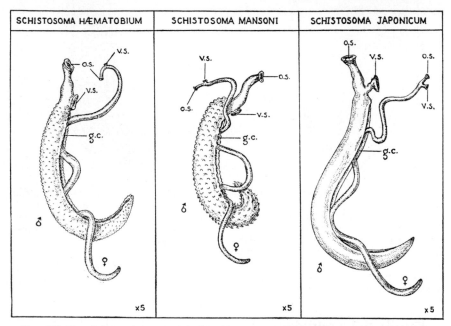

| SCHISTOSOMA HÆMATOBIUM | SCHISTOSOMA MANSONI | SCHISTOSOMA JAPONICUM |

FIG. IX–10.—Schematic representation of important schistosomes of man. *g.c.*, gynecophoric canal; *o.s.*, oral sucker; *v.s.*, ventral sucker. (Belding, *Textbook of Clinical Parasitology*, courtesy of D. Appleton-Century Company.)

species as *S. mattheei* but *S. intercalatum* may be a race of *S. bovis* which has become adapted to man. Snails belonging to the genus *Bulinus* serve as intermediate hosts for *S. bovis*. Another species parasitic in cattle, sheep, goats, carabao, antelope, and occasionally in dogs and horses is *S. spindale* which may be the same species as *S. nasale*. It too occurs in Africa and southern Asia and uses snails of the genera *Planorbis*, *Indoplanorbis* and *Lymnaea*. *S. incognitum* occurs in the pig in India.

Other genera are *Ornithobilharzia*, *Gigantobilharzia*, *Bilharziella*, *Trichobilharzia* and *Pseudobilharziella*. The relationships of these flukes are not well understood and deserve much more study. Sexes are separate, the female is often longer than the male and more slender. Females range from about 3 to about 15 mm. (usually less than 10) but one species (*Gigantobilharzia acotyles*) in the abdominal veins of the black-headed gull may reach 165 mm. The species from man will serve to illustrate the morphology, functions and life cycles of the entire group.[12]

The important schistosomes of man are *Schistosoma japonicum*, *S. hematobium*, and *S. mansoni*. Since there is great similarity among all these species only *S. japonicum* will be described in detail. Comparisons of adult morphology are shown in figure IX–10.

Schistosoma Japonicum. This blood fluke occurs in Japan, Korea, the Philippines, Sulawesi (Celebes), China and Taiwan (Formosa). The overall incidence of infection is from 10 to 25 per cent. In Taiwan the fluke is unusual in that it does not infect man, occuring only in various other mammals. In every other respect it appears to be identical with *Schistosoma japonicum* found elsewhere in the Far East. A recent report that a case of human trypanosomaisis was found in southern Taiwan has not been verified. The woman involved probably ate some meat heavily infected with *Schistosoma* eggs which then passed through her intestine. The commonest host of the Taiwan species is the rat but the fluke may be found in shrews and bandicoots. Various laboratory animals may also be infected. In other countries important reservoir hosts include pigs, dogs, cats, carabao, cattle, goats, horses, deer and various rodents.

Male *Schistosoma japonicum* average 15 × 0.5 mm. An oral sucker lies at the anterior end and a ventral sucker is situated at the end of a short anterior projection from the body. The body forms a groove along much of its length, thus appearing somewhat like a narrow boat. The female lies within this depression which is called the *gynecophoral canal*. The integument is smooth except for minute spines in this canal and on the suckers. There is no muscular pharynx and the intestinal ceca unite posteriorly forming a single cecum. There are usually seven testes located near the anterior end of the body, and ducts from the testes join to form a seminal vesicle which leads to a short duct which in turn opens at the genital pore situated just posterior to the pedunculate ventral sucker. A muscular cirrus is lacking.

Females average 20 × 0.3 mm. thus being both longer and narrower than the males. The gynecophoral canal is not long enough to enclose the extended female, so loops of its body generally can be seen extending from the canals. The ovary is situated in the posterior half of the body and from it extends a long, fairly straight uterus which, in mature worms, is filled with 50 to 300 eggs. A genital pore opens just behind the ventral sucker. Numerous vitelline glands lie on either side of the long median vitelline duct in the posterior quarter of the body.

The worms live chiefly in the superior mesenteric veins where the females extend their bodies from the male or leave the male and lay eggs (Fig. IX–12) in small venules or capillaries of the intestine. The oval to rounded eggs require a few days to develop into mature miracidia. The egg shell measures 90 × 60 microns and possesses a minute lateral hook usually difficult to see. Masses of eggs cause

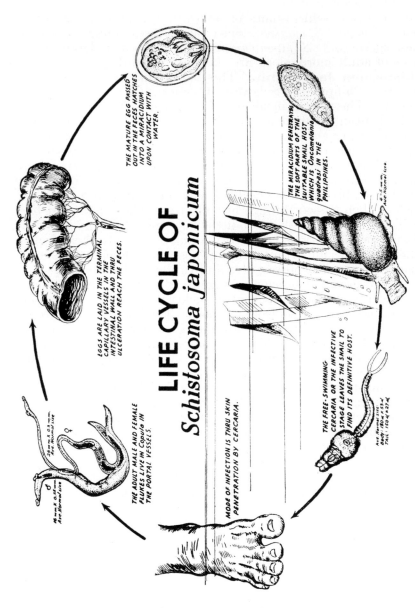

LIFE CYCLE OF
Schistosoma japonicum

THE MATURE EGG PASSED OUT IN THE FECES HATCHES INTO A MIRACIDIUM UPON CONTACT WITH WATER.

THE MIRACIDIUM PENETRATES THE SOFT PARTS OF THE SUITABLE SNAIL HOST, WHICH IS *Oncomelania quadrasi* IN THE PHILIPPINES.

EGGS ARE LAID IN THE TERMINAL CAPILLARY VESSELS IN THE INTESTINAL WALL AND THRU ULCERATION REACH THE FECES.

THE FREE-SWIMMING CERCARIA OR THE INFECTIVE STAGE LEAVES THE SNAIL TO FIND ITS DEFINITIVE HOST.

THE ADULT MALE AND FEMALE FLUKES LIVE IN COPULA IN THE PORTAL VESSELS.

MODE OF INFECTION IS THRU SKIN PENETRATION BY CERCARIA.

Fig. IX–11.—Life cycle of *Schistosoma japonicum*. (Pesigan, courtesy of Santo Tomas J. Med.)

pressure on the thin venule walls which are weakened by secretions from the histolytic glands of the miracidia within the eggs. The walls rupture and the eggs get into the intestinal lumen and thus to the outside. Up to 3500 eggs a day may be laid by a single worm, and in a heavy infection there may be thousands of worms in the blood vessels. See figure IX–11 for the life cycle.

Hatching takes place in water. Although pH, salinity, temperature and other environmental factors are important, factors within the

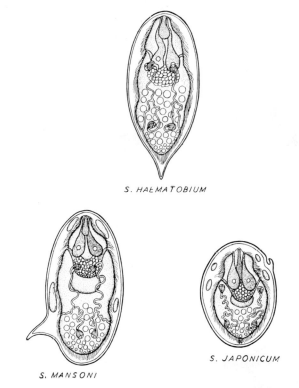

S. HAEMATOBIUM

S. MANSONI

S. JAPONICUM

FIG. IX–12.—Eggs of *Schistosoma*. (Redrawn from various authors.)

egg probably play a major role in the hatching process. The released miracidia can live for a few hours during which time they actively swim about as though "in search" of their molluscan host. These hosts are various species of the minute snail *Oncomelania* (Fig. IX–13). The miracidia penetrate the snail's foot or body by means of histoloytic gland secretions, the process requiring only a few minutes. Within the snail the cilia are shed and the miracidia become sporocysts. These sporocysts enlarge and the germ cells within them develop into a second generation of sporocysts which mature in the digestive gland of the snail. Germ cells within the second generation sporocysts give rise to cercariae thus skipping the usual redia generation. About a month is required from miracidial penetration of the snail to emergence of cercariae. These cercariae possess forked tails, hence the name "schistosoma" or "split body." They usually emerge during the early part of the night and are large enough (335 microns overall length) to be seen with the unaided eye. They are active swimmers but may hang motionless from the surface of the water.

Penetration of man or other mammals usually occurs within forty-eight hours, and the life span of the cercariae is limited to a very few days. Penetration is probably similar to the following description of this process for *Schistosoma mansoni*.[16] When the cercariae come in contact with the skin of an appropriate host they "loop" for variable

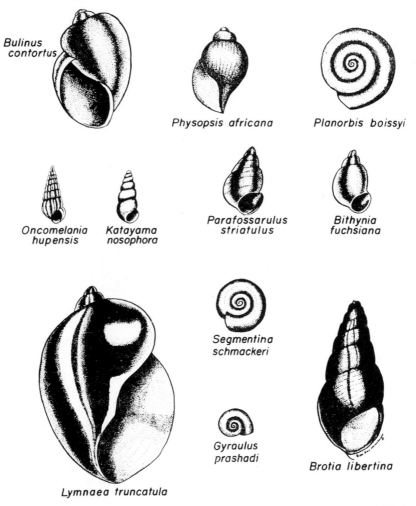

FIG. IX–13.—First intermediate hosts of human flukes. (United States Naval Medical School Laboratory Guide.)

periods of time by attaching themselves alternately with the oral and ventral suckers. When unattached, the oral end of the body constantly probes into every irregularity encountered. Points of entry include, wrinkled areas, the bases of follicular eminences, points of scale attachment, distal hair-skin angles, orifices or follicular canals and entry sites used by previous cercariae.

Eventually the cercariae become closely attached by their oral suckers and they assume a vertical or oblique position with relation to the surface. At this time the body is elongated and slender, and the muscular oral sucker is thrust into the entry site. Penetrating cercariae apparently release an enzyme from glands at their anterior ends. Several pairs of large glands are usually located on each side of the mid-line, and they empty through long narrow ducts at the anterior end of the larva in the neighborhood of the oral sucker. Although the exact nature of the secretion of the penetration glands is not known, some cercariae apparently produce hyaluronidase, an enzyme that dissolves hyaluronic acid, one of the principal substrates of connective tissue. Ramming motion and partial eversion of the sucker bring the openings of the ducts from the penetration glands into contact with the stratum corneum. Through these ducts the gland content is secreted into the host tissue. Alternate contraction and elongation of the body and energetic movements of the tail accompany thrusts of the oral sucker. Elongation of the body at the time the oral sucker initially probes into the entry site permits the cercariae to push into very small crevices. Thus attached and buried orally, the body is contracted and the diameter increased, with the result that the breach in the host tissue is enlarged. This sequence of slenderizing the body while the oral tip is being thrust deeper, and then contracting the body and pouring out glandular secretions seems to be the regular means of enlarging the entry pores for gradual penetration. Constant tail activity provides added forward thrust, but tail thrust is not a necessity since tailless cercariae have been seen penetrating the host. Exploratory time for the cercariae is about 1.8 to 2.3 minutes and entry time about three to seven minutes.

Migration through the body commences with entry into minute lymphatic vessels, thence to the heart and circulatory system. Young flukes leave the blood vessels in the liver where they develop to maturity. After several weeks they pass from the liver back into the circulatory system and remain in the superior mesenteric veins. Copulation takes place and the females enter the gynecophoral canals of the males. Usually from one to two months elapse from the time of penetration by cercariae to the appearance of schistosome eggs in human feces. The life span of adult worms is usually between five and thirty years and there may be several thousand individuals in one host.

Symptoms and pathology are related to the numbers of worms, tissues infected and sensitivity of the host.[11] Penetration of the skin by cercariae may give rise to minute rash, lesions or itching. Dermal schistosomiasis, caused by non-human species is described below. Migrating worms usually cause little or no damage or symptoms but occasionally there are serious reactions such as a pneumonia resulting from the invasion of the lungs. The liver-inhabiting phase may be symptomless but may be marked by enlargement and tenderness of this organ and toxic reactions. Other symptoms include: cough, fever, diarrhea, eosinophilia, enlargement of spleen and liver, anemia, ascites and an extreme wasting away so that the arms, legs and body in general become alarmingly thin and the abdomen is huge with fluid (Fig. IX–14). Ulceration and necrosis of tissues in the intestine are characteristic. Details of pathogenicity need much more study.

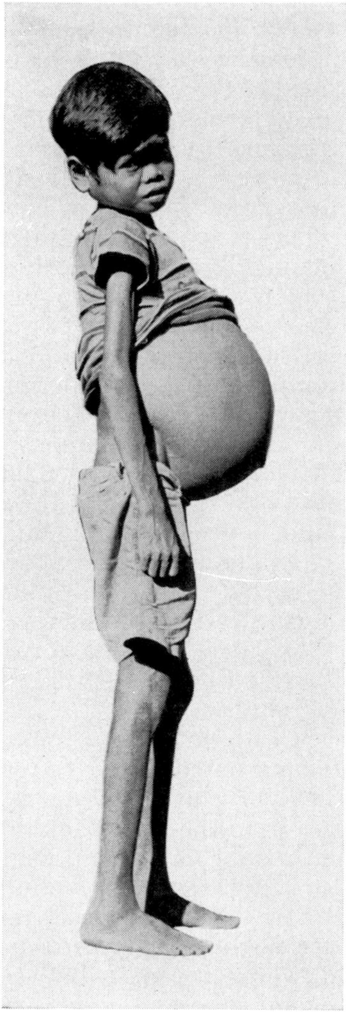

Prognosis is good in light cases where the patient does not become reinfected. It is grave in cases of long duration and in undernourished persons who often expose themselves to the cercariae. Man and animals can develop some immunity after a previous infection.[15] Even the snail, *Australorbis glabratus*, shows immune reactions against *Schistosoma mansoni*. Promising research is being carried out by Hsü and Hsü[9] and others using the non-human Taiwan strain of *S. japonicum* as an antigen for building up immunity. These workers injected cercariae of this strain into monkeys, and they found that the animals were resistant to subsequent challenge infections with the human type strain from Japan.

Treatment is as yet rather unsatisfactory although the following drugs have been used with some success: sodium antimony tartrate, potassium antimony tartrate (= tartar emetic), fouadin (= stibophen), antimony dimercaptosuccinate and miracil (lucanthione) hydrochloride.

Diagnosis should be based on finding eggs in the feces or in biopsied tissue. Complement fixation reaction, dermal tests and slide flocculation tests are of value.

Fig. IX–14.—Advanced case of schistosomiasis in a Filipino boy. Courtesy of Dr. Robert E. Kuntz, U.S., N.M.R.I., Bethesda, Maryland.

Prevention and control involve education of the people using infected waters, development of sanitary waste disposal measures, providing clean drinking water and destruction of the snail vectors.[13]

Schistosoma haematobium lives primarily in the blood vessels of the urinary bladder and adjacent areas. The male worm is about 13 mm. long by 1 mm. wide; the female is long and slender, being about 20 by 0.25 mm. She is able to extend her body in a quick snake-like manner from the gynecophoral canal of the male into small blood vessels where her eggs are deposited, and then withdraw to the "safety" of the canal. The eggs of this species are characterized by a pointed projection on the terminal end. This spine aids in the passage of the egg through blood vessel walls and other tissues to the lumen of the bladder or gut. The main intermediate hosts of *Schistosoma haematobium* are snails belonging to the families Physidae and Bulinidae (Fig. IX–13).

Schistosoma mansoni is the blood fluke which lives mainly in branches of the inferior mesenteric veins. Wild rodents may be reservoirs of infection. The eggs of this species measure 114–175 × 45–68 microns and they possess a spine which is not terminal but which projects from the shell on one side near the end of the egg. Miracidia enter several types of snails but primarily those of the family Planorbidae.[2] Mature male *S. mansoni* in the mesenteric portal system (of mice and hamsters) are necessary for the sexual maturation of the female worms.[14] If the male worms have not reached sexual maturity the female worms do not mature.

A review of studies of the glycolytic enzymes of *Schistosoma mansoni* to determine if these enzymes of the parasite are the same as comparable ones in the host was presented by Bueding (in Cole, 1955).[4] The enzymes studied were phosphoglucose isomerase, lactic dehydrogenase, and hexokinases. Differences definitely existed in the nature of the enzymes catalyzing the same reactions in *S. mansoni* and in the host, and it was found that these differences may occur at different levels. Phosphoglucose isomerase of the parasites could be distinguished from that of host muscle (rabbit) only by the use of immunological procedures. Lactic dehydrogenase of the worms and of host muscle differed from each other in their behavior toward specific antibodies, and in their affinities for one of their substrates, and in the effect of the hydrogen ion concentration on their activities. Hexokinases of the parasite and of the host differed in kinetics as well as in substrate specificities. Glucosamine showed a selective toxicity for *S. mansoni*. This selective toxicity was detected as a result of observations on the substrate specificities of schistosome hexokinases and the occurrence of a specific glucosamine kinase in the parasites. The selectiveness of the action of immune sera on enzymes of the worm has demonstrated the possibility of interfering with the functional integrity of the parasite without altering the normal functioning of similar enzymes of the host. The significance of this possibility for a more rational approach to the chemotherapy of schistosomiasis is obvious.

develops into a sporocyst which produces the first generation of rediae which, in turn, produces the second generation of rediae. During the hot months of summer there is usually only one redia generation. Rediae give rise to cercariae which leave the snail, often at night, and swim to aquatic vegetation and encyst as metacercariae. One or two months are required for development from the miracidium to the metacercaria stage. The vertebrate host acquires infection by ingesting the metacercariae with water plants or drinking water. In the intestine of man the parasite excysts and migrates through the gut wall and the body cavity to the liver where it takes up residence in bile passages. Two months are required to reach maturity in the liver or gallbladder. Eggs pass down the bile ducts into the intestine and out to soil or water. The entire life cycle may require as much as five months for completion.

The degree of pathogenicity of liver flukes to man depends on many factors, particularly on the number of worms present and the organ or organs infected. Mechanical and toxic damage are characteristic. The parasite occasionally gets into the lungs, brain or other tissues. Pain in the region of the liver, abdominal pain, diarrhea, fever and anemia are some of the usual symptoms. A study of experimentally infected mice has shown that young flukes feed on hepatic cells and that "blood is inevitably included in the diet."[6] If infected raw liver is eaten, immature flukes can become attached to the buccal or pharyngeal membranes causing pain, irritation, hoarseness or coughing. Diagnosis depends primarily on finding the eggs in stool specimens. Emetine hydrochloride is a standard drug used in treatment.

Fasciola gigantica is a related fluke with a similar life cycle and is common in cattle and other ruminants in Asia, Africa and a few other areas. It is exceedingly rare in man. *F. gigantica* is not as broad but longer than *F. hepatica* measuring 25 to 75 mm. by 3 to 12 mm.

Fasciolopsis buski (Fig. IX–19) is a big relative of *Fasciola hepatica*. It may reach 75 mm. in length but is usually smaller. Its life cycle[3] is similar to that of *Fasciola hepatica* but the adult lives in the intestine of man and pigs. Most cases of infection have been found in China, and there is a low incidence in India. Man acquires the fluke by eating water chestnuts (*Eliocharis*) or the nuts of the red caltrop (*Trapa*) or other water plants on which the metacercariae occur. Hexylresorcinol and beta-naphthol are two anthelminthics used against fasciolopsiasis.

Another genus is *Fascioloides*, represented by *F. magna*, a large liver fluke in cattle, sheep, moose, deer, and horses. It is an oval fluke up to 26 by 100 mm. in size. The life cycle is similar to that of *Fasciola hepatica*.

The injurious or lethal effects of extracts of worm tissues on bacteria can be demonstrated by grinding worms with sand, adding saline, filtering and adding the filtrate to bacteria cultures. Filtrates thus obtained from *Fasciola gigantica* and *Ascaris vitulorum* show marked bacteriostatic action.[7]

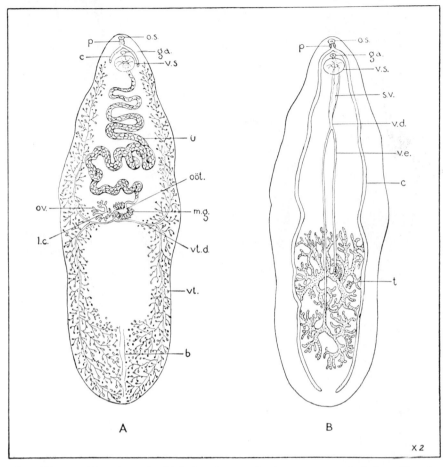

FIG. IX–19.—*Fasciolopsis buski A*, female reproductive organs, ventral view; *B*, male reproductive organs and digestive tract, ventral view.

b, bladder; *c*, ceca; *g.a.*, genital atrium; *m.g.*, Mehlis' gland; *l.c.*, Laurer's canal; *oot*, ootype; *o.s.*, oral sucker; *ov.*, ovary; *p.*, pharynx; *s.v.*, seminal vesicle; *t.*, testes; *u*, uterus; *v.d.*, vas deferens; *v.e.*, vas efferens; *v.s.*, ventral sucker; *vt.*, vitellaria; *vt.d.*, vitelline duct. (Adapted from Odhner, 1902). (Belding, *Textbook of Clinical Parasitology*, courtesy of Appleton, Century and Crofts.)

SUBORDER PARAMPHISTOMATA

Family Paramphistomatidae (= Amphistomidae).   The anterior end of these flukes possesses a mouth but no sucker.   The single sucker, or acetabulum, is located at the posterior end.   The general shape of the body, which is often covered with papillae, is unlike the typical leaf-shape of other flukes since it frequently is rounded and sometimes looks more like a gourd or a pear with a hole in the top end.   Common genera are *Homalogaster*, *Gastrodiscus*, *Watsonius* and *Gigantocotyle*.   The life history of *Gigantocotyle explanatum*, a liver fluke of domestic ruminants in India, is illustrated in figures IX–20, 21.

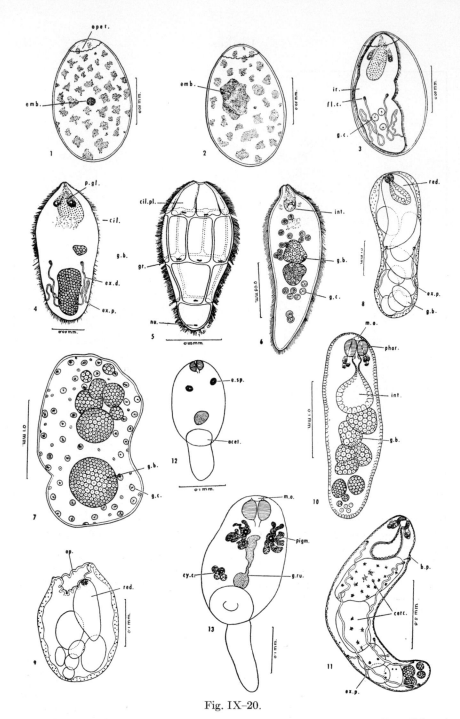

Fig. IX–20.

Fig. IX–20 and 21.—The life history of *Gigantocotyle explanatum*, a liver fluke of domestic ruminants.

1–19, Gigantocotyle explanatum. All figures drawn with the aid of a camera lucida. *1*, Egg, from uterus. *2*, Egg, embryo partially developed. *3*, Egg, with miracidium. *4*, Miracidium, alive. *5*, Miracidium, showing ciliated epidermal plates. *6*, Miracidium, stained with Ehrlich's haematoxylin. *7*, Sporocyst, early stage. *8*, Sporocyst, late stage. *9*, Sporocyst, 28 days old. *10*, Redia, free early stage. *11*, Redia, later stage.

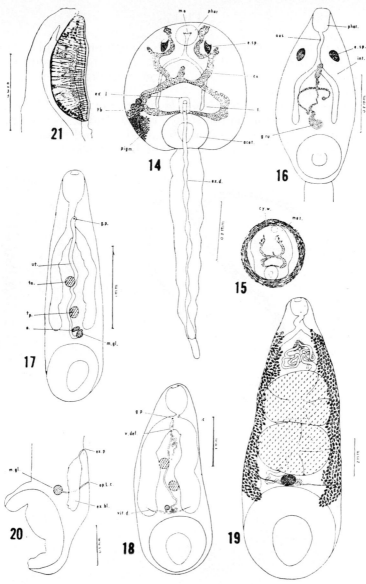

Fig. IX—21.

12, Cercaria, free within the shell of snail, early stage. *13,* Cercaria, free within the
shell of snail, later stage. *14,* Cercaria, free swimming. *15,* Metacercaria, on leaf.
16, Cercaria, free, stained with aceto-carmine. *17,* Immature adult from final host.
18, Immature adult from final host. *19,* Gravid adult from final host, ventral view.
20, Adult, sagittal section of posterior half. *21,* Adult, sagittal section of pharynx.
acet., acetabulum. *b.p.,* birth pore. *cerc.,* cercaria. *cil.,* cilia. *cil.pl.,* ciliated epidermal
plate. *cy.c.,* cystogenous cells. *cy.w.,* cyst wall. *emb.,* embryo. *e.sp.,* eye spot. *ex.bl.,*
excretory bladder. *ex.d.,* excretory duct. *ex.p.,* excretory pore. *fl.c.,* flame cell. *g.b.,*
germinal ball. *g.c.,* germ cell. *g.p.,* genital pore. *gr.,* groove. *g.ru.,* genital rudiments
Int., intestinal caecum, intestine. *met.,* metacercaria.
m.gl., Mehlis' gland. *mir.,* miracidium. *m.o.,* mouth opening. *nu.,* nucleus. *oes.,*
oesophagus. *op.,* opening. *oper.,* operculum. *op.L.c.,* opening of Laurer's canal.
ov., ovary. *p.gl.,* penetration glands. *phar.,* pharynx. *pigm.,* pigment. *red,.* redia.
t., tail. *t.,a.,* testis, anterior. *t.,p.,* testis, posterior. *ut.,* uterus. *v.def.,* vas deferens.
vit., vitellaria. *vit.d.,* vitelline duct. (Singh, courtesy of J. Parasitol.)

(217)

Watsonius watsoni is a species which is normally found in monkeys and has once been reported from man. It is about 9 mm. long and was found in a man's intestine in large numbers where it was apparently pathogenic.

Gastrodiscoides (= *Gastrodiscus*) *hominis* (Fig. IX–22,C,D) is common in the intestine of man in some areas of India, Assam and a few other places. The worm is about 6 mm. long and possesses a large disc-like portion of the body within which is a sucker.

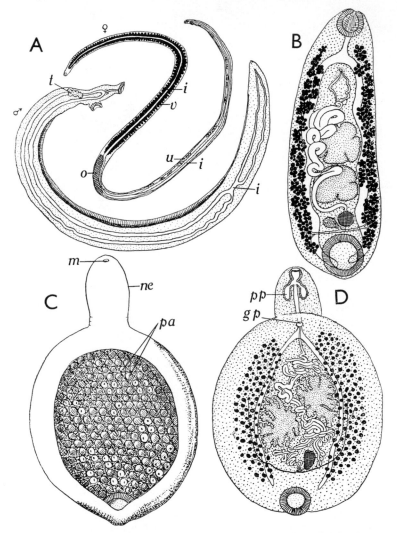

Fig. IX–22.—Schistosomatidae (*A*) and Paramphistomatidae (*B–D*) of mammals *A, Schistosoma bovis*, male and female. *B, Paramphistomum cotylophorum. C,D, Gastrodiscus*, showing external characters in ventral view (*C*) and internal organs (*D*). *gp*, genital pore; *i*, intestine; *m*, mouth; *ne*, neck; *o*, ovary; *pa*, papillae; *pp*, pharyngeal pouch; *t*, testes; *u*, uterus; *v*, vitelleria. (Dawes, *The Trematoda*, courtesy of the University Press, Cambridge.)

Paramphistomum (= *Cotylophoron*) *microbothriodes* possesses a sucker around the genital pore. The fluke lives in the rumen of cattle and other ruminants, and may be found in South Africa and the United States, although the identity of the species in these two countries has been questioned. In appropriate snail hosts the usual sequence of sporocyst, redia, and cercaria appear. The cercariae leave the snail and encyst as metacercariae on vegetation. There is no evidence that the adult flukes are pathogenic but the immature forms in the small intestine cause inflammation, edema, hemorrhage and destruction of the intestinal villi. Carbon tetrachloride is often used for treatment. See figure IX–22,*B*.

SUPERORDER EPITHELIOCYSTIDIA

The cercaria possesses a thick-walled epithelial bladder and a single tail that is reduced in size or lacking.

ORDER PLAGIORCHIIDA

Family Dicrocoeliidae. These flattened and somewhat translucent flukes occur in the gut, gallbladder, bile ducts, liver, or pancreatic ducts of amphibians, reptiles, birds, and mammals. The ovary is situated behind the testes and the uterus fills most of the posterior part of the body. Common genera are *Eurytrema*, *Dicrocoelium* and *Brachycoelium*.

Eurytrema pancreaticum (Fig. IX–23) is a parasite of the pancreatic ducts of hogs, water buffaloes and cattle in the Orient and of some camels and monkeys in the Old World. It has also been reported from the duodenum of sheep and goats in South America, and it was once found in man. The fluke measures about 12 by 7 millimeters.

Dicrocoelium dendriticum (= *D. lanceolatum*) (Fig. IX–24) is an elongated narrow fluke which measures about 8 by 2 mm. and is known as the *lancet fluke*. It occurs in the bile ducts of cattle, sheep, goats, horses, camels, rabbits, pigs, deer, elk, dogs, and occasionally man, and it is worldwide in distribution. The fluke has a well-developed ventral sucker which is larger than the anterior sucker, unbranched ceca, slightly lobed testes which are almost tandem, no spines on the cuticle, and vitelline glands which occupy the middle third of the body. The eggs of *D. dendriticum* must be eaten by an appropriate snail before they will hatch. The snails are land forms (*Cionella lubrica*), so a cycle of larval fluke growth without swimming stages had to develop. There are two sporocyst stages and the cercariae aggregate in masses called slime balls in the respiratory chamber of the snail. These slime balls are deposited on the soil or grass as the snail crawls along. Although sheep, or other final hosts, may possibly acquire the infection by eating the slime balls or even the snails, ants (*Formica fusca*) may serve as secondary hosts by eating these masses of cercariae, and the sheep acquire their infections by eating the ants.[10]

Family Microphallidae.   This group somewhat resembles the Heterophyidae. They are small, some species being less than 1 mm. long, although many of them are closer to 2 mm. in length. The body tends to be thick, pear-shaped and spiny. The two branches of the

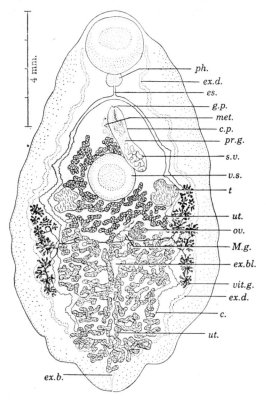

Fig. IX-23.—*Eurytrema pancreaticum.*   Abbrev.:   *c.*, cecum;   *c.p.*, cirrus pouch; *es.*, esophagus; *ex.b.*, excretory bladder; *ex.d.*, excretory duct;   *ex.p.*, excretory pore; *g.p.*, genital pore; *m.*, mouth; *M.g.*, Mehlis' glands; *met.*, metraterm; *ph.*, pharynx; *pr.g.*, prostate glands; *ov.*, ovary; *s.v.*, seminal vesicle *t.*, testis; *ut.*, uterus; *vit.g.*, vitelline glands; *v.s.*, ventral sucker. (Looss in Chandler and Read, *An Introduction to Parasitology,* courtesy of John Wiley and Sons.)

intestine are unusually short and there is a penis papilla. The usual host is a shore bird such as a sea gull, plover, godwit, sandpiper or tern in which the parasites are found in the intestine.

Representative genera are *Microcephalus, Maritrema, Levinseniella, Spelotrema, Spelophallus* and *Gymnophallus.*   Sexually mature flukes belonging to the genus *Gymnophallus* inhabit the gallbladder, intestine, ceca and bursa Fabricii of shore birds. Asexual generations of these parasites occur in bivalve mollusks,

and they produce cercariae (from sporocysts) which belong to the
Dichotoma group of furcocercous larvae. Some of the intermediate
hosts from which cercarial stages and sporocysts of this genus have
been reported are: *Mytilus edulus*, *Macoma balthica*, *Scrobicula
tenuis*, *Cardium edule*, and *Hiatella arctica*. Upon emerging from the
first intermediate host the cercariae attach themselves to the mantle
or body-wall of bivalve or gastropod mollusks where they develop
as unencysted metacercariae which almost reach definitive size, and
are easily mistaken for adults. These metacercariae produce lesions
on the mantles of their hosts, sometimes accompanied by deposition
of nacreous material. Such pearly formations in the mantle of the

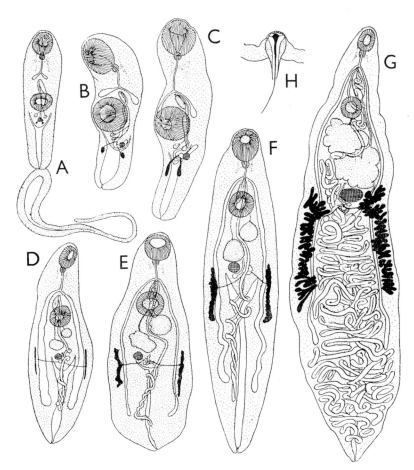

FIG. IX–24.—Stages of *Dicrocoelium dendriticum* developing in the definitive host.
A, *Cercaria vitrina*, removed from cyst. *B–F*, juvenile flukes collected —16 days after
infection: *B*, 8; *C*, 9; *D*, 12; *E*, 14; and *F*, 16 days old. *G*, full-grown fluke. *H*, a touch
papilla (on the suckers of the adult). (After Neuhaus, 1939.) (The magnifications of
ABC/DEF/G stand in the relation 5:1/2:4/1.) (Dawes, *The Trematoda*, courtesy of The
University Press., Cambridge.)

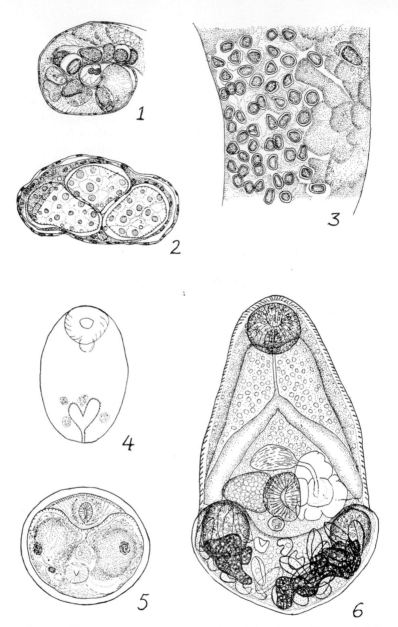

Fig. IX–25.—Developmental stages of *Levinseniella minuta*; Figures 1–5 from the snail, *Hydrobia minuta*. Figure *4* from a slightly compressed living larva, other figures from fixed and stained specimens.

1, Tip of abdomen of *Hydrobia minuta*, experimental infection, showing daughter sporocysts and developing cercariae. *2*, Sporocyst, 0.078 mm. long, with germ balls, from a snail other than the one shown in *1* and *3*. *3*, Portion of abdomen of snail shown in *1*, compressed laterally, with an unencysted cercaria in the upper right corner, between lobes of the digestive gland, and many encysted metacercariae; same scale as *1*; dorso-ventral measurement, 0.75 mm. *4*, Cercaria, 0.086 mm. long, from haemal sinus of *H. minuta*, showing oral sucker, pharynx, excretory vesicle, and cell aggregates which are incipient stages of the acetabulum and gonads. *5*, Encysted metacercaria, cyst 0.09 mm. in diameter, from *H. minuta*, experimental infection. *6*, Adult specimen, 0.17 mm. long, from a white mouse. (Stunkard, courtesy of J. Parasitology.)

Mytilus edulis, Donax truncatus and other bivalves are not uncommon, and have often been reported as caused by a distome trematode.

Another representative species is *Levinseniella minuta,* a tiny fluke that averages only about 0.16 mm. long and 0.1 mm. wide. Its general appearance and life history is given in Figure IX–25.[17] The normal vertebrate host is the scaup or other diving duck, but white mice easily become infected in the laboratory. Snails eat the fluke eggs which hatch into miracidia and then develop into sporocysts. Cercariae emerge from the sporocysts and encyst, forming the metacercaria stage in the snail. Ducks become infected by eating infected snails.

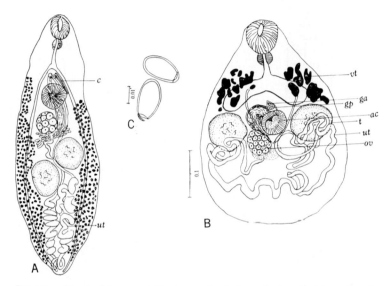

Fig. IX–26.—*Plagiorchis vespertilionis* on the left and *Acanthatrium jonesi* on the right, eggs of the latter between. Both flukes are found in Korean bats.

All figures were drawn with the aid of a camera lucida. The projected scale has value in millimeters indicated in each figure. Abbreviations used: *ac,* acetabulum; *as,* atrial spine; *c,* cirrus; *e,* egg; *ga,* genital atrium; *gp,* genital pore; *isv,* internal seminal vesicle; *ov,* ovary; *pm,* prostatic mass; *t,* testis; *ut,* uterus; *vt,* vitellaria.

A, Plagiorchis vespertilionis, ventral view. *B, Acanthatrium jonesi,* ventral view. *C, Acanthatrium jonesi,* eggs. (Sogandares-Bernal, courtesy of J. Parasitol.)

Family Plagiorchiidae. These flukes are found mainly in the intestines of frogs, snakes and lizards but they may occur in amphibians, birds and bats (Fig. IX–26). The family is large, containing hundreds of species. The flukes are small or only moderately large and are covered with spines; the two suckers are not far apart and there is a Y-shaped urinary bladder. The parasites also live in the respiratory tract, urogenital tract and sometimes the gallbladder. After leaving the snail, young worms (cercariae) penetrate aquatic insect larvae (Fig. IX–27), crayfish, or tadpoles. The vertebrate host acquires the infection by eating one of these transport hosts.

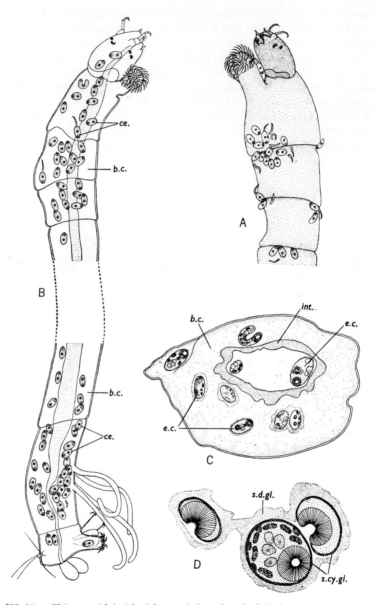

Fig. IX–27.—Chironomid (midge) larvae infected with fluke larvae.
A, Anterior extremity of chironomid larva showing accumulation of cercariae on the surface in the junctions between the segments. B, Anterior and posterior extremities of chironomid larva showing numerous cercariae in body cavity, not yet encysted. C, Transverse section through chironomid larva showing encysting cercariae in body cavity and alimentary canal. D, Three cercariae in process of encysting, from body cavity of chironomid larva. b.c. body cavity; ce. cercaria; e.c. encysting cercaria; int. intestine; s.cy.gl. secretion from cytogenous glands; s.d.gl. secretion from dorsal glands. (Rees, courtesy of Parasitology.)

Common genera are *Plagiorchis*, *Glyphthelmins*, *Opisthoglyphe*, *Renifer*, *Haematoloechus* (= *Pneumoneces*, the common lung fluke of frogs), *Prosthogonimus* and *Sympetrum*. Most of the flukes are only a few millimeters long but some may reach 20 millimeters in length or more.

Family Allocreadiidae. Common intestinal flukes of marine and freshwater game fishes such as trout and bass belong to this family. *Crepidostomum*, *Bunodera*, *Allocreadium*, *Hamacreadium*, *Plagioporus*, and *Pharyngora* are the more common genera. Usually they are small, often not longer than one or two millimeters. The cuticle is not spinous. In some genera (*Crepidostomum* and *Allocreadium*) the rediae are found in small bivalves and the metacercariae occur in other bivalves, crayfish, amphipods or May fly nymphs. Other genera utilize snails as the first intermediate host and various other animals as the second intermediate host. *Helicometrina elongata* (Fig. IX–28) about 4 mm. long, lives in the small intestine of a tidepool fish (*Caularchus meandricus*) in Bodega Bay, California.

Family Troglotrematidae. Most of the genera belonging to this family are less than 10 mm. long and some may be only 1 or 2 mm. in length. In general, the group is composed of rather thick, spinous or scaly flukes that have an oval outline and live in various organs and sinuses of birds and mammals.

The genus *Paragonimus* is of special interest to us because it contains the common lung fluke of man, *Paragonimus westermani*. The following account of the genus is from various sources but primarily from the thorough review by Yokogawa *et al.*[19]

Species generally considered valid at the present time are: *Paragonimus westermani* (= *P. ringeri* and *P. edwardsei*), found in man, dog, cat, pig, and many other mammals; *P. kellicotti*, in the cat, dog, pig, mink, goat, fox and in experimental animals; *P. ohirai*, in the pig, dog, weasel, badger, wild boar and in experimental animals; *P. iloktsuensis*, in the rat and dog; and possibly *P. compactus*. These lung flukes all have the same general characteristics and life cycle.

Paragonimus westermani is one of the most important trematodes of man in some areas of the world, especially in the Far East. It has been found in Korea, Japan, China mainland, Taiwan, Philippines, Indonesia, Africa, India, some Pacific islands, Peru and Ecuador. The incidence of infection ranges from 7 to 44 per cent.

Anatomical details of an adult *Paragonimus westermani* are shown in Fig. IX–29. There is no true cirrus or cirrus pouch. The fluke is usually about 10 × 5 × 4 mm. in size. It is plump, reddish in color and covered with minute cuticular spines. It usually lives in the lungs, often paired with another one, and is enclosed within a cyst. Many other organs, however, may harbor the worms.

Eggs (Fig. VIII–9), which average 87 × 50 microns, are brownish in color and sometimes are present in such numbers that they give the sputum a brown or rust tinge. These operculated eggs are coughed up from the lungs and are expectorated, or swallowed and

15

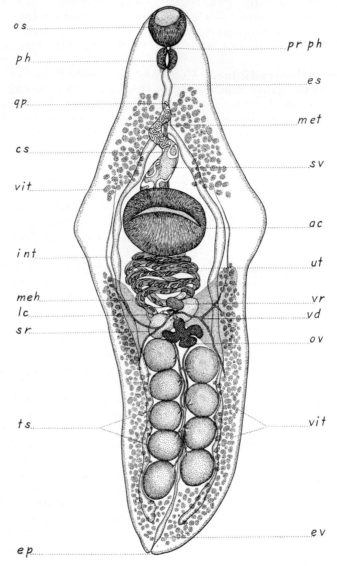

FIG. IX–28.—*Helicometrina elongata* from a tidepool fish. × 42. Drawn from a stained whole mount with the aid of a camera lucida. Lateral bulges in the acetabular region are partially due to pressure during fixation. The vasa efferentia and the interconnections of the smaller female ducts were added to the drawing from studies on sectioned material.

Ac, acetabulum; *cs,* cirrus pouch; *ep,* excretory pore; *es,* esophagus *ev,* excretory vesicle; *gp,* genital pore; *int,* intestine; *lc,* Laurer's canal; *meh,* Mehlis' gland; *met,* metraterm; *os,* oral sucker; *ov,* ovary; *ph,* pharynx; *pr pa,* prepharynx; *sr,* seminal receptacle; *sv,* seminal vesicle; *ts,* testes; *ut,* uterus; *vd,* vitilline duct; *vit,* vitellaria; *vr,* vitelline reservoir. (Noble and Park, courtesy of Trans. Amer. Miscros. Soc.)

leave the body with feces. After two to several weeks of development in moist soil or water they hatch and the miracidia swim about until a suitable snail appears. See Figure IX–29A for the life cycle.

Hatching is initiated by a sudden increase in activity of the larva inside the egg. The animal may at first lunge at the operculum but it soon flattens its anterior end against this structure. A series of violent contractions then occurs and the posterior portion of the body is extended until the operculum suddenly flies back as on a hinge. Water passes through the exposed vitelline membrane causing it to swell and extend through the opercular opening. A bubble is pro-

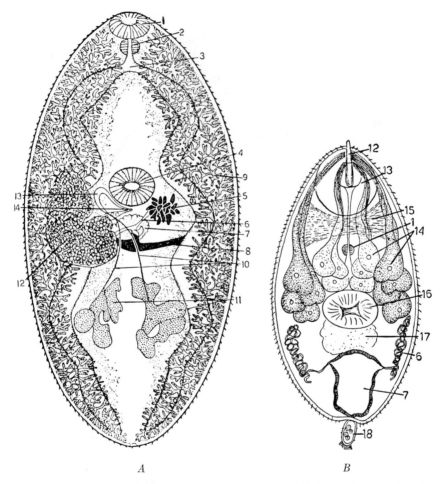

A   B

FIG. IX–29.—A, *Paragonimus westermani* adult (after Chen, 1940). *1*, oral sucker; *2*, pharynx; *3*, intestine; *4*, acetabulum; *5*, ovary; *6*, oviduct; *7*, ootype; *8*, yolk ducts; *9*, yolk glands; *10*, sperm ducts; *11*, testes; *12*, uterus; *13*, cirrus sac; *14*, gonopore. *B*, Cercaria (after Amed, 1932.) *1*, pharynx; *6*, protonephridia; *7*, bladder; *12*, stylet; *13*, oral sucker; *14*, penetration glands; *15*, brain; *16*, acetabulum; *17*, primordium of reproductive system; *18*, tail. (Hyman, *The Invertebrates*, courtesy of the McGraw-Hill Book Company.)

duced which may become larger than the egg itself, forming a transparent sac into which the miracidium finally forces itself. The larva swims rapidly about inside this sac until the membrane is ruptured and the ciliated worm swims away.[1]

Mature miracidia average 0.08 × 0.04 mm. in size and are covered with 4 rows of ciliated ectodermal plates. Snails belonging to the genera *Melania*, *Oncomelania*, *Semisulcospira*, *Hua*, *Thiara*, *Pomatiopsis* and *Brotea* are the common first intermediate hosts. These snails are usually found in swift mountain streams, often away from towns or villages. Infection of the snails probably depends primarily

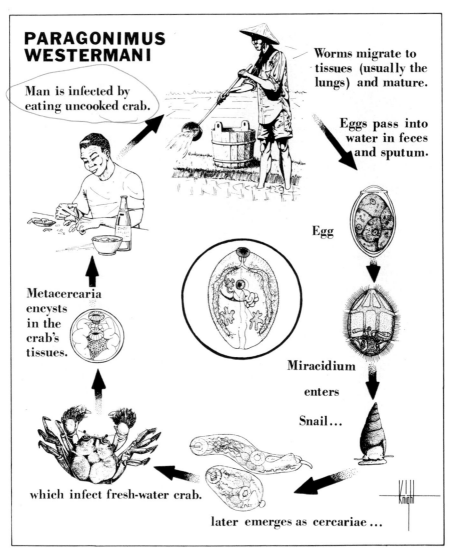

PARAGONIMUS WESTERMANI

Man is infected by eating uncooked crab.

Worms migrate to tissues (usually the lungs) and mature.

Eggs pass into water in feces and sputum.

Egg

Metacercaria encysts in the crab's tissues.

Miracidium enters Snail...

which infect fresh-water crab.

later emerges as cercariae...

Fig. IX–29A. —Life cycle of *Paragonimus*. (Original.)

on animal reservoir hosts rather than on man. The incidence in snails is surprisingly low. Out of hundreds of snails examined in endemic areas in the Philippines, we have found only 2 per cent infected. Miracidia shed their ciliated plates during the act of penetrating the snail. The mother sporocyst generation develops free in the lymphatic system, usually along the esophagus, stomach or intestine.

First generation rediae emerge from the sporocyst about four weeks after infection. Second generation rediae appear in the digestive gland from sixty-three to seventy days after infection.

Microcercous cercariae emerge from the snail. They are ellipsoidal and possess a short tail with a spiny tip. The body is covered with small spines and a prominent stylet lies in the dorsal side of the oral sucker. There are two types of penetration glands plus two irregular rows of mucoid glands on each side of the body. Cercariae of *P. westermani* in the laboratory do not readily escape from snails.

Cercariae enter a crayfish or a crab. Crabs belonging to the genera *Potomon*, *Eriocheir*, *Sesarma* and *Parathelphusa* are the usual second intermediate hosts. Crabs probably ingest the cercariae. Possibly cercariae penetrate the crabs immediately after molting when the joint membranes are soft, although Yokogawa[18] believes this penetration does not occur since he found metacercariae only in blood vessels. Metacercariae (0.34–0.48 mm.) in the crustacea may be found in the gills, heart, muscles of the legs and body, liver or reproductive organs. Infected crayfish usually belong to the genera *Cambaroides* and *Cambarus*. The time between infection of the crustacean and appearance of mature metacercariae in its tissues may be several weeks to several months.

When a new host eats uncooked or poorly cooked crayfish or crabs, the metacercariae excyst in the intestine within an hour of ingestion. The minute worms are pinkish in color and possess a large, elongate, sac-like bladder. They penetrate the intestinal wall and usually go through the diaphragm to the pleural cavity. They may wander around the abdominal cavity for twenty days or more and enter various organs in which they may even reach sexual maturity. Even after penetrating the diaphragm, they may never get to the lungs but enter the liver or other tissue. A heavy infection of the liver frequently is observed in experimental animals. In animals there are usually two worms in a lung cyst but this phenomenon rarely occurs in man, one worm being the rule. Eggs appear in the sputum 2.5 to 3 months after a man eats infected crustacea.

Excysted metacercariae have been observed to enter wounds and mucous membranes of experimental animals. Possibly some vertebrate hosts acquire infection by eating metacercariae freed from their crab hosts. It has been noticed that in an aquarium where infected crabs are kept, there may be a few free metacercariae. These cysts may fall from tissues when crabs fight. Crabs are often prepared for cooking on chopping blocks and the juice left on the block may contain metacercariae which adhere to foods subsequently prepared on

the same block or to the fingers of the cook. The raw juice of fresh
crabs is used in various preparations in Korea and the Philippines.
Crabs are often "pickled" or salted or dipped in wine or vinegar before eating. These treatments rarely kill all metacercariae. The
encysted parasites can live several days in a dead crab, one or two
days in diluted rice wine, or three weeks in an ice chest at $10°$ C in
10 per cent formalin.

Immunity to paragonimiasis has received very little study, but
undoubtedly some immunity is developed. The incidence of infection is much lower in children under ten years old than in older
children or adults. A host sex factor seems to be operative since in
Korea 80 per cent of the cases in children are boys. Perhaps this
simply reflects a difference in the eating habits or other behavior of
boys.

Symptoms of infection include a cough, profuse expectoration,
occasional appearance of blood in sputum, pain in chest, brown
sputum and muscular weakness. Pathology involves bleeding spots
where worms penetrate tissues, leucocyte infiltration, tearing of
muscles, scar tissue. host allergic reaction, and fibrous cyst formation
around worms. These cysts may contain blood-tinged material,
purulent chocolate-colored fluid, worm eggs, living worms, dead
worms or no worms. Migration of the worms to other tissues or
organs may or may not be troublesome. Cerebral involvement can
be extremely serious. The eggs are distributed widely throughout
the host and cause inflammation. Secondary bacterial infection may
occur.

Diagnosis consists primarily of finding the eggs in sputum or feces
but the clinical picture is of value. Intradermal and complement
fixation tests are useful.

Treatment with emetine hydrochloride has been recommended
for many years. Control should involve treatment of patients, elimination of reservoir hosts, disinfection of sputum and feces of patients, destruction of snails, crabs and crayfish, prevention of human
infection by cysts freed from second intermediate host, and education against eating raw or poorly cooked or preserved crabs or crayfish. Chloroquine, emetine plus prontosil or, better, emetine with
solfonamide are effective modern drugs.

Nanophyetus (= *Troglotrema*) *salmincola* is known by the curious
name "salmon poisoning fluke." Microbial pathogens are commonly transmitted to vertebrate hosts by ectoparasites, but some years
ago parasitologists were startled by the discovery that this trematode
has taken the place of an arthropod vector of a rickettsial agent
causing a serious disease in dogs. The tiny fluke is roughly oval in
shape, about a millimeter in length, and lives in the intestine.
Eggs are about 40 by 70 microns in size. Various snails (*e.g. Goniobasis silicula*) serve as the first intermediate host within which develop cercariae similar to those of *Paragonimus westermani*. These
cercariae penetrate salmon and other fishes, and enter the kidneys.
The parasite becomes infected with a rickettsia, *Neorickettsia*

helmintheca, which causes a serious disease in the natural final host which eats the salmon. Dogs, foxes, raccoons, and other fish-eating mammals harbor the fluke and may thus become infected with the rickettsia. Fever, vomiting, dysentery are some of the more severe symptoms. Apomorphine and oleoresin of aspidium are good anthelminthics. The mortality rate is fairly high but recovery confers immunity.

ORDER OPISTHORCHIIDA

Family Opisthorchiidae. The habitat of these lanceolate distomes is the bile passages of vertebrates. Suckers are small, the ovaries are located in front of the testes, and a genital pore occurs just in front of the ventral sucker. The life cycle involves a snail and fish or amphibian intermediate hosts, and the usual miracidia, sporocyst, redia, cercaria, and metacercaria stages.

The best-known member of the family is the Chinese liver fluke, *Opisthorchis sinensis* (= *Clonorchis sinensis*). Its prevalence in China is evident from the common name but it is also found in Korea, Japan and other southeast Asia countries. The incidence of infection in man reaches 15 to 70 per cent in local areas and 100 per cent in reservoir hosts such as cats, dogs, tigers, foxes, badgers and mink. This fluke (Fig. IX–30) averages about 18 by 4 mm. in size. The eggs (27 by 16 microns) are shaped somewhat like an electric light bulb with a distinct "door" or operculum on top. They are readily killed by desiccation but can live 6 months at 0° C if kept moist. The life cycle (Fig. IX–31) includes a snail (e.g. *Bithynia*), which eats the eggs, and freshwater fishes of the minnow and carp families to which the cercariæ swim. These larval flukes penetrate the skin of the fish and encyst as metacercariae. Man gets the infection by eating uncooked, infected fish. The normal route of this fluke to the liver appears to be through the host's intestinal mucosa by penetration, and transference to the liver by the portal blood system. The incubation period in man is about 3 weeks. Although in man a few dozen worms is about an average infection, there was reported one case with 21,000 worms! Cats, dogs, tigers, and other fish-eating mammals may also become infected.

Symptoms, if any, include eosinophilia, nausea, epigastric pain, edema, diarrhea, vertigo, fluid in body tissues, and wasting of the body. The drug of choice is chloroquine. Prevention rests mainly on cooking all freshwater fish from endemic areas. Diagnosis is confirmed by finding the eggs in fecal samples.

Opisthorchis felineus (= *O. tenuicollis*) is found in much of Europe and the Orient. It averages about 10 by 2½ mm. in size, and it lives in the liver of man, cats, dogs, foxes, and other mammals. The life cycle is similar to that of *O. sinensis*, eggs being eaten by a suitable snail such as *Bithynia* (= *Bulimus*) *tentaculata*. Liberated cercariae possess penetration glands and large tails, and they are active swimmers. They become attached to various species of fish, drop their tails, penetrate the skin under scales, and become metacercariae in the skin or muscles. Man and other vertebrate hosts become infected by ingesting uncooked or partially cooked, infected fish. The mature metacercariae in fish sometimes reach a diameter of 300 microns, so they can be seen as tiny spots with the naked eye. In the vertebrate host they excyst and make their way to the bile ducts of the liver where they mature.

A few dozens of these worms in the human liver seem to cause no appreciable harm. When the number gets into the hundreds there may be pain, congestion, liver enlargement, bile stones, and cirrhosis. There is no effective treatment. See also Figure IX–32A, B,C.

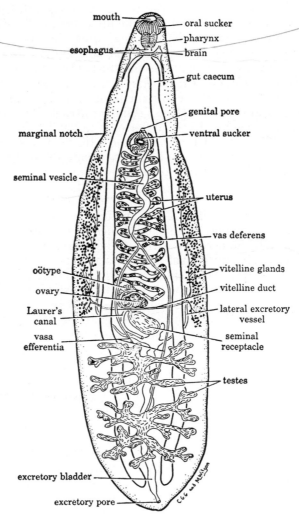

FIG. IX–30.—*Opisthorchis sinensis.* Dorsal view of adult. (Brown, *Selected Invertebrate Types,* courtesy of John Wiley & Sons, Inc.)

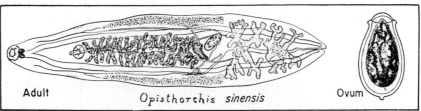

Fig. IX–31.—Epidemiology of opisthorchiasis (= clonorchiasis). (Mackie, Hunter and Worth, *A Manual of Tropical Medicine*, courtesy of W. B. Saunders & Co.)

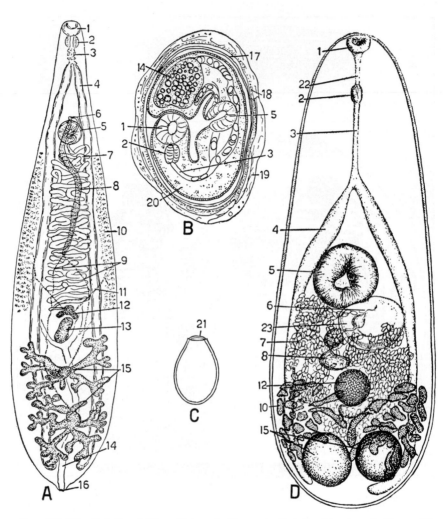

Fig. IX–32.—Opisthorchiidae, Heterophyidae. *A, Opisthorchis sinensis (from slide, courtesy A. E. Galigher)*, human liver fluke. *B*, Metacercaria of *O. sinensis (after Komiya and Tajimi, 1940). C*, Capsule of *O. sinensis (after Looss, 1907a). D, Heterophyes heterophyes (after Witenberg, 1929)*, intestinal fluke of mammals.

1, oral sucker; *2*, pharynx; *3*, esophagus; *4*, intestine; *5*, acetabulum; *6*, gonopore; *7*, uterus; *8*, seminal vesicle; *9*, sperm duct; *10*, yolk glands; *11*, yolk ducts; *12*, ovary; *13*, seminal receptacle; *14*, bladder; *15*, testes; *16*, nephridiopore; *17*, inner cyst wall; *18*, outer cyst wall; *19*, host part of cyst wall; *20*, metacercaria coiled in cyst; *21*, operculum; *22*, buccal tube; *23*, gonotyl. (Hyman, *The Invertebrates II*, courtesy of McGraw-Hill Book Company.)

Family Heterophyidae. These small intestinal flukes live in birds and mammals including dogs, cats, and man. The parasites are usually only 1 or 2 mm. long, rarely reaching 3 mm. Some are distomes and some monostomes, and the cuticle is scaly, at least on the anterior part of the body. The general shape of the body is ovoid or pyriform, and the ovary is located in front of the testes or testis. The metacercaria stage occurs in fishes or amphibians.

Heterophyes heterophyes is a minute fluke (Fig. IX–32) averaging 1.3 by .35 mm. and it may be pear-shaped, oval or somewhat elongated. The outer surface is covered with spine-like scales. The mid-ventral surface seems to possess two adjacent suckers, but careful examination shows that one of them is the genital opening. This organ is retractile and it may be called a genital sucker or a *gonotyl*. The life cycle is similar to that of *Opisthorchis felineus*. The oval eggs average about 28 by 15 microns, thus they are smaller than many protozoan cysts. They resemble the eggs of related species and must be eaten by the right species of snail to survive. Metacercariae occur in various fishes and may be ingested by man with his fish dinner. The adult parasite lives in the intestine and normally it causes little harm, but it may produce pain and diarrhea. Eggs of this species and related forms may also find their way into the blood stream and cause mild to serious trouble in organs into which they filter. The fluke is especially prevalent throughout the Orient. There are a number of related species which occasionally get into man (*Cryptocotyle lingua, Haplorchis yokogawai, Heterophyes katsuradai, H. brevicaeca,* and *Diorchitrema sp.*). *Cryptocotyle lingua* lives in dogs between the intestinal villi and in the lumen, and causes considerable damage due, in the main, to mechanical factors. A heavy infestation causes the production of a great deal of mucus, sloughing of tissue, pressure atrophy and necrosis.

A more important related fluke is *Metagonimus yokogawai* (Fig. IX–33). It, too, lives in the small intestine of man, dogs, cats, and it has even been found in pelicans. It occurs in the Orient and in a few other places. This fluke is only slightly larger than *Heterophyes heterophyes* and it has a similar life cycle, the metacercariae encysting in freshwater trout and in other salmonoid and cyprinoid fishes. A diagnostic character of the adults is the eccentric position of the ventral sucker which is located about half way between the anterior and posterior ends of the body but to the right of the midline. After ingestion of the metacercariae by man the young worms grow to maturity in two to three weeks. Infection may produce colicky pains and diarrhea.

Family Hemiuridae. These flukes are elongated, cylindrical worms with a non-spinous cuticle. They are sometimes called *appendiculate* flukes, and they vary in length from a few millimeters to 15 millimeters. A characteristic feature of the body of some of them is its division into an anterior *soma* and a posterior *ecsoma*. These two parts may be telescoped together, the ecsoma being withdrawn into the soma. The dividing line between the thick-walled anterior part and the thin-walled posterior part is often clearly evident as a constriction (Fig. IX–34). Often the vitellaria consist of a few large bodies rather than many scattered particles. The flukes usually inhabit the gut, stomach, gallbladder, esophagus, or pharynx of marine fishes, and they are worldwide in their dis-

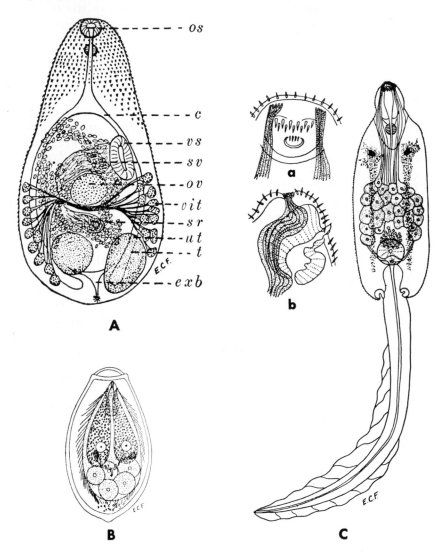

Fig. IX–33.—*A*, Adult specimen of *Metagonimus yokogawai*, ventral view. × 36. *c*, cecum; *ex b*, excretory bladder; *os*, oral sucker; *ov*, ovary; *sr*, seminal receptacle; *sv*, seminal vesicle; *t*, testis; *ut*, uterus; *vit*, vitellaria; *vs*. ventral sucker. (After Faust.)

B, Egg of *M. yokogawai*, with mature miracidium. × 1300. (After Faust.)

C, Cercaria of *M. yokogawai*. × 200. *a*, *b*, Ventral and lateral aspects of anterior end, showing relationship of lytic gland ducts and integumentary spines to oral opening; greatly enlarged. (Adapted in part from Faust, 1929, in part from Yokogawa, 1931.) (Faust and Russell, *Clinical Parasitology*, Lea & Febiger.)

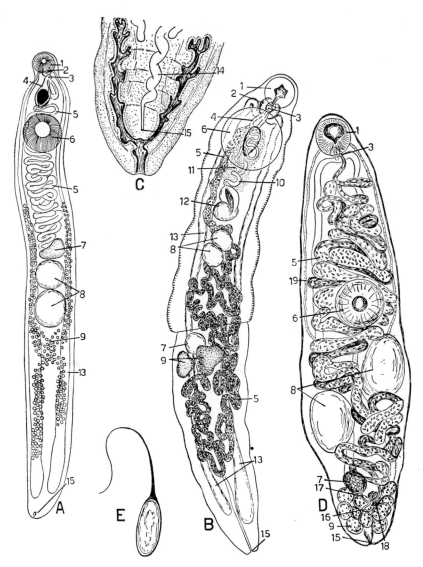

Fig. IX–34.—Azygiidae, Hemiuridae. *A, Otodistomum,* to 100 mm. long, from the stomach of a skate, from life. *B, Hemiurus* (after Looss, 1908) with rear end extended. *C,* Rear part of same with rear end telescoped into the interior *(after Looss,* 1908). *D, Halipegus* nonappendiculate hemiurid, from the oral cavity of frogs. *E,* Capsule of *Halipegus.* *(D and E, after Krull,* 1935).

1, oral sucker; *2,* pharynx; *3,* gonopore; *4,* cirrus sac; *5,* uterus; *6,* acetabulum; *7,* ovary; *8,* testes; *9,* yolk glands; *10,* sperm duct; *11,* prostatic glands; *12,* seminal vesicle; *13,* intestine; *14,* bladder; *15,* nephridiopore; *16,* yolk duct. *17,* oviduct; *18,* ootype; *19,* nephridium. (Hyman, *The Invertebrata II,* courtesy of McGraw-Hill Book Company.)

tribution. Sample genera are *Hemiurus*, *Aphanurus*, *Sterrhurus* and *Lecithochirium*.

Nonappendiculate genera include *Hysterolecitha* and *Derogenes*. The latter (Fig. IX–35) is the most widely distributed digenetic trematode of fishes,[5] being found in cod, flounder, sturgeon, sole, salmon, mackerel, halibut and many others. The parasite is usually found in the stomach of its vertebrate host but it may occur in the intestine. *Hysterolecitha trilocalis* (Fig. IX–37) is found on the gills of the mudsucker, *Gillichthys mirabilis*, an unusual site "preference" for an adult digene.

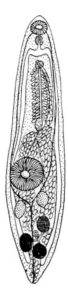

FIG. IX–35.—*Derogenes varicus.* × 30. (Dawes, *The Trematoda*, courtesy of the University Press, Cambridge.)

Halipegus (Fig. IX–36) is generally placed in a separate family (Halipegidae), and it commonly occurs in frogs and salamanders. Nonciliated miracidia are eaten by snails within which sporocysts, rediae, and cercariae are produced. The latter are eaten by insect larvae or by copepods.

Family Didymozoidae. These peculiar flukes usually live in pairs in cysts or cavities of their marine fish hosts. They may occur in the body cavity, kidney, body surface, esophagus, gut, musculature, subcutaneous tissue, pharynx or other places. The worms may have a broad posterior portion of the body (*Didymocystis*) or they may be thread-like (*Nematobothrium*). Most of them are hermaphroditic but in some (*Wedlia*, *Köllideria*) the sexes are separate. The ventral sucker is absent in members of this family, the pharynx is reduced or absent and the life histories are not known (Fig. IX–38). In at least one cyst-dwelling species (*Kollikeria filicollis*) the

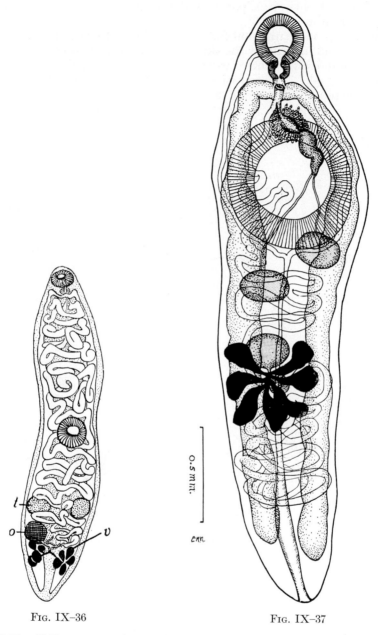

FIG. IX-36   FIG. IX-37

FIG. IX-36.—*Halipegus ovocaudatus*. (Dawes, *The Trematoda*, courtesy of The University Press, Cambridge.)

FIG. IX-37.—*Hysterolecitha trilocalis*. Composite drawing of mature adult. The uterine coils have been reduced to numbers below average conditions and eggs omitted in order not to obscure other organs. Ventral view. (King and Noble, courtesy of Jour. Parasitology.)

sexes are not entirely separate but the functional "males" and "females" are dimorphic.

One of the most unusual flukes, probably belonging to this family, may be found just under the skin of the sunfish, *Mola mola*. We have tried to remove the entire worm from the fish but find it an almost impossible task. The parasite is over 20 feet long and lies in tangled masses extending from one side of the host to the other, winding in and out through fin supports and dipping down between muscle masses.

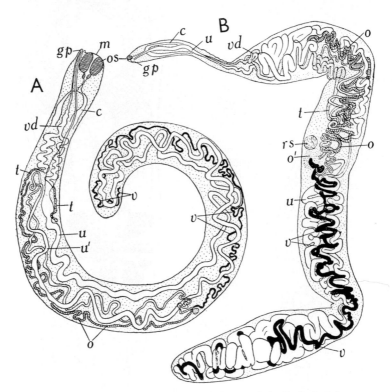

Fig. IX–38.—Two species of *Didymozoon*. *A, D. scombri. B, D. faciale. c*, cecum; *gp*, genital pore; *m*, mouth; *o*, ovary; *o'*, ootype; *os*, oral sucker; *rs*, seminal receptacle; *t*, testis; *u*, uterus; *u'*, descending limb of uterus; *v*, vitellaria; *vd*, vas deferens. (Dawes, *The Trematoda*, courtesy of University Press, Cambridge.)

BIBLIOGRAPHY

1. AMEEL, D. J., 1934. *Paragonimus*, its Life History and Distribution in North America and Its Taxonomy (Trematoda-Troglotrematidae). Amer. J. Hyg., *19*, 279–317.
2. BARBOSA, F. S., 1962. Problèmes de Nomenclature au Sujet des Vecteurs Actuels et Potentiels de *Schistosoma mansoni* en Afrique et en Amérique. Ann. Parasitol. Hum. Comp., *37*, 861–865.
3. BARLOW, C. H., 1925. Life Cycle of *Fasciolopsis buski*. Amer. J. Hyg., Monogr. Ser. 4.

4. COLE, W. H., 1955. *Some Physiological Aspects and Consequences of Parasitism.* Rutgers U. Press, New Brunswick, New Jersey, 90 pp.
5. DAWES, B., 1956. *The Trematoda (With Special Reference to British and Other European Forms.)* Cambridge, at the Univ. Press. 644 pp.
6. DAWES, B., 1962. On the Growth and Maturation of *Fasciola hepatica* L. in the Mouse. J. Helminthol., *36*, 11–38.
7. GHARIB, H. M., 1961. A Preliminary Note on the Bacteriostatic Properties of Some Helminths of Animals. J. Helminthol., *35*, 225–232.
8. GRODHAUS, G., and KEH, B., 1958. The Marine, Dermatitis-producing Cercaria of *Austrobilharzia variglandis* in California. (Trematoda: Schistosomatidae). J. Parasitol., *44*, 633–638.
8a. HOFFMAN, GLENN L., 1960. Synopsis of Strigeoidea (Trematoda) of Fishes and their Life Cycles. U.S. Fish and Wildlife Serv. Fish Bull., *60* (175), 439–469.
9. HSÜ, S. Y. L. and HSÜ, H. F., 1961. New Approach to Immunization Against *Schistosoma japonicum.* Science, *133*, No. 3455, p. 766.
10. KRULL, W. H., 1956. Experiments Involving Potential Definitive Hosts of *Dicrocoelium dendriticum* (Rudolph, 1891) Looss, 1899: Dicrocoeliidae. Cornell Vet., *46*, 511–525.
11. LINCICOME, D. R. (Ed)., 1962. Frontiers in Research in Parasitism: I. Cellular and Humoral Reactions in Experimental Schistosomiasis. Exper. Parasitol., *12*, 211–240.
12. MALEK, E. A., 1961. The Ecology of Schistosomiasis. In: May, J. M. (ed.), *Studies in Disease Ecology*, Chapt. 10. Hafner Publ. Co., N. Y., 613 pp.
13. McMULLEN, D. B., 1963. Schistosomiasis Control in Theory and Practice. Amer. J. Trop. Med. Hyg., *12*, 288–295.
14. MOORE, D. V., YOLLES, T. K., and MELENEY, H. E., 1954. The Relationship of Male Worms to the Sexual Development of Female *Schistosoma mansoni.* J. Parasitol, *40*, 166–185.
15. NEWSOME, J., 1956. Problems of Fluke Immunity: with Special Reference to Schistosomiasis. Trans. Roy. Soc. Trop. Med. Hyg., *50*, 258–274.
16. STIREWALT, M. A. and HACKEY, J. R., 1956. Penetration of Host Skin by Carcariae of *Schistosoma mansoni.* I. Observed Entry Into Skin of Mouse, Hamster, Rat, Monkey, and Man. J. Parasitol., *42*, 565–580.
17. STUNKARD, H. W., 1958. The morphology and Life History of *Levinseniella minuta* (Trematoda: Microphallidae) J. Parasitol., *44*, 225–230.
18. YOKOGAWA, M., 1952. Studies on the Biological Aspects of the Larval Stages of *Paragonimus westermanii*, Especially the Invasion of the Second Intermediate Hosts. (II). Jap. J. Med. Sci. & Biol., *5*, 501–515.
19. YOKOGAWA, S., CORT, W. W., and YOKOGAWA, M., 1960. *Paragonimus* and Paragonimiasis. Exper. Parasitol., *10*, 81–205.

CHAPTER X

Phylum Platyhelminthes, Class Cestodea, Introduction, Subclass Cestodaria

INTRODUCTION

THE class Cestoidea consists of parasites (commonly called tape-worms) which as adults live in the intestines of vertebrates, and whose bodies are usually white or yellowish, ribbon-like and divided into short segments called *proglottids*. Larval stages live in a wide variety of invertebrates and vertebrates. A few forms (Cestodaria) are not segmented. The holdfast (head) is the *scolex*, and it is armed with hooks or "suckers" or both, while below the scolex is the neck (zone of proliferation) and the body, or *strobila*. Whereas each larval stage of a cestode is unquestionably an individual organism, the adult can be considered to be a "linear colony of highly specialized zooids."[17] "The preponderance of evidence appears to support the opinion that the adult cestode is an individual rather than a colony."[15]

Hooks in some species are attached to an anterior *rostellum* which may or may not be retractable. Some types of holdfasts are called *bothria* or *bothridia* after the Greek word meaning "hole" or "trench." Bothria are usually slit-like grooves with weak suction powers, as in *Dibothriocephalus latus* (Fig. X–9). Bothridia (or *phyllidia*, meaning "like a leaf") are leaf-like in appearance and may have thin, flexible margins. The order Tetraphyllidea, as the name indicates, possesses four-leaf bothridia. There are many variations in shape. Another type of sucker-like organ is the cup-like *acetabulum* which occurs on the scolex of the pork or beef tapeworm, *Taenia* (Fig. XI–15). The proglottids, which number from 3 to more than 3,000, become pro-gressively more mature toward the posterior end of the tapeworm. The terminal segments, especially in the more primitive families of cestodes, may sometimes become detached at an early stage in their development and live and mature independently in the intestine of their host. More commonly, however, the terminal gravid or ripe proglottids become little more than sacs filled with eggs. The cestoidea possess no digestive, circulatory, respiratory or skeletal organs. It would seem that everything possible has been eliminated in order to produce a thoroughly efficient reproductive machine. Ganglia and nerve cords occur, but no specialized sense organs.

Each proglottid normally has a complete set of male and female reproductive organs. Occasionally the male organs disappear before

(242)

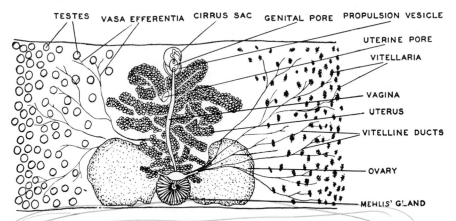

FIG. X–1.—Proglottid of the fish tapeworm *Dibothriocephalus latus*. (Cable, *An Illustrated Laboratory Manual of Parasitology*, courtesy of Burgess Publishing Co.)

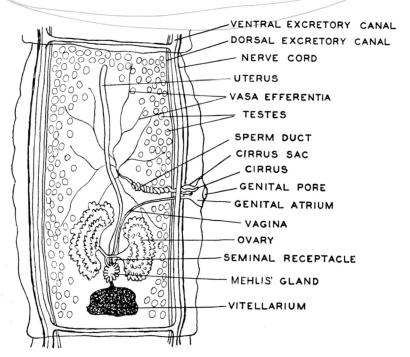

FIG. X–2.—A mature proglottid of *Taenia pisiformis*, found in the dog and in other mammals. (Cable, *An Illustrated Laboratory Manual of Parasitology*, courtesy of Burgess Publishing Co.)

the female organs become functional. These organs are fundamentally similar to those of most flukes but there is a vaginal canal which opens to the outside. There may be a duplication of reproductive organs in each proglottid. Self-fertilization, involving the sexual structures of a single proglottid, or reciprocal fertilization between proglottids of the same worm, may occur. Reciprocal fertilization between proglottids of different worms may also take place if more than one tapeworm is present in the same region of the host's intestine. Some proglottids in mature strobila may become sexually undifferentiated because of nutritional deficiency. Crowding possibly prevents parts of the strobila from coming in contact with the mucosa of the host from which they receive a protein-synthesizing enzyme.[6]

A single tapeworm may lay thousands of eggs a day and one to two million eggs during its lifetime. Scattered *testes* occur throughout each proglottid, and the *vitellaria*, or yolk glands, are commonly grouped in one clump but may also be dispersed along the lateral margins of the worm. These and other reproductive organs are illustrated in Figures X–1 and 2.

The organization of the reproductive organs may be used to divide the cestodes into two groups.[12] In Group I are placed those worms with vitellaria scattered throughout the peripheral region of the proglottid (Pseudophyllidea and Tetrarhynchidea), or with these yolk glands occurring in broad or narrow lateral masses (Tetraphyllidea, Proteocephalidea and Lecanicephalidea). In some species (Pseudophyllidea) the eggs are thick-walled, oval and operculated, as in flukes, whereas in others (Tetraphyllidea) the eggs are thin-walled, round and non-operculated.

In Group II are placed the cestodes with compact vitelline glands usually located in the mid-line of the proglottid. Two small, median glands occur in the Mesocestoididae, but in some of the Anoplocephalidae vitelline glands are absent. Eggs of the group are usually protected by the *embryophore* (Fig. X–3). Figures X–4 and 5 illustrate these two groups.

The early embryology of tapeworms is a subject still filled with many unknown steps. Students with a flair for microtechnique and a sound knowledge of biochemistry can add much to our knowledge.

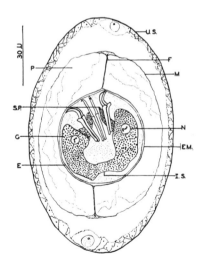

Fig. X–3.—Oncosphere of *Raillietina cesticillus*. Ventral view of a *R. cesticillus* larva enclosed in embryonic membranes. *E*, embryo boundary; *EM*, embryophore; *F*, filament; *G*, gland; *I.S.*, *isthmus*. *M*, membrane from macromeres and yolk material; *N*, nucleus; *P*, protein substance; *S.P.*, secretory pore; *U.S.*, uterine shell. (Reid, courtesy of Trans. Amer. Micros. Soc.)

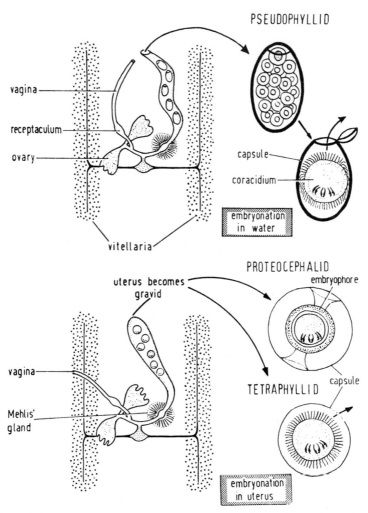

PSEUDOPHYLLID

vagina

receptaculum

ovary

capsule

coracidium

embryonation
in water

vitellaria

PROTEOCEPHALID

uterus becomes
gravid

embryophore

vagina

Mehlis'
gland

capsule

TETRAPHYLLID

embryonation
in uterus

Fig. X–4.—Diagrammatic representation of genitalia and eggs of cestodes in Group I: with extensive vitellaria. (Smyth and Clegg, courtesy of Experimental Parasitology.)

Egg shell formation in the pseudophyllid, *Schistocephalus solidus* (Group I), has received detailed study,[12] but little is known of this process in other tapeworms. The reproductive organs and egg shell formation of the family Pseudophyllidae are closely related to those of digenetic trematodes as is described on pages 173–179. Shell globules are released from the vitelline cells and coalesce around the mass of these cells surrounding the ovum. These globules form the egg shell (Fig. VIII–7). In cyclophyllidean cestodes, with small vitellaria, few cells, sometimes only one, surround the egg. We have yet to learn how the thick inner *embryophore*, so characteristic of *Taenia* and other genera, is formed (Figs. X–3 and 6).

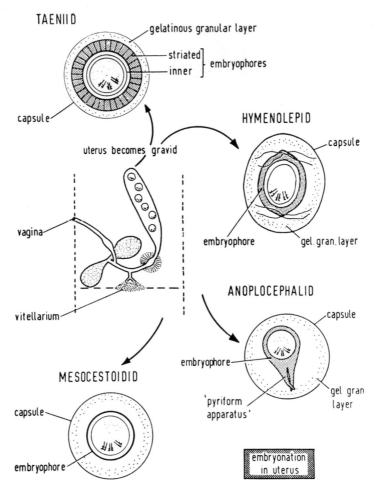

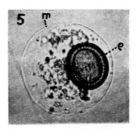

Fig. X–6.—*Taenia saginata*. Photomicrograph of egg. *m*, external membrane of the egg; *e*, embryophore containing oncosphere or six-hooked embryo. (Gradwohl and Kouri, *Clinical Laboratory Methods and Diagnosis*, courtesy of C. V. Mosby Co.)

The nervous system of cestodes consists of relatively few ganglia and nerves located primarily in the anterior end of the worm (Fig. X–7). There are three to five longitudinal nerve cords extending the length of the body with lesser nerves attached to them.

The "excretory" or osmoregulatory system is similar to that of flukes, consisting of flame cells (flame bulbs) connecting with transverse and longitudinal collecting tubules (Fig. X–2 and 8). A pair of

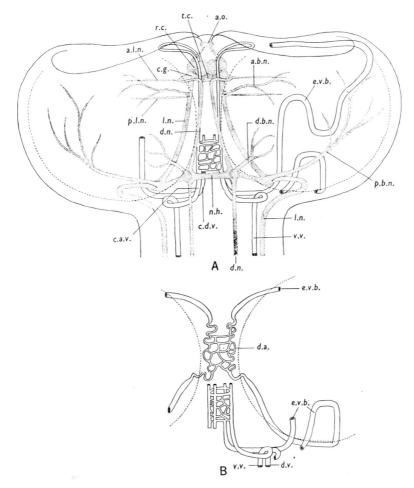

FIG. X–7.—The scolex of *Tetrabothrius affinis* showing nervous system. This tapeworm is from the Blue Whale, *Balaenoptera musculus*. *a.b.n.* anterior bothridial nerve; *a.l.n.* antero-lateral nerve; *a.o.* apical organ; *c.a.v.* central ascending branch of ventral vessels; *c.d.v.* central descending branch of ventral vessel; *c.g.* cerebral ganglion; *d.a.* anastomosis of dorsal excretory vessels; *d.b.n.* dorsal bothridial nerve; *d.n.* dorsal nerve; *d.v.* dorsal excretory vessel; *e.d.b.* excretory vessel of dorsal bothridium; *e.v.b.* excretory vessel of ventral bothridium; *l.n.* lateral nerve; *n.h.* nerve hexagon; *p.b.n.* posterior bothridial nerve; *p.l.n.* postero-lateral nerve; *r.c.* ring commissure; *t.c.* transverse commissure; *v.a.* anastomosis of ventral excretory vessels; *v.v.* ventral excretory vessel. (Rees, courtesy of J. Parasitology.)

longitudinal vessels passes along each side of the body. Fluid flows anteriorly in the smaller, dorsal vessel and posteriorly in the larger, ventral vessel. These vessels generally open directly to the surface but a caudal excretory vesicle and a caudal excretory pore may be present.

The exact function of the excretory vessels is in doubt but it seems clear that in addition to the usual role of ridding the body of certain metabolic wastes, these tubules help to maintain hydrostatic pres-

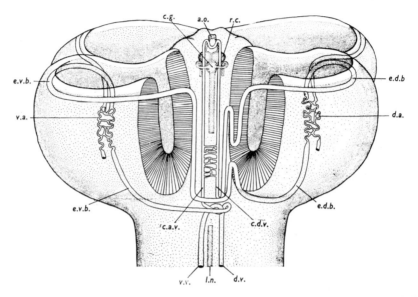

Fig. X–8.—Scolex of *Tetrabothrius affinis*. Reconstruction of the left half of the excretory system with part of the bothridia removed. See Fig. X–7 for legend. (Rees, G., courtesy of Parasitology.)

sure. To study the excretory products *in vivo* presents extreme difficulties, so one has to rely either on analogies with free-living organisms or on studies with parasites in culture. The very important outer covering of the worm is a cuticle, while under it occurs a parenchyma. "There seems to be little control over the osmotic entry or loss of water in larvae of adult cestodes."[8] Longitudinal as well as transverse and dorso-ventral muscles are located in a sub-cuticular zone and in the parenchymal zone. Transmission of waves of contraction is apparently inherent in the muscle fibers. Detached, ripe segments often move actively.

Adult tapeworms are generally more host specific than are other groups of parasitic worms. Larval tapeworms, however, are rarely host specific (see Chapter XXV, p. 618). This situation is the reverse of that found in trematodes. Tapeworms apparently evoke the production of antibodies in the host when the parasites are in either the tissue phase or in the lumen of the gut.

A number of species of cestodes (e.g. *Taenia taeniaeformis*, *Cysticercus fasciolaris*) contain large amounts of inorganic substances localized in *calcareous corpuscles*. This material is especially common in larval stages and it apparently serves to buffer body acids.[16]

The physiology of tapeworms has received much attention but we are only beginning to understand the complex biochemical nature of these organisms. One obstacle is the great difficulty in maintaining tapeworms in the laboratory outside of the host long enough, and under sufficiently normal conditions, to obtain reliable results from experiments. The composition of the worm itself presents us with unusual difficulties. For example, there is a linear gradient in metabolic rate along the strobila, so observations made on proglottids at one point in the body may be different from those made on other proglottids a short distance away. Extreme care must be exercised in analyzing the results of experiments, and definite notice must be taken of the region of the tapeworm under analysis.

With the aid of an electron microscope Rothman[10] has recently described minute projections which cover the surface of *Hymenolepis diminuta*. He has called these projections "microtriches" (sing. "microthrix") and he suggests that they serve to increase the absorptive area of the body surface, to help hold the worm next to the gut lining, and to agitate the adjacent gut fluids. Similar projections have been seen in other cestodes. Within the cuticle are "pore canals" which are not really canals but are "globules of the environmental medium that have been taken in by pinocytosis and formed into vacuoles." Also in the cuticle are mitochondria.

Energy production in adult tapeworms appears to be independent of oxygen. The worms depend on the breakdown of glycogen for their energy source. In general, the kinds of carbohydrates which can be utilized by tapeworms *in vitro* are limited, as indicated by the fact that most of the tapeworms studied[7] are capable of fermenting only certain monosaccharides. Anoplocephalids, however, use certain disaccharides. Because of differences between the physiology of the host and that of its tapeworm, the quality of carbohydrate ingested by the host has a direct bearing on the growth and reproduction rates of the worm. Some of the effects of carbohydrates on the worm may be due to preliminary effects on the physiochemical characteristics of the habitat. As numbers of tapeworms in one host increase, their average size decreases. This reaction is known as the *crowding effect* and it may be the result of competition for utilizable carbohydrate among the worms (see p. 574). Variations in the quantity of carbohydrate ingested by the host modify the competitive effects of one tapeworm species on another because different species are not affected proportionally. Seasonal changes in the behavior of tapeworms and in their carbohydrate content may be correlated with the feeding behavior of the host. The imposition of the dynamics of gut physiology on the specific carbohydrate requirement of cestodes may be of importance in the distribution of

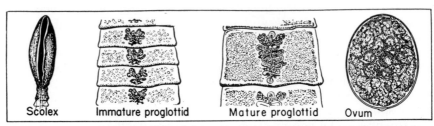

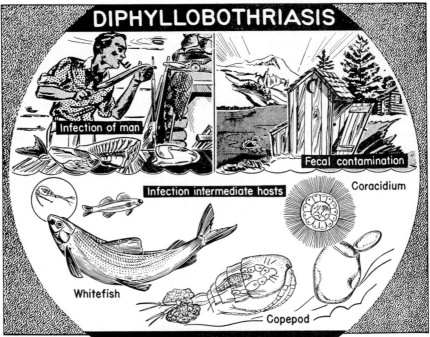

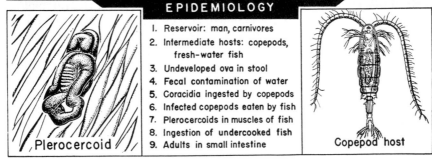

FIG. X–9.—Epidemiology of dibothriocephaliasis (= diphyllobothriasis) (Mackie, Hunter and Worth, *A Manual of Tropical Medicine*, courtesy of W. B. Saunders Co.)

the parasites and in the selection of species of parasites which appear and prosper in a particular host.[7]

LIFE CYCLES

Tapeworm life cycles involve several types of organisms. See Smyth (1963)[11a] for a review of the biology of cestode life histories. The fish tapeworm, *Dibothriocephalus latus* (Fig. X–9), whose eggs

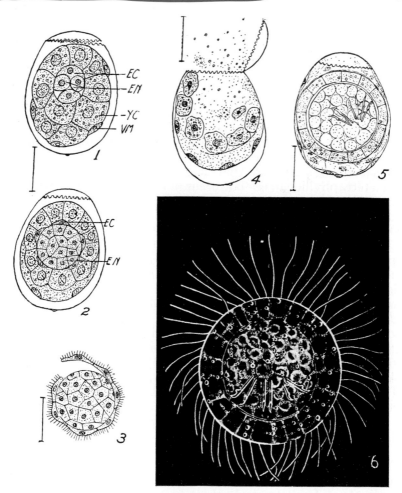

FIG. X–10.—*Dibothriocephalus latus* eggs and coracidium.

1, 2, Segmented eggs, showing origin of ectoderm and endoderm. Tissues shrunk away from the eggshell owing to fixation. (Modified after Schauinsland.) *3,* Immature embryo, showing development of cilia. (After Schauinsland.)

4, Egg just after liberation of the coracidium. *5,* Egg a few hours before hatching. *6,* Vogel's figure of the coracidium by dark field illumination.

Abbreviations: *EC,* ectodermal cell; *EN,* entodermal cell; *VM,* vitelline membrane; *YC,* yolk cell. The lines near the figures represent 0.02 mm. (Vergeer, courtesy of Papers. Mich. Acad. Sci., University of Michigan Press.)

possess a cap-like "door" or operculum, will be used as our first example. The early embryo within the egg develops three pairs of hooks and thus is known as a *hexacanth* embryo or *oncosphere* (Fig. X–3). If this embryo hatches and becomes free-swimming it is a *coracidium* (Fig. X–10). Copepods (e.g. *Diaptomus*) eat the coracidia of *Dibothriocephalus* and the young worms migrate into the body cavity (hemocoel) becoming *procercoid* larvae. The next host is a fish which eats the copepod. Salmon, trout, perch, pike and other varieties of fish thus become infected. The procercoid is liberated in the fish intestine and it makes its way into the muscles. Here it elongates into a *plerocercoid* larva (Figs. X–9 and 11). Because of an early mistake in identification the plerocercoid larva was thought to be another type of worm and was called a *sparganum*. The name persists, and when a fish is found infected with plerocercoids it is said to be "suffering" from sparganosis. A sparganum, or plerocercoid, may be minute or, in a few species, several inches in length. Fish-eating mammals, including man, act as final hosts. Spargana develop into mature tapeworms in the intestine, and eggs appear a few weeks after infection.

It has been suggested that plerocercoid larvae of an elasmobranch tetraphyllidean cestode occur in most genuine oriental pearls.[1] Apparently the oyster feeds on small crustaceans which harbor the first intermediate host of the tapeworm.

Other common types of tapeworm life cycles are represented by *Taenia, Echinococcus* and *Hymenolepis* (page 270). These genera display six types (with variations) of immature tapeworms. (1) *Oncosphere*, a hooked embryo within the egg; (2) *plerocercus*, a solid, rounded worm with deeply retracted head; (3) *plerocercoid*, solid, elongated, with scolex not deeply retracted; (4) *cysticercoid*, with scolex retracted into a small bladder, with or without a solid tail (sometimes a cysticercoid with a tail is called a *cercocystis*); (5) *cysticercus* (= *bladderworm*), a rounded cyst or bladder into which the scolex is invaginated; (6) *multiple cysts* and many scoleces, a modification of the cysticercus.

The oncosphere moves with its hooked end in advance; later this portion with larval hooklets is constricted off as a *cercomere*, and atrophies. The scolex develops at the opposite end. Thus there is a definite metamorphosis in the life cycle between the oncosphere and the cysticercoid stage.

Factors which cause larval tapeworms to excyst are, of course, of fundamental importance to the life cycle of these worms. It is exceedingly difficult to study these factors *in vivo*, so most investigators resort to *in vitro* laboratory studies. Much light can be thrown on life processes this way but the student must keep in mind that "test tube" conditions are never exactly like conditions in living animals, so conclusions may be misleading. Excystment of the cysticercoid stages of *Hymenolepis diminuta, H. citelli, H. nana* and *Oochoristica symmetrica* have recently been studied.[9] In one experiment larvae were reared in appropriate beetles and the cysticer-

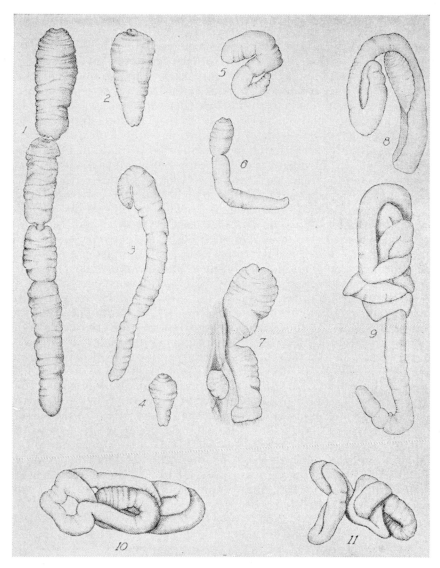

FIG. X–11.—Plerocercoids of *Dibothriocephalus latus*. *1*, Old preserved plerocercoid of *D. latus* showing deep constrictions. × 5. *2, 3, 4, 5* and *6*, Young plerocercoids of *D. latus* preserved while in flesh to show normal positions. × 11¼. *7*, The same, with part of the flesh of the fish still in position. × 11¼. *8, 9, 10* and *11*, Large living plerocercoids as seen in the flesh. × 5. (Vergeer, courtesy of J. Infectious Diseases.)

coids were dissected out, washed and placed on cover slips. Substances tested were placed on the coverslips which were inverted over welled slides. Only the larvae of *O. symmetrica* excysted in bile salts at room temperature. Only the larvae of this worm and of *H. diminuta* excysted in bile salts at 37° C. All four cysticercoid larvae excysted in bile salts when trypsin was added. These results certainly indicate that bile salts (sodium cholate, glycocholate or taurocholate) and trypsin in the intestine of living mammal hosts are probably responsible for excystation of the infective larval forms of these four tapeworms. Studies by other workers have shown that pepsin probably plays a major role in excystation, and that bile salts appear to be required for evagination of the scolex of larvae.[11a]

The rapid advances that have recently been made in our understanding of the biochemistry and physiology of tapeworms have been reviewed by Read and Simmons (1963).[7a] These authors listed some physiological modifications which may be correlated with obligate parasitism of tapeworms. The modifications include: "nutritional dependence on carbohydrate for growth and reproduction coupled with the limitation effected by the capacity to use only simple sugars; limited ability to perform transamination reactions; a general incapacity to digest complex organic molecules from the surrounding medium; very active membrane transport systems associated with the outer surface and showing stereospecificity for various classes of small organic molecules such as monosaccharides and amino acids; an incapacity of many species to osmoregulate but with obvious adaptations to the osmotic pressures and ionic strengths of vertebrate body fluids; and specific reactions of oncospheres and later larval stages to physiochemical factors involved in establishment within a host. The limited information available suggests that, except for carbohydrate, the nutritional requirements of tapeworms may not be much more complicated than those of vertebrates. The physiological specializations thus far delineated in tapeworms strongly support the hypothesis that the broad determinant of obligate parasitism in this group of organisms is dependence on the chemical regulatory mechanisms possessed by their vertebrate hosts. Tapeworms seem to lack many functions usually associated with maintenance of a steady state."

CLASSIFICATION

The classification followed here is primarily that of Hyman, but modified slightly on the basis of the reviews by Stunkard.[14,15] Three minor orders (Aporidea, Disculicepitidea, Nippotaenidea) have been omitted. A few families are discussed but no attempt is made to list all of them, and only a few species are described. For details on classification see the works of Hyman,[2] Spasskii,[13] Stunkard,[15] Wardle and McLeod,[17] and Yamaguti.[18]

CLASSIFICATION OF THE CESTOIDEA

Phylum Platyhelminthes

Class Cestoidea

Subclass Cestodaria

Order Amphilinidea
Order Gyrocotylidea

Subclass Cestoda

Order Tetraphyllidea
Order Diphyllidea
Order Lecanicephalidea
Order Proteocephalidea
Order Tetrarhynchidea (= Trypanorhyncha)
Order Pseudophyllidea
Families include : Diphyllobothriidae, Caryophyllidae
Order Cyclophyllidea
Families include: Davaineiidae, Dilepididae, Hymenolepidae, Taeniidae, Anoplocephalidae, Linstowiidae, Mesocestoididae.
Order Spathebothridea

SUBCLASS CESTODARIA

In this group[5] of worms there is no scolex, and the body is not segmented; these cestoides are therefore sometimes called *monozoic* in contrast with the *polyzoic* forms with proglottids. The two orders of Cestodaria given below are also characterized by larval stages which possess ten hooks in contrast with the six hooks of practically all the orders of Cestoda. The general appearance of the Cestodaria is more like a fluke than like the usual concept of a tapeworm. The worms may be found in the intestine and body cavity of fishes. The cestodarians have generally been considered to be the most primitive of the cestoides, but there is considerable evidence that they are progenetic plerocercoid larvae. See page 671 for a discussion of their phylogeny.

ORDER AMPHILINIDEA

Amphilina foliacea, which lives in the body cavity of the sturgeon, *Acipenser,* is an oval, flat worm without a scolex or digestive tract and with a protrusible proboscis. It is hermaphroditic with the ovary located near the posterior end of the body and the testes scattered throughout the animal. There is a long, loosely coiled uterus, a vagina, and male and female openings, both at the posterior end of the body. Adults range in length from a few millimeters to about 40 millimeters.

The life history[3] of *Amphilina foliacea* starts with the egg which

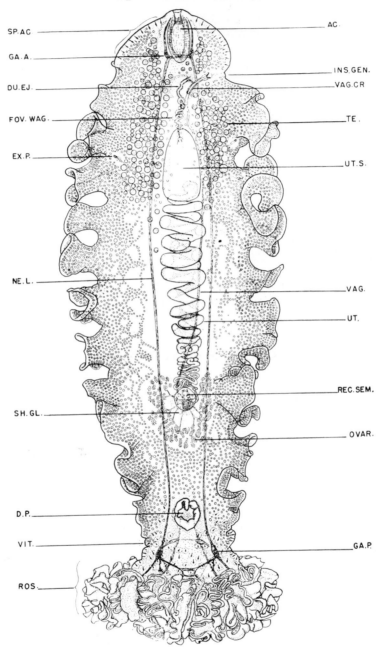

SP.AC.

GA.A.

DU.EJ.

FOV. WAG.

EX.P.

NE.L.

SH.GL.

D.P.

VIT.

ROS.

AC.

INS.GEN.

VAG.CR

TE.

UT.S.

VAG.

UT.

REC.SEM.

OVAR.

GA.P.

FIG. X–12.—*Gyrocotyle fimbriata*, dorsal aspect. × *57*. *AC.* acetabulum; *D.P.* dorsal pore of funnel; *DU.EJ.* ejaculatory duct; *EX.P.* excretory pore; *FOV.WAG.* fovea Wageneri (ventral); *GA.A.* anterior ganglion; *GA.P.* posterior ganglion; *INS.GEN.* genital notch; *NE.L.* longitudinal nerve trunk; *OVAR.* ovary; *REC.SEM.* receptaculum seminis; *ROS.* rosette; *SH.GL.* shell gland; *SP.AC.* acetabular spines; *TE.* testicular follicles; *UT.* uterus; *UT.S.* uterine sac; *VAG.* vagina (slender portion); *VAG.CR.* vagina (thickened terminal section); *VIT.* posterior limit of vitelline follicles. (Lynch, courtesy of J. Parasitology.)

develops into a ciliated larva while still in the uterus of the mother worm. This larva is called a *lycophore* or *decacanth* and it does not emerge from the egg until it is eaten by the second host, an amphipod. In the crustacean host the larva makes its way into the body spaces and develops into a procercoid, then into a plerocercoid stage. The latter is infective to the sturgeon which eats the amphipod. Sexually mature worms contain larval hooklets. They are *progenetic* plerocercoid larvae.[4]

ORDER GYROCOTYLIDEA

These elongated flat worms are non-segmented and they live in the spiral intestine of chimaeroid fishes (Holocephali). *Gyrocotyle urna* and *G. fimbriata* are representative species. The genus *Gyrocotyle* consists of worms whose bodies are composed of one segment dorsoventrally flattened. At the anterior end is a muscular sucker, the *acetabulum*, and at the posterior end occurs a funnel-shaped *haptor* with a small anterior dorsal pore and a wide posterior opening. The borders of this opening are thin and are folded in a complex manner forming the rosette. The lateral borders of the body, which has spines on its surface, are thin and undulant or ruffled. The vaginal pore is dorsal in position, the male genital pore is ventral, and the uterine pore is ventral, all three pores occurring in the anterior fourth of the body.

Little is known of the life cycles of these parasites. A ten-hooked ciliated larva emerges from the egg and apparently gets directly into the host tissues without using an intermediate host.[11]

Gyrocotyle fimbriata lives in the intestine of the ratfish, *Hydrolagus colliei*, which may be caught along the western coast of the United States. The parasites average 32 mm. in length but range from 13 to 63 mm. Their general anatomy is described above, and other details may be seen in Figure X–12.

BIBLIOGRAPHY

1. BAER, J. G., 1951. *Ecology of Animal Parasites.* The University of Illinois Press, Urbana. 224 pp.
2. HYMAN, L. H., 1951. *The Invertebrates: Platyhelminthes and Rhynchocoela. The Acoelomate Bilateria.* Vol. II. McGraw-Hill Book Co. 550 pp.
3. JANICKI, C. and ROSEN, F., 1928. Die Lebensgeschichte von *Amphilina foliacea G.* Wagen., Parasiten des Wolgasterlets, nach Beobachtungen und Experimenten. Arb. Biol. Wolga-Station, Saratow, *10*, 101–134.
4. JANICKI, C. and ROSEN, F., 1930. Über die jungsten Zustande von *Amphilina.* Zool. Anz., *90*, 190–205.
5. JOYEUX, Ch. and BAER, J. G., 1961. Classe des Cestodaires. Cestodaria Monticelli. In: GRASSÉ, P. *Traité de Zoologie.* Tome IV. p. 327–346. Masson et Cie Éditeurs. Libraires de l' Acad. Méd. Paris.
6. READ, C. P., 1951. The "Crowding Effect" in Tapeworm Infections. J. Parasitol., *37*, 174–178.
7. READ, C. P., 1959. The Role of Carbohydrates in the Biology of Cestodes. VIII. Some Conclusions and Hypotheses. Exp. Parasitol., *8*, 365–382.

17

7a. READ, C. P. and SIMMONS, J. E., JR., 1963. Biochemistry and Physiology of Tapeworms. Physiol. Rev., *43*, 263–305.
8. ROGERS, W. P., 1962. *The Nature of Parasitism. The Relationship of Some Metazoan Parasites to Their Hosts.* Academic Press, New York and London, 287 pp.
9. ROTHMAN, A. H., 1957. The larval development of *Hymenolepis diminuta* and *H. citelli.* J. Parasitol., *43* (6), 643–646.
10. ROTHMAN, A. H., 1963. Electron Microscopic Studies of Tapeworms: The Surface Structure of *Hymenolepis diminuta* (Rudolphi, 1819) Blanchard, 1891. Trans. Amer. Micros. Soc., *82*, 22–30.
11. RUSZKOWSKI, J. S., 1932. Études sur le Cycle Evolutif et sur la Structure des Cestodes de mer. II. Sur les Larves de *Gyrocotyle urna* (Gr. et Wagen.). Bull Intern. Acad. Polon. Sci., Sér B., pp. 629–641.
11a. SMYTH, J. D., 1963. *The Biology of Cestode Life-Cycles.* Tech. Communication No. 34, Commonwealth Bur. Helminthol., St. Albans, Herts, Eng. 38 pp.
12. SMYTH, J. D. and CLEGG, J. A., 1959. Egg-Shell Formation in Trematodes and Cestodes. Exp. Parasitol., *8*, 286–323.
13. SPASSKII, A. A., 1951 (1961). *Essentials of Cestodology.* Ed. by K. I. Skrjabin, Vol. I. *Anoplocephalate Tapeworms of Domestic and Wild Animals.* Acad. Sci. USSR, Moscow. Publ. in Engl. by Israel Prog. Sci. Transl. Birron & Cole. 783 pp.
14. STUNKARD, H. W., 1953. Life Histories and Systematics of Parasitic Worms. Systematic Zool., *2*, 7–18.
15. STUNKARD, H. W., 1962. The Organization, Ontogeny, and Orientation of the Cestoda. Quart. Rev. Biol., *37*, 23–34.
16. VON BRAND, T., MERCADO, T. I., NYLEN, M. U., and SCOTT, D. R., 1960. Observations on Function, Composition and Structure of Cestode Calcareous Corpuscles. Exper. Parasitol., *9*, 205–214.
17. WARDLE, R. A. and McLEOD, J. A., 1952. *The Zoology of Tapeworms.* Univ. Minn. Press., 780 pp.
18. YAMAGUTI, S., 1959. *Systema Helminthum.* Vol. II. *The Cestodes of Vertebrates.* Interscience Publ. Inc., N. Y. 860 pp.

CHAPTER XI

Phylum Platyhelminthes, Subclass Cestoda

THESE flatworms typically possess a scolex bearing hooks and suckers, the strobila consists of three to many proglottids, and the embryo usually has six hooklets.

ORDER TETRAPHYLLIDEA

These tapeworms are commonly found in the intestines of elasmobranch fishes (sharks, rays, etc.) and are characterized by four bothridia (= phyllidia) on the scolex. These "suction" organs of attachment are usually broad and leaf-like or trumpet-like and they may be relatively simple or complex. The worms are moderate in size, usually not exceeding 10 cm. in length, with at most only a few hundred proglottids. The ovary is bilobed, and each lobe is constricted horizontally; the vagina is dorsal to the uterine sac, and the yolk glands occur as two marginal bands. There are two families: Phyllobothriidae and Onchobothriidae. Life cycles of the various genera have not been completely worked out, but they are basically similar to the pseudophyllids (p. 260).

ORDER LECANICEPHALIDEA

Like the tetraphyllids, these tapeworms live in the intestines of elasmobranch fishes. The two groups of worms are similar in many respects but the scolex of the lecanicephalids consists of two main parts in tandem. The anterior portion may be bulb-like (many possess tentacles or suckers); and the posterior part may bulge like a cushion and bear four suckers. The group is composed of small tapeworms with relatively few proglottids and with more-or-less cylindrical bodies. Complete life cycles have not yet been described. There are three families: Lecanicephalidae, Cephalobothriidae and Discocephalidae.

ORDER PROTEOCEPHALIDEA

The order includes only one family, Proteocephalidae, but it is a large group with many well-known species. The worms inhabit the intestines of amphibia, reptiles and freshwater fishes. One species, *Lintoniella adhaerens*, has been found in the hammerhead shark. The worms, in general, are only a few centimeters long with mature proglottids which are longer than they are broad. The scolex is varied but usually possesses four simple suckers flush with the surface of the body and near the anterior tip. There may or may not be an extension of the scolex beyond the suckers. This extension sometimes possesses hooks. Vitellaria occur in two marginal bands.

The life cycle involves an oncosphere which develops into a plerocercoid larva in the body cavity of a copepod (*Cyclops*). The copepod is eaten by fish or amphibia in which the adult worm develops, or these vertebrates serve as intermediate hosts when they are eaten by larger fish, amphibia or reptiles. In these cases the plerocercoid larvae are usually in the liver or other organ of the first vertebrate host and, when eaten, remain in the intestine of the second vertebrate host.

ORDER DIPHYLLIDEA

The single genus *Echinobothrium* contains a few species, such as *E. typus*, *E. affine*, *E. longicolle* and *E. benedeni*. The adults occur in the intestines of elasmobranch fishes while the larval stages inhabit marine mollusks and crustaceans. The group is characterized by a scolex which possesses large hooks at its anterior end and two large, boat-like bothridia, each formed by a fusion of two of these sucker-like attachment organs. The long "neck" of the worm is spiny, and the entire worm is small, possessing fewer than twenty proglottids.

ORDER TETRARHYNCHIDEA (=TRYPANORHYNCHA)

The scolex of these tapeworms possesses four long tubes within each of which lies a slender tentacle armed with rows of hooks (Fig. XI-1). These tentacles can readily be extended from the scolex and withdrawn into the tubes. In addition, the scolex possesses two to four bothridia which are not usually well developed. The entire holdfast end of the worm is long and cylindrical. Yolk glands are usually distributed in a "sleeve-like" layer in the cortex of each proglottid; the testes extend into the region behind the ovary; the vagina and its opening are ventral to the cirrus pouch; the sperm duct does not cross the vagina before entering the cirrus pouch; the eggs do not reach the oncosphere stage in the uterus.

These tapeworms are usually less than 100 mm. in length and may be only a few millimeters long. They normally inhabit elasmobranchs, especially the spiral valve. Larval stages are common in teleost fishes.

ORDER PSEUDOPHYLLIDEA

An important characteristic of this group of tapeworms is the presence of two *bothria* on the scolex instead of suction cups. A

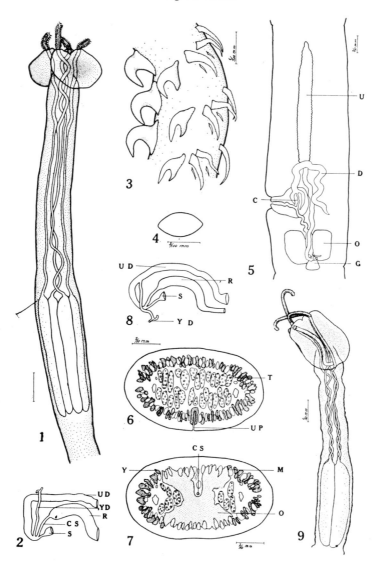

Fig. XI–1.—*Tentacularia musculara* found in elasmobranch fishes.

1, Tentacularia musculara, scolex, whole mount. *2, Tentacularia musculara*, diagram of genital complex. *3, Tentacularia musculara*, mid-portion of proboscis.

4, Tentacularia musculara, egg. *5, Tentacularia musculara*, semi-diagrammatic drawing of proglottid, whole mount. *6, Tentacularia musculara*, transverse section through uterine pore.

7, Tentacularia musculara, transverse section through ovary. *8, Tentacularia megabothridia*, diagram of genital complex. *9, Tentacularia megabothridia*, scolex, whole mount.

C, cirrus; *CP*, cirrus pouch; *CS*, canalis seminalis; *D*, vas deferens; *G*, shell gland; *M*, longitudinal muscle; *O*, ovary; *OD*, oviduct; *R*, receptaculum seminis; *S*, "Schluckapparat;" *T*, testis; *U*, uterus; *UD*, uterine duct; *UP*, uterine pore; *V*, vagina; *Y*, vitellaria; *YD*, vitelline duct. (All drawings and semi-diagrammatic drawings were made with the aid of a camera lucida. Diagrams were made from reconstructions.) (Hart, courtesy of Trans. Amer. Micros. Soc.)

bothrium is simply a groove. In this order it is usually not specialized. (Fig. X–9). In some species the bothrium is a short longitudinal slit-like groove whereas in others it is a wider depression. In either case the bothria possess weak hold-fast properties. In some groups of worms the margins of the bothria are joined, forming a tube. The length of worms of this order varies from a few millimeters to 25 meters or more. Some forms are *monozoic*, that is, possessing a body without segmentation, but most of them are *polyzoic* which term refers to the familiar divisions of the body (strobila) into proglottids.

Only one set of reproductive organs usually occurs in each proglottid but a few species of worms possess two sets. The genital opening is often on the mid-ventral surface, or even mid-dorsal, but it may also occur laterally. The ovary is bilobed, yolk glands are numerous and scattered, and the uterus opens to the outside on the ventral surface.

Haplobothrium globuliforme (Fig. XXVI–4, p. 673) has four retractile, spined "tentacles" that suggest a relationship with the tetrarynchs, but the anatomy of its gravid segments places it with the pseudophyllids. The life cycle of this cestode includes a coracidium which is eaten by *Cyclops* within which it develops into a procercoid larva. A bony fish (*e.g.* the bullhead, *Ameiurus nebulosus*) eats the crustacean and the procercoid is liberated and develops into a plerocercoid in the liver of the fish. A ganoid fish, *Amia calva*, eats the bullhead and so becomes infected. (See p. 672).

Family Diphyllobothriidae. *Dibothriocephalus latus* is an important parasite of man, but most of the several genera of this family are parasites of marine mammals. *D. latus*, the "fish" or "broad" tapeworm (formerly named *Diphyllobothrium latum*) has a scolex which is almond-shaped, measuring 2 to 3 by 0.7 to 1 mm. with deep dorsal and ventral grooves (*bothria*). The anterior one-fifth of the body is composed of small immature segments while the rest consists of mature and gravid segments (Fig. X–9). The entire worm ranges from 3 to 10 or more meters in length. Most of the segments are wider than long, but most of the posterior gravid segments are longer than wide. The testes are numerous, small, roundish bodies situated in the lateral folds or dorsal side of the body. The vas deferens is much convoluted and proceeds anteriad from the midplane at the beginning of the posterior third of the body. It enlarges into a seminal vesicle, and ends in a muscular cirral organ which is median in position, approximately between the first and second third of the body.

The ovary is symmetrically bilobed and is located in the posterior third of the proglottid with Mehlis' gland (see page 243) between the lobes. Vitelline glands occupy the same lateral fields as do the testes but the former are ventral to the latter. The uterus is in the form of a rosette, occupying the middle field of the proglottid. The vagina is a narrow, coiled tube, its coils interspersed with those of the uterus.

Dibothriocephalus latus eggs (Fig. X–9) are broadly ovoidal, yellowish to golden brown, operculated, 55 to 76 by 41 to 56 microns and are non-embryonated when voided with the feces of the host. The life cycle is described on page 251. The adult worms may be found in the small intestine of man, pig, dog, cat, or many other mammals. Some of these parasites may have both birds and mammals as definitive hosts. The intermediate hosts are freshwater copepods and fishes.

Symptoms of infection are often absent. Sometimes digestive discomfort, anemia, abdominal pains, nervous disorder or enteritis occur in man. If a mature *Dibothriocephalus latus* is situated in the proximal part of the small intestine, the host and the worm may compete for vitamin B_{12}. If enough of this vitamin is removed by the worm the host may suffer from pernicious anemia.[2] Drugs used in treatment include oleoresin of aspidium, carbon tetrachloride, atabrine, chiniofon and acranil. If the scolex is not found, several months should elapse before a negative diagnosis is made. Prevention consists of thoroughly cooking fish before eating, or of freezing them at −10 °C for twenty-four hours. Reservoir hosts should be eliminated if possible, and untreated sewage should be prevented from flowing into freshwater lakes or rivers.

Sparganosis may occur in man from infection by the plerocercoid larvae of tapeworms belonging to the genus *Spirometra*. The normal hosts for these larvae are frogs, snakes or amphibious mammals. Southsea islanders occasionally used crushed fresh frogs as a poultice, and have been known to acquire plerocercoids from this practice.

Another member of the genus *Dibothriocephalus*, *D. erinacei* (= *D. mansoni*), is more strictly a dog and cat form, and it has a particularly interesting life cycle. Coracidia emerge from the eggs and are eaten by copepods which in turn are eaten by young frogs. If procercoid larvae have developed within the copepods, the frogs become infected and plerocercoid stages occur in the adult amphibians. In certain areas of the Philippines about 12 per cent of the frogs were found to be infected.[13] The number of plerocercoids, or spargana, in a single frog ranges from one to twenty-five, and they are located mainly in the hind legs and abdomen. Oral transfer to cats and dogs results in the establishment of the adult tapeworms in the intestine.

Family Caryophyllidae. These little worms live in fishes, with the exception of *Archigetes* which lives in freshwater annelid worms. The uterus opens between the male and female apertures. The holdfast is either a vague depression or groove, or it may be entirely undifferentiated. There is only one set of reproductive organs. Although this family is often placed as a separate order (Caryophyllidea), there is convincing evidence that the worms are paedogenetic plerocercoids of pseudophyllids.[8]

Pliovitellaria wisconsinesis averages about 5 mm. long by 1 mm. wide and lives in the intestine of the shiner (*Notemigonus crysoleucas auratus*) and in the minnow (*Hyborhynchus notatus*) in Wisconsin. It

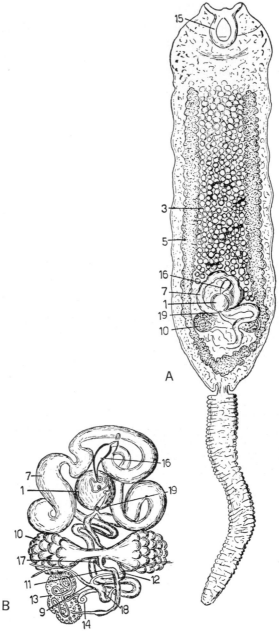

Fig. XI–2.—Pseudophyllidea. *A, Archigetes,* from the oligochaete worm *Tubifex. B,* Sex organs of *Archigetes* (after Wisniewski, 1930).

1, cirrus sac; *2,* coils of uterus; *3,* testes; *4,* spermiducal vesicle; *5,* yolk glands *6,* common uterovaginal pore; *7,* uterus; *8,* vagina; *9,* yolk ducts; *10,* ovary; *11,* oviduct; *12,* beginning of vagina; *13,* shell gland; *14,* beginning of uterus; *15,* bothrium; *16,* seminal vesicle; *17,* oviduct; *18,* yolk reservoir; *19,* common gonopore; *20,* male pore. (Hyman, *The Invertebrates,* courtesy of McGraw-Hill Book Company.)

has a poorly defined scolex, elongate body which is oval in cross section, 42 to 64 testes, large cirrus sac, H-shaped ovary and terminal excretory bladder. The sexual apertures and ovary are situated within the posterior half of the body. *Archigetes* (Fig. XI–2) from the worm, *Tubifex*, has been the object of considerable speculation on the phylogeny of cestodes (see p. 674).

ORDER CYCLOPHYLLIDEA

Most of the important tapeworms of man and of domestic animals belong to this order. The order is also well represented among the tapeworms of birds but not so well among those of the amphibians and reptiles. Like the pseudophyllids, members of this order have a wide range in length. Some of them are only a few millimeters long, while others may reach a length of 30 meters. An important characteristic of the group is the presence of four well-developed suckers on the scolex. As one might expect, however, some species possess weak suckers or lack them entirely. The anterior tip of the scolex usually projects as a *rostellum* which may or may not bear hooks and may be retractable (Fig. XI–3). Proglottids are usually

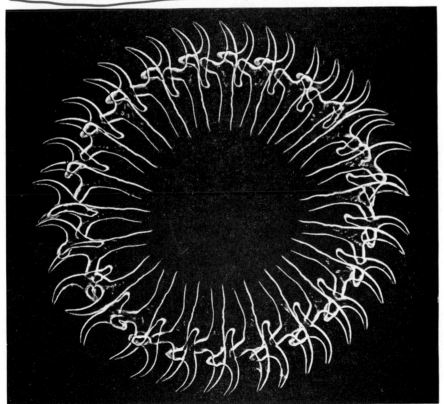

Fig. XI–3.—Hooks on the scolex of the tapeworm *Taenia pisiformis* (Courtesy of Amer. Inst. Biol. Sci. Drawing by D. W. C. Marquardt.)

flattened, and the genital apertures are located marginally on one or both sides. The ovary is typically bilobed or fan-shaped and the testes consist of scattered granules. The yolk gland is usually compact, lying posterior to the ovary. The gravid uterus usually possesses many lateral branches. Ripe terminal segments become sacs of eggs containing developing embryos. Almost all of the species are hermaphroditic but the genus *Dioecocestus* (and a few others) is dioecious. The male and female strobila of the latter can be recognized by their difference in shape.

Arthropods, annelids or mollusks serve as intermediate hosts; and amphibians (rarely), reptiles, birds, and mammals harbor the adult tapeworms.

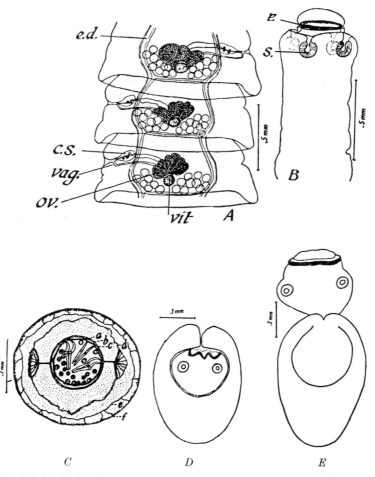

Fig. XI–4.—*Raillietina cesticillus*. *A*, mature segments. *B*, scolex. *C*, oncosphere. *D*, cysticercoid, invaginated. *E*, cysticercoid, evaginated. *a*, surface layer of oncosphere; *b, c, d, e, f*, the five membranes of the oncosphere, *c.s.*, cirrus sac; *e.d.* excretory (osmoregulatory) canal; *ov.*, ovary; *r*, rostellar hooks; *s*, unarmed sucker; *vag.*, vagina.; *vit.*, vitellaria (Lapage, *Veterinary Parasitology*, courtesy of Oliver and Boyd Ltd.).

Family Davaineidae.   The scolex of these small to moderately large tapeworms possesses hooks, suckers, and a cushion-shaped rostellum. Eggs occur in capsules. An important species is *Raillietina* (= *Skrjabinia*) *tetragona*, a common tapeworm of domestic fowl. This worm may reach 25 cm. in length.   Larval stages occur in ants or in maggots of the house fly.

Raillietina cesticillus is probably the best-known member of the family because it is a common tapeworm of poultry.   Chickens, pheasants, guinea fowl and wild birds are often infected.   The adult

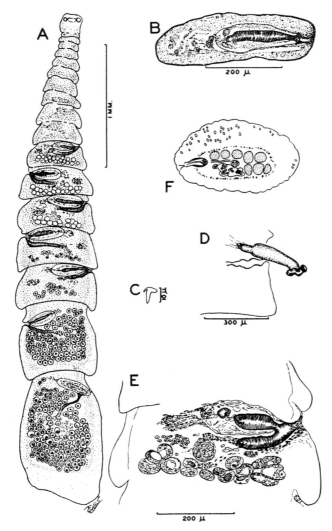

Fig. XI–5.—*Davainea meleagridis*, a tapeworm from the turkey. *A*, Whole specimen, whole mount. *B*, Transverse section of mature segment. *C*, Rostellar hook. *D*, Everted cirrus. *E*, Frontal section of mature segment. *F*, *Davainea andrei*, transverse section of mature segment (Jones, after Fuhrmann, Proc. Helminth. Soc. Wash.).

worm may reach 130 mm. in length and is about 2 mm. wide. The
four suckers are small and there are 400 to 500 minute hooks which
circle the scolex. Eggs are passed from the host with feces and are
eaten by the intermediate host which may be one of several species
of beetles or even the house fly. In the insect, cysticercoids are
formed and the bird becomes infected by eating the insect. Figure
XI–4 illustrates the stages in the life cycle. Figure X–3 shows the
oncosphere within and out of the egg (see Reid[5]).

   Davainea meleagridis is a small member of the family found in
the turkey, *Meleagris gallopavo*. Mature specimens are only 5 mm.
long by 950 microns wide. The scolex is about 165 microns wide.
When one remembers that the limit of vision with the unaided eye
is about 100 microns he can appreciate the difficulty encountered
in hunting for such tiny tapeworms. The worm is illustrated in
Figure XI–5.

   Family Dilepididae. *Dipylidium caninum* (Fig. XI–6) is
worldwide in distribution and is common in the small intestine of
dogs, cats and other carnivores but rare in man. The few infections
that do occur in man are usually in children. The tapeworm averages
about a foot in length (10 to 70 cm.) and it can be recognized by the
elongated, somewhat almond-shaped mature proglottids. The
rhomboidal scolex possesses an anterior projection, the *rostellum*,
which is armed with several transverse rows of hooks and can be
retracted into a rostellar sac. Below the rostellum are four prominent
suckers. A mature proglottid contains two sets of reproductive

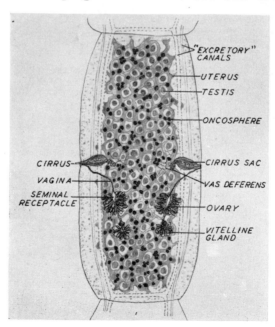

Fig. XI–6.—*Dipylidium caninum*, mature proglottid. The uterus forms a network
around the testes. (After various authors.)

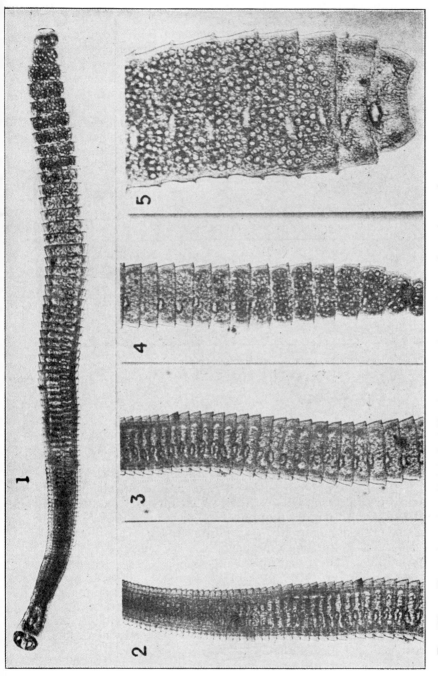

FIG. XI-7.—*Hymenolepis nana.* (Originals of Kouri.) *1*, Complete specimen. Photomicrograph ×26. *2, 3,* and *4,* Anterior, center, and posterior thirds of the parasite, respectively. Photomicrograph ×40. *5,* Posterior fourth of the parasite ×100. The gravid segments are filled with eggs. Most of the caudal segments are completely emptied. The third from last has partially lost its ova. (Gradwohl and Kouri, *Clinical Laboratory Methods and Diagnosis,* courtesy of C. V. Mosby Co.)

organs with an opening on each side of the body. The uterus develops as a network of canals or cavities. Hooked eggs, 24 to 40 microns in diameter, occur in oval packets of 5 to 20 eggs each. Ripe proglottids containing these packets, or balls of eggs, break loose from the strobila and look like active little worms about the size and shape of a pumpkin seed. When they reach the outside they rupture, and the eggs may be ingested by larvae of the fleas, *Ctenocephalides canis*, *C. felis*, or the human flea, *Pulex irritans*, or adult biting lice, *Trichodectes canis*. Within these vectors the eggs hatch and migrate to the body cavity. By the time the insect has reached maturity the tapeworm has developed through the procer-

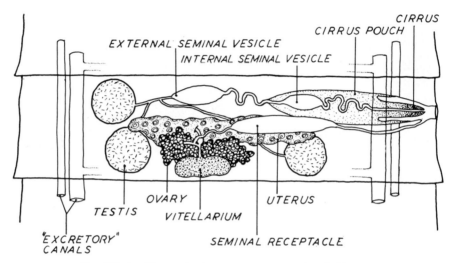

Fig. XI–8.—*Hymenolepis nana*, mature proglottid. (Original.)

coid and into a cysticercoid stage. Dogs and cats get the fleas or bits of them into their mouths and, if swallowed, the parasite is carried to the intestine where the cysticercoid stage matures into an adult tapeworm. Children apparently get infected fleas or parts of them under their fingernails and become themselves infected by putting their fingers into their mouths.

Symptoms in children are absent to mild. Diagnosis involves finding egg packets or entire proglottids in feces. Treatment consists of the use of oleoresin of aspidium (male fern) or quinacrine. Dogs and cats and their sleeping quarters should be kept as clean as possible, their bodies "wormed" often, and treated frequently with insecticides. Diphenthane is a drug used effectively against the worm in dogs. (See also under *Multiceps multiceps*, p. 279).

Family Hymenolepidae. *Hymenolepis nana* is a common cosmopolitan species found in man as well as in rats and mice. Since the parasite averages only about 32 mm. (usually 25 to 40) in length it is called the "dwarf tapeworm" (Fig. XI–7). The rostellum of

Hymenolepis nana is retractable, like that of *Dipylidium caninum*, but it possesses a single ring of hooks. Proglottids are wider than long, and they contain one set of reproductive organs (Fig. XI–8).

The life cycle is unusual for tapeworms (Fig. XI–9). Eggs (30 to 50 microns in diameter) which reach the outside may be ingested by grain beetles or fleas in which the oncospheres develop into tailed cysticercoids, but often these eggs are swallowed directly by man or mouse, and when the oncospheres are liberated they develop into

Fig. XI–9.—*Hymenolepis nana*, indirect life cycle. The adult tapeworm may be in a rat or man, the egg passes from the vertebrate body and is eaten by a beetle in which the tailed cysticercoid develops. The verterbrate eats the beetle and thus acquires the parasite. (Original.)

tailless cysticercoids in the intestinal villi. Thus the intermediate stage in the life cycle can be eliminated. The cysticercoids mature, drop into the lumen of the gut and develop into adult tapeworms in from one to two weeks. The life span is short and senescence is evident.

The incidence of infection in man ranges from less than one per cent to 28 per cent. The numbers of worms in one host may be high. Seven thousand of them were taken from one human patient. Symptoms of infection are usually mild, if any, but toxic reactions such as nervous disorders, sleeplessness, diarrhea and intestinal pain may occur. Atabrine, acranil and hexylresorcinol crystoids are three effective drugs used in treatment. Diagnosis is best made by finding *Hymenolepis nana* eggs in stool specimens.　Preventative measures include personal cleanliness, destruction of rats and mice and a well-balanced diet to promote resistance to infection.

Hymenolepis diminuta is a common rat and mouse tapeworm, and only occasionally gets into man.　The incidence of infection in man is usually less than 1 per cent but in favorable localities (*e.g.* a few areas of India) it may run as high as 6 per cent.　The maximum number of worms recorded from one man is 19.　The worm averages 45 cm. in length, thus being considerably larger than *Hymenolepis nana*.

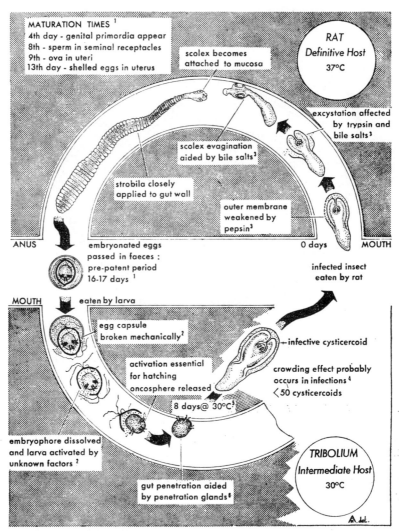

FIG. XI–10.—Life cycle of *Hymenolepis diminuta* and some physiological factors relating to it. (Details from Roberts, Voge and Berntzen, Rothman, Schiller, Voge and Turner, based on *Taenia saginata* Silverman and Maneely from J. D. Smyth, Commonwealth Bureau of Helminthology, Technical Communication Number 34.)

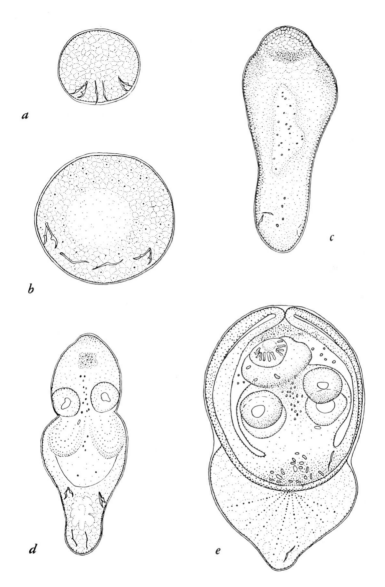

Fig. XI–11.—Five stages in the growth of *Hymenolepis diminuta* and *H. nana*.

a, Stage 1. Solid sphere, showing paired hooks and external membrane. *b*, Stage 2. Cavity and dispersal of oncosphere hooks. *c*, Stage 3. Two body divisions, elongation of cavity and anterior zones of sucker and rostellum primordia.

d, Late stage 3. Process of withdrawal, showing separation of "neck" tissue, which will become layer immediately envloping scolex. *e*, Stage 4. Withdrawn scolex, enlarged rostellum with partly developed hooks, and clearly demarcated suckers.

All drawings freehand, relative size indicated by oncosphere hooks (10–12μ). (Voge and Heyneman, courtesy of Univ. Calif. Publ. Zool.).

Its size, however, is partly a function of the age of the rat host, but the basis for this relationship is not well understood (see p. 574). Eggs of *H. diminuta* are similar to those of *H. nana* but lack the polar filaments of the latter. *H. diminuta*, unlike *H. nana*, has an indefinite life span and does not show aging. The life cycle (Fig. XI–10) requires an intermediate host in which the cysticercoids develop. Many kinds of insects serve as this host, *e.g.*, grain beetles, earwigs, fleas, dung beetles, cockroaches. The pattern of larval development of the tapeworms, *H. diminuta* and *H. nana*, has been clarified by Voge and Heyneman.[10] There are five stages (Fig. XI–11) in the growth of the cysticercoid larva in the intermediate host, *Tribolium confusum*. (1) A hexacanth stage in the hemocoel of the flour beetle. (2) An enlarged spherical larva containing an eccentric cavity. (3) An elongated, larger larva with the beginnings of a forebody, midbody and hindbody. (4) A young cysticercoid with a partially differentiated scolex withdrawn into the midbody. (5) A mature scolex at the anterior end and a tail at the posterior end.

Hymenolepis has received a large share of the research on the physiology and biochemistry of tapeworms. The sizes and reproductive rates of this parasite are related to carbohydrate ingestion of the host. Glucose absorbed from the host gut is actively transported by the worm to its own tissues. Many studies of the degradation of carbohydrate and of the krebs cycle have been made with this animal.

The role of lipids in the metabolism of *Hymenolepis diminuta* has been studied by many investigators but their functions remain obscure. The synthesis of fat by the tapeworm may "buffer" the rapidly formed organic acids by chemical synthesis to neutral fats.[11] There seems to be no real evidence that the fat is used as a source of energy. The amount and nature of fat is altered by environmental conditions, as is shown by changes which occur when a different species or strain of host is used in experiments.

Symptoms of infection are mild, and quinacrine and oleoresin of male fern are the drugs of choice in treatment. Control of the tapeworm consists of keeping rats and mice away from stored fruits and grains, keeping insects away from such material and by being careful not to eat insect-contaminated food.

Family Taeniidae. The "pork tapeworm," *Taenia solium* (Fig. XI–12), is, as the common name indicates, one which man can acquire from eating uncooked pork. It is a cosmopolitan worm with a length of 2 to 7 meters and a scolex with a rounded rostellum. The scolex is equipped with large hooks which alternate with small hooks, giving the appearance of a double ring. There are four prominent, round suckers. The gravid proglottid (Fig. XI–13) is longer than wide and contains a single set of reproductive organs. Gravid proglottids can be distinguished from those of *T. saginata* (see below) by a uterus possessing 5 to 10 arms or branches. The parasite is fairly common in Europe but rare in parts of the Orient, America, and England. Man is the only definitive host. Camels, dogs, monkeys and man may serve as intermediate hosts in addition to the pig.

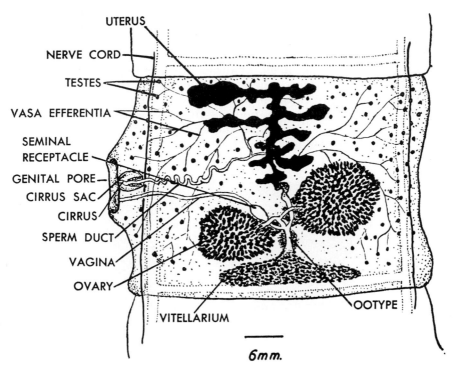

UTERUS
NERVE CORD
TESTES
VASA EFFERENTIA
SEMINAL RECEPTACLE
GENITAL PORE
CIRRUS SAC
CIRRUS
SPERM DUCT
VAGINA
OVARY
VITELLARIUM
OOTYPE

6mm.

Fig. XI–12.—*Taenia solium*, the pork tapeworm. Mature proglottid. (Noble and Noble, *Animal Parasitology Laboratory Manual.*)

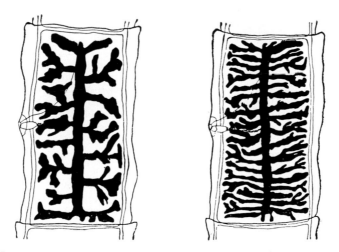

Fig. XI–13.—*Taenia saginata* on the right and *T. solium* on the left, gravid proglottids showing uterine pattern. (Roudabush, *An Aid to the Diagnosis of Helminths Parasitic in Humans*, courtesy of Wards Natural Science Establishment.)

The life cycle of *Taenia solium* starts with a thick-walled round egg averaging about 38 microns in diameter. It contains the characteristic embryo with three pairs of hooks. Usually the eggs remain in proglottids which become isolated and pass from the body of the host. Pigs, man, dogs, or other animals ingest these eggs in contaminated food. Oncospheres are liberated in the small intestine and make their way through the gut wall to blood vessels and are carried to all parts of the body. In various organs, especially muscles, the larval worms leave the blood stream and develop into the *cysticercus* or bladderworm stage (Fig. XI–14). The muscles of

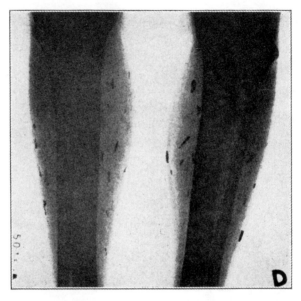

Fig. XI–14.—X-ray of the lower limbs of a case of generalized cysticercosis, attended at the outpatient department of the Institute of Tropical Medicine (Director, Prof. P. Kouri) of the University of Havana. (Original photograph of Kouri, Basnuevo, and Sotolongo.) Note the calcified *Cysticercus* in the soft tissues. (Gradwohl and Kouri, *Clinical Laboratory Methods and Diagnosis*, courtesy of C. V. Mosby Co.)

hogs may sometimes become so filled with these parasites (sometimes called *Cysticercus cellulosae*) that the meat is called *measly pork*. The fluid within these cysticerci is largely composed of host blood plasma. Man usually acquires the adult tapeworm by eating uncooked or poorly cooked infected pork. The bladderworm becomes evaginated in the intestine, hook and suckers enable the young worm to become attached to the gut wall, and a new worm develops into maturity.

Symptoms of adult tapeworm infection may be absent or there may be mild general reactions. Rarely there is diarrhea, loss of weight, nervous symptoms and even perforation of the intestinal tract. Symptoms of cysticercus infection in man depend on extent of infection and location of the bladderworms. Cysticercosis of the brain would obviously produce symptoms different from cysticercosis of the forearm muscles. Diagnosis of intestinal infection is based on finding proglottids or eggs in stool specimens and is confirmed by finding the scolex. Quinacrine, oleoresin of male fern, antiphen and atabrine are effective drugs used in treatment against the adult worms. If the scolex is not recovered, 4-6 months are necessary to be sure the entire worm is no longer present. Treatment for cysticercosis, other than surgery, is of little value. Prevention consists in thoroughly cooking all pork before eating it. Proper sewage disposal is important.

Cysticercosis. As is apparent from the above discussion, bladderworms can be more serious to the host than can the adult worms. Some of these parasites were first discovered as larval stages and thought to be adults of new species or genera, and so were given new names. Later it was found that they were stages in the life cycles of other parasites, so two sets of names arose for the organisms. For example, *Cysticercus tenuicollis* is the thin-necked bladderworm of domestic ruminants, but a study of its complete life cycle shows it to be the larval stage of *Taenia hydatigena* of dogs. *Cysticercus ovis* causing sheep "measles" is the larva of *Taenia ovis* of dogs.

The larval stage of the tapeworm, *Taenia solium*, is only one of several types of bladderworms of pigs. *Cysticercus cellulosae* has also been reported from other domestic mammals. This parasite usually measures about 5 by 10 mm. when fully mature and infective to man. Sometimes the cysticerci are so numerous as to occupy more than one-half of the total volume of a piece of flesh. The worms are characteristically located in the connective tissue of striated muscles but they may be found in any organ or tissue of the body. Various authorities disagree as to the site of "preference." Belding[1] lists possible infected tissue in the following order: tongue, neck, shoulder, intercostal muscles, abdominal muscles, psoas, femoral, posterior vertebral. The U.S.D.A. Yearbook 1942,[9] lists heart, head, diaphragm, abdomen, tongue.

Although the tongue is high on the "preference" list, there is nothing in the available literature to indicate that this organ is always the first "choice" of the worms. Some veterinarians apparently believe that if the cysticerci are not found in the tongue of hogs, one can safely assume they will not be found in any other place. In other words, manipulation of the tongue will reveal 100 per cent of the infested animals. None of the authors quoted above gives the slightest indication that this idea is true. In the U.S.D.A. Yearbook[9] is the following statement, "Bladderworms of swine can be diagnosed with certainty as a rule only after the death of the animal, when parasites may be seen on the surface of the heart and other muscles."

Lightly infected carcasses may be approved for human consumption after removal of visible cysts and thorough sterilization. Heavy infestations should be condemned. There are no definite symptoms of bladderworm infestation in animals, and there is no known practical treatment for removal of the parasites from swine.

Taenia saginata is the cosmopolitan "beef tapeworm," also called the "unarmed tapeworm" because the scolex does not possess hooks (Fig. XI–15). It is more prevalent in man than is *Taenia solium* and, as the common name indicates, it can be transferred to man from uncooked beef. It is longer than the pork species, usually measuring from 5 to 10 meters, and it lives in the small intestine. One extreme specimen reached 25 meters in length, about three times as long as the entire human intestine. In general it is similar in structure to *T. solium* but the uterus in gravid proglottids possesses fifteen to thirty dichotomous branches (Fig. XI–13) and the entire strobila is longer than that of *T. solium*, possessing from 1,000 to 2,000 proglottids. Another difference is the active behavior of a separated gravid segment of *T. saginata*. This activity may cause much discomfort when the proglottid migrates out through the anus.

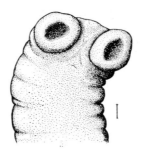

Fig. XI–15.—*Taenia saginata*, scolex. The beef tapeworm. The line on the right represents 0.22 mm. (Original.)

The life cycle is essentially similar to that of *Taenia solium* and starts with an almost identical egg (Fig. XI–16). Ova are expelled only from detached proglottids which migrate to the perianal area. They can be picked up on "Scotch" tape.[5a] The intermediate hosts are cattle, buffalo or other ungulates, in which the bladderworm stage is called *Cysticercus bovis*. Heavy infections cause the "measly" condition to occur primarily in jaw muscles and in the heart. Man is probably the only definitive host and he acquires the infection by swallowing the cysticerci in uncooked, infected beef. Symptoms and treatment are the same as for the pork species.

Taenia pisiformis (about 500 mm. long) possesses a life cycle much like that of *T. solium*. The intermediate hosts are rabbits, rats, squirrels or some other rodent which might be eaten by dogs. Oncospheres usually are found in the liver of these animals while the infective stage, the cysticercus, inhabits the peritoneal cavity. The rodents are eaten by dogs, cats, wolves, foxes and other carnivores which thus become the definitive hosts.

Taenia taeniaeformis (= *T. crassicollis*) is a tapeworm which occurs in domestic and wild cats. The adult worm apparently does little damage but the larval form, called *Cysticercus fasciolaris* may cause considerable damage to the rat or mouse host in which it is normally found. The larva gets into the rodent liver and there becomes encapsulated. A serious cancer-like growth apparently may arise from this encapsulation.

Multiceps multiceps is normally found in dogs and wolves and is similar to *Taenia solium* in appearance. When the eggs are eaten

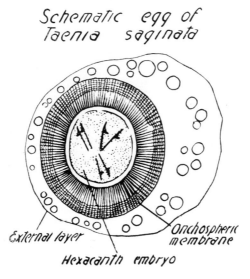

Schematic egg of
Taenia saginata

External layer

Onchospheric membrane

Hexacanth embryo

FIG. XI–16.—Schematic drawing of egg of *Taenia saginata*. (Adapted by Kouri.) (Gradwohl and Kouri, *Clinical Laboratory Methods and Diagnosis*, courtesy of C. V. Mosby Co.)

by ruminant animals such as sheep, cattle, and by horses, or related wild mammals, the larvae develop into the bladder stage, each of which contains many scoleces (Fig. XI–17). This larval stage is a *coenurus* (= *Coenurus cerebralis*). It resembles a brood capsule of *Echinococcus granulosus* (see below). Although it may develop in almost any tissue it often occurs in the brain, causing giddiness. Thus the common name "gid worm" or "gid tapeworm." It is most prevalent in sheep but has rarely occurred in man, probably due to accidental ingestion of eggs from dog feces. Prognosis in man is grave and there is no effective treatment. Dogs acquire the adult tapeworm by eating infected parts of sheep.

Drugs used in treatment against the adult worm in dogs are diphenthane, nemural, arecoline, kamala or 2 per cent hydrogen peroxide. These drugs are also used against *Dipylidium caninum* and other tapeworms.

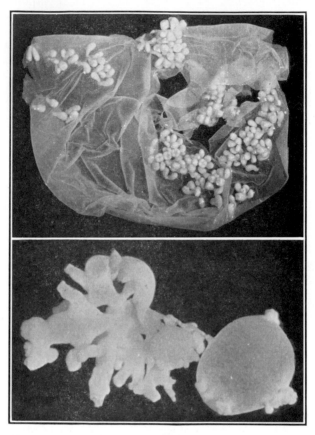

Fig. XI–17.—Racemose type of coenurus of *Multiceps*. (Faust and Russell, *Clinical Parasitology*, Lea & Febiger.)

Echinococcus granulosus causes the most serious larval tapeworm infection in man. It is called the "hydatid worm" (Fig. XI–18) because it forms *hydatid cysts* in various organs. The normal host for the adult parasite is the dog in which hundreds of the worms may occur in the small intestine. Wolves and jackals also harbor the adult worm, and in some areas foxes are probably infected. The parasite is especially common in sheep-raising countries such as Australia, parts of South America and the Middle East. See Gemmell,[4] Stephens,[7] Webster and Cameron.[12] The entire tapeworm consists of four segments, including the scolex, and it is only 3 to 5 mm. long. The scolex has a retractible rostellum armed with a double circle of hooks, and there are four moderately sized suckers. Only a single ripe proglottid occurs at any one time and it, although tiny, somewhat resembles that of *Taenia solium*. Apparently the adult worms do little damage to the host.

The important part of the life cycle, so far as its pathogenicity is concerned, is the larval stage which may occur in man, cattle, sheep, camels, horses, moose, deer, pigs, rabbits, etc. These hosts ingest *Echinococcus granulosus* eggs which are almost identical with those of *Taenia* sp. The oncospheres are liberated in the intestine and, as in other species, make their way to various organs, especially the lungs and liver. The spleen, kidneys, heart, brain, or even bone may be infected. In these organs the oncosphere develops into a

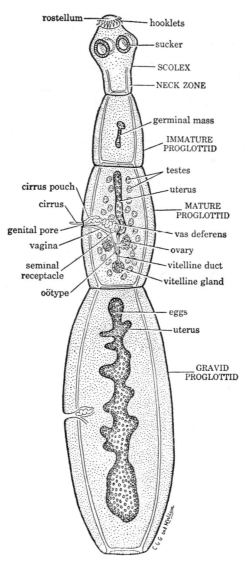

FIG. XI–18.—*Echinococcus granulosus*, surface view of whole worm. (Brown, *Selected Invertebrate Types*, courtesy of John Wiley & Sons Inc.)

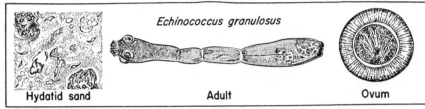

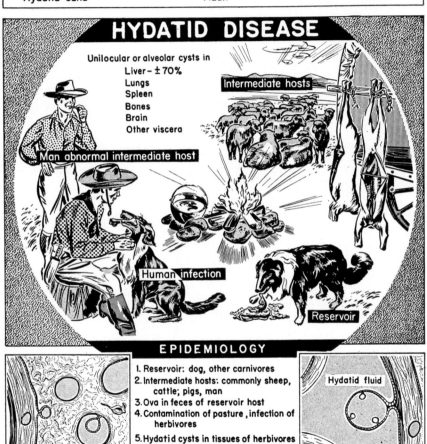

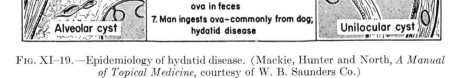

Fig. XI–19.—Epidemiology of hydatid disease. (Mackie, Hunter and North, *A Manual of Topical Medicine*, courtesy of W. B. Saunders Co.)

spherical cyst (Fig. XI–19) or hydatid and it may grow to a diameter of 15 cm. (6 inches!). The size and shape of the cyst may be limited by the organ or space in which it develops. The inner lining of the cyst is germinative and gives rise to scoleces, brood capsules and daughter cysts. Brood capsules and scoleces may become free from their attachments and form a loose mass on the floor of the cyst (Fig. XI–20). This mass is known as "hydatid sand." The cyst is

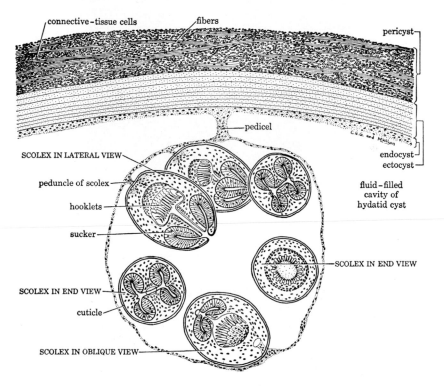

Fig. XI–20.—*Echinococcus granulosus*, portion of the hydatid. (Brown, *Selected Invertebrate Types*, courtesy of John Wiley & Sons Inc.)

filled with "hydatid fluid." There may be as many as two million scoleces in a large cyst which might contain 2 liters of fluid. Old enormous cysts have been reported containing over 15 liters of fluid. These fluid-filled cysts are *unilocular* and they may persist for years. They may develop within bone, thus forming osseous hydatid cysts. Figure XI–21 shows a cyst-like mass, somewhat larger than a fist, taken from the abdomen of a woman in New York. The small (0.5 to 2.5 cm. in diameter) echinococcal cysts it contained are illustrated in Figure XI–22.

In heavily endemic areas 50 per cent of the dogs are infected with adult worms, and up to 90 per cent of the sheep and cattle and 100 per cent of the camels may be infected with hydatid cysts. The in-

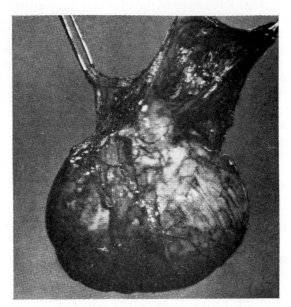

FIG. XI–21.—*Echinococcus* cyst, somewhat larger than a fist. (Bohrod, courtesy of Medical Radiology and Photography.)

FIG. XI–22.—Small cysts taken from the mass illustrated in Figure XI–21. (Bohrod, courtesy of Medical Radiology and Photography.)

cidence of hydatid disease in man may run as high as 20 per cent (in a few areas in South America) but it is usually much lower.[3]

An even more serious condition occurs when the cyst becomes irregular, filled with connective tissue and gelatinous masses, and grows like a malignant tumor with metastasis. This type is a *multilocular* or *alveolar* cyst. It is part of the life cycle of *Echinococcus multilocularis* (= *E. sibiricensis*). This tapeworm, found chiefly in Europe and northern Asia, looks much like a small *E. granulosus*. In length it ranges from 1.4 to 3.4 mm. The testes lie posterior to the cirrus sac and the uterus does not possess lateral pouches. Although dogs or cats may harbor the adult worm, the principal host is the fox. Intermediate hosts are usually mice in which the liver may become heavily infected. The many pockets which may be formed are the basis for the name *multilocular*. Some authorities believe that this species is a variety of *E. granulosus*.

Damage by any cyst is, of course, related to the size of the cyst and to its location. Simple cysts seem to do little harm to animals, although pressure on surrounding organs may be of consequence. Rupturing cysts may cause allergic responses, and enlarging cysts may destroy bone or impair the normal functioning of other organs. Large or migrating cysts can be serious. Although the adult worms do not live long, the cysts may remain alive for many years. Host tissue reactions, toxemia, eosinophilia, pressure effects, obstruction of blood vessels and other factors indicate the presence of the parasites.

Treatment of dogs for adult tapeworms consists of administering such drugs as those listed under *Multiceps multiceps* above. The only treatment for infection by the cyst is by surgery, and this procedure is often unsuccessful or impractical. Prevention consists mainly of keeping dogs free from infection and avoiding accidental ingestion of tapeworm eggs. Obviously the best way to prevent dogs from becoming parasitized by those worms with intermediate hosts is to prevent dogs from eating the intermediate hosts. To prevent man from becoming infected with the cysts personal hygiene is important. Keep dogs clean; don't pet infected dogs; never allow a dog to "kiss" your face.

Family Anoplocephalidae. Members of this family[6] possess scoleces without hooks, and female reproductive organs may be single or double. The parasites live in the intestines of birds, herbivorous animals, and primates; and the cysticercoid stage occurs in oribatid mites. A few genera (e.g. *Avitellina*) lack yolk glands.

Adult worms which live in the small intestines of ruminants are: *Moniezia expansa*, *M. benedeni* and *Thysanosoma actinioides*. All may inhabit any grazing animal, domestic or wild, but *T. actinioides*, the fringed tapeworm, and *M. expansa* (Fig. XI–23) are usually found in sheep, whereas *M. benedeni* is more often found in cattle. The life history of the cattle worm is unknown but that of the two sheep forms involves the oribatid (galumnid) or "beetle" mites, (*e.g. Galumna longipluma*). Tapeworm eggs with host feces contaminate pastures. Oribatid mites creep over the soil, usually in the evening, and probably accidentally ingest the worm eggs with their natural food. Within two to five months the young tapeworms have developed into the cysticercoid stage in the mites. Sheep eat mites which often cling to forage grass. Cysticercoids are released in the sheep intestine and there they mature. About thirty days after eating the mites, sheep begin to void a new generation of tapeworm eggs or proglottids. Adult *Moniezia expansa* reach a length of 600 cm. (20 feet). The mature proglottids are wider than

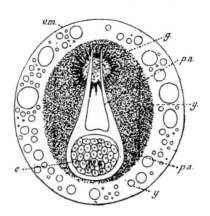

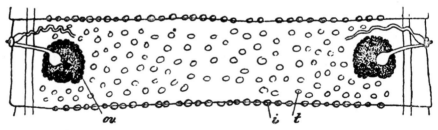

Fig. XI–23.—*Moniezia expansa.* Proglottid and egg. Proglottid showing the interproglottidal glands (*i*) arranged around a series of blind sacs and extending across the segment, *t*, testis; *ov*, ovary. (After Mönnig.) Egg, showing the pyriform apparatus (*p.a.*); *v.m.*, vitelline membrane; *g*, granular mass; *y*, yolk, *e*, embryo. (After Raillet.) (Lapage, *Veterinary Parasitology*, courtesy of Oliver and Boyd Ltd.)

long. *M. benedeni* and the related species *Bertiella studeri* and *B. mucronata* have been reported as accidental parasites of man.

Family Linstowiidae. These worms are small to medium in size. The scolex is unarmed but otherwise the parasites resemble members of the family Davaineidae (p. 267). They are primarily inhabitants of insectivorous animals, and the larval stages occur in beetles. Because of the unarmed scolex and other features, the group is sometimes placed as a subfamily of the Anoplocephalidae. An important genus is *Inermicapsifer. I. madagascariensis* is unusual in that a few cases of human infection have been reported, although it is normally a parasite of rats. The adult worm is about 40 cm. in length. The life cycle has not yet been worked out. The genus *Raillietina* of the family Davaineidae has sometimes been listed as a synonym of *Inermicapsifer*, thus adding to confusion of cestode taxonomy.

Family Mesocestoididae. Members of this family are found as adults in birds and mammals. They are small to medium in size; the holdfast has 4 prominent suckers but no rostellum; the genital aperture is median and on the ventral surface of the body; eggs occur in a posterior paruterine organ.

ORDER SPATHEBOTHRIDEA

These small forms were formerly included with the order Pseudophyllidea. They never have true bothrias or suckers; there is no external segmentation, but some internal proglottisation; the uterus opens between the male and female apertures; medullary testes are in 2 oval lateral bands; the ovary is rosettiform or bilobed and the operculated eggs have thick shells. Adults appear to be sexually functionless, neotenic procercoids, and they occur in the more ancient groups of fishes.

BIBLIOGRAPHY

1. BELDING, D. L., 1952. *Textbook of Clinical Parasitology.* Appleton-Century-Crofts, Inc., New York. Second Edition. 1139 pp.
2. BONSDORFF, B. VON., 1956. *Diphyllobothrium latum* as a Cause of Pernicious Anemia. Exper. Parasitol., *5*, 207–230.
3. CAMERON, T. W. M. and WEBSTER, G. A., 1961. The Ecology of Hydatidasis. In: May, J. M. (ed.), *Studies in Disease Ecology,* Chapter 7. Hafner Publ. Co., N. Y., 613 pp.
4. GEMMELL, M. A., 1960. Advances in Knowledge on the Distribution and Importance of Hydatid Disease as World Health and Economic Problems During the Decade 1950–1959. Helminth. Abst., *29*, 355–369.
5. REID, W. M., 1948. Penetration Glands in Cyclophyllidean Oncospheres. Trans. Amer. Micros. Soc., LXVII, 177–182.
5a.RIJPSTRA, A. C., SMIT, A. M., and SWELLENGREBEL, N. H., 1961. How and Where to Search for the Ova of *Taenia saginata.* Tropical Geogr. Med. Amsterdam, *13*, 160–166.
6. SPASSKII, A. A., 1961. *Anoplocephalate Tapeworms of Domestic and Wild Animals.* 730 pp. (This book is Vol. 1 of Skrjabin, K. I., *Essentials of Cestodology.* Acad. Sci. USSR, Moscow.) Publ. in English for N.S.F., Wash. D.C. and the Dept. Agric., U.S.A. by the Israel Program for Sci. Transl.
7. STEPHENS, W. H., 1961. Hydatids in Humans. Tasmanian J. Agric., *32*, 185–187.
8. STUNKARD, H. L., 1962. The Organization, Ontogeny, and Orientation of the Cestoda. Quart. Rev. Biol., *37*, 23–34.
9. U.S.D.A. YEARBOOK, 1942. *Keeping Livestock Healthy.* 1942 Yearbook of Agriculture, Washington, D.C. 1271 pp.
10. VOGE, M. and HEYNEMAN, D., 1957. Development of *Hymenolepis nana* and *Hymenolepis diminuta* (Cestoda: Hymenolepididae) in the Intermediate Host *Tribolium confusum.* Univ. Calif. Pub. Zool., *59*, 549–580.
11. WARREN, M. and DAUGHERTY, J., 1957. Host Effects on the Lipid Fraction of *Hymenolepis diminuta.* J. Parasitol., *43*, 521–526.
12. WEBSTER, G. A. and CAMERON, T. W. M., 1963. Some Preliminary Observations on the Development of *Echinococcus* in vitro. Can. J. Zool., *41*, 185–196.
13. YUTUC, LOPE. 1951. Observations on Manson's tapeworm, *Diphyllobothrium erinacei* Rudolphi, 1819, in the Philippines. Phil. Jour. Sci., *80*, (1): 33–51.

CHAPTER XII

Phylum Acanthocephala

THE phylum Acanthocephala is composed of thorny-headed worms, so-called because of the many thorn-like hooks on the proboscis. *Acanth* means a thorn and *cephala* refers to the head, so the name is apt. These cosmopolitan worms are all endoparasitic as adults in the digestive tracts of terrestrial and aquatic vertebrates from fish to man but especially in fishes. They are whitish parasites whose bodies are wrinkled or smooth, and whose range in length is from about 1 mm. to over a meter. Hundreds of young stages have been found in a single intermediate host; and the vertebrate host may harbor thousands of the adult worms.

The proboscis and associated structures are called the *presoma*. The rest of the body is the *trunk*. Small spines occur on the trunk in some genera (e.g. *Corynosoma strumosum* in seals). The proboscis, neck and trunk may become modified as accessory anchoring devices, such as a bulb-like inflation of the anterior end and a general covering of cuticular spines. The body cavity is a fluid-filled space between the viscera and the body wall in adults, and is a *pseudocoel* rather than a true coelom. There is no digestive tract or true circulatory system in either adult or larval worms. The "lacunar system" is probably a circulatory system of sorts. Sexes are separate, females are almost always larger than males, and the posterior aperture, or *gonopore*, is the only body opening. Tissues in general have lost cellular identity and there are few nuclei in the entire body.

The body wall consists of a thin cuticle, a thick syncytial, fibrous, 3-layered epidermis, a thin dermis and a thin double syncytial muscular layer (inner longitudinal, outer circular). The inner layer of the epidermis contains a network of spaces or *lacunae* which contain nutritive fluid and function as a food-distributing mechanism. The number of nuclei in the body wall is approximately constant for each species, at least in early stages, and often throughout life.

The proboscis is an anterior, globular to cylindrical structure bearing rows of recurved hooks or spines which serve to attach the worm to the gut of its host. In some species the proboscis of the adult and that of the infective larva are identical in appearance; in others the adult proboscis may become markedly modified. In some worms it is permanently anchored in host tissue, as in *Filicollis* in birds, *Polymorphus* in ducks and *Pomphorhynchus bulbocolli* in fish. The proboscis possesses retractor and invertor (protractor)

(288)

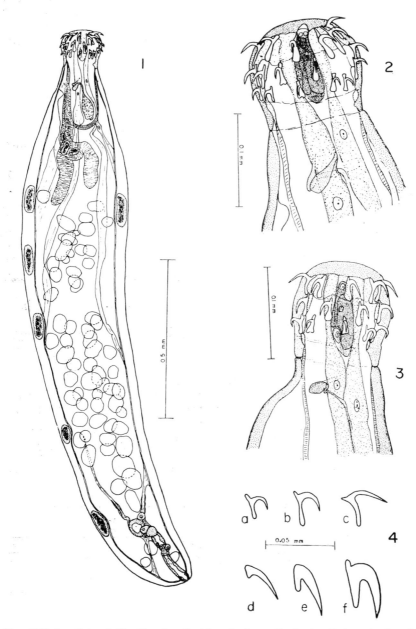

FIG. XII–1.—*Octospiniferoides chandleri* female from *Gambusia affinis* and other fish. (1) Adult; (2) and (3) Proboscis; (4) Comparison of hooks of *O. chandleri* with those of *O. macilentis*. (Bullock, courtesy of J. Parasitol.)

muscles and can usually be withdrawn into a receptacle or muscular *proboscis sac*. This sac extends into the body cavity from the neck region. The hooks on the proboscis are of many varieties of size, shape, number and arrangement and thus are of considerable taxonomic value (Fig. XII–1).

Lemnisci are paired organs, usually elongated and pendulus, which extend, two to a worm, into the body cavity from the neck region. They apparently serve as fluid reservoirs when the proboscis is invaginated. There is considerable histochemical evidence that the lemnisci may also serve a metabolic function—especially for fat metabolism. They are often surrounded by muscles at their basal portion.

Ligament sacs extend from the proboscis sheath or from the adjacent body wall and form tubes which surround the reproductive organs. There may be only one ligament sac. A *ligament strand* is attached to the gonads and extends the length of the ligament sacs.

Protonephridia serve as excretory organs. They consist of flame bulbs and collecting tubules which occur in some members of the class Archiacanthocephala. The flame bulbs are grouped into two masses attached to the reproductive organs and empty via a canal or bladder into the sperm duct or uterus.

The nervous system consists mainly of a ganglion in the proboscis sheath and of nerves which connect the ganglion to other organs and tissues of the body. In addition, a pair of genital ganglia, with nerves, occurs in the male. *Sense organs* are found in the proboscis and in the penis and male bursa.

Male reproductive organs consist of a pair of *testes*, one behind the other, and a common *sperm duct* formed by the union of a duct from each testis. The common duct leads through the *penis* to the outside. There is usually a cluster of large *cement glands* which empty into the common sperm duct, sometimes via a cement gland reservoir. The penis projects into an eversible *bursa*. This cup-like terminal structure with a thick, domed cap is used to hold the female during copulation (Fig. XII–2).

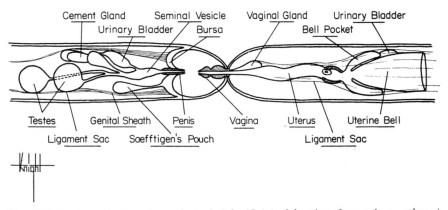

FIG. XII–2.—Sexual union of acanthocephalids. (Original drawing after various authors.)

Female reproductive organs consist of an *ovary* fragmented into *ovarian balls* which lie in the ligament sac or are free in the pseudocoel. A *uterine bell*, at the end of the ligament sac is a funnel or cup-like structure which receives ova from the ovarian balls. At the base of the uterine bell is the *uterine tube* and two associated bell pouches. The uterine tube empties into the elongated *uterus*. A *vagina* connects the uterus to the terminal opening, or *gonopore*.

During copulation the male discharges sperm into the vagina. Then secretions from the cement glands block the exit, thus prevent-

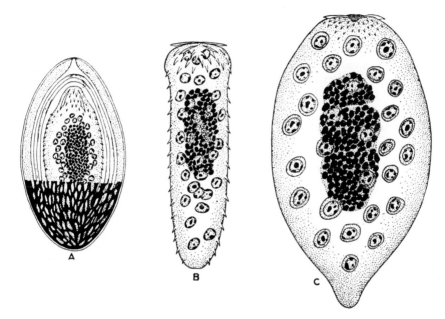

Fig. XII–3.—Shelled embryo and acanthor stages of *Macracanthorhynchus hirudinaceus* (Pallas) to show details not available at magnification adopted for life cycle plate. Redrawn from Kates (1943). Magnification approximately 500 diameters. A. "Egg" or shelled embryo. Surface appearance shown only on lower pole; on remainder of drawing membranes are shown in optical section. B. Acanthor, stage I, from lumen of mid gut of beetle larva. Note the larval rostellar hooks and small body spines. C. Acanthor, stage II, after penetrating the wall of the mid gut of the beetle larva, about five to twenty days after artificial infection. (Van Cleave, courtesy of J. Parasitol.)

ing escape of sperm. In some species of worms, the cement gland secretions form a cap over the entire terminal end of the female. Fertilized eggs go through early embryological development in the ligament sac or pseudocoel. When eggs emerge from the gonopore they contain a hooked larva called the *acanthor* (Fig. XII–3). Eggs must be eaten before the embryo will hatch.

The life cycles of Acanthocephala need much study. Little is known specifically about these cycles in most species but they all undoubtedly follow the same general plan. Each female usually has only one reproductive cycle. At the time of copulation all of the eggs are subject to fertilization and the female may become greatly distended with stored eggs which she is able to discharge selectively over a long period of time. The eggs are normally spindle-shaped, often resemble diatoms, and are commonly eaten by aquatic insects and crustaceans. The intermediate hosts for acanthocephalids of fishes are usually benthic crustaceans: amphipods (*Gammarus*, *Pontoporeia*), isopods (*Asellus*), ostracods (*Cypris*). Snails and aquatic insects sometimes act as either transport hosts or as secondary intermediate hosts.

Some species of acanthocephalids may require a second and even a third intermediate host, but usually only a single invertebrate host is involved. There is no superimposed multiplicative cycle as that which occurs in the flukes, no asexual or parthenogenetic development. From each zygote arises one adult.

A life cycle scheme involving two invertebrate hosts has been given by Petrochenko[10] (1956), as follows:

```
  ┌──────────────→  Adult worm in final host        ─────────────┐
  │                                                               ↓

Larva encysted                                    Eggs containing larva
   in carrier host                                 free in environment


  ↑_____        Larva in invertebrate host    ←────────┘
  │
```

Petrochenko suggested that only the first intermediate host is required, the second one being a carrier. Carrier hosts can be either vertebrates or invertebrates. Within the invertebrate host the *acanthor* is liberated from the egg and develops into the *acanthella*. After several weeks or more, the acanthella becomes a juvenile which is sometimes called a *cystacanth* and which differs from an adult primarily by being sexually immature. The term "juvenile" should be used only when the larva resembles the adult. The vertebrate host becomes infected by eating the arthropod intermediate host or a carrier host. Sexual development occurs in the final host. Since host specificity towards the intermediate host is pronounced as compared with the freedom of "choice" of vertebrate hosts, the distribution of acanthocephalids is largely determined by these invertebrate hosts. Some birds, for example, acquire *Corynosoma* by eating fish. This genus occurs in aquatic birds and marine mammals. The fish is presumably a transport host. DeGiusti[2] has made a significant observation on the life cycle of *Leptorhynchoides thecatus*, a parasite of the rock bass, *Ambloplites rupestris*. An amphipod is the intermediate host, but if the fish swallows an amphipod containing a juvenile worm that has not quite completed its full development, the parasite does not become mature in the intestine of the final host, but it penetrates the gut wall and becomes encysted in the mesenteries.

Macracanthorhynchus Hirudinaceus

Macracanthorhynchus hirudinaceus (Fig. XII–4 and XII–5) has rarely been found in man but it is a common species in hogs where it occurs in the small intestine attached to the gut wall. It is usually large, the females ranging from 20 to 65 cm. in length while the males range from 5 to 10 cm. The largest worms may be about the width of an ordinary pencil. The animal is flattened in normal life but it soon becomes cylindrical when collected and preserved. Irregular transverse folds give the worm a wrinkled appearance. The small protrusible proboscis is armed with hooks in six spiral rows of six rows each. The body tapers from just behind the proboscis to the posterior end where there occurs a bell-like bursa. Testes are located in the anterior half of the male worm.

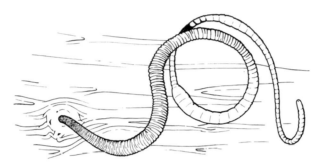

Fig. XII–4.—*Macracanthorhynchus hirudinaceus* adult attached to the gut wall of a pig. (Original.)

Female worms produce eggs containing mature acanthors. One female may contain as many as 10,000,000 eggs. Eggs (67–110 × 40–65 microns) leave the pig's intestine with feces and they become widely scattered. They are extremely resistant to adverse environmental conditions and remain viable for years. Birds may carry the eggs on their feet or may even eat them with contaminated food and pass them unharmed through their own bodies. The usual invertebrate host is a larval beetle which eats the eggs.

Cockchafer beetles, *Melolontha vulgaris*, rose chafer beetles, *Cetonia aurata*, water beetles, *Tropisternus collaris*, and various species of dung beetles are the common hosts. Eggs hatch in the beetle gut and the acanthor uses its hooks to bore through the intestinal wall to the hemocoel where it develops into the acanthella which gradually develops most of the adult characteristics. By the end of six weeks to three months the juvenile (cystacanth) stage is reached. The beetle may be eaten by a second intermediate host but usually it is devoured by the final host. This juvenile is thus the infective stage for pigs or man. The life span of the adult in the pig is usually less than a year. Although 400 acanthors have been found in

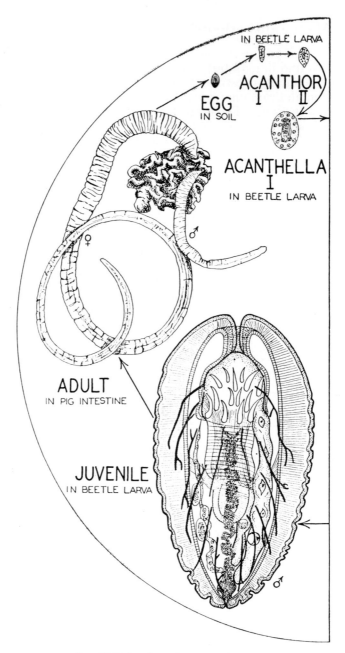

IN BEETLE LARVA

ACANTHOR
I II

EGG
IN SOIL

ACANTHELLA
I
IN BEETLE LARVA

ADULT
IN PIG INTESTINE

JUVENILE
IN BEETLE LARVA

FIG. XII–5.—*Legend on opposite page.*

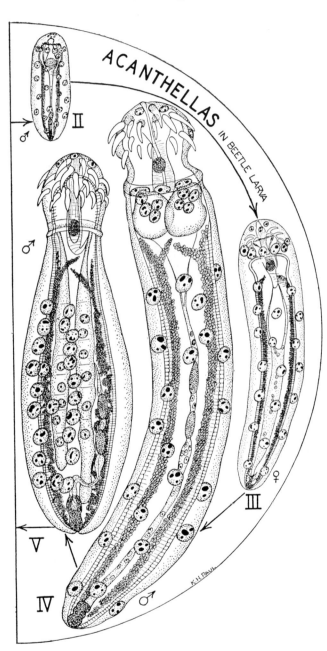

Fig. XII–5.—The life cycle of *Macracanthorhynchus hirudinaceus* (Pallas), the thorny-headed worm of swine. Drawings of adult worms about natural size; all other stages at fairly uniform magnification of approximately 38 diameters. The elongated, branching, dark bodies in the juvenile are the nuclei which will become the giant nuclei of the sub-cuticula in the adult. (From Van Cleave, after Kates, courtesy of Jour. Parasitology.)

one naturally infected beetle, there are usually fewer than 30 worms in a pig. Occasionally dogs and other mammals which might eat beetles are found to be parasitized by this worm.

Ulceration, necrotic areas, anemia and even penetration of the intestinal wall with subsequent peritonitis may occur in serious infections. There is no really satisfactory drug, but some benefit is derived from administering carbon tetrachloride, nicotine sulfate or sodium sulfate. Control consists mainly of sanitary measures in raising pigs, such as rearing them on concrete floors, and prompt removal of pig feces.

Moniliformis Moniliformis

Moniliformis moniliformis is a cosmopolitan acanthocephalan in the small intestine of rats, mice, dogs, and cats. The worms have a beaded appearance due to annular thickenings. Males range from 4 to 13 cm. in length while females are 10 to 30 cm. long. The proboscis possesses 12 to 15 rows of hooks. Eggs, 85 to 120 × 40 to 50 microns, are eaten by beetles (*Blaps gigas, Tenebrio molitor, Calandra orizae*) or by cockroaches (*Blatta orientalis, B. germanica*). The life history closely resembles that of *Macracanthorhynchus hirudinaceus*. Juveniles appear in four to six weeks and there may be as many as 100 juveniles in one cockroach. The infection rate in rats varies but may run as high as 20 per cent in *Rattus alexandrinus*. Frogs, toads, and lizards have been suggested as possible paratenic hosts. Oleoresin of male fern is used in treatment. The acanthocephalan requires carbohydrate for growth. Growth of the worm ceases when the rat is placed on a diet devoid of carbohydrate.

Moniliformis dubius is also common in rats and has been reported from man. There is some doubt whether or not this is the same species as *M. moniliformis*. This problem has been "settled" several times by the taxonomic "lumpers" and "splitters."

Other Species

Polymorphus minutus (Family Polymorphidae) is a small bright orange acanthocephalan in the small intestine of chickens, ducks and possibly geese and other water birds. The male is about 3 mm. long and the female up to 10 mm. It can cause serious disease in domestic and wild fowl. The intermediate host is the amphipod, *Gammarus pulex*. A closely related species, *Filicollis sphaerocephalus*, is also found in aquatic birds. The invertebrate host is a crustacean.

Filicollis anatis is a small species in the intestine of ducks, geese and other water birds. The male is 6 to 8 mm. long and the female 10 to 25 mm. *Asellus aquaticus*, a freshwater isopod, is the intermediate host. *Neoechinorhynchus* is common in turtles and fish.[8]

CLASSIFICATION

Affinities of this phylum to other worms are not clear (see Evolution p. 674). Developmental stages are more similar to those of flatworms than to the nematodes, but the group is closest to the cestodes though distinctly separate. There are about 500 known species, probably many more not yet described. The following classification is from Watson[13] and Hyman.[7] Hyman designated the three main groups below as Orders instead of Classes. Some minor families have been omitted from the list.

Class 1. ARCHIANCATHOCEPHALA. "Parasites of terrestrial birds and mammals in which the proboscis hooks are arranged in concentric circles, trunk spination is lacking, the main lacunar channels are median in position, protonephridia are generally present, two persistent ligament sacs are found in the females and eight cement gland cells in the male."

Family Gigantorhynchidae. Elongate worms in birds and Central and South American anteaters; no protonephridia. *Mediorhynchus.*

Family Oligacanthorhynchidae. Elongate worms often curved, coiled or even spirally rolled; short spheroid or ovoid proboscis; protonephridia usually present; in birds and mammals. *Macracanthorhynchus, Oncicola, Hamanniella.*

Family Moniliformidae. Elongate worms; body somewhat twisted; in rodents and other terrestrial mammals; no protonephridia. *Moniliformis.*

Family Pachysentidae. Short, stout worms; body usually straight, in carnivores and other terrestrial mammals. Proboscis short; protonephridia present. *Onicola.* This family is considered a synonym for part of Oligacanthorhynchidae by Van Cleave and Golvan.

Class 2. PALAEOACANTHOCEPHALA. "Parasites of fish, aquatic birds and marine mammals in which the proboscis hooks are arranged in alternating radial rows, trunk spines are frequently present, the main lacunar channels are lateral, protonephridia are absent, the single ligament sac ruptures in females and the male usually has six cement gland cells."

Family Rhadinorhynchidae. Usually with spiny trunk; elongate proboscis; elongate worms in fishes. *Rhadinorhynchus, Telosentis, Illiosentis, Leptorhynchoides.*

Family Gorgorhynchidae. Short proboscis; in fishes. *Serrasentis, Gorgorhynchus.*

Family Echinorhynchidae. No trunk spines; in fishes and amphibians. *Echinorhynchus, Acanthocephalus.*

Family Pomphorhynchidae. Long, slender, cylindrical neck, usually with prominent, bulbous swelling at anterior end; in fishes. *Pomphorhynchus.*

Family Polymorphidae. Relatively short, straight, often plump worms in aquatic birds and marine mammals; proboscis of various shapes; spines often on anterior part of trunk; neck and foretrunk frequently sharply differentiated from hindtrunk. *Polymorphus, Filicollis, Corynosoma, Bolbosoma* (in whales).

Class 3. EOACANTHOCEPHALA. "Parasites of fish and turtles in which the proboscis hooks are arranged in alternating radial rows, trunk spines may or may not be present, the main lacunar channels are lateral, protonephridia are absent, two persistent ligament sacs are found in the female and a syncytial cement gland with a reservoir in the male."

Family Quadrigyridae. With trunk spines. *Pallisentis* (spiny girdle); *Quadrigyrus* (no spiny girdle).

Family Neoechinorhynchidae. Without trunk spines, rather small worms with giant epidermal nuclei; in fishes. *Neoechinorhynchus, Octospinifer, Octospiniferoides.*

For further information on the Acanthocephala see Baer,[1] Golvan,[3-6] Hyman,[7] Kates,[9] Petrochenko,[10] Van Cleave,[11,12] and Yamaguti.[14]

BIBLIOGRAPHY

1. BAER, J. G., 1961. Embranchement des Acanthocéphales. M. Grassi, P. Traité de Zoologie. Tome IV. pp. 731–782.
2. DeGIUSTI, D. L., 1949. The Life Cycle of *Leptorhynchoides thecatus* (Linton), an Acanthocephalan of Fish. J. Parasitol., *35*, 437–460.
3. GOLVAN, Y.-J., 1958. Le Phylum des Acanthocephala. Première Note. Sa Place dans l'Échelle Zoologique. Ann. Parasit. Hum. Comp., *33*, 538–602.
4. GOLVAN, Y.-J., 1959. Le Phylum des Acanthocephala. Deuxieme Note. La Classe des Eoacanthocephala (Van Cleave 1936). Ann. Parasit. Hum. Comp., *34*, 5–52.
5. GOLVAN, Y.-J., 1960. Le Phylum des Acanthocephala. Troisième Note. La Classe des Palaeacanthocephala (Meyer 1931). Ann. Parasit. Hum. Comp., *35*, 138–165.
6. GOLVAN, Y.-J., 1962. Le Phylum des Acanthocephala (Quatrième Note). La Classe des Archiacanthocephala (A. Meyer 1931). Ann. Parasitol. Hum. Comp., *37*, 1–72.
7. HYMAN, L. H., 1951. *The Invertebrates: Acanthocephala, Aschelminthes and Entoprocta.* Vol. III, McGraw-Hill. N. Y. 572 pp.
8. HOPP, W. B., 1954. Studies on the Morphology and Life Cycle of *Neoechinorhynchus emyais* (Leidy). An Acanthocephalan Parasite of the Map Turtle, *Graptemus geographica* (Le Sueur). J. Parasitol., *40*, 284–299.
9. KATES, K. C., 1943. Development of the Swine Thorn-headed Worm, *Macarcanthorhynchus hirudinaceus* in its Intermediate Host. Am. J. Vet. Res., *4*, 173–181.
10. PETROCHENKO, V. I., 1956. *Acanthocephala of Wild and Domestic Animals.* Publ: AN, S.S.S.R., I.
11. VAN CLEAVE, H. J., 1947. A Critical Review of Terminology, for Immature Stages in Acanthocephalan Life Histories. J. Parasitol., *33*, 2, 118–125.
12. ———— 1953. *Acanthocephala of North American Mammals.* Illinois Biological Monogr., *23*, Nos. 1–2, Univ. Illinois Press, Urbana, 179 pp.
13. WATSON, J. M., 1960. *Medical Helminthology.* Baillière Tindall & Cox, 7 and 8 Henrietta St., London, 487 pp.
14. YAMAGUTI, S., 1964. Systema Helminthum. Vol. V. Acanthocephala. Interscience Publ. N. Y. and London, 423 pp.

CHAPTER XIII

Phylum Nematoda
Introduction, Class Secernentea (= Phasmidia), Orders: Rhabditida: Strongylida

INTRODUCTION

PHYLUM Nematoda contains an almost unbelievable number of free-living worms in water and soil, and an impressive number of parasitic species in plants and animals. Biology students are constantly finding thread-like worms coiled in the muscles, connective tissue or other organs of laboratory-dissected animals. Fishes, especially, are notorious for their burden of worms. Hundreds of individual worms and several species are often found in one host. Insects and other invertebrates have their own roundworm parasites. Morphological or behavioral changes of the host sometimes occur after heavy infestation. Many nematodes have yet to be described, and the host-parasite relationships are just beginning to be understood. Some parasitic nematodes possess their own parasites. Thus *Aphelenchoides parietinus*, a soil nematode parasitic in plants, may be infected with a microsporidian. Fossil nematodes are known. The worm, *Heydonius antiguus*, was found projecting from the anus of the beetle, *Hesthesis immortua*, in Rhine lignite. Various other species have been found in amber.

Nematology is certainly an open field for anyone interested in investigating parasites. The worms are generally round in cross-section; hence they are called "roundworms" in contrast with the "flatworms." These worms should not be confused with the segmented worms or annelids, represented by earthworms. For general references to the nematodes see: Baker,[1] Fairbairn,[11] Goodey,[12] Hyman,[15] Lavoipierre,[16] Rogers,[20] Sasser and Jenkins,[24] Skrjabin *et al.*,[26] Stoll,[27] Tromba,[29] Thorne,[30] and Wallace.[31,32]

Morphology. A generalized picture of some of the organ systems of nematodes is given in Figure XIII–1. The neck or tail region of these worms may bear cuticular fin or wing-like flanges. In the neck these structures are known as *cervical alae* (singular, *ala*) whereas those on the tail are *caudal alae*. The latter may be supported by fleshy papillae and are used as copulatory organs.

Muscles are well developed in the body wall, and the outside of the worm is covered by a non-nucleated cuticle.[4] This cuticle is usually tough and protective and it may be smooth or covered with spines (Fig. XIII–2). In many adult nematodes nine separate layers, composed mostly of protein, have been identified in the cuticle.[10] This outer covering is subject to keratinization or polyphenol-quinone-tanning or both, and hence is resistant to the action of the host digestive enzymes.[17] The number of nuclei or cells in the epidermis, and the number of muscle cells remains constant, at least in juvenile forms and in some species of adults. The alimentary canal is a fairly simple tube beginning with the mouth at the anterior end and ending at the anus near the posterior tip of the animal. A muscular esophagus is situated near the mouth, and a slight enlarge-

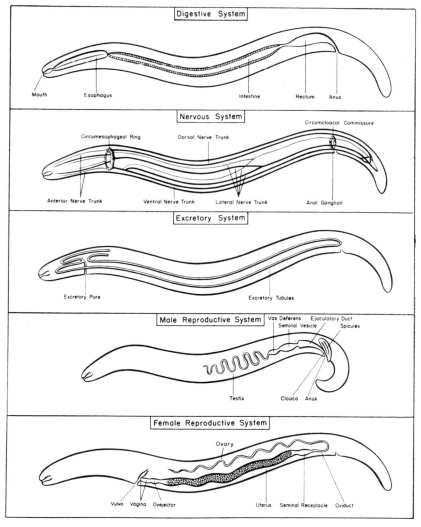

FIG. XIII–1.—Major organ systems of roundworms. (United States Navy Medical School Laboratory Guide.)

ment, the rectum, is near the anus. The nervous system basically consists of a ring of nervous tissue around the esophagus (Fig. XXVI–6, p. 678) and another nerve ring around the posterior region of the intestine, with longitudinal nerves connecting the rings and extending to the extremities of the body.

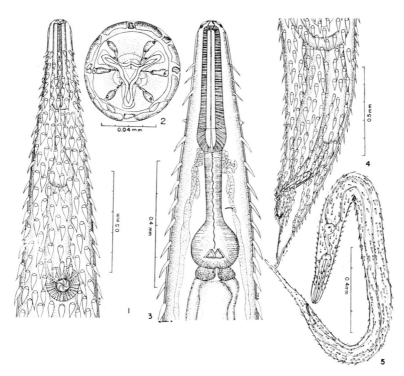

FIG. XIII–2.—*Paratractis hystrix* a nematode parasite of the large intestine of the water turtle, *Podocnemis dumeriliana*, showing pronounced spiny body surface. (Sarmiento, courtesy of J. Parasitology.)

   1.   Anterior portion of female, showing the arrangement of cuticular projections and the excretory pore.

   2.   En face view of the head.

   3.   Anterior portion, showing the esophagus and papillae.

   4.   Posterior end of female. Lateral view.

   5.   Larva, bearing cuticular projections.

Phasmids (Fig. XIII–3) are small post-anal organs associated with the nervous system in many parasitic nematodes. These structures have an obscure function but they are frequently called "chemoreceptor" organs. They are pouch-like and possess a minute canal leading to the outside, and they are often marked by the presence of small papillae. The glands are used as a basis of classification. Thus we may speak of the *Aphasmidia* (without phasmids) and the *Phasmidia* (with phasmids). See pages 310 and 366 for further discussion of these groups. Probably all nematodes possess a pair of similar organs in the head region. These chemoreceptors are called *amphids*.

The excretory system varies considerably in this phylum. The Class Secernentea possesses longitudinal ducts which open to the outside through a midventral pore which is associated with a ventral gland and excretory duct. The longitudinal ducts are often connected by a cross tube giving the whole apparatus an "H" shape. The Class Adenophorea usually possesses a single excretory gland which is cervico-ventral in position and opens by way of a short duct through a pore on the mid-ventral line. Ammonia is the major end-product of nitrogen metabolism in the infective stages of the parasites. Urea and uric acid are frequently present.

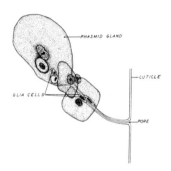

Fig. XIII–3.—A phasmid in a female *Spironoura*. The phasmid gland is a flushing (or "scent"?) gland, and the opening to the outside is a post-anal lateral pore. Redrawn from Chitwood and Chitwood. (Chitwood, B. G. and Chitwood, M. B. 1950. An Introduction to Nematology. p. 168, Fig. F. Copyright by the Authors.)

Blood vessels are not present in the nematodes but body fluids bathe the various organs, and these body fluids possess hemoglobin. Hemoglobins may also occur in the tissues of the body wall. These pigments have an affinity for oxygen in some but perhaps not in all nematodes. The requirement for oxygen varies greatly among worms, but even those worms which are the most completely anaerobic may still require minute amounts of free oxygen.

The hemoglobin in body fluids may be a by-product of digestion, playing no role in respiration, but that in the body wall probably accepts oxygen from the surrounding medium. The common stomach worm of ruminants, *Haemonchus contortus*, and the cecal worm of fowl, *Heterakis gallinae*, utilize molecular oxygen readily under laboratory conditions, and presumably their tissue hemoglobin plays the same role *in vivo*.

Reproduction. Nematodes are dioecious and commonly exhibit sexual dimorphism. This condition of one sex being of a different size, shape or color from the other, reaches an extreme state of development in *Trichosomoides crassicauda*, a parasite of the urinary bladder of the rat. In this species the male worm is a tiny creature, compared with the female, and he lives like a parasite in her uterus.

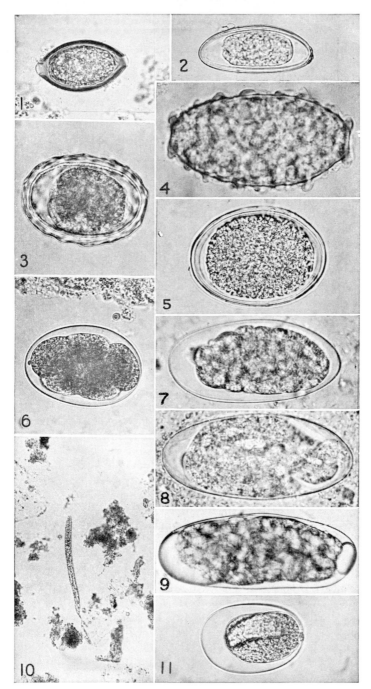

Fig. XIII–4.—Nematode eggs; 1, *Trichuris trichiura*; 2, *Enterobius vermicularis*: 3, *Ascaris lumbricoides*, fertilized egg; 4, *Ascaris*, unfertilized eggs; 5, *Ascaris*, decorticated egg; 6, Hookworm; 7, *Trichostrongylus orientales*, immature egg; 8, *Trichostrongylus*, embryonated egg; 9, *Heterodera marioni*; 10, *Strongyloides stercoralis*, rhabditiform larva; 11, *Strongyloides* egg (rarely seen in stool). All figures × 500 except 10 (75×) (Mackie, Hunter and Worth, *A Manual of Tropical Medicine*, courtesy of W. B. Saunders Co.)

(303)

The female reproductive system consists of one or two long coiled tubules which unite to form a vagina which opens through a vulva. The vulva is usually located on the anterior portion of the body. The distal ends of the tubes are the ovaries, the portions next to them are the oviducts while the remainder are the uteri. The single ovary condition is called *monodelphic* whereas worms with two ovaries are referred to as *didelphic*. Rarely are there *polydelphic* forms. The physalopterid nematodes belong to the latter group.

The chemistry of nematode eggs has received considerable study but only a start has been made on a complete understanding of the complicated processes involved in the formation and composition of the egg shell, and the exact role that each layer plays. Eggs of Strongyloidea, Oxyuroidea and Ascaridoidea (Fig. XIII–4) all have primary envelopes produced by the eggs themselves and consisting of lipid coats, membranes and shells. Many variations among simple, complex, thin and thick layers are found. The egg membranes of Strongyloidea and the exterior egg shell of Oxyuroidea consist of quinone-tanned proteins, whereas the interior egg shell of Oxyuroidea consists of chitin. Egg shells of Ascaridoidea are constructed of protein lamellae with chitin layers interposed, and are covered with an exterior membrane which consists of a quinone-tanned protein. Some ascarids have tertiary envelopes produced by the uterine wall.[18]

Male worms possess reproductive organs which are likewise modifications of long coiled tubes. The single *testis* is the distal end of a tube which continues as the *vas deferens* which joins the lower end of the gut at the *cloaca*. Before this junction occurs, the vas deferens enlarges and forms a *seminal vesicle*, or storage sac, for sperm. In some species of worms the sperm resemble amebas. The terminal end of the male organs may be called the *ejaculatory duct*. Transfer of sperm to the female worm is aided by a pair of *spicules* (Fig. XIII–16) in many species of roundworms. These long structures are sclerotized and they may be thrust out through the cloaca, and may serve the additional function of tactile sensory organs. Another male structure, the *gubernaculum*, is a sclerotized thickening of the cuticle in some species of worms. This organ lies on the dorsal side of the cloaca and probably helps to guide the spicules as they are thrust out. A larger organ, the *telemon*, lies on the ventral and lateral walls of the cloaca. It, also, develops as a thickening of the cuticle and serves to help direct the spicules in copulation. The posterior end of some male species of this type of worm is flared and curved in such a manner as to suggest a hood. This structure is called the *copulatory bursa* (Fig. XIII-16) and it helps the male worm to hold itself to the female during copulation. The walls of the bursa may be supported by finger-like rays. The number and arrangement of these rays serve as diagnostic features in species identification.

LIFE CYCLES OF NEMATODE WORMS

Life cycles occur in a variety of ways among the thousands of species of nematodes that infect animals. Early developmental stages within the egg are basically the same for all nematodes and are well represented in Figure XIII-5 which illustrates the process in the egg of *Contracaecum aduncum*, a parasite of marine fish. One

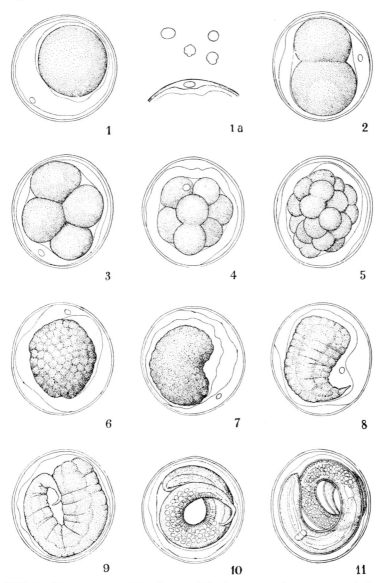

FIG. XIII–5.—Development within the egg of *Contracaecum aduncum*, a nematode of fish. (St. Markowski, courtesy of Bull, Acad. Polonaise Sci. et Lett.)

of the simplest life cycles is exhibited by *Trichuris* (= *Trichocephalus*) *trichiura* (Fig. XIII–6), the common whipworm of man, and by similar species in many other mammals.

The eggs of the whipworm pass out of the body with feces and develop into embryos within a few weeks. They are then infective to a new host and gain entrance to this host by being ingested. Embryo-

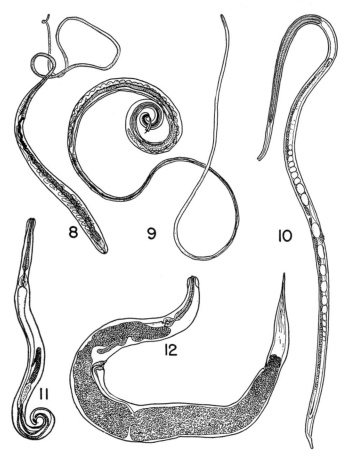

Fig. XIII–6.—*Trichuris trichiura.* 8 female × 7; 9, Male showing characteristic coiling of the hindbody, × 7. 10, *Strongyloides stercoralis* female, × 75. 11 and 12, *Enterobius vermicularis*, 11, mature male × 26; 12 gravid female, × 26. (Beaver, courtesy of Am. J. Clin. Pathology.)

nated eggs may remain viable for many months if they remain in moist areas. When ingested, the infective eggs are passed to the cecum where they are hatched and where, in about four weeks, they mature. As is characteristic of nematodes, the sexes are separate. Mating occurs as soon as the adult stage is reached, and not long thereafter the females start producing their eggs. For further details see p. 372.

Molting is characteristic among nematodes and involves the casting off the sheath or cuticle which surrounds the larva or juvenile. Juveniles molt once to several times during their growth to maturity. Generally they do not become infective until after the second molt (third-stage larvae). Some species of larvae (Fig. XIII–7) retain this cuticle as a potective sheath which thus becomes a diagnostic character. When molting occurs within a host, the process is possibly controlled by the endocrine system of the worms and stimulated by factors in the host fluids which surround the worms.[21]

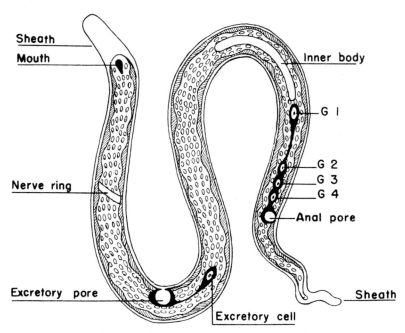

Sheath

Mouth

Inner body

G 1

G 2
G 3
G 4

Nerve ring

Anal pore

Excretory pore

Sheath

Excretory cell

FIG. XIII–7.—A juvenile (microfilaria) nematode showing the sheath and other structures. (United States Navy Medical Guide Laboratory Manual.)

A nematode parasite which shows an unusually variable type of life cycle is the threadworm, *Strongyloides stercoralis*. Under optimum environmental conditions the adult worms live in the soil and carry on a non-parasitic existence. When environmental conditions are unfavorable the juveniles become infective to a new host. For further details see p. 311.

Many filarial worms make use of insect vectors. *Wuchereria bancrofti*, causing "elephantiasis" in man, is one of the best known examples (p. 354).

The development of various species of filarial nematodes to the infective stage in their arthropod hosts has been described as taking place in muscles, the fat-body, the parenchyma, Malpighian tubes and in the hemocoel, but no one has reported this development as occurring in the nervous system, gonads, alimentary canal or salivary glands.[16]   Wherever they do develop, the juvenile worms (Fig. XIII–8) are usually highly specific to the particular type of tissue selected.

Many parasitic roundworms, after entering an arthropod host, become surrounded by chitin or other special membrane, or become impregnated with a brown deposit which forms a "capsule" around them.   Studies have shown that this encapsulation or melanin deposit is a defense mechanism on the part of the host.[16] Sometimes this reaction occurs only when a parasite is introduced into an abnormal host.

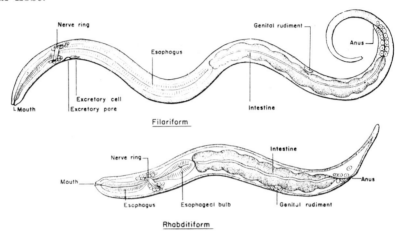

Fig. XIII–8.—Juveniles of intestinal roundworms. (United States Navy Medical School Laboratory Guide.)

Larva Migrans.   Larval nematodes frequently get into an unsuitable host and are unable to continue their normal development. Instead, they may wander in the host tissues until they die and are absorbed, or encapsulated, or reach the outside. The migration of these worms in the "wrong" host is called *larva migrans.* Most cases in man are acquired from infected dogs or cats. Prevention, therefore, consists of deworming these animals.[3]

Cutaneous larva migrans occurs in man when his skin is penetrated by filariform larvae of the cat hookworm, *Ancylostoma brasiliense,* or, less frequently, by the dog hookworm, *A. caninum,* and other species. The condition is called "creeping eruption" of the skin and is characterized by visible tracks with red, painful, swollen advancing ends, often associated with intense itching.[2] *Visceral larva migrans* in man is due to the wandering of second-stage larvae from the dog nematode, *Toxocara canis,* and, more rarely, from other species of *Toxocara.* Children often become infected by swallowing eggs from infected puppies. Lesions have been reported from many organs including the liver, brain and eye. Chronic eosinophilia is a common symptom of this disease.[9]

GENERAL CONTROL

Control of some of the more important nematodes is mentioned with the discussion of the various species below. One of the newest ideas for the control of nematodes, however, is the use of predacious fungi. Some of these fungi can be grown in culture on synthetic media but others must be grown in their natural hosts. The endozoic fungus, *Harposporium anguillulae*, for example, sends its mycelia throughout the tissues of nematodes of the genera *Rhabditis* and *Panagrellus*.

The drug dithiazanine (3:3¹-diethylthiadicarbocyanine iodide) has been found to be effective against the whipworm (*Trichuris*), the common round worm (*Ascaris*), the strongyle worm (*Strongyloides*), and the pinworm (*Enterobius*), thus making this drug a broad-spectrum anthelminthic. The recommended dose is an oral administration of 200 mg. two or three times daily for five days. There are apparently no significant side effects.

Bephenium hydroxynaphthoate, a quartenary ammonium compound, has received extensive trials as an anthelminthic. A single dose of 3 grams of the base preparation was found to be at least as effective against hookworm and other roundworm infections in man as is tetrachlorethylene, and it had the added advantage of not producing toxic side effects. This drug is also known under the name of *alcopara*. Stilbazium iodide is also a promising general anthelminthic.[14a]

CLASSIFICATION

Hyman[15] has presented strong evidence for grouping, as classes, the Rotifers, Gastrotricha, Kinorhyncha, Nematoda and Nematomorpha under the phylum Aschelminthes (a term meaning "worms with a cavity"). Other authorities prefer to consider each of these groups as a separate phylum. We have adopted Thorne's (1961)[30] system of classification; therefore we are referring the nematodes to a separate phylum, but we are using the term "Nematoda" instead of "Nemata." Only those orders and superfamilies containing parasitic representatives will be listed below. For further discussions of problems of systematics and taxonomy in nematology see Coninck.[7]

CLASSIFICATION OF THE PARASITIC NEMATODES

Phylum Nematoda
  Class Secernentea (= Phasmidia)
    Order Tylenchida
      Superfamily Tylenchoidea
        Examples: *Ditylenchus, Pratylenchus, Heterodera*
    Order Rhabditida
      Superfamily Rhabditoidea
        Example: *Strongyloides*

Order Strongylida
  Superfamily Strongyloidea
    Examples: *Stephanurus, Oesophagostomum, Ancylostoma, Syngamus*
  Superfamily Trichostrongyloidea
    Examples: *Haemonchus, Ostertagia, Cooperia, Nippostrongylus,*
             Nematodirus, Trichostrongylus, Hyostrongylus
  Superfamily Metastrongyloidea
    Examples: *Dictyocaulus, Metastrongylus*
Order Ascaridida
  Superfamily Ascaridoidea
    Examples: *Toxocara, Toxascaris, Ascaris, Heterakis*
  Superfamily Oxyuroidea
    Examples: *Oxyuris, Enterobius, Ascaridia.*
Order Spirurida
  Superfamily Spiruroidea
    Examples: *Gongylonema, Gnathostoma*
  Superfamily Thelazioidea
    Example: *Thelazia*
  Superfamily Filarioidea
    Examples: *Ornithofilaria, Wuchereria, Brugia, Onchocerca, Loa,*
             Dirofilaria
Order Camallanida
  Superfamily Dracunculoidea
    Example: *Dracunculus*
Class Adenophorea (=Aphasmidia)
  Order Dorylaimida
  Superfamily Dorylaimoidea
    Examples: *Xiphinema, Trichodorus*
  Superfamily Mermithoidea
    Example: *Agamermis*
  Superfamily Trichinelloidea
    Examples: *Capillaria, Trichinella, Trichuris*
  Order Dioctophymatida
  Superfamily Dioctophymatoidea
    Examples: *Dioctophyme, Eustrongylides*
Class Nematomorpha
    Example: *Gordius*

CLASS SECERNENTEA (=PHASMIDIA)

ORDER TYLENCHIDA

(Plant nematodes—see page 376)

ORDER RHABDITIDA

SUPERFAMILY RHABDITOIDEA

The evolution of a parasitic mode of life among roundworms might well have started with groups like the rhabditoids (see p. 677). Many of these worms live in decaying flesh, dung, decomposing plant material or in other similar substances where transfer to the intestine of an animal or to tissues of a plant is relatively easy. Members of this large order possess head sense organs in the form of papillae, and the amphids are reduced to small pockets.

Rhabditis coarctata must be carried as ensheathed juveniles on the surface of dung beetles to fresh dung before they can mature. Another species, *R. ocypodis*, is carried on the gills of crabs. Still another type, *Pristionchus aerivora*, gets into the head of a termite, usually kills the host, and then feeds on its body. A more typically parasitic rhabditoid is *Cephalobium microbivorum* which lives as an adult in the intestine of crickets.

Parasitic nematodes in the lungs of amphibia (e.g. *Rhabdias bufonis* = *Rhabditis nigrovenosa*) and reptiles belong to the family Rhabdiasidae, and certain parasitic worms in the intestines of mammals belong to the family Strongyloididae. The latter family contains worms of considerable importance to man.

Strongyloides stercoralis

This intestinal parasite of man is world-wide in its distribution but is found primarily in warm countries. The incidence of infection is usually very low but may be as high as 25 per cent in favorable areas. Chimpanzees, dogs, cats are possible reservoir hosts but some authorities believe the worms in these animals belong to different species. Related species occur in numerous other mammals. Parasitic females of *S. stercoralis* are about 2 mm. long by 50 microns wide, while the free-living males average .7 mm. long by 45 microns wide. They are called "threadworms" and the disease which they produce is known as "strongyloidiasis."

Strongyloides stercoralis (Fig. XIII–9) shows considerable variability in its life cycle, apparently being able to adjust the type of its development to changing demands of the environment. Under optimum conditions of moisture, temperature and food availability, the adult worms live in the soil. This free-living period begins with an egg which develops into four rhabditiform stages (Fig. XIII–10), the last one forming an adult male or female. The cycle may be repeated many times, and it is essentially the same as that of any non-parasitic soil nematode.

When environmental conditions become unfavorable, however, a second type of life cycle occurs. The free-living adults mate and produce young worms that pass through two rhabditiform stages and two filariform stages. The latter are infective to man. These juveniles may infect dogs and cats by being eaten, but in man they usually penetrate the skin.

On contact with the skin, the worms (Fig. XIII–11) burrow through to small blood vessels. The course of the juveniles through the body via the blood stream, lungs, mouth and the intestine, is the same as that of hookworm larvae (page 323). They may, however, mature in the lung spaces and remain there. After fertilization, the adult males pass out of the body with the feces, and the females (average 2.2 mm. × 40 microns) penetrate the intestinal mucosa and start laying

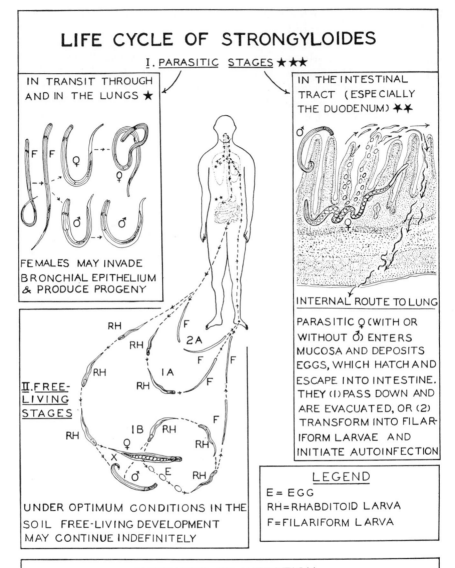

LIFE CYCLE OF STRONGYLOIDES

I. PARASITIC STAGES ★ ★★

IN TRANSIT THROUGH
AND IN THE LUNGS ★

FEMALES MAY INVADE
BRONCHIAL EPITHELIUM
& PRODUCE PROGENY

IN THE INTESTINAL
TRACT (ESPECIALLY
THE DUODENUM) ★★

INTERNAL ROUTE TO LUNG

PARASITIC ♀ (WITH OR
WITHOUT ♂) ENTERS
MUCOSA AND DEPOSITS
EGGS, WHICH HATCH AND
ESCAPE INTO INTESTINE.
THEY (1) PASS DOWN AND
ARE EVACUATED, OR (2)
TRANSFORM INTO FILAR-
IFORM LARVAE AND
INITIATE AUTOINFECTION

II. FREE-
LIVING
STAGES

UNDER OPTIMUM CONDITIONS IN THE
SOIL FREE-LIVING DEVELOPMENT
MAY CONTINUE INDEFINITELY

LEGEND

E = EGG
RH = RHABDITOID LARVA
F = FILARIFORM LARVA

METHODS OF INFECTION

1. FILARIFORM LARVAE ENTER SKIN IN CONTACT WITH SOIL
   A. FOLLOWING DIRECT RH→F LARVAL DEVELOPMENT
   B. FOLLOWING FREE-LIVING CYCLE IN THE SOIL
2. FILARIFORM LARVAE DEVELOP BEFORE LEAVING PATIENT
   A. FOLLOWING DEPOSITION ON THE SOIL, ENTER EXPOSED SKIN
   B. ENTER PERIANAL SKIN AND INITIATE AUTOINFECTION
   C. ENTER INTESTINAL MUCOSA, MIGRATE TO LUNG AND
      INITIATE AUTOINFECTION

E.C.F.
1950

FIG. XIII–9.—Diagrammatic representation of the potential whole life cycle of *Strongyloides*. (Faust and Russell, *Clinical Parasitology*, Lea & Febiger.)

eggs which average 50 by 32 microns (Fig. XIII–4). The duodenum is possibly the site of "preference," but the worms may be found elsewhere in the intestine. The eggs hatch in host tissue and the new juveniles migrate from the tissue to the lumen of the intestine and so find their way outside to soil.

A third type of life cycle of *Strongyloides stercoralis* involves *autoinfection*. Newly-hatched juveniles in the intestine may remain in the lumen of the gut, develop into filariform juveniles and burrow through

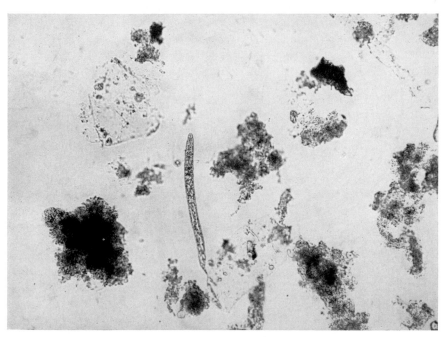

Fig. XIII–10.—*Strongyloides stercoralis*, rhabditiform larva. (Roudabush, *An Aid to the Diagnosis of Helminths Parasitic in Humans*, courtesy of Ward's Natural Science Establishment Inc.)

the mucosa and into blood vessels. They are then carried to the lungs and make their way back to the intestine, as described above, and mature. Other filariform juveniles may crawl through the anus and re-enter the body by penetrating the skin of the perianal region. They also go to the lungs and from there to the intestine. Autoinfection, however, appears to be rare.

Symptoms may occur with the penetration of the juveniles through the skin. Itching and swelling of the area is typical. Penetration of the lungs may cause coughing, a bronchial pneumonia and other pulmonary disorders. Worms in the intestinal mucosa sometimes cause diarrhea, abdominal pain, anemia, loss of weight, constipation or bloody feces. There may also be allergic effects. Probably the best drug for treatment is gentian violet but others are more or less successful (*e.g.* dithiazanine, hexylresorcinol, diethylcarbamizine citrate).

Strongyloides simiae is a similar species in monkeys and apes. This species and some others (*S. cebus* and *S. fülleborni*), also found in these hosts, should probably be grouped into one species and called *Strongyloides fülleborni. S. ratti* has been described from rats.[22]

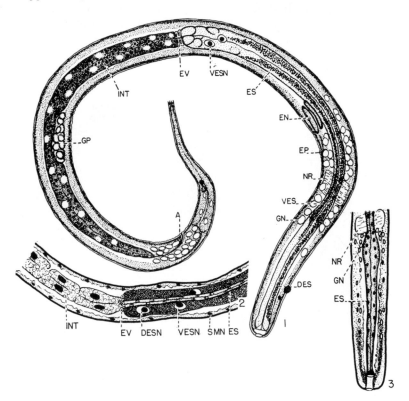

Fig. XIII–11.—*Strongyloides stercoralis.* 1, larva after twelve days in rat abdominal muscle (unstained). × 600. 2, 3, larva in lamina propria of human colon (stained). × 620. DES, dorsal esophageal gland; DESN, nucleus of dorsal esophageal gland; EN, nucleus of excretory cell; EP, excretory pore; ES, esophagus; EV, esophago-intestinal gland; GN, ganglionic nucleus; GP, genital primordium; INT, intestine; NR, nerve ring; SMN, somatic muscle nucleus; VES, ventral esophageal gland; VESN, nucleus of ventral esophageal gland. (Nichols, courtesy of J. Parasitology.)

ORDER STRONGYLIDA

SUPERFAMILY STRONGYLOIDEA

The male worms of this order possess an expanded posterior end which is known as a *bursa* and which sets them apart from most of the other nematodes. Females possess a pointed tail. The mouth is not surrounded by the conspicuous lips which characterize the ascaroids, and the esophagus does not possess a bulb.

This order contains many highly important parasitic roundworms of domestic animals and of man. Most of them are bloodsucking worms which grasp a portion of the intestinal mucosa in their mouths and are apparently able to keep the blood from clotting by secreting an anticoagulant. The intestinal lumen is essentially anaerobic but parasites are able to obtain oxygen from the host red blood cells which they eat. The presence of fresh blood in the worms gives some of them a bright red color. A much more reliable characteristic of the group is the bursa, mentioned above. This bell-shaped extension of the cuticle is supported by rays which exhibit a definite pattern. For a general taxonomic treatment of the group see Skrjabin.[26a]

Stephanurus Dentatus

This nematode (Fig. XIII–12) is the common kidney worm of pigs, and it may also be found in the liver, lungs, spleen, muscles, spinal canal, and body cavities.

Male worms are from 20 to 30 mm. long, while the females are from 30 to 45 mm. They are thicker than the lungworms and they appear black and white because some internal organs may be seen from the outside.

Female worms in the kidneys produce oval eggs which average a little more than 100 microns in length, and thus can just barely be seen without a microscope. The eggs pass down the ureter, into the urinary bladder and to the outside with urine. A heavily infected pig may pass a million eggs a day.

In moist shaded soil the eggs hatch into tiny free-living larvae which grow and molt twice within the next three to five days. The

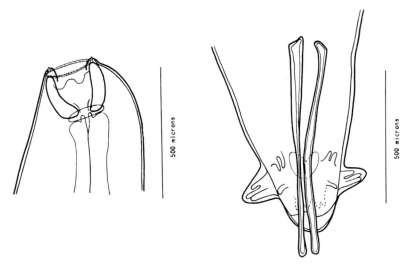

Fig. XIII–12.—*Stephanurus dentatus* anterior and posterior end of male. (Morgan and Hawkins, *Veterinary Helminthology*, courtesy of Burgess Publishing Co.)

young worms are then infective to pigs which eat them with contaminated food.   Larvae may also get into their host through cuts or
sores on the skin or they may even penetrate the unbroken skin.
Within the body, larvae find their way via blood and lymph vessels
to the liver where they may remain for several months.   Then the
parasites make their way to the kidneys where they mature.   The
entire life cycle usually requires six to eight months.   Most larvae
do not reach maturity.

Larvae and adults cause abscesses, hemorrhage, adhesions, loss
of weight and death.   The economic loss in the United States due
to this worm alone has been estimated to be at least $72,000,000
annually.

Treatment is ineffective.   Good management practices help to
keep down infection.   Keeping the area around hogs dry and exposed
to sunlight prevents the development of enormous numbers of eggs
and larvae.

Oesophagostomum

The various species of *Oesophagostomum* have a common general
type of life cycle and it can be represented by *O. dentatum* (Fig.
XIII–13), the nodular worm of swine.   In this cosmopolitan species
the males are about 9 mm. long, while the females average about 12

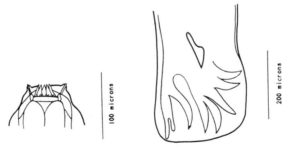

Fig. XIII–13.—*Oesophagostomum dentatum*, anterior and posterior end of male. (Morgan
and Hawkins, *Veterinary Helminthology*, courtesy of Burgess Publishing Co.)

mm.   The species name is based on the presence of a ring of tooth-
like projections bordering the mouth, and a ring of very short projections within the buccal capsule.   The male possesses a pair of
slender spicules about 1 mm. long and a tri-lobed bursa.   The vulva
of the female is posterior in its position.

The life cycle begins with the fertilized eggs which are about
70 to 40 microns in size. The eggs escape the host with feces and, in
moist soil, they hatch in a day or two.   After another few days or a
week, the larvae have developed into the infective stage and are now
ready to be eaten by a hog.   If the worms get into the large intestine
they penetrate the intestinal wall, causing inflammation and the
formation of nodules about 1 mm. in diameter—thus the common

name of the worm. Other species produce larger nodules. Eventually the juveniles leave the nodules, enter the lumen of the intestine and develop into sexually mature worms.

Symptoms of infection range from none to anemia, weakness, diarrhea and emaciation. Phenothiazine is an effective drug used in treatment. A strict diet of skim milk for a few days is also effective. Control measures center around efforts to prevent contamination of food by infected feces.

Oesophagostomum columbianum, the sheep nodular worm, and *O. venulosum* are common nematode worms of the intestines of farm mammals, especially sheep and goats. Eggs similar to those of hookworms usually leave the body of the host with feces and hatch in moist soil, but some eggs hatch within the body of the host. In a few days the larvae grow into the infective stage and crawl on vegetation. If eaten by sheep or some other host the parasites reach the intestine. Each worm is liberated from a sheath which surrounds it, and burrows into the lining of the small or large intestine. Host tissue reacts to *O. columbianum* by forming a tumor-like nodule around one or more embedded larvae. These nodules may reach 25 mm. in diameter, and they may occasionally be found in man. In young hosts the larvae remain in the nodules for only a week or two but in old, more immune, animals they may remain for months. Eventually the worms emerge into the lumen of the gut and become mature. Adults are about the size of hookworms (12 mm. long), sexes are, as usual, separate. Soon after they mature, mating occurs and a new generation of eggs appears.

A nodular intestinal lining is known as "pimply gut" or "knotty gut." The presence of worms may be indicated by emaciation, dysentery, loss of weight, brittle yellow wool on sheep, progressive weakness or secretion of mucus. Phenothiazine is the drug of choice in treatment for adult worms. Larval worms in the nodules are not affected by anthelminthics.

Syngamus Trachea

The gapeworm, *Syngamus trachea* (Fig. XIII–14), is a red nematode which lives in the trachea of various species of poultry, and derives its common name from the fact that heavily infected birds apparently try to get rid of the annoyance caused by this worm by gaping, coughing, swallowing, or stretching the neck. Male worms average about 4 mm. in length, while the females are usually about 7 mm. The male and female worms are permanently fused so as to unite the genital openings of each worm. Eggs are coughed up by the host, swallowed, and find their way outside with feces. In moist soil the eggs become infective in a week or two, depending on the temperature, and may be eaten by a chicken or some other bird, or the eggs may hatch outside and the larvae eaten. The worm is versatile in its life history; the larvae may enter an earthworm, slug, or snail, or the egg may be eaten by one of these intermediate hosts. Chickens or other birds can thus become infected by eating snails, slugs or earthworms. Within the birds the larvae penetrate the gut wall and make their way, via the circulatory system, to the lungs where they penetrate the blood vessel wall and other tissues and enter the lung cavities, and crawl to the trachea where they become established. Within about two weeks they are mature.

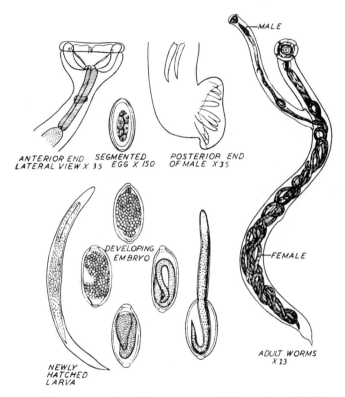

ANTERIOR END SEGMENTED POSTERIOR END
LATERAL VIEW X 35 EGG X 150 OF MALE X 35

DEVELOPING EMBRYO

MALE

FEMALE

ADULT WORMS X 13

NEWLY HATCHED LARVA

FIG. XIII–14.—*Syngamus trachea*, the gapeworm. Redrawn from M. Neveu-Lemaire. (Courtesy of Vigot Fréres, Paris.)

Birds may become suffocated if the worms are present in large numbers. Barium antimony tartrate is fairly successful in treatment. General cleanliness in bird management is extremely important, and care should be taken not to raise birds in areas which are contaminated from previous infections.

Hookworms

Family Ancylostomidae. These worms possess a well-developed buccal capsule which contains ventral teeth or cutting plates. The male bursa is normally well-developed. The name "hookworm" is said to arise from the dorsad-bent position of the anterior end. It is also purported to arise from the hook-like appearance of the bursal rays.

Dogs and cats are hosts to four common species of hookworms: *Ancylostoma caninum* (in dogs), *A. tubaeforme* (in cats), *A. braziliense* (primarily in cats), and *Uncinaria stenocephala* (in dogs, foxes, wolves). The last two may also occasionally be found in man.[5,6]
The life histories of these worms are essentially similar to that of *A. duodenale* of man (see below), but the possibility of insects acting as paratenic hosts should not be overlooked. A fourth species, *Necator americanus* of man, has been reported from dogs but it is quite rare in this host. *Uncinaria lucasi* is the worst enemy of fur seal pups on the Pribilof Islands. During the two-month stay of these young seals on the rookeries they die by the thousands from hookworm infection, covering the rookeries with their dead bodies.[19]

Hookworms are, in general, host specific but the larval stages may penetrate the skin of "foreign" hosts. Thus the larvae of *Ancylostoma braziliense* sometimes enter and burrow around in human skin. They cause intense itching, and the affliction is known as "creeping eruption." The major damage of adult worms is to the intestinal wall to which they attach and from which they suck blood. Bloody diarrhea, anemia and death are common, especially in puppies. About 630 million people have hookworms, and the estimated daily loss of blood due to this disease is the equivalent of the total volume of blood of 1,500,000 persons.[28] Dr. N. D. Stoll[28] has recently stated, "Now that malaria is being pushed back, hookworm remains *the* greatest *infection* of mankind in the moist tropics and subtropics. In my view, it outranks all other worm infections of man combined, with the possible exception of ascariasis, in its production of human misery, debility, and inefficiency in the tropical world."

Many other varieties of hookworms occur in vertebrates, but they all are essentially similar in structure and in their life cycle. A common species of man, *Ancylostoma duodenale*, will be discussed as a representative of the entire group.

Ancylostoma Duodenale

The two most important hookworms of man are *Ancylostoma duodenale*, the Oriental species, and *Necator americanus*, the American hookworm. Modern travel has provided ample opportunity for both species to become world-wide in their distribution.

Ancylostoma duodenale (Fig. XIII–15, 16) is a hookworm which can be found in the small intestine of millions of people, chiefly in Europe, Africa and the Orient. It is primarily a species infecting man and is the dominant species in the Mediterranean area, India, China and Japan. The male worm is 8 to 11 by 0.4 to 0.5 mm. in size. The posterior end of its body is flared and forms a *bursa* which is supported by fleshy rays with a characteristic pattern. A pair of long spicules passes from the genital canal to the outside through the cloaca. They are used during copulation to aid in the transfer of

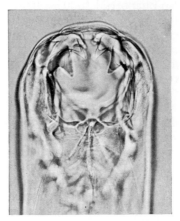

Fig. XIII–15.—En face of view of *Ancylostoma*. (Whitlock, *Diagnosis of Veterinary Parasitisms*, Lea & Febiger.)

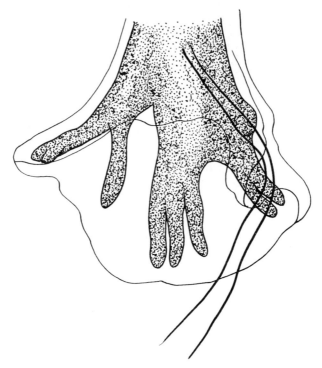

Fig. XIII–16.—Copulatory bursa of the hookworm *Ancylostoma duodenale*, lateral view. The two heavy, parallel lines on the right, extending beyond the posterior tip of the worm, are schematic representations of the spicules which are usually difficult to distinguish in preserved slide preparations. The rays of one side only are shown. The dorsal side is on the left. (Original.)

sperm. A *gubernaculum*, sclerotized as are the spicules, is present and is also used during copulation to help guide the spicules. The females average 10 to 13 by 0.6 mm. in size. The posterior end of the body tapers to a rather blunt point. The vulva is located at a point about two-thirds the length of the body from the anterior end. Eggs are ovoidal, thin-shelled (compared with those of the tapeworm *Taenia*) and measure 56 to 60 by 34 to 40 microns. When they are found during fecal examinations they are usually already in the early stages of segmentation (Fig. XIII–17).

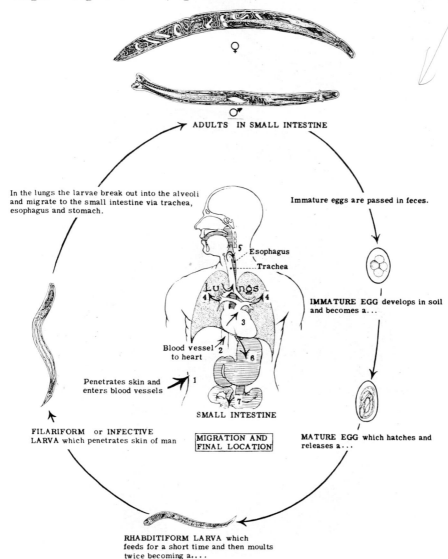

FIG. XIII–17.—Life cycle of hookworms. (Courtesy of National Naval Medical Center, Bethesda, Maryland.)

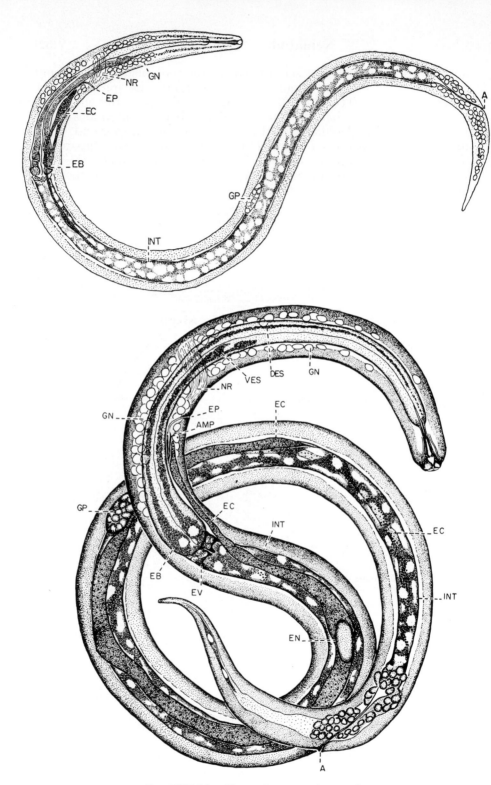

Fig. XIII–18.—*(Legend on opposite page)*

The life cycle starts with a fertilized egg which, by the time it reaches the soil, is well on its way to forming a juvenile. The daily output of eggs from a single female worm is probably from 10,000 to 20,000. Within twenty-four hours, in moist, warm soil, rhabditiform larvae (Fig. XIII–8) hatch from the eggs. Oxygen is essential for hatching and for further development. Larvae grow rapidly, molt twice, and in about a week become non-feeding slender filariform juveniles (Fig. XIII–18). This stage (third stage larva) is infective to man. The young worms crawl to a high point of dirt, vegetation, or bit of rock, so long as it is moist, and wait for a new host to come along. Excess water at this stage of the life cycle is injurious to the worms. Alternate wetting and drying is particularly harmful, hence frequent rains, with dry weather in between, tend to rid the soil of hookworm juveniles.

If a filariform juvenile comes in contact with the skin of a new host, it burrows into the skin and, if it gets deep enough, enters a blood or lymph vessel and is eventually carried to the lungs. Here it leaves the blood stream, penetrates the lung tissue, and arrives in the air spaces or alveoli. From the lungs the worm passes up the air tube to the mouth cavity and is swallowed, and thus arrives in the small intestine. A final molt occurs and the young worm attaches itself to the wall of the intestine, begins to suck blood, and matures to the adult stage. About five weeks elapse between penetration of the skin and the production of new eggs. A patient suffering from severe hookworm disease may discharge with his feces six million eggs per day. A single hookworm may produce in its lifetime (about five years) up to fifty-four million eggs. Adult female worms may invade the intestinal epithelium and lay eggs. Only rhabditiform larvae have thus far been found in this locality, but if they develop into filariform larvae in the host the danger of autoinfection is obvious.

Symptoms of infection start with the "ground itch" which occurs during the penetration of the skin by filariform larvae. If pyogenic bacteria enter with the larvae there may be itching, burning, crythema, edema and vesicle formation. "Creeping eruption" (cutaneous larva migrans, see p. 308) may occur if human skin is penetrated by larvae of other species of hookworms from animals or even by the species from man (Fig. XIII–19). Pulmonary inflammation and minute hemorrhages are associated with lung penetration. Anemia is the principal host reaction to intestinal infection by adult worms. Other symptoms are undernourishment, pallor, fever,

---

Fig. XIII–18.—Typical hookworm infective juveniles (unstained). The more coiled worm is the dog hookworm, *Ancylostoma caninum*, ×700, the other is the hookworm of man, *Necator americanus* ×430. *A*, anus; *AMP*, excretory ampulla; *DES*, dorsal esophageal gland; *EB*, esophageal bulb; *EC*, excretory column; *EN*, nucleus of excretory canal; *EP*, excretory pore; *EV*, esophago-intestinal valve; *GN*, ganglionic nucleus; *GP*, genital primordium; *INT*, intestine; *NR*, nerve ring; *VES*, ventral esophageal gland. (Nichols, courtesy of J. Parasitology.)

abdominal pains, diarrhea, listlessness, myocarditis and eosinophilia. Diagnosis is confirmed by finding hookworm eggs in stool specimens. Treatment includes a diet to promote blood formation, and the use of bephenium hydroxynaphthoate (drug of choice), tetrachlorethylene, hexylresorcinol or dithiazanine. Control measures include proper sewage disposal and education of the people in endemic areas concerning sources of infection. It is possible that acquired immunity plays a major role in restraining hookworm infection in man.[28]

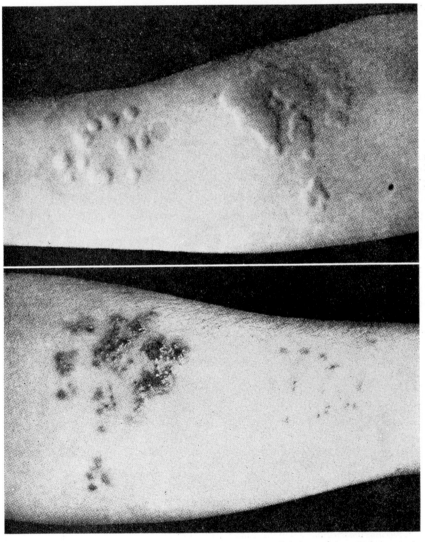

FIG. XIII-19.—(*Upper*). Urticaria-like elevations on the arm sixty minutes after penetrations by larvae of *A. caninum* and *Necator americanus*. Near the wrist smaller reactions followed penetrations of *A. braziliense* of a boy-to-cat strain.

(*Lower.*) Seventeen hours after penetrations. (Dove, courtesy of Amer. J. Hyg.)

Some autopsy material in Java has revealed, in the lining of the human small intestine, nodules containing not only adult specimens of *Ancylostoma duodenale* but eggs and larvae as well. This discovery suggests a method of autoinfection, but the extent of its prevalence is unknown.

Necator americanus (Fig. XIII–20) follows the same general life cycle and, from the medical point of view, presents essentially the

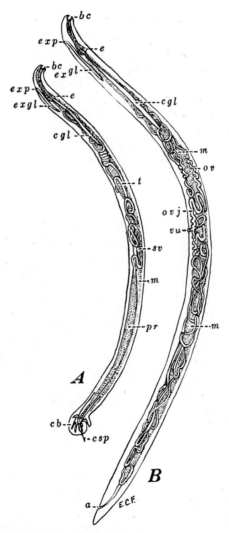

Fig. XIII–20.—*Necator americanus* adults, lateral view. *A*, male; *B* female. *a*, anal pore; *bc*, buccal capsule; *cb*, copulatory bursa; *c gl*, paired cephalic gland; *c sp*, copulatory spicules; *e*, esophagus; *ex gl*, excretory gland; *ex p*, excretory pore; *m*, midgut; *ov*, ovary; *ovj*, ovejector; *pr*, prostate gland; *sv*, seminal vesicle, *t*, testis; *vu*, vulva. × 18. (Original adaptation from Lane.) (Faust and Russell, *Craig and Faust's Clinical Parasitology*, courtesy of Lea & Febiger.)

same problems as does *Ancylostoma duodenale*. Some authorities recommend tetrachorethylene, given with oil of chenopodium, as the drug of choice against *N. americanus*. *A. ceylonicum* is a rare intestinal worm of man in southeast Asia. It was formerly believed to be the same species as *A. braziliense*.

SUPERFAMILY TRICHOSTRONGYLOIDEA

Haemonchus Contortus

Haemonchus contortus (Fig. XIII–21), the twisted stomach worm or wireworm, is a world-wide inhabitant of the abomasum of sheep, goats, cattle and of other ruminants. Females measure 18 to 30 mm. in length, while males are from 10 to 20 mm. long. The common names arise from the fact that in the female the white ovaries are twisted around the red intestine. The male is a more uniform red.

The life cycle begins with eggs, about 85 by 45 microns, which pass from the host to the ground. Here they hatch and within four days they have reached a sheathed infective stage. A new host acquires the parasite by eating the infective larvae with grass or other food.

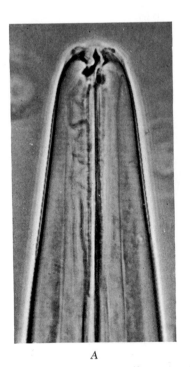
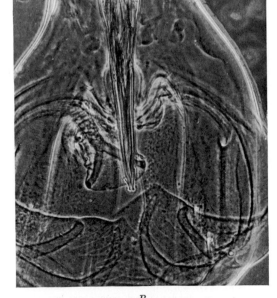

A   B

FIG. XIII–21.—*A*, Lateral view of anterior end of *Haemonchus*. × 400. *B*, Spicules and bursa of *Haemonchus*. Note barb on spicules and asymmetrical dorsal lobe. × 138. (Whitlock's *Diagnosis of Veterinary Parasitisms*, Lea & Febiger.)

The effect on the host is anemia, digestive disturbances, loss of weight, often a swelling under the jaw and susceptibility to other infectious agents. Drugs used in treatment include copper sulfate, nicotine sulfate and phenothiazine. *Haemonchus placei* in cattle is a similar species.

Ostertagia Ostertagi

Ostertagia ostertagi (Fig. XIII–22) is another stomach worm of ruminants. It lives in the abomasum and, rarely, in the intestine.

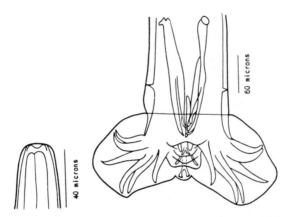

FIG. XIII–22.—*Ostertagia ostertagi*, anterior and posterior ends of male. (Morgan and Hawkins, *Veterinary Helminthology*, courtesy of Burgess Publishing Co.)

Its common name is the brown stomach worm or the medium worm and it is smaller than *Haemonchus contortus*. Males average about 7 mm., and females about 9 mm. in length.

The life cycle of this worm is similar to that of *Haemonchus contortus*, the infective third stage larvae appearing on the fifth and sixth day after the eggs reach the ground. Symptoms of infection include anemia, diarrhea and emaciation. Treatment involves tetrachlorethylene or phenothiazine. Other species are *Ostertagia circumcincta* and *O. trifurcata* both in sheep and goats, *O. lyrata*, in cattle, and *O. bisonis* in bison.

Cooperia Punctata

Cooperia punctata (Fig. XIII–23) is a small, reddish worm which may be found in many countries in the small intestine of various ruminants, especially cattle. The males average a little over 5 mm. long, and the females about 6 mm. in length. The life cycle is not fully known but it probably resembles that of *Haemonchus contortus*. Symptoms of infection in calves include diarrhea, weakness, anemia and emaciation. Various anthelminthics have been tried in treatment with varying success. Other species include *Cooperia curticei*, in sheep and goats, *C. oncophora*, *C. pectinata*, in cattle and *C. bisonis* in the abomasum of bison.

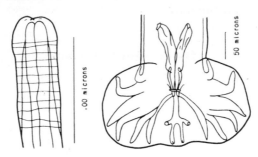

FIG. XIII–23.—*Cooperia punctata*, anterior and posterior ends of male. (Morgan and Hawkins, *Veterinary Helminthology*, courtesy of Burgess Publishing Co.)

Nippostrongylus Brasiliensis

Nippostrongylus brasiliensis (= *N. muris*), a small reddish worm, is a common parasite of the small intestine of wild rats but it is normally not found in laboratory rats. The worm has been used in various studies of the physiology of parasitic worms. The male is 3 to 4 mm. in length, whereas the female is 4 to 6 mm. In both sexes the head is somewhat enlarged. In the male the bursa is asymmetrical in shape and the spicules are long and slender. Eggs pass from the intestine of the host, and the young worms within them develop into the infective stage in one day under favorable environmental conditions. The life cycle is similar to that of the hook worm, *Ancylostoma duodenale* (p. 319), and the adult stage is reached in about a week. After entering the host body the larvae go first to the lymph glands where they are cleansed of their bacteria and other foreign material, then to the lungs.[11a] For details see Haley.[13,14]

Nematodirus Spathiger

Nematodirus spathiger (Fig. XIII–24) is a common parasite of cattle and sheep and occurs in the small intestine. The male is from 10 to 15 mm. in length and the female varies between 15 and 23 mm. Third-stage larvae are, as usual, the infective stage, and they are eaten by cattle or sheep while the hosts feed on grass or other vegetation. The symptoms of infection are not pronounced but probably infected cattle exhibit the same symptoms as occur with other intestinal worms, but to a milder degree. Another species in cattle is *N. helvetianus*.

Trichostrongylus

Seven or eight species of *Trichostrongylus* (*e.g. T. axei*, *T. colubriformis*, *T. vitrinus*, *T. capricola*, *T. orientalis*) have been reported from man. All of these worms are also found in domestic animals. *T. colubriformis*, for example, causes "black scours" in ruminants. It usually occurs in the small intestine. *T. axei* is found in the abomasum of ruminants and in the stomach and small intestine of horses. The others are also parasitic in ruminants. The world incidence of infection in man is probably not over 1 to 2 per cent. In some areas of the Orient, however, there is a 10 to 20 per cent infection. Local areas of Iran show infection rates as high as 60 per cent. In general, the appearance and life cycle of these worms resemble hookworms.

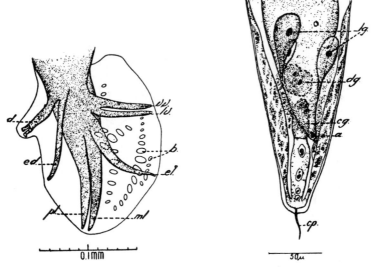

Fig. XIII–24.—*Nematodirus spathiger* posterior ends of male and female, the latter shows the terminal process (cp). *d*, dorsal ray in the distinct dorsal lobe; *ed*, externodorsal ray; *pl*, posterolateral and *ml*, medio-lateral rays close together for most of their length; *e.l.*, externo-lateral ray separate from the other laterals; *l.v.*, lateroventral and *v.v.* ventro-ventral rays close together; *lg* latero-ventral gland; *dg*, dorsal gland; *cg*, caudal gland; *a*, anus. (May, Proc. U. S. Nat. Museum).

Trichostrongyles have a rather unpretentious anterior end, simply tapering to a blunted point without any accessory structures and without a prominent buccal capsule. Males possess a posterior copulatory bursa and paired copulatory spicules which are thick, short, irregular and brown in color. The life cycle is relatively simple. Adults (6 to 8 mm. long) live in the small intestine, and eggs leave the host with feces. The eggs are greenish in fresh stools, slightly longer and narrower than those of hookworms and are more pointed at one end. In the soil there is a period of a few days before the larvae hatch and develop into the infective stage. During this free-living stage they are sheathed and are resistant to desiccation. Man becomes infected by swallowing the larvae, usually with contaminated food or drink, though the larvae may penetrate human skin. In the intestine of man the larvae mature in about twenty-five days, and the adult worm may live for eight years. Symptoms of infection, including anemia, are usually absent or mild.

Treatment is usually of little value in removing the worms although carbon tetrachloride, tetrachlorethylene and phenothiazine are used. Since the eggs are easily confused with those of hookworms, many cases of trichostrongyliasis have gone unreported. The world incidence of this disease in man is undoubtedly higher than usually believed. Probably more than 50,000,000 persons throughout the world harbor these worms. The incidence of infection in animals is extremely high.

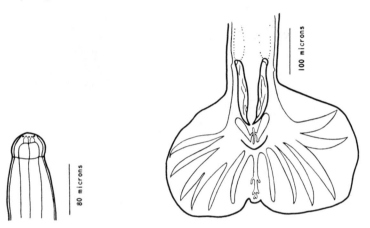

Fig. XIII–25.—*Hyostrongylus rubidus*, anterior and posterior ends of male. (Morgan and Hawkins, *Veterinary Helminthology*, courtesy of Burgess Publishing Co.)

Hyostrongylus Rubidus

Hyostrongylus rubidus (Fig. XIII–25) is the red stomach worm of swine and is world-wide in its distribution. The males are from 4 to 7 mm., and the females from 5 to 10 mm. long. Eggs in the soil hatch in thirty-nine hours and the infective third stage larvae develop in one week. Pigs become infected by eating these larvae. As with the other worms described above, *H. rubidus* sucks blood. Carbon bisulfide is the recommended drug for treatment.

SUPERFAMILY METASTRONGYLOIDEA

Metastrongylus

In this group the buccal capsule is absent or rudimentary; bursa reduced or absent; vulva situated near anus; and the worms usually require an intermediate host. Metastrongyles are called "lungworms," and they inhabit the respiratory or circulatory systems of carnivores, ungulates, rodents and primates throughout the world.

The members of one family (Pseudaliidae) infect the lungs of dolphins and porpoises.[8]

Metastrongylus elongatus (=*apri*), *M. salmi* and *Choerostrongylus* (=*Metastrongylus*) *pudendotectus* are all thread-like, white worms which may reach 60 mm. in length, although some are considerably shorter. They live in air passages of the lungs of pigs where they lay their eggs. These eggs are coughed up, swallowed, and passed from the host with feces. Various species of earthworms belonging to the genera *Helodrilus*, *Lumbricus* and *Diplocardia* eat the eggs which then hatch in the earthworm intestine. Young larval parasitic worms leave the lumen of the gut and enter the walls of the esophagus, crop, gizzard and intestine. After a period of growth they enter the circulatory system of the annelid. In about a month they are infective to swine which eat the earthworms. Larvae are released into the pig intestine whose walls they penetrate, making their way, via the lymphatic and blood vessels to the lungs. In three or four weeks after being eaten by pigs, the larvae have matured in the lungs and start producing eggs.

Infected pigs suffer from malnutrition, lung hemorrhage, difficult breathing and coughing. Young pigs may be killed by the parasites. The worms may carry the virus of swine influenza.[25] No one seems to worry about the effect of larval worms on the earthworms.

Treatment has so far been unsuccessful. Infection may be reduced by clean surroundings and other sound management practices.

An eosinophilic meningoencephalitis of man caused by a metastrongylid lung worm of rats has been reported.[23] Its method of transmission is unknown.

Dictyocaulus

Dictyocaulus viviparus (Fig. XIII–26), the lungworm of cattle may be found in other large mammals such as moose, elk, bison, deer or pigs. Worm eggs are produced in the lungs of the host and often hatch before leaving the body. The larvae or eggs are coughed up and are usually swallowed, and pass from the body with feces. Unhatched eggs are usually hatched at this time. It has been estimated that an infected animal can pass five million of these first-stage larvae a day. In about four days in moist soil the larvae develop into the second and then the third stage. The latter is the infective stage which may be ingested by cattle or some other host. From the host intestine the larvae migrate via the lymphatics or blood stream to the lungs, trachea or bronchi. Here they mature, and undergo a prepatent period of about a month. The adults are white, thread-like and 5 to 8 cm. long. They cause difficult breathing, coughing, foaming around the mouth, loss of appetite, diarrhea, fever, and even death. Five thousand larvae can kill a calf. There is no effective treatment. *Dictyocaulus filaria*, the thread lungworm, *Mullerius capillaris*, the hair lungworm, and

Protostrongylus rufescens, the red lungworm, are the commoner varieties affecting sheep and goats in the United States.

Both the thread lungworm and the red lungworm possess life cycles involving the coughing up of eggs which are swallowed and pass out of the body and hatch in the soil. The larvae go through a period of development, crawl on pasture grass and are eaten by the host. Young worms penetrate the intestinal wall and make their way, via the blood and lymph vessels, to the lungs where they mature.

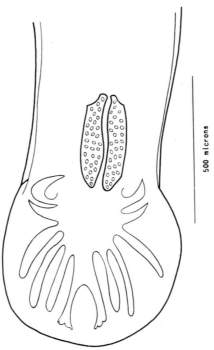

500 microns

Fig. XIII–26.—*Dictyocaulus viviparus,* posterior end of male. (Morgan and Hawkins, *Veterinary Helminthology,* courtesy of Burgess Publishing Co.)

The hair lungworm is different. Its larvae in the soil must enter a snail or slug, and develop in this intermediate host for about two weeks, although they may remain in the snail or slug for many weeks. To complete the cycle the mollusk must be eaten by a suitable vertebrate host.

Symptoms of infection with the hair lungworm vary from none to severe coughing and loss of weight. Secondary bacterial infection may be serious. Treatment is not satisfactory.

BIBLIOGRAPHY

1. BAKER, A. D., 1962. *Check List of the Nematode Superfamilies Dorylaimoidea, Rhabditoidea, Tylenchoidea, and Aphelenchoidea.* E. J. Brill, Leiden, 261 pp.

2. BEAVER, P. C., 1956. Larva Migrans, Exper. Parasitol., *5*, 587–621.
3. BEAVER, P. C., 1959. Visceral and Cutaneous Larva Migrans. Pub. Health Repts., *74*, 328–332.
4. BIRD, A. F., 1958. Further Observations on the Structure of Nematode Cuticle. Parasitol., *48*, 32–37.
5. BURROWS, R. B., 1962. Comparative Morphology of *Ancylostoma tubaeforme* (Zeder, 1800) and *Ancylostoma caninum* (Ercolani, 1859). J. Parasitol., *48*, 715–718.
6. CAMERON, M. D., 1962. The Six Hookworms of Man, Dog and Cat: Their Modes of Infection and Treatment. Southwest Vet., *15*, 292–295.
7. CONINCK, DE L., 1962. Problems of Systematics and Taxonomy in Nematology Today. Nematologica, *7*, 1–7.
8. DOUGHERTY, E. C., 1944. The Lungworms (Nematoda: Pseudaliidae) of the Odontoceti. Part I. Parasitol., *36*, 80–94.
9. DUGOID, I. M., 1961. Chronic Endophthalmitis Due to *Toxocara*. Brit. J. Ophthalm., *45*, 705–711.
10. FAIRBAIRN, D., 1957. The Biochemistry of *Ascaris*. Exper. Parasitol., *6*, 491–554.
11. ————, 1960. The Physiology and Biochemistry of Nematodes. In: *Nematology, Fundamentals and Recent Advances*. Eds. J. N. Sasser and W. R. Jenkins. Univ. of North Carolina Press. Chapel Hill. p. 267–296.
11a. GHARIB, H. M., 1961. A Preliminary Note on the Bacteriostatic Properties of Some Helminths of Animals. J. Helminthol., *35*, 225–232.
12. GOODEY, J. B., 1957. *Laboratory Methods for Work with Plant and Soil Nematodes*, Technical Bulletin No. 2, Ministry of Agriculture, Fisheries and Food. London.
13. HALEY, A. J., 1961. Biology of the Rat Nematode *Nippostrongylus brasiliensis* (Travassos, 1914). I. Systematics, Hosts and Geographic Distribution. J. Parasitol., *47*, 727–732.
14. HALEY, A. J., 1962. Biology of the Rat Nematode, *Nippostrongylus brasiliensis* (Travassos, 1914). II. Preparasitic Stages and Development in the Laboratory Rat. J. Parasitol., *48*, 13–23.
14a. HSIEH, H. C., BROWN, H. W., CHEN, E. R., CHEN, C. Y., and SHIH, C. C., 1963. Treatment of *Fasciolopsis buski*, *Ancylostoma duodenale*, *Ascaris lumbricoides*, *Trichuris trichiura*, and *Enterobius vermicularis* Infections with Stilbazium Iodide. J. Parasitol., *49*, 425–427.
15. HYMAN, L. H., 1951. *The Invertebrates: Acanthocephala, Aschelminthes, and Entoprocta*. 572 pp. Vol. III. McGraw-Hill Book Co., New York.
16. LAVOIPIERRE, M.M.S., 1958. Studies on the Host-Parasite Relationships of Filarial Nematodes and Their Arthropod Hosts. II. The Arthropod as a Host to the Nematode: A Brief Appraisal of Our Present Knowledge, Based on a Study of the More Important Literature from 1878–1957. Ann. Trop. Med. & Parasitol., *52*, 326–345.
17. MONNÉ, L., 1959. On the External Cuticles of Various Helminths and their Role in the Host-Parasite Relationship. A Histochemical Study. Arkiv. Zool., *12*, 343–358.
18. MONNÉ, L. and HÖNIG, G., 1954. On the Properties of the Egg Envelopes of Various Parasitic Nematodes. Arkiv. Zool., *7*, 261–272.
19. OLSEN, O. W., 1957. A Fur Seal Pup is Born. Turtox News, *35*, 32.
20. ROGERS, W. P., 1962. *The Nature of Parasitism. The Relationship of Some Metazoan Parasites to Their Hosts*. Academic Press, New York and London, 287 pp.
21. ROGERS, W. P. and SOMMERVILLE, R. I., 1957. Physiology of Exsheathment in Nematodes and its Relation to Parasitism. Nature, *179*, 619–621.
22. ROMAN, E. 1956. Specificité Parasitaire de *Strongyloides ratti*, du Surmulot. Effects de la Cortisone sur l'Infestation d'Autres Rongeurs par ce Nématode. Ann. Parasitol. Humaine et Comp., *31*, 552–571.
23. ROSEN, L., CHAPPELL, R., LAQUEUR, G. L., WALLACE, G. D., and WEINSTEIN, P. P., 1962. Eosinophilic Meningoencephalitis Caused by a Metastrongylid Lung-Worm of Rats. J. Amer. Med. Assoc., *179*, 620–624.
24. SASSER, J. N. and JENKINS, W. R., 1960. *Nematology. Fundamentals and Recent Advances, With Emphasis on Plant Parasitic and Soil Forms*. Univ. North Carolina Press, Chapel Hill, N. C., 480 pp.
25. SHOPE, R. E., 1943. The Swine Lungworm as a Reservoir and Intermediate Host for Swine Influenza Virus. III. Factors Influencing Transmission of the Virus and the

Provocation of Influenza. IV. The Demonstration of Masked Swine Influenza Virus in Lungworm Larvae and Swine Under Varied Conditions. J. Exper. Med., *77*, 111–126, 127–138.

26. SKRJABIN, K. I. (ed.), 1960. *Essentials of Nematology*. Vol. III. *Trichostrongylids of Animals and Man*. Israel Program for Scientific Translations (for N.S.F. & Dept. Agric. Wash. D.C.), 704 pp.

26a. SKRJABIN, K. I. (ed.) 1962. *Key to Parasitic Nematodes*. Vol. III. *Strongylata*. Israel Program for Sci. Transl. (N.S.F. & Dept. Agric. Wash. D.C.), 890 pp.

27. STOLL, N. R., 1962a. Biology of Nematodes Parasitic in Animals. J. Parasitol., *48*, 830–838.

28. STOLL, N. R., 1962b. On Endemic Hookworm, Where Do We Stand Today? Exptl. Parasitol., *12*, 241–252.

29. TROMBA, F. G., 1962. Immunology of Nematode Diseases. J. Parasitol., *48*, 839–845.

30. THORNE, G., 1961. *Principles of Nematology*. McGraw-Hill Book Co., N. Y. 553 pp.

31. WALLACE, H. R., 1961. The Bionomics of the Free-living Stages of Zoo-parasitic and Phyto-parasitic Nematodes—A Critical Survey. Helminthol. Abst., *30*, 1–22.

32. WALLACE, H. R., 1962. The Future of Nematode Ecology. J. Parasitol., *48*, 846–849.

CHAPTER XIV

Phylum Nematoda
Orders: Ascaridida, Spirurida, Camallanida

ORDER ASCARIDIDA

SUPERFAMILY ASCARIDOIDEA

THREE prominent lips around the mouth are important characteristics of this group of worms. Usually there is no pronounced posterior bulb in the esophagus, but there is, in the majority of species in this order, a ventriculus which sometimes has appendages, and an intestinal cecum which projects forward alongside the esophagus. The tails of both males and females come to a point but the female tail is blunter. The tail of the male is usually coiled. Members of this order are primarily parasites of vertebrates, and some species are of considerable economic importance.

Species of nematodes belonging to this order are especially abundant in fishes, amphibia, reptiles and birds. For example, *Porrocaecum* and *Contracaecum* are found in many fishes, birds, and marine mammals; *Raphidascaris* is a common parasite of fishes; *Angusticaecum* inhabits amphibians and reptiles; members of the family Anisakidae are widespread in aquatic or fish-eating vertebrates; and *Ophidascaris*, whose juvenile stages may be found in frogs and salamanders, is a parasite of reptiles. Some species of veterinary or medical significance are described below.

The life cycles of the ascaridoids usually involve one or more intermediate hosts. That of *Ascaris lumbricoides* (see below) represents an unusual form of behavior. See Hartwich[9] for a consideration of the morphology and taxonomy of these worms.

Toxocara and Toxascaris

Toxocara canis (Figs. XIV–1, 2) and *Toxascaris leonina* are intestinal roundworms of dogs and cats and related carnivores. Another species, *Toxocara cati*, seems to be limited to cats. Adult worms may be 5 to 18 cm. long, and they possess one-host life cycles. Infections are normally obtained by eating worm eggs. Eggs hatch and complete their first molt in the host duodenum, and then penetrate the intestinal wall from where they may migrate to other organs. In *T. canis* the transference of larvae may occur by transmission of second-stage larvae from the female host to the liver of the fetus, or from newborn hosts to the mother. *T. leonina* may be transmitted by the migration of the third-stage larvae from the host intestinal wall to the intestinal lumen.[18]

These intestinal roundworms are especially harmful to puppies. The animals lose their appetite, and their abdomens tend to enlarge. Large numbers of worms are often passed with feces, or sometimes coughed up. The juveniles frequently cause larva migrans in man (see p. 308).

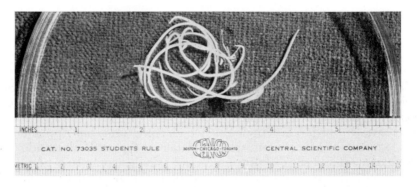

Fig. XIV–1.—*Toxocara canis* adults. (Courtesy of Dow Chemical Co.)

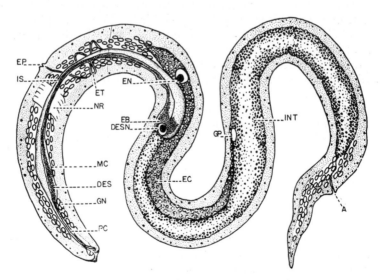

Fig. XIV–2.—Infective second-stage *Toxocara canis* larva pressed from egg (× 624). A, anus; DES, dorsal esophageal gland; DESN, nucleus of dorsal esophageal gland; EB, esophageal bulb; EC, excretory column; EN, nucleus of excretory cell; EP, excretory pore; ET, excretory tubule; GN, ganglionic nucleus; GP, genital primordium; INT, intestine; IS, isthmus; MC, metacorpus; NR, nerve ring; PC, procorpus. (Nichols, courtesy of J. Parasitology.)

Ascaris Lumbricoides

When a man has "worms," he probably harbors the common intestinal roundworm, *Ascaris lumbricoides* (Fig. XIV–3). This parasite is world-wide in its distribution and in some localized areas of the Orient its incidence of infection is 100 per cent. The worm possesses typical nematode structures and is often used in biology laboratories as a representative of the Nematoda. A very closely related species, *A. suum*, lives in the intestines of pigs.[17]

Ascaris lumbricoides is the largest nematode of the human intestine. An adult female may reach 50 cm. in length (almost 2

FIG. XIV–3.—*Ascaris lumbricoides*, adults. (Courtesy of Dow Chemical Co.)

feet), but the average is about 27 cm. Males average about 22 cm. in length. Characteristically, nematode males are smaller than the females. There may be only one worm in the intestine or there may be many. After medication, one man expelled 667 worms. An autopsy of another man revealed 1,488 worms, an astonishing burden of large parasites to be carried in the intestine. The writers have seen patients in the Orient so heavily parasitized with worms that a bowel movement produced nothing but a large mass of ascarids and tapeworms. It has been estimated that the glycogen consumption in one year of all the ascarids in all the people of China is equal to the carbohydrate value of 143,000 tons of rice.

This worm looks like a slim white earthworm without segments. There are three prominent lips surrounding the mouth, each lip possessing a pair of minute papillae on its lateral margin (Fig. XIV–4). The mouth cavity leads to a muscular esophagus which is at-

22

tached to the mid-intestine. The latter organ extends almost to the extremity of the body where it empties into a short rectum. The rectum opens directly through the anus in the female and into the cloaca in the male. The ability of *Ascaris* to digest foodstuffs is not thoroughly understood. Amylase, lipase, esterase and protease have been found in the intestine of this worm but the exact role these enzymes play is still uncertain.

The cuticle, an epidermal secretion, contains fibrous protein as well as small amounts of carbohydrates and lipids. About 74 per cent of the cuticle, however, is water. This highly important membrane of roundworms has been studied extensively, with conflicting reports. In *Ascaris* it consists of three main layers. (1) A resistant outer cortex which is not digested by pepsin or trypsin but can be digested by ficin and papain. This cortex may be keratin or collagen or quinone-tanned protein. (2) A softer middle layer which is some-

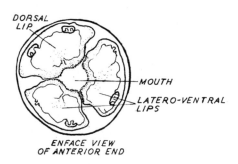

FIG. XIV–4.—*Ascaris lumbricoides*, anterior end. (Original.)

what spongy and easily digested by pepsin and trypsin. (3) A three-part layer of fibers embedded in a matrix. This layer can be digested by pepsin but not by trypsin. The fibers are probably collagen.

Ascaris possesses two distinct types of hemoglobin: (1) that which comprises about 2 per cent of the hemolymph, and (2) a type which occurs in the body-wall of the worm. The functions of these hemoglobins are obscure. Their respiratory function is questionable since under anaerobic conditions the body-wall hemoglobin is deoxygenated in six hours but the hemolymph hemoglobin remains unchanged. In general, composition of the hemolymph is similar to the composition of the host intestinal fluids, so far as total ions, solids and ash are concerned. More specifically the hemolymph of *Ascaris* is composed of 4.9 per cent proteins of which 2.8 per cent are albumens and 2.1 per cent are globulins. Magnesium, calcium and potassium are kept at fairly regular concentrations in this fluid but sodium passes freely through the cuticle. The worm behaves like an osmometer.

The reproductive tissues of this roundworm and of *Parascaris* contain a waxy alcohol which has the empirical formula $C_{33}H_{68}O_4$

and which contains two readily esterified hydroxyl groups and a third oxygen atom which is firmly bound in an unspecified manner. The names *ascaroside* A, B, and C have been given to the three components of this substance. The functions of these and other lipids are beginning to be understood but much remains to be done. Most of the lipids of *Ascaris* are deposited in the reproductive tissues, especially the ovaries and uterine eggs, and undoubtedly they are catabolized during embryonation. Starving worms apparently are unable to utilize these lipids. Even other lipids, such as the triglycerides, phospholipids and sterols found in contractile tissues are not readily available for energy metabolism.[6]

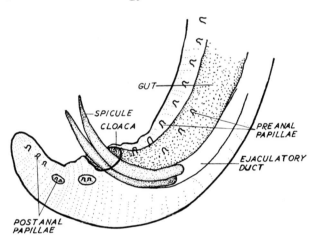

FIG. XIV–5.—*Ascaris lumbricoides.* Diagram of the posterior end of a male worm. The spicules emerge from the ventral surface of the worm. (Original.)

Males range from 15 to 32 cm. in length, with a width of from 2 to 4 mm. The posterior end curves ventrally. Male genitalia form a long coiled tube situated in the posterior half of the body, consisting of testis, collecting tubule and ejaculatory duct, the latter opening into the cloaca. Dorsal to the outer end of the ejaculatory duct is a pocket into which a pair of spicules is retracted (Fig. XIV–5). A gubernaculum is lacking. There are numerous preanal and postanal papillae.

In females the vulva lies near the junction of the anterior and middle thirds of the body, and it leads to the vagina which branches to form the paired genital tubules. Each tubule consists of a seminal receptacle, uterus, oviduct and ovary. These tubules are more or less parallel with each other and they follow a tortuous course throughout the posterior two-thirds of the body. The uterus is wider than are the other parts of the tubule, and it accommodates the eggs.

The life cycle of *Ascaris lumbricoides* starts with the fertilized egg within the body of the female. These fertilized eggs, 45 to 75 by 35 to

50 microns, are ovoidal with a thick transparent shell and an outer
coarsely mamillated, albuminous covering. They are not embryonated when voided with the feces of the host. Unfertilized eggs are
longer, narrower, more elliptical and usually possess an irregular
albuminous coating. Each female may lay as many as 200,000 eggs
per day. The eggs are laid in the intestine of the host, so there is
ample opportunity for soil contamination in areas lacking modern
sanitation. The shell of *Ascaris* eggs is highly resistant to desiccation
and to chemicals. Eggs in 10 per cent formalin have remained viable
for weeks and have developed active larvae within them.

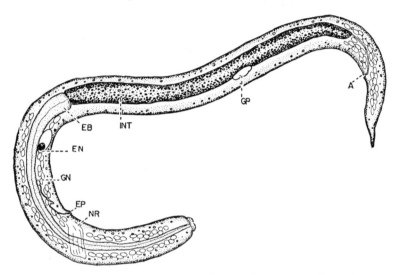

Fig. XIV–6.—*Ascaris lumbricoides*, second stage juvenile × 684. *A*, anus; *EB*,
esophageal bulb; *EN*, nucleus of excretory cell; *EP*, excretory pore; *GN*, ganglionic
nucleus; *GP*, genital primordium; *INT*, intestine; *NR*, nerve ring; (Nichols, courtesy of
J. Parasitology.)

Growth and molting of the embryo occur within the egg but the
larvae do not hatch in the soil. Full embryonation requires 2-3
weeks. When the eggs have developed to the second stage juvenile
(Fig. XIV–6) they are infective to man, and when ingested they
reach the small intestine where they are hatched. Hatching is a
complicated process which has been described as follows.[16] Dissolved
host gaseous carbon dioxide at low redox potentials, undissociated
carbonic acid and the pH are all involved in producing a stimulus
which causes the eggs to produce a hatching fluid which contains the
enzymes esterase, chitinase and possibly a protease. The esterase
alters the vitelline membrane of the eggs permitting the other
enzymes to hydrolyze the hard shell. The inner membrane forms a
bulge at this point and the larvae escape by stretching and finally
bursting through this bulge. Occasionally the entire shell is hydro-
lyzed, leaving only the thin vitelline membrane surrounding each

larva which then ruptures the membrane. The larvae are now in the part of the body where one would expect them to remain and mature. Instead, they seem to possess a wanderlust, and they burrow through the intestinal wall to the lymphatics or blood vessels and make the same tour through the body as do hookworm larvae. They go through the heart and to the lungs where they spend a week or more, then migrate to air spaces, up the trachea to the mouth and are swallowed. Back in the small intestine, from which they started, they now remain and mature. The tour through the body suggests that these ascarids have evolved from an ancestor related to the hookworm and have simply eliminated the free-living larval stage in the soil (see page 323).

The odds against any one egg reaching maturity are indicated by the vast numbers of eggs produced by one female. As mentioned above, one worm may produce as many as 200,000 eggs per day. A worm probably does not live for more than a year, but if it should live that long and produce eggs at this rate, it would produce 73,000,000 eggs during its lifetime. If many worms are present at one time we can easily understand why an unconcentrated fecal smear is almost certain to contain some eggs.

Symptoms of *Ascaris* infection vary with the phase of the infection. Immature worms leaving the intestine and migrating through the body can cause annoying or serious trouble depending on where they go. Headache, muscular pain, coughing or fever are typical symptoms. If a young worm 5 to 7 cm. long should leave the intestine and wander up the alimentary canal to creep out of the nostrils, its appearance would be more embarrassing than serious. But if the worm should pierce the gut wall and get into the heart or brain it could cause death. Larval worms which migrate into lung spaces and which remain there for several days or more can produce pulmonary symptoms. Adult worms in the intestine frequently produce no symptoms. In susceptible hosts or in cases of heavy infection there may be vague discomfort, no appetite, occasional intestinal pain, nausea, diarrhea, or constipation. Poorly nourished children in areas of heavy infection may reveal lumps of worms on rectal examination. Masses of worms are palpable through the abdominal wall.

Prevention and treatment include use of sanitary water and proper sewage disposal, thorough washing or cooking of suspected foods, and use of the drugs hexylresorcinol, oil of chenopodium, tetrachlorethylene, dithiazanine, leche de higuéron, piperazine citrate, gentian violet or hetrazan.

Heterakis

The remarkable association beteeen the protozoan flagellate, *Histomonas meleagridis*, which causes *blackhead* in poultry, and the cecal worm, *Heterakis gallinae* (Fig. XIV–7), has already been mentioned (p. 42). The male worm averages about 10 mm. in length while the female is usually about 13 mm. long. Eggs pass from the host with feces, and are eaten by earthworms which serve as vectors.[13a] When infected worms are swallowed by chickens, turkeys, and presumably by ducks, geese, guinea fowl, quail or other birds, they hatch within a few hours and the freed larvae burrow into the cecal mucosa for a day or two. They return to the cavity of the cecae and mature in three to four weeks. The distribution of this worm is probably world-wide.

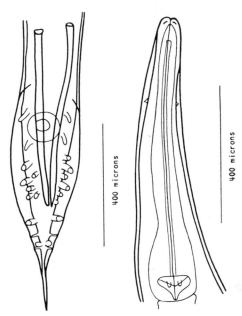

FIG. XIV-7.—*Heterakis gallinae,* posterior and anterior ends of a male. (Morgan and Hawkins, *Veterinary Helminthology,* courtesy of Burgess Publishing Co.)

Although the presence of the adult nematode worms seems to have little effect on the host, the eggs of the worm apparently carry the histomonad flagellate, *Histomonas meleagridis,* which may cause serious disease, especially to turkeys. The problem of how and when the protozoan parasite enters the egg, and when it leaves, is still to be learned but there is evidence that the larval worm as well as the egg may carry the flagellate.

SUPERFAMILY OXYUROIDEA

Oxyuroids are characterized by an esophagus with a posterior bulb, males with one or two equal spicules, and both males and females with pointed tails (few exceptions in some males). All members of the order are parasitic, primarily in vertebrates, and their common name is *pinworm.*[11a] There are no intermediate hosts. General anatomy of the group is represented in Figures XIV-8, 9 which show

Pharyngodon mamillatus from the rectum of the lizard, *Eumeces algeriensis*, and *Thelandros bulbosus* from the cecum and rectum of the lizard, *Chalicides ocellatus polylepis*.[5] Females of the former worm average 5.5 mm. in length whereas the males average 2.9 mm.

Oxyuris equi is the common pinworm in the cecum and colon of horses. Males average about 11 mm. long, whereas the females may be over 100 mm. in length (40 to 150). The worm is definitely patho-

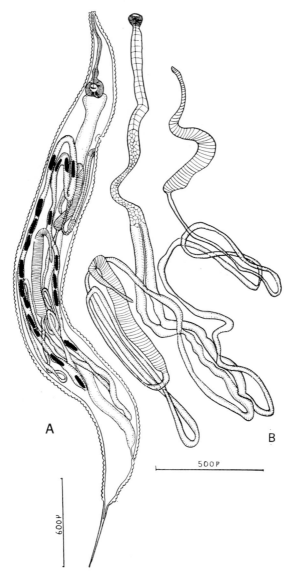

Fig. XIV–8.—*Pharyngodon mamillatus* from the rectum of a lizard showing, A, a young female, and, B, the dissected genital structures. (Chabaud and Golvan, courtesy of Arch. de l'Institute Past. du. Maroc.)

genic and heavy infestations may cause considerable irritation to horses which tend to rub the base of the tail region on fences or other objects. Sheep, rabbits, and other vertebrates may become infected with related species.

One genus, *Syphacia* (Fig. XIV–10), is found in the intestine of rats and mice, and an accidental infection has been reported from man. Persons handling rats and mice always run the risk of acquiring rodent parasites but, fortunately, these parasites are rarely pathogenic to man. *S. muris* appears to be the common species in rats and *S. obvelata* the common species in mice. There is some evidence of the possibility of cross infection between these hosts. The

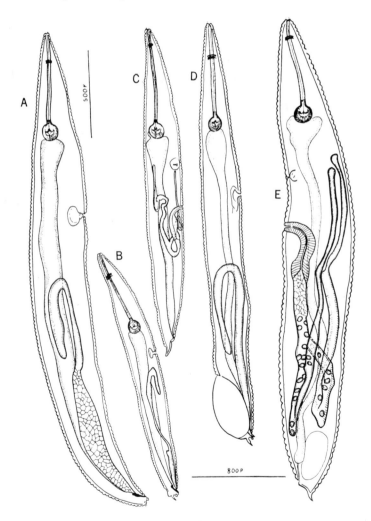

FIG. XIV–9.—*Thelandros bulbosus* from the cecum and rectum of a lizard. Lateral alae have been omitted. A, B, and D, males; C and E, females. (Chabaud and Golvan, courtesy of Arch. de l'Institut Past. du Maroc.)

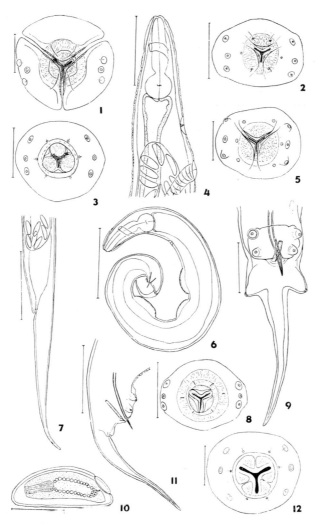

Fig. XIV–10.—*Syphacia*, several species from the intestines of various mammals showing especially the oral region. (Tiner and Rausch., courtesy of Natural History Miscellanea.)

Scales for Figures 1, 5, and 12 represent 25 μ; for 2 and 8, 30 μ; for 3, 9, and 10, 50μ; for 4 and 6, 300 μ; for 7, 500 μ; for 11, 100 μ.

1. *En face* view of *S. thompsoni* from *Glaucomys sabrinus macrotis*, in Wisconsin (U. S. N. M. Helm. Coll. No. 37156). 2. *En face* view of *S. obvelata* from *Microtus* in Alaska. (U.S.N.M. Helm. Coll. No. 37157). 3. *En face* view of *S. citelli* (U. S. N. M. Helm. Coll. No. 37152).

4. Anterior end of *S. arctica*, female. 5. *En face* view of *S. arctica*. (U. S. N. M. Helm. Coll. No. 37150). 6. Male *S. arctica*.

7. Tail of female, *S. arctica*. 8. *En face* view, *S. peromysci* from *Peromyscus maniculatus bairdii* in Wisconsin (U. S. N. M. Helm. Coll. No. 37155). 9. Ventral view, posterior extremity of *S. arctica*.

10. Egg of *S. arctica*. 11. Side view, posterior extremity of *S. arctica*. 12. *En face* view, *S. eutamii* from (type locality and host) *Eutamias minimus*, Grand Marias, Minn. (U. S. N. M. Helm. Coll. No. 37154).

worms bear a superficial resemblance to *Enterobius vermicularis* (see below) but the "tail" of both male and female is long and pointed. Males average about 1.3 mm. in length, and females about 4.5 mm. *Syphacia* eggs (125 by 35 microns) tend to be oval in outline but one side is flattened.

The human stomach is usually free from worms. The oxyuroid, *Diploscapter coronata*, however, is occasionally taken from this organ in people whose gastric hydrochloric acid level is abnormally low.

Although most of the oxyuroids are found in vertebrates, insects may be parasitized by these worms. The mole cricket, *Gryllotalpa*,

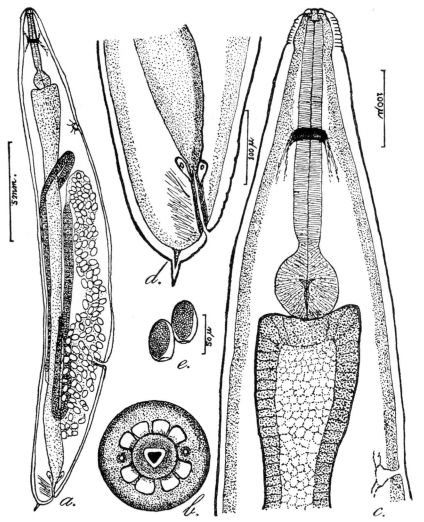

Fig. XIV–11.—*Periplaneticola periplaneticola* from the mole cricket. *a*, Adult female, entire, lateral view. *b*. Female, head, en face view. *c*. Female, anterior region. *d*. Female, tail, lateral view. *e*. Egg. (Basir, courtesy of Records of the Indian Museum.)

for example, may harbor any of the following forms: *Gryllocola gryllocola, Gryllophila gryllophila, Talpicola talpicola, Mirzaiella asiatica* and *Periplaneticola periplaneticola*[2] (Fig. XIV–11).

Ascaridia Galli

This nematode (Fig. XIV–12) is a common large parasite of the small intestine of various domestic and wild birds. It has a worldwide distribution. The males average about 50 mm. long, and the females may be longer than 100 mm. although they are usually about

Fig. XIV–12.—The common chicken roundworm, *Ascaridia galli.* (Courtesy of Dow Chemical Co.)

90 mm. in length. These worms possess a preanal sucker. Eggs do not hatch in the soil but when infective and eaten by a suitable host they hatch in the intestine. During part of the growth period the juveniles burrow into the intestinal mucosa for a few days, but sometimes this burrowing does not occur. Occasionally young worms wander elsewhere in the host body, even getting into the oviduct and becoming enclosed within the egg shell.

The infection may be serious, even resulting in death. Drugs used in treatment are carbon tetrachloride, nicotine and iodine preparations. Good management practices are of great importance in controlling infections.

Enterobius Vermicularis

Enterobius vermicularis (Fig. XIII–6) is the cosmopolitan pin-worm or seatworm of man. The adult parasite is usually most abundant in the cecum and appendix. It is a short whitish worm shaped like a narrow spindle. A pair of lateral cephalic alae or wings is situated at the anterior end. The mouth possesses three lips or labia, and the mouth cavity leads to an esophagus with an extra or prebulbar swelling and a distinct bulb. Males range from 2 to 5 by 0.1 to 0.2 mm. in size, and each possesses a strongly curved posterior end. At this end there is a pair of small caudal alae ("wings") which are supported anteriorly and posteriorly by pairs of papillae. The

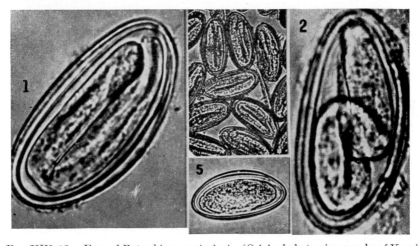

FIG. XIV–13.—Eggs of *Enterobius vermicularis*. (Original photomicrographs of Kouri.) The eggs are asymmetrical, double walled, colorless, and contain a tadpole-shaped or worm-shaped embryo. *1* and *2*, Egg with vermiform embryo. (The embryo emerges through the convex part, located in the cephalic pole of the egg—the adherence zone.) 5, non-embryonated egg. (After Gradwohl and Kouri, *Clinical Laboratory Methods and Diagnosis*, courtesy of C. V. Mosby Co.)

gubernaculum is lacking and, in contrast to *Ascaris* (p. 337), there is but one spicule. Females range from 8 to 13 by 0.3 to 0.5 mm. in size, each with a long tapering tail. The anus lies at the junction of the middle and posterior thirds of the body, and the vulva is situated in front of the junction of the anterior and middle thirds of the body. Eggs (Fig. XIV–13) are flattened on the ventral side, which shape gives them a distinct appearance. They measure 50 to 60 by 20 to 30 microns, possess relatively thick shells, and are embryonated when laid.

The life cycle, as in all sexually produced animals, begins with the fertilized egg. The eggs are usually not deposited in the host's intestine but they remain in the body of the female worm until she crawls through the host anus, usually at night. A person can sometimes feel the worms crawling in his rectum. The female worm contains about 11,000 eggs, and the pressure of these eggs sometimes causes her to burst, scattering them on the body of the host or on the bed clothes. If the worm does not burst, she rapidly discharges her eggs, dies and becomes desiccated. In women and girls, a pinworm may crawl into the genital opening and cause inflammation and irritation. The person infected may experience intense itching in the anal region or only a mild tickling sensation. Children, especially, may become irritable and not sleep well. The general symptoms are anal or vaginal pruritis, sleeplessness, irritability, nausea, constipation or diarrhea. As has been noted, these symptoms are common to many kinds of intestinal parasites, so they are of little diagnostic value. Frequently there are no symptoms. Eggs are scattered about on clothes, bedclothes, hands and on the body of persons infected, and even in the dust of the room. In classrooms up to 300 eggs have been found per square foot (30 cm. square) of dust. The eggs mature rapidly and are infective within a few hours.

Man becomes infected by inhaling contaminated air, sucking fingers after scratching infested areas, or possibly through food or drink. When the mature eggs are swallowed, they hatch in the small intestine and the larvae migrate to the cecum, appendix, colon or ileum where they mature to adults in about a month. Male and female worms may become attached to the gut wall and produce inflammation. It has been estimated that about 209,000,000 people in the world are infected with this worm. Unlike the condition with most worms we have been describing, man is the only host for *Enterobius vermicularis*. Non-human forms occur in the chimpanzee, the lar gibbon and the marmoset. Children are more commonly infected than are adults, and the parasite is more prevalent in cooler countries than in hot climates where children wear fewer clothes.

Prevention and treatment include frequent laundering of night clothes and bedding, keeping hands and fingernails clean, frequent bathing, keeping rooms as dust-free as possible, and using the following drugs: gentian violet, terramycin, hexylresorcinol, piperazine, santonin, tetrachlorethylene, phenothiazine, pyrvinium pamoate, or dithiazanine. A small enema (60 to 90 ml.) of tap water gives immediate and sometimes lasting relief from itching.

ORDER SPIRURIDA

SUPERFAMILY SPIRUROIDEA

Males of this group do not possess a bursa. Both sexes of these slender worms of moderate size usually possess two lateral lips surrounding the mouth, but there may be four or six small labia. The esophagus does not possess a bulb. The buccal capsule is cuticularized and, in the female, the vulva is usually located near the middle of the body. Most males possess unequal spicules.

These worms are parasites of the digestive tract, respiratory system, eyes, nasal cavities and sinus sacs of vertebrates. The life cycle involves one or two intermediate arthropod hosts (*e.g.* beetles, grasshoppers, flies, cockroaches, crustaceans). In a typical life cycle, thick-walled embryonated eggs from the final host are swallowed by the arthropod which is subsequently eaten by the final host.

Gnathostoma Spinigerum

These short, fat worms are normally parasites of cats and of other animals, and only accidentally of man.[15] The worms are world-wide in distribution but are found mainly in the tropics. In the normal host they live in stomach tumors; thus eggs get to the outside with feces. The eggs hatch into free-swimming larvae which are eaten by small crustacea such as *Cyclops* which, in turn, are eaten by invertebrates or vertebrates which themselves are eaten by cats. The parasites must develop, in turn, in each of these hosts to become infective to the next host. Adults are from 3 to 5 cm. long and about 8 mm. wide. They possess distinct, enlarged, spiny heads and the spines continue down one-half of the body.

In man the worms are often found in an immature condition in skin tumors although they may become lodged in almost any other organ.

Echinocephalus pseudouncinatus is a related species which lives in the pink abalone, *Haliotis corrugata*, and probably the green abalone (*H. fulgens*).[14] The worms burrow through the "foot" of the mollusk and encyst in the ventral portion of this muscle. The life cycle is unknown but larvae of related species have been found in other mollusks, and other members of the genus are parasitic in the spiral valve of sting-rays.

Gongylonema

Gongylonema pulchrum (Fig. XIV–14) is a parasite of sheep, goats, pigs, horses, cattle and of other mammals in which it lies embedded

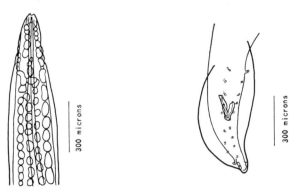

Fig. XIV–14.—*Gongylonema pulchrum* anterior and posterior ends of male. (Morgan and Hawkins, *Veterinary Helminthology,* courtesy of Burgess Publishing Co.)

in the mucosa or submucosa of the esophagus and oral cavity. It is world-wide in distribution. Males may reach 62 mm. in length and females may be as long as 145 mm. Eggs pass from the host in feces and are eaten by dung beetles or by cockroaches in which the larval worms develop. In about a month after ingestion these larvae become encysted in the insect and are infective to a new vertebrate host which eats the insect. Man is occasionally infected. One wonders what sort of man could bring himself to eat cockroaches or dung beetles.

SUPERFAMILY THELAZIOIDEA

Thelazia

Thelazia callipaeda, the oriental eye worm, and *T. californiensis* are nematode worms which are normally found in the eyes of vertebrate animals and occasionally the eyes of man. They range from 5 to 20 mm. in length and usually lie on the surface of the eyeball. When disturbed they tend to make their way under the eyelids, or into the conjunctival sac. The genus is characterized by a mouth without definite lips, short buccal cavity, male with or without alae, usually numerous preanal papillae, spicules usually unequal, ovoviviparous, occurring in the eyes, nasal chambers, mouths of mammals and birds, in the air-sacs of birds and the intestine of fishes.

SUPERFAMILY FILARIOIDEA

These long, thin, tapering worms include several species which are important parasites of man and of animals. The worms are mostly moderate in size but some are relatively long. There are no lips around the mouth, the buccal capsule is small or rudimentary, the esophagus does not possess a bulb, males have spicules but no bursa, the vulva of the females is anterior, and the females may be oviparous or ovoviviparous. The life cycle invovles a blood-sucking insect.[10] Adults are often called, "filarial worms" and the larvae are known as "microfilariae" (Figs. XIII–7; XIV–15, 16). Genera of common interest to parasitologists include *Loa*, *Wuchereria*, *Brugia*, *Onchocerca*, *Acanthocheilonema*, (= *Dipetalonema*) *Mansonella*, *Dirofilaria*, *Stephanofilaria* and *Ornithofilaria*.

Larval filarial worms are *microfilariae*. The term was formerly used as a genus name. Sometimes the larval stage of a filarial species is still designated as a separate genus. Thus the larvae of *Wuchereria bancrofti* may be written as *Mf. bancrofti*. See Kessel[13] for a discussion of the ecology of filariasis, and Friedheim[7] for a consideration of chemotherapeutic control.

Ornithofilaria Fallisensis

Ornithofilaria fallisensis is a parasite which inhabits the subcutaneous tissue of domestic and wild ducks in Canada. A careful

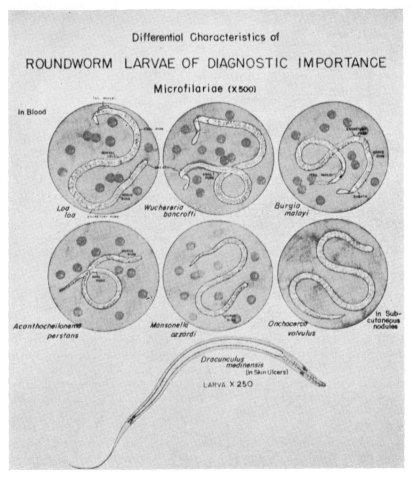

Fig. XIV–15.—Microfilariae of importance in human parasitology. (United States Navy Medical School Laboratory Guide.) (The magnifications are reduced to about $\frac{5}{8}$ of the numbers indicated.)

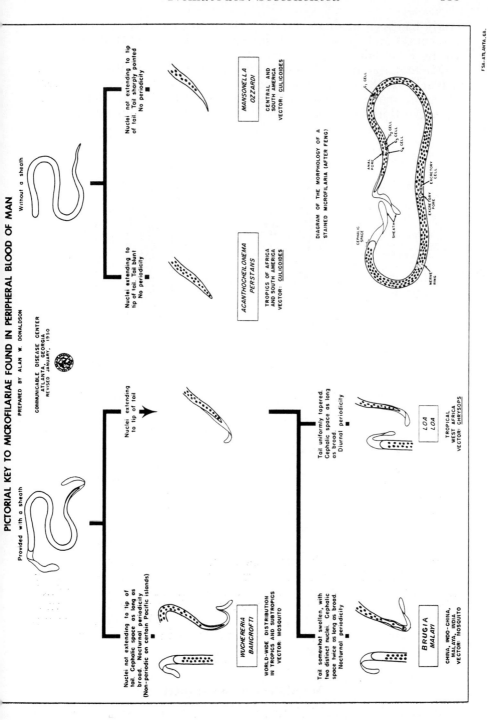

FIG. XIV–16.—Microfilariae found in peripheral blood of man. (Federal Security Agency U. S. Pub. Health Service.)

23

study has been made of the lfe cycle of this parasite in white Pekin
ducklings[1] and the results of this study will serve as an introduction
to the Filarioidea.

Microfilariae in the blood of ducklings are taken into the body of
a black fly (*Simulium venustum, S. parnassum*). In the hemocoel
of the fly the young worms (Fig. XIV–17, XIV–18) develop into the
infective third-stage larvae in one to two weeks, depending on the

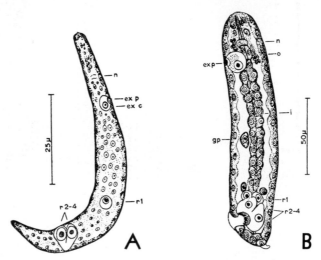

Fig. XIV–17.—Developmental stages of *Ornithofilaria fallisensis*. (Anderson, courtesy
of Canad. J. Zool.)
   A. Early larva showing division of first rectal cell, lateral view.
   B. Advanced first-stage larva with well-formed esophagus and intestine, lateral view.

a pl = anal plug ("nail-like structure" of Brug)	o = esophagus
ex c = excretory cell	r = rectum
ex p = excretory pore	r 1–4 = rectal cells ("genital cells"
gp = genital primordium	of most authors)
i = intestine	r 1 = rectal lumen
n = nerve ring	

temperature. When the fly bites a duck the worms are introduced
into the bird blood and they migrate to subcutaneous tissues where
they mature. Mating occurs, and the females produce young which,
after about a month from the time the bird becomes infected, can be
found in the peripheral blood of the host. These minute young
worms exhibit diurnal periodicity, appearing in the peripheral blood
only during the daytime.

Wuchereria Bancrofti

Wuchereria bancrofti lives in the lymphatic vessels of man in
tropical countries and, like many other nematode worms, gives

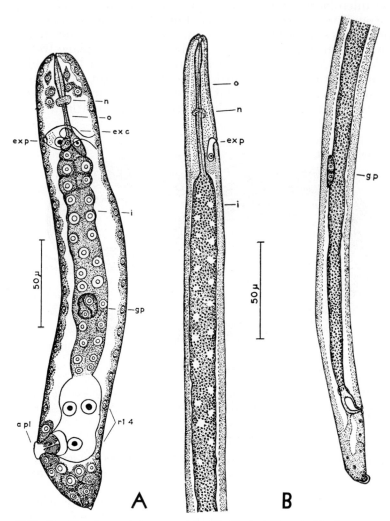

Fig. XIV–18.—Developmental stages of *Ornithofilaria fallisensis*. (Anderson, courtesy of Canad. J. Zool.)

A. Newly emerged second-stage larva, lateral view.

B. Third-stage larva from head of fly, lateral view, anterior and posterior ends. See Figure XIV–17 for legend.

birth to young (Fig. XIV–19). During development, the egg shell becomes a transparent sheath around the embryo before birth and the young are born already well advanced beyond the egg stage. These microfilariae make their way through the lymph and blood to the surface vessels of the body. They are about 270 microns long. In most places of the world where the parasite is endemic (*e.g.* Africa) this migration to the periphery of the body takes place from about 10 P.M. to 4 A.M., and the microfilariae can rarely be found in surface vessels at other times during the day or night. In Samoa, and some other areas, however, the microfilariae occur in the peripheral circulation primarily during the early morning and late afternoon,

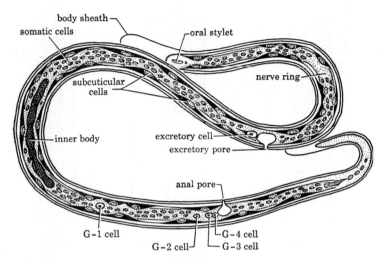

Fɪɢ. XIV–19.—*Wuchereria bancrofti* microfilaria juvenile. G refers to a genital cell. (Redrawn from Fülleborn, from Brown, *Selected Invertebrate Types,* courtesy of John Wiley & Sons, Inc.)

coinciding with those hours during which the people are usually out of their houses and working in the fields (for a brief discussion of this cycle see under *periodicity* p. 29).

Whatever the cause of the migration of young worms to the peripheral circulation, if they are there when man is bitten by a mosquito (*Culex, Anopheles, Aëdes, Psorophora, Mansonia*) they are taken into the stomach of the insect, and, if in the appropriate species, they begin a period of growth and migration which usually requires about two weeks. During this time the microfilariae molt a few times and elongate to become infective filariform larvae. They may migrate to various parts of the mosquito's body during their development, but most of them eventually reach the mouth parts where they are in a position to penetrate the skin or wound when the insect bites another man (or the original host). Apparently, larvae are dropped on the surface of the skin by the mosquito.

The details of penetration of the larvae of *Wuchereria bancrofti* through human skin is still somewhat obscure. Experiments have been made by placing the infective larvae on intact skin, on scarified skin and on areas which have been pierced with a needle to simulate a mosquito bite. In each of these experiments the worm larvae

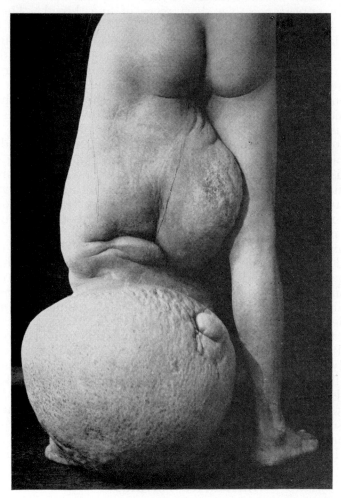

Fig. XIV-20.—Elephantiasis of the left leg. (Courtesy of the Mayo Clinic.)

failed to get through the skin. Apparently the mosquito is needed, indicating an absolute dependency on the intermediate host. See page 472 for a description of mosquitoes and their life cycle.

Worm larvae travel from the point of entry into human skin to the lymphatics where they mature to adults. The time required from the bite of the mosquito to the appearance of microfilariae in the peripheral blood is about one year. The blocking of lymph vessels by masses of adult worms, and growth of host tissue at the blocked area, cause the swelling of extremities so characteristic of advanced cases of this type of filariasis. When the disease has caused the enlargement of such organs as the scrotum, breast, and legs, it is called *elephantiasis* (Fig. XIV–20).

Adult female worms average 82 mm. long and 0.25 mm. wide — similar in appearance to a short piece of fine thread. The males average 40 mm. in length by 0.1 mm. in width. The head is only slightly larger than the tapering posterior end, and the mouth is a simple hole without lips or other organs. The mouth leads directly into the esophagus, without a buccal cavity, and the esophagus does not possess the bulges and constrictions so characteristic of some other nematode worms. The vulva opens to the outside of the body in the mid-region of the esophagus. The male possesses two spicules of unequal length, and a gubernaculum.

Symptoms range from none to fever, tenderness of infected parts, eosinophilia, inflammation, and transient swelling. Anxiety caused by fear is of considerable importance. Thick blood smears are preferable in examinations for the microfilariae. Drugs of some value are hetrazan and arsphenamide. Prevention involves the use of DDT and other insecticides, mosquito control measures and moving from areas of infection.

Brugia malayi is the cause of widespread filarial disease of man in the Far East from Korea south through China, Philippines, Malaya, Indonesia and New Guinea, as well as Ceylon and India. It is transmitted by mosquitoes of the genera *Mansonia* and *Anopheles*, and occurs also in monkeys and cats. Clinical features include adenitis, periodic lymphangitis and elephantiasis typically involving the feet and legs. The microfilariae exhibit nocturnal periodicity. For further details see Buckley[3] and Wilson.[20]

Closely related to *Brugia malayi* is *B. pahangi* which is found principally in carnivores, but also in a wide range of other kinds of mammals, including primates. It has been reported from Malaya and East Pakistan, and has been transmitted to man experimentally. The mosquito vectors are species of *Mansonia*, *Aëdes* and *Armigeres*. The microfilaria, *B. patei*, has been found in dogs and cats in East Africa. For details of *B. pahangi* see Buckley,[3] and Schacher.[16a]

Onchocerca Volvulus

Onchocerca volvulus (= *caecutiens*) (Fig. XIV–21) is a subcutaneous parasite which causes the disease known as onchocerciasis in man in Africa and tropical America. The adult worms are usually found in fibrous skin tumors which appear as nodules almost anywhere on the body, but rarely on the lower parts of the legs. The life cycle starts with the fertilized egg within the body of the female. This zygote develops into a microfilaria (Fig. XIV–22) which escapes the egg membranes and leaves the mother worm. Many thousands of microfilariae, 250 to 300 microns long, gather in the nodules, wander

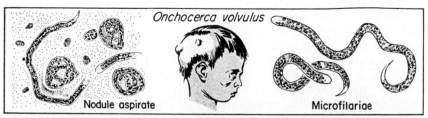

FIG. XIV–21.—Epidemiology of onchocerciasis. (Mackie, Hunter and North, *A Manual of Tropical Medicine,* courtesy of W. B. Saunders Co.)

in connective tissues and find their way into superficial lymphatic vessels. Apparently, they do not get into blood vessels.

The insect vector is the black fly, *Simulium* (Fig. XVIII–10, page 479), several species of which may bite man and so pick up the microfilariae. Within the fly the young worms migrate to thoracic muscles and develop into the rhabditiform, then the filariform stage in about a week. Filariform larvae migrate to other tissues, especially the proboscis, and when the fly bites again the filariae get back into human skin or subcutaneous connective tissue. Within a year mature worms appear in nodules, and the cycle is complete.

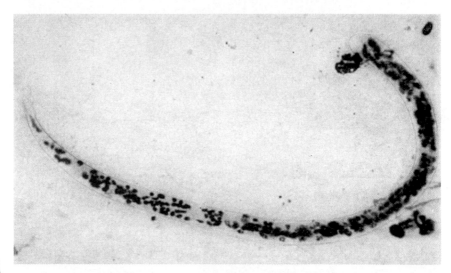

Fig. XIV–22.—*Onchocerca volvulus*, microfilaria from scarification preparation. (Photomicrograph by Zane Price, in Markell and Voge, *Diagnostic Medical Parasitology*, courtesy of W. B. Saunders Co.)

Adult males are 20 to 50 mm. long and the females may reach 700 mm. (28 inches)[11] but they are usually shorter. The worms occur in a tangled mass in the nodules. A light infection consists of a single nodule but occasionally over one hundred nodules appear on one person. Usually these nodules contain degenerating worms, whereas healthy adult worms are more often found free in subcutaneous tissues.

The infection usually causes an itching dermatitis, but the original nodule is commonly painless. As the nodules increase in number and age they may become filled with pus. They gradually become fibrous and eventually are calcified. Sometimes skin involvement is not accompanied by nodular formation. A serious infection occurs when the worms get into the eye. There is no satisfactory drug treatment, but surgical removal of the nodules usually has good results. Hetrazan, cortisone and prednisone seem to be beneficial in some cases. Control consists of destroying black flies directly with insecticides and by eliminating their breeding places. See Burch.[4]

Loa Loa

Loa loa (Fig. XIV–23) is the eye-worm of Africa. The adult parasite averages about 50 mm. in length and it lives in the connective tissues of various parts of the body of man and monkeys. Female worms deposit sheathed embryos (microfilariae) which migrate to the blood stream and are taken up by the bite of a horse fly or mango fly (*Chrysops dimidiata* or *C. silacea*) belonging to the family Tabanidae. The fly feeds during all daylight hours but its biting peak

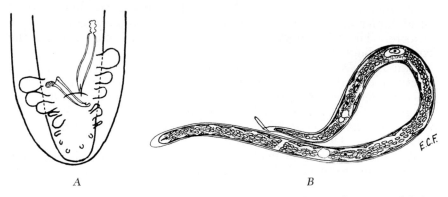

A   B

Fig. XIV–23.—*Loa loa*. *A*, Posterior end of male, ventral view, showing caudal alae, papillae and copulatory spicules. × 180. (From Faust, after Yorke and Maplestone's *Nematode Parasites of Vertebrates*, courtesy of J. and A. Churchill, Ltd.)

B, Microfilaria of *Loa loa*. × 666. (From Faust, after Fülleborn, Arch f. Schiffs u. Tropen-Hygiene; courtesy of Johann Ambrosius Barth.)

is during the middle of the day. Intercapillary feeding is probably impossible, and microfilariae are ingested from a blood pool charged with an anticoagulant from the fly. Apparently little, if any, damage is done to the insect.[8] The parasites become infective filariform larvae within the insect in about ten days and they are transferred to man by the bite of the fly. The worms probably take the best part of a year to mature and they wander in connective tissue, periodically crawling over the eye just under the corneal conjunctiva.

Monkeys may possibly serve as host reservoirs for this worm. The parasite can be transmitted by practically all species of *Chrysops*, but the exact pathway of larval migration either in the fly or in the mammalian host has not yet been determined. As with many other larvae of nematode worms, the microfilariae of *Loa loa* are periodic in the life cycle. During the day the larvae remain in the peripheral circulation where they can be picked up easily by the blood-sucking fly, whereas at night they are concentrated in lung capillaries. It is still a mystery as to how this periodicity is controlled, but it is not completely dependent on such agencies as oxygen tension, CO_2 concentration or exercise, although some physiological factors are involved.

The infection is usually painless, but allergic responses may occur. Hetrazan is used in treatment, and the worms can be removed from the eye fairly easily.

Dirofilaria

Dirofilaria immitis lives in the pulmonary artery and heart of the dog and in some wild carnivores such as the fox or wolf. It is commonly transmitted by mosquitoes and fleas, and is world-wide in distribution. The first larval stage develops in the hemocoel of the insect abdomen, and the second stage develops in the hemocoel of the abdomen and thorax. The insect seems not to be affected by the parasite. The adult male worm is about 14 cm. long, whereas the female is about 27 cm. in length.

Immature *Dirofilaria* of various species may infect man as conjunctival or subcutaneous parasites. One species from the conjunctivae has been named *D. conjunctivae* but it probably belongs to the genus *Nochtiella*, a relatively small filaria in which the caudal papillae of the males exhibit a distinct asymmetry in number and distribution. Occasionally adult *Dirofilaria* have been reported from man, an abnormal host, but there is no evidence that viable microfilariae are produced by female *Dirofilaria* in man.

ORDER CAMALLANIDA

SUPERFAMILY DRACUNCULOIDEA

Nematodes belonging to this order do not possess definite lips, but six conspicuous labial papillae and eight external papillae are present. The esophagus generally has a muscular portion and a posterior, broader, glandular portion.

The Guinea worm, *Dracunculus medinensis* (Figs. XIV–24) occurs in Africa, parts of Asia and rarely in South America. Areas of abundant rainfall are freer from the worm than are drier locations. The adult female measures between 750 and 1200 mm. in length (up to 4 feet) with a diameter of about 1.25 mm. The male is much shorter, averaging only about 25 mm. in length. These worms live in the connective tissue of man and other vertebrates, especially just under the skin, and they can migrate from one site to another.

The life cycle starts with the development of young worms within the body of the female parasite. By the time the young are ready to emerge from the uterus, the female has produced a hole in the host's skin into which a portion of the worm's uterus projects. When the infected host skin comes in contact with water, as when bathing or washing clothes, myriads of young worms pass from the uterus

into the water. The larvae are approximately 600 microns long.
As they swim around, some of them may be eaten by the small
freshwater crustacean, *Cyclops* (Fig. XVI–8). Several species of the
intermediate host are involved, among them being *C. bicuspidatus,*
C. cornatus and *C. leuckerti.* Within this crustacean vector the
young Guinea worms migrate to the hemocoel, undergo one or two
molts and become infective in ten to twenty days. The definitive
hosts (man, dogs, cats, or various wild mammals) acquire the infection by ingesting infected *Cyclops* in drinking water. In these
crustacea the larvae leave the *Cyclops* while it is being digested, and

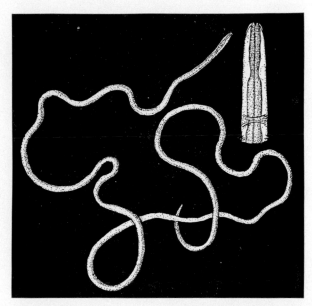

Fig. XIV–24.—*Dracunculus medinensis*, the Guinea worm. A female specimen is shown
with an enlarged view of the anterior end. (Original.)

penetrate the host's intestinal wall. They migrate to connective
tissue where they mature in about a year. After fertilization the
males die and are absorbed by the host. When the females become
gravid they migrate to the skin which they pierce, thus providing
the locus for the development of a small ulcer.

Symptoms are absent until a skin sore begins to form. Then there
may be nausea, diarrhea, giddiness, skin rash, itching or asthma.
The sore is usually on feet, legs or arms but occasionally on other
parts of the body, the location corresponding to the parts which
most often get wet. At first there occurs a reddish pimple which
enlarges and then develops a blister which eventually breaks.
The sore is usually not much over 5 mm. in diameter but it can get
considerably larger, and sometimes it becomes secondarily infected
with bacteria.

Phenothiazine emulsion injected into the muscle near the worms is of some value in treatment. Surgical removal of the worms is the best procedure. Some Africans and Asians remove the worms by slowly winding them on small sticks (Fig. XIV–25), but this feat must be done gradually, a few centimeters a day, or the worm will break and cause severe inflammation. Control measures center around keeping people with the sores from contaminating wells, laundry and bathing waters, and encouraging *Cyclops*-eating fish to become established in streams or ponds used by the people.

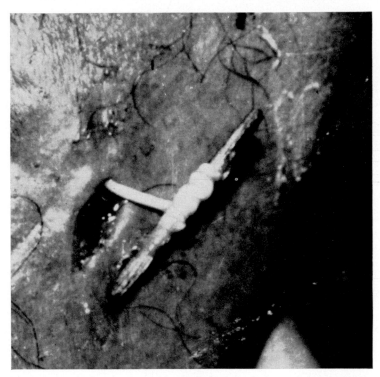

Fig. XIV–25.—The nematode, *Dracunculus medinensis*, being removed from the arm by slow winding on a match stick. (Courtesy, Institute of Parasitology and Malariology, University of Teheran, School of Medicine.)

BIBLIOGRAPHY

1. Anderson, R. C., 1956. The Life Cycle and Seasonal Transmission of *Ornithofilaria fallisensis* Anderson, A Parasite of Domestic and Wild Ducks. Canadian J. Zool., *34*, 485–525.

2. Basir, M. A., 1942. Nematodes Parasitic in *Gryllotalpa*. Mus. Univ., India, *44*, 95–106.

3. Buckley, J. J. C., 1958. Occult Filarial Infections of Animal Origin as a Cause of Tropical Pulmonary Eosinophilia. East African Med. J., *35*, 493–500.

4. Burch, T. A., 1961. The Ecology of Onchocerciasis. In: May, J. M. (ed.), *Studies in Disease Ecology*. Chapter 4. Hafner Publ. Co., N. Y., 613 pp.

5. CHABAUD, A. G. and GOLVAN, Y. J., 1957. Miscellanea Helminthologica Maroccana XXIV. Nematodes Parasites de Lezards de la Foret de Nefifik. Arch. de l'Institut Pasteur du Maroc., 7, 447–469.
6. FAIRBAIRN, D., 1955. Lipids of the Female Reproductive Organs in *Ascaris lumbricoides.* Canadian J. Biochem. and Physiol., *33* (1), 31–37.
7. FRIEDHEIM, E. A. H., 1963. Missing Links in Chemotherapeutic Control of Filariasis. J. Trop. Med. Hyg., *66*, 102–105.
8. GORDON, R. M., 1955. The Host-Parasite Relationships in Filariasis. Trans. Roy. Soc. Trop. Med. Hyg., *49*, 496–507.
9. HARTWICH, G., 1954. Die Vorderdarmstrukturen, das Exkretionssystem sowie der Kopfbau der Ascariden und ihre taxonomische Bedeutung. Wiss. Ztschr. Univ. Halle, Math. Nat., *3*, 1171–1212.
10. HAWKING, F. and WORMS, M., 1961. Transmission of Filaroid Nematodes. Ann. Rev. Entomol., *6*, 413–429.
11. HYMAN, L. H., 1951. *The Invertebrates: Acanthocephala Aschelminthes and Entoprocta.* Vol. III, McGraw-Hill Book Co. 572 pp.
11a.INGLIS, W. G., 1961. The Oxyurid Parasites (Nematoda) of Primates. Proc. Zool. Soc. London, *136*, 103–122.
12. KAGAN, I. G., 1960. Trichinosis: A Review of Biologic, Serologic and Immunologic Aspects. J. Inf. Dis., *107*, 65–93.
13. KESSEL, J. F., 1961. The Ecology of Filariasis. In: May, J. M. (ed.), *Studies in Disease Ecology,* Chapter 3. Hafner Publ. Co. N. Y., 613 pp.
13a.LUND, E. E., WEHR, E., and ELLIS, D., 1963. Role of Earthworms in Transmission of *Heterakis* and *Histomonas* to Turkeys and Chickens. J. Parasitol., *49* (No. 5, Sect. 2), 50.
14. MILLEMANN, R. E., 1951. *Echinocephalus pseudouncinatus* n.sp. A Nematode Parasite of the Abalone. J. Parasitol., *37*, 435–439.
15. MIYAZAKI, I., 1960. On the Genus *Gnathostoma* and Human Gnathostomiasis, With Special Reference to Japan. Exp. Parasitol., *9*, 338–370.
16. ROGERS, W. P., 1958. Physiology of the Hatching of Eggs of *Ascaris lumbricoides.* Nature *181*, 1410–1411.
16a.SCHACHER, J. F., 1962. Morphology of the Microfilaria of *Brugia pahangi* and of the Larval Stages in the Mosquito. J. Parasitol., *48*, 679–692.
17. SCHWARTZ, B., 1959. Experimental Infection of Pigs with *Ascaris suum.* Am. J. Vet. Res., *20*, 7–13.
18. SPRENT, J. F. A., 1959. The Life History and Development of *Toxascaris leonina* (von Linstow 1902) in the Dog and Cat. Parasitol., *49*, 330–371.
19. THORNE, G., 1961. *Principles of Nematology.* McGraw-Hill Book Co., N. Y., 553 pp.
20. WILSON, T., 1961. Filariasis in Malaya. A General Review. Trans. Roy. Soc. Trop. Med. Hyg., *55*, 107–129.

CHAPTER XV

Phylum Nematoda
Class Adenophorea (= Aphasmidia)
Orders: Dorylaimida, Dioctophymatida
Class Nematomorpha

SUPERFAMILY MERMITHOIDEA

These slim, smooth nematodes range in size from a few millimeters to 50 cm. in length. They are free-living in the soil or in water as adults but are parasitic during the larval stages, especially in insects but also in other invertebrates. There is no buccal capsule, and the long (sometimes one-half body length) esophagus proceeds directly from the mouth opening. The intestine consists of two or more rows of enlarged cells filled with food reserves.

Agamermis decaudata (Fig. XV–1) is parasitic in the body cavity of grasshoppers. Young worms, 5 to 6 mm. long, in moist soil, enter grasshopper nymphs but in so doing the worms usually leave half of their bodies outside. There is a node or breaking point at about the middle of the body, and at this point the two portions of the worm part company, the anterior half taking up its residence in the insect and the posterior half disintegrating in the soil. The necessary or-

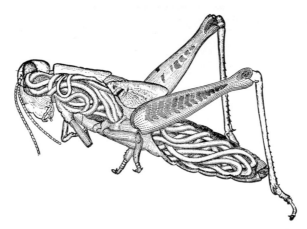

Fɪɢ. XV–1.—Grasshopper infected with juvenile *Agamermis decaudata*. (Hyman, *The Invertebrates* courtesy of McGraw Hill Book Co.)

gans for continuing life and for reproduction accompany the anterior half, so all is well. After remaining in grasshoppers for one to several months the worms emerge through the body wall and lie in the soil during the winter. The next spring they mature, mate, produce eggs which hatch and liberate more young which enter other grasshoppers, and so the cycle is complete.

The burden of worms which a grasshopper may carry is enormous, as can be seen in the illustration, and obviously considerable damage to the viscera may result in death. Some insects become infected by eating mermithid eggs. These parasites may infect crustacea, spiders and snails, in addition to insects.

SUPERFAMILY TRICHINELLOIDEA

The anterior portion of the body of these worms is filamentous, sometimes markedly so, while the posterior part is wider and often considerably shorter. The mouth is not surrounded by lips, the buccal capsule is small or rudimentary, the esophagus lacks a bulb and is a slender tube lying in a few (sometimes only one) rows of large cells called *stichocytes*. These stichocytes are collectively known as the *stichosome*. The anus is terminal in both the male and female. Males usually possess a single ensheathed spicule but some of them lack a copulatory apparatus. The vulva is normally located near the junction of the two portions of the body. Most females are oviparous and the life cycle is usually direct, but a few species make use of an intermediate host.

Capillaria

The cropworm, *Capillaria annulata*, (Fig. XV–2) of poultry uses an earthworm in its life cycle. Eggs are deposited in the mucosa

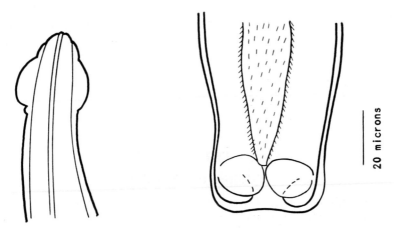

Fig. XV–2.—*Capillaria annulata*. Anterior and posterior ends of the male. (Morgan and Hawkins, *Veterinary Helminthology*, courtesy of Burgess Publishing Co.)

of the crop and are freed when this layer sloughs off and is carried down the intestine. The eggs become embryonated in a few weeks and are eaten by earthworms. Poultry become infected by eating the infected earthworms. The larval nematodes are liberated in the bird's crop, penetrate the mucosa, and mature to adults which soon mate, and a new batch of eggs is produced. Adult males average about 15 mm. in length, whereas the females average about 40 mm. Since heavily infected birds do not eat well, they lose weight, become thin and often die.

Capillaria hepatica is a liver-worm which infects rodents, ground squirrels, rabbits, beavers, monkeys and other animals, and occasionally man. The worm sometimes causes hepatic cirrhosis but

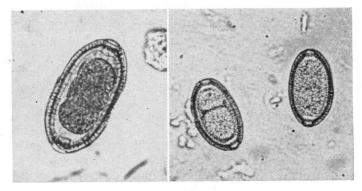

FIG. XV–3.—*Capillaria hepatica.* Photomicrographs of the eggs of the parasite, obtained from lesions produced by this parasite in the liver of a rat. (Gradwohl, Kouri, *Clinical Laboratory Methods and Diagnosis,* courtesy of C. V. Mosby Co.)

probably is not especially pathogenic. The brown, pitted, thick-shelled eggs (Fig. XV–3) (about 50 microns in diameter) are discharged in the liver but do not develop further unless freed from the liver and exposed to air. A new host acquires the infection by eating decomposed infected liver or the feces of an animal that has eaten infected liver. In the new host the eggs hatch in the intestine and the young larvae burrow through the intestinal wall and make their way to the liver where they mature. Adult males are about 4 mm. long and 100 microns wide, whereas the females are twice as wide and about 10 mm. long.

FAMILY TRICHINELLIDAE

Trichinella Spiralis

The trichina worm, *Trichinella spiralis* (Fig. XV–4, 5), causes the widespread disease *trichinosis.*[4] At least 30,000,000 people in the United States are infected with the larvae of this worm. Some estimates are as high as 60,000,000. It is especially prevalent in

Europe and in the United States and, curiously enough, rare or absent in most of the Orient and Australia.

Adult female worms average 3-4 mm. long by 60 microns wide. Adult males average about 1.5 mm. long by 45 microns wide and possess two large conical posterior papillae. The worms live in the intestinal mucosa of the duodenum and jejunum of man, pigs, wild boars, rabbits, walruses, rats, beavers, raccoons, skunks, seals, bears, polar bears, ermine, wolves, wolverine, lynx and many other mammals. The incidence of infection in the arctic marine mammals is not high. Experimental infections of adults have been established in birds. The parasites show typical nematode structures, and they differ from many roundworms in that the females do not lay eggs.

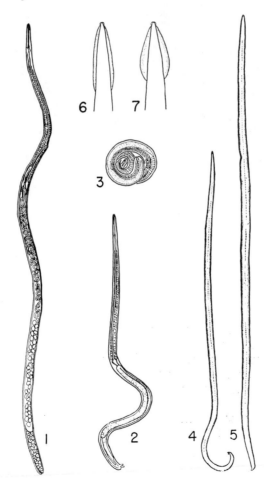

FIG. XV–4.—*Trichinella spiralis* adults compared with *Ascaris* and *Toxocara*. 1–3. *Trichinella spiralis*. 1, adult, female × 67; 2, adult male, × 67; 3, infective stage larva × 97. 4 and 5. *Ascaris lumbricoides*. 4, male with typical flexion of posterior end, × ⅜; 5, female, × ⅜. 6 and 7. *Toxocara* spp. Anterior end showing cervical alae. 6, *T. canis* ×7½; 7, *T. cati* (*mystax*), × 7½. (Beaver, courtesy of Amer. J. Clin. Path.)

The testis of *Trichinella* spiralis is a hollow tube with the germinal zone covering the entire inner wall. The ovary is also a hollow tube but the germinal zone occurs only on the ventral wall. Larval worms develop within the slender female. The larvae average about 100 microns in length when they emerge from the vulva, and one adult female may produce 1500 larvae in from three to four weeks. These young worms burrow through host tissues to the blood vessels, and they are carried to all parts of the body. They may leave the vessels and enter any organ, and they have been recovered (in hogs) from the stomach wall, testes, liver, brain, lungs, intestinal wall, pancreas, wall and contents of the urinary bladder, heart and spinal

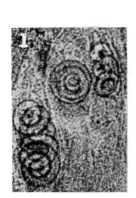

Fig. XV-5.—*Trichinella spiralis.* (Experimental infestation of white rat. Original photomicrographs [of Kouri] of material supplied by Dr. G. Bachman, Puerto Rico.) *1,* Larvae in diaphragm muscle; *6,* larvae freed by artificial digestion of muscle. (Gradwohl and Kouri, *Clinical Laboratory Methods and Diagnosis,* courtesy of C. V. Mosby Co.)

cord. The vast majority of the larvae, however, enter striated muscles, especially the diaphragm, intercostals, extraocular, lingual, larynx, pectoral, biceps, deltoid, gluteus and gastrocnemius. Here they gradually become encapsulated and eventually calcified. In the diaphragm of one human case 1000 larvae per gram of muscle were found. They may live for six months or as long as thirty years. The life cycle can continue only if the infected muscle is eaten by another host.

Man usually becomes infected by eating uncooked pork. In the small intestine of man the larvae are liberated and grow to sexual maturity in two days. The males probably die soon after copulation, and the viviparous females live for about a month producing young most of the time. Adult worms are essentially harmless. There are a variety of infection chains such as: rat to rat, pig to pig, pig to rat.

Symptoms of infection in man usually appear during the second week after he swallows infected pork. These symptoms include

LIFE CYCLE OF TRICHINELLA SPIRALIS

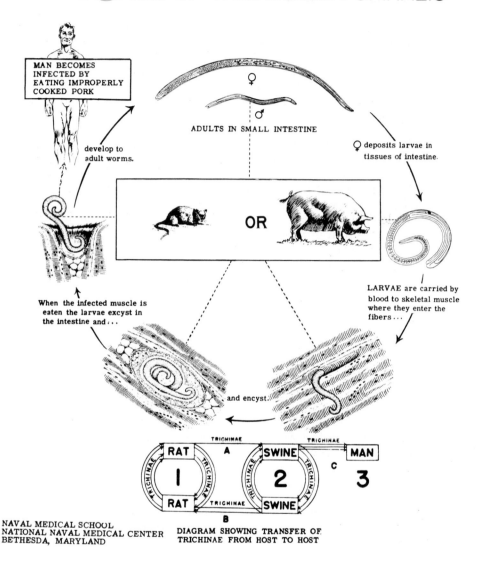

MAN BECOMES INFECTED BY EATING IMPROPERLY COOKED PORK

develop to adult worms.

ADULTS IN SMALL INTESTINE

♀ deposits larvae in tissues of intestine.

OR

When the infected muscle is eaten the larvae excyst in the intestine and ...

LARVAE are carried by blood to skeletal muscle where they enter the fibers ...

and encyst.

TRICHINAE
RAT | A | SWINE | | MAN
TRICHINAE | 1 | TRICHINAE | 2 | C | 3
RAT | TRICHINAE | SWINE
B

NAVAL MEDICAL SCHOOL
NATIONAL NAVAL MEDICAL CENTER
BETHESDA, MARYLAND

DIAGRAM SHOWING TRANSFER OF TRICHINAE FROM HOST TO HOST

169

Fig. XV–6.—Life cycle of *Trichinella spiralis*. (Courtesy of National Naval Medical Center, Bethesda, Maryland.)

headache, hemorrhages under the skin, fever, difficult breathing, edema, soreness of the infected muscles and eosinophilia. There is no specific drug against trichinosis. Intramuscular injection of adrenal hormones shows promise. Hetrazan and piperazine are possibly of some benefit. Intradermal skin tests aid in diagnosis. Prevention consists of cooking meat (especially pork) thoroughly to kill the larvae. Quick freezing (lowering the temperature immediately to —35° C.) apparently kills most of the larvae, and ionizing radiation (X-rays, gamma rays, high energy electrons) seems also to be effective. Meat scraps fed to hogs should be sterilized and rats and mice should be eliminated.

A dermal test for trichinosis consists of injecting into the skin 0.1 ml. of a 1:10,000 dilution of powdered worms. One-tenth of a gram of washed, dried powdered worms is mixed with 1 liter of sterile normal saline. A positive reaction indicates the presence of *Trichinella* but is not proof of infection since such a reaction may be evoked by the presence of related parasites.

A serological test consists of placing living *Trichinella* juveniles in the blood serum of a person suspected of harboring the parasite. If antibodies are present, a precipitate forms around the worms, especially at body openings. For details see Kagan (1960).[4]

Trichuris Trichiura

(= Trichocephalus Trichiurus)

This worm is one of the commonest helminth parasites of man, especially in tropical and subtropical regions, and apparently the same species lives in pigs and monkeys. Similar species may be found in many other animals. *Trichuris trichiura* eggs found in the gut contents of the frozen body of an Inca girl in Chile, buried at an elevation of 17,658 feet at least 450 years ago, indicate the presence of this parasite in South America before the Spanish conquest, and raise an interesting question as to the possible New World origin of *Trichuris*. It is world-wide in its distribution.

Trichuris trichiura (Figs. XV–7, 8) is commonly known as the whipworm because of the characteristic shape of its body. The anterior three-fifths is a capillary tubule which contains the esophagus; and the posterior two-fifths are more fleshy and contain the intestine and sex organs. The esophagus has a reduced musculature and is associated with a row of large secretory cells.

Male worms, with a ventrally coiled caudal extremity, measure 30 to 45 by 0.6 mm. There is a single spicule which protrudes through the retractable sheath at the posterior end of the body. The sheath possesses a bulbous end and is beset with numerous recurved spines. The female measures 35 to 50 by 0.7 mm. The vulva lies at the anterior extremity of the fleshy portion of the body. Eggs are barrel-shaped, brown in color, with an outer and an inner shell and transparent polar prominences; and they measure 50 to 54 by about 23 microns.

The life cycle begins with eggs which are deposited in the cecum, appendix, ileum, colon or rectum, where the adults live. The eggs pass from the host body to the soil with feces and they develop embryos within a few weeks. These eggs may remain viable outside of the host for many months if they lie in moist areas, but development of the larvae within them may be delayed by dryness or cold, and when a favorable weather change occurs, the bulk of the accumulated organisms continues development, thus making possible a massive

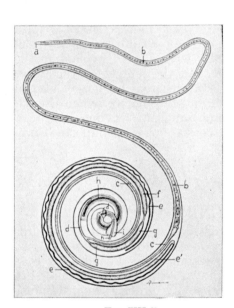

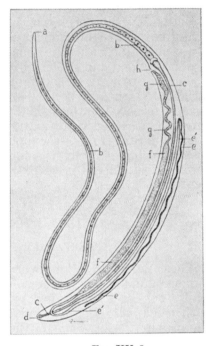

Fig. XV–7.   Fig. XV–8.

Fig. XV–7.—Male *Trichuris trichiura*. (After Guiart, modified by Kouri in "Lecciones de Parasitologia y Medicina Tropical." Courtesy of Editorial Profilaxis S.A., Havana, Cuba.) *a, b, c, d,* Digestive tract; *a,* mouth in the anterior end of the parasite; *b, b,* esophagus occupying the entire length of the thin portion of the parasite and formed by a fine duct which passes through a single layer of cells; *c, c,* intestine; *d, d,* cloaca; *e, e', f, g, h, i,* male genitalia; *e, e,* testicle; *e'* vas deferens; *f,* seminal vesicle; *g, g,* ejaculatory duct; *h, h,* spicule; *i,* sheath or thorny prepuce. (Gradwohl and Kouri, *Clinical Laboratory Methods and Diagnosis,* courtesy of C. V. Mosby Co.)

Fig. XV–8.—Female *Trichuris trichiura*. (After Guiart, modified by Kouri in "Lecciones de Parasitologia y Medicina Tropical." Courtesy of Editorial Profilaxis S.A., Havana, Cuba.) *a, b, d, d.* Digestive tract; *a,* mouth in the anterior end of the parasite; *b, b,* esophagus in the thin portion. It is formed by a fine duct which passes through a single layer of cells; *c, c,* intestine; *d,* anus; *e, e', f, g, h,* female genitalia, simple; *e', e',* oviduct; *f, f,* uterus filed with eggs; *g, g,* long and sinuous vagina; *h,* vulva. (Gradwohl and Kouri, *Clinical Laboratory Methods and Diagnosis,* courtesy of C. V. Mosby Co.)

infection. Embryonated eggs are infective to a new host, and they gain entrance to this host by being eaten. Obviously the more chances there are for fecal contamination of food and water the greater the incidence of infection. When ingested, eggs are passed to the cecum where they hatch and where the young larvae burrow into the intestinal wall. After a few days they leave the intestinal wall and may go to some other part of the intestine to mature. In a few months mature worms are ready to mate and produce eggs, thus completing the cycle. See also Figure XIII–4(1) page 303. Four molts are required from egg to adult.

Symptoms of infection are usually absent. Rarely there may be digestive disorders and anemia, toxic disturbances, intestinal obstruction or even perforation of the gut wall. Sometimes there are symptoms which are similar to those of hookworm infection. A heavy infection may cause inflammation, eosinophilia, hemorrhage, diarrhea, blood and mucus in feces, dyspnea, nausea, loss of weight, abdominal pain, fever and prolapse of the rectum. Secondary bacterial infection may occur. Diagnosis is confirmed by finding the eggs in feces. Treatment is difficult, but the following drugs have proven to be at least partially successful: leche de higuéron (latex of a fig), mixture of oil of chenopodium and tetrachlorethylene, hexylresorcinol (given orally or as an enema) and dithiazanine. Sanitary sewage disposal and personal cleanliness are obvious important preventive measures.

ORDER DIOCTOPHYMATIDA

SUPERFAMILY DIOCTOPHYMATOIDEA

These moderate to long worms each possess a mouth lacking lips but surrounded by papillae. There is no bulb on the esophagus. Males possess a bell-shaped bursa without rays. Females lay eggs with thick, pitted shells, and end-plugs. Birds and mammals are the primary hosts. Some of the worms may use fishes as intermediate hosts. *Eustrongylides*, *Hystrichis* and *Dioctophyme* are genera of particular interest to parasitologists. The latter will serve to illustrate the order.

Dioctophyme renale is, as the name indicates, a kidney worm. Since the males range in length from 140 to 450 mm. and the females range from 200 to 1,000 mm. in length, the common name of the parasite is the giant kidney worm. These reddish worms may be found in the kidneys of the dog, wolf, raccoon, mink, weasel, otter, fox, marten, seal and other mammals in the United States and the Orient. Apparently the parasites occupy the right kidney much more frequently than the left one. Destruction of the kidney may be complete.

The life cycle involves two intermediate hosts. Eggs pass from the mammal with urine and they require about six months to develop into infective juveniles. These eggs are ingested by branchiobdellids which are leechlike oligochaete worms commensal on gills of crayfishes. Nematodes escape from the egg and migrate to various organs of the oligochaete, and eventually encyst. When the second intermediate host, the black bullhead, *Ameiurus melas melas*, eats the infected branchiobdellids (or the crayfish with worms attached) the nematodes are liberated and they migrate to the fish mesenteries where they again encyst. The final host acquires the infection by eating infected fish.

CLASS NEMATOMORPHA (= GORDIACEA)

Occasionally when one looks in farmyard water-troughs he sees a long (up to 1 meter), narrow, dark-brown worm. Because of a common notion that horse hairs become transformed into these worms they are popularly called "horsehair worms," "hair worms" or "hair snakes." Horse hairs, of course, have nothing to do with the worms. In the United States there are two common varieties, *Gordius robustus* and *Paragordius varius*. In Europe the common species is *Gordius aquaticus*.

Adults and larvae possess a degenerate, non-functional digestive tract. Food is absorbed through the integument. The anterior end of the adult is translucent with a dark ring behind the clear area. The posterior portion of the male ends in two broad branches,

Fig. XV-9.—Larva of *Gordius aquaticus*, the "Horsehair Worm." (Baer, *Ecology of Animal Parasites*, courtesy of University Illinois Press.)

and the posterior portion of the female is usually bluntly tapered but it may end in three broad branches.

The life cycle begins with the egg. Each female lays one million or more eggs in strings in water or in moist soil. Within each egg there develops an embryo which possesses an armed proboscis and head region which is separated from the rest of the body by a septum (Fig. XV–9). The proboscis becomes a perforating organ which enables the larva to emerge from the egg. Soon after escaping, the young worm encysts and may be eaten by many kinds of animals. If an appropriate insect eats the cyst the wall is digested and the released worm makes its way to the body cavity or to fat bodies where it starts to mature to the adult stage. A cyst may remain viable in water for two months. If eaten by an inappropriate host (*e.g.* some insects, snails, certain fishes) the cyst wall is digested but the parasite secretes a new cyst covering and is able to withstand passage through the intestine and thus gets back to soil or water. In this manner the worm may be transported long distances. If eaten again, this time by a suitable insect, it can reach the adult stage. Just before reaching maturity in the insect the worm escapes, possibly with the aid of a digestive enzyme. Worms do not leave the insect unless they can enter water. During their stay in the insect they may bring about castration of their hosts. In water the worms copulate and soon afterwards egg laying commences. In the fall of the year after all eggs have been laid the adults die. See Hyman[3] for details.

NEMATODES PARASITIC IN PLANTS

Although most of the important plant nematodes belong to the order Tylenchida which is listed first in our scheme of classification they are considered here at the end of the nematode discussion because they and the order Dorylaimida contain parasites that live in or on plants.

The nematode parasites of plants are often called "eelworms" (Fig. XV–10). They do enormous damage to cultivated plants and cause the loss of many millions of dollars a year to farmers. This loss is due to the direct damage done by the worms and by other organisms which enter the damaged areas. Nematodes may even transmit plant viruses. Fanleaf of grapes, for example, is a virus disease which is spread by the dagger nematode, *Xiphinema index.*[2]

In structure, plant nematodes are much like the familiar ascarid worms in vertebrate digestive tracts but they are much smaller. The smallest are only about 400 microns long, while few reach a length of much over 3 to 4 mm. One of the most characteristic structures in these worms is a stylet, or spear, in the anterior end. This structure apparently helps the parasites to penetrate plant tissues. Life cycles consist of eggs, larvae and adults but the details vary considerably depending on the species of nematode, species

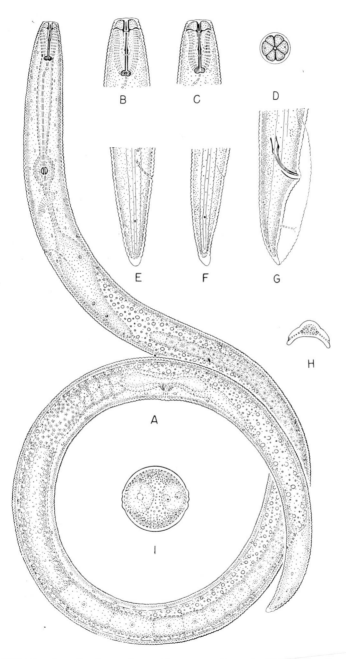

Fig. XV–10.—*Pratylenchus vulvus*. Structure of root-lesion nematode. *A*—Adult female. *B* and *C*—Heads of females. *D*—Face view of female. *E* and *F*—Female tails. *G*—Male tail. *H*—Diagrammatic cross-section through male tail. *I*—Cross-section through female body. Greatly magnified. Maggenti and Allen, courtesy of Calif. Agriculture, University of California, Division of Agricultural Sciences.)

of plant host and on temperature and other environmental factors. In general, the female worm lays eggs which hatch either in the soil or in the host plant. If the host plants are not available, the eggs frequently will not hatch but will remain dormant for years. Even larval stages of some forms can remain alive for a surprisingly long time. The larvae of the wheat nematode, for example, can live in galls for twenty years. In any case, once nematode larvae get into a plant, they begin to feed on plant tissues. Probably all crop and ornamental plants may be attacked by nematode parasites.

Some nematode worms are ectoparasitic on parts of plants which appear above the ground. *Aphelenchoides besseyi*, for example, feeds on the surfaces of leaves or on the developing buds. This parasite may also be endoparasitic, feeding on tissues within the stems and leaves of the strawberry plant. *A. ritzema-bosi* may even be ectoparasitic on some parts of gooseberry or blackberry plants and endoparasitic on other parts. Apparently the host plant determines the nature of the parasitism. Gall formation is one of the responses to endoparasitic activity. Galls may be formed in stem tissues or in a leaf or even in flowering tissues. *Anguina* spp. will produce galls in various flowering and other parts of plants. *Ditylenchus dipsaci* is a stem and bulb nematode which lives in the stems of wheat, alfalfa, potato, and leaves of onion, daffodil, garlic and other plants. Intercellular lamellae of the host plant break down and the tissues become loose and spongy. Secondary infection may be produced by bacteria or fungi. *D. dipsaci* may live for as long as twenty-one years in the dry state.

Underground parts of plants may be attacked by either ectoparasites or endoparasites or by both. The ectoparasitic worms simply lay their eggs on or near roots and when young worms hatch they start to feed on the tender parts of roots, such as the tip. *Trichodorus* and *Xiphinema* are two genera whose species behave in this manner. Plant roots swell and the plant becomes stunted or dies. These worms ordinarily do not actually enter plant tissues. Many other species do, however, penetrate into the underground parts of plants. *Pratylenchus* (Fig. XV–12), *Radopholus*, *Ditylenchus* and *Helicotylenchus* (Fig. XV–11) are genera whose species get into roots and usually lay their eggs inside the plant.

The biochemical aspects of the method of injury to potato stems by the nematode *Ditylenchus destructor* has been analyzed by Myuge.[6] He kept the worms for one day in water and then analyzed the water for enzymes and other substances. He found that the water contained amalyse and proteolytic enzymes which contained sulfhydril groups and which were especially active in a weakly-acid medium. Apparently the nature of necrosis caused by the worms consists in protein coagulation due to ammonia poisoning, consequent dehydration and protein oxidation. Starch hydrolysis leads to disruption of natural osmosis followed by a dehydration of

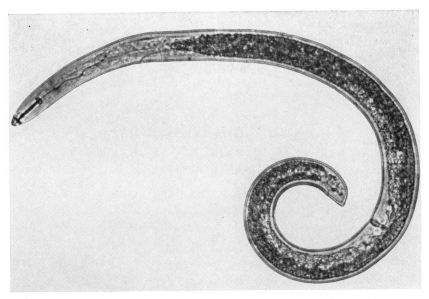

Fig. XV–11.—Mature female of *Helicotylenchus dihystera*—a plant pathogenic nematode. (Courtesy of W. T. Mai, Cornell University.)

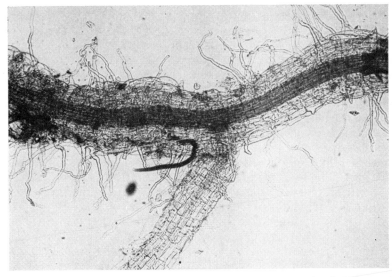

Fig. XV–12.—Larva of *Pratylenchus penetrans* entering an orchard grass rootlet. (Courtesy of W. T. Mai, Cornell University.)

affected tuber tissues. There also occurs an increase in size of plant cells bordering on the focus of invasion.

Some plant nematodes are host specific while others seem to have little preference for host plants. Some groups (*Aphelenchoides* and *Ditylenchus*) possess representatives which are even able to live and reproduce on fungi as well as on higher plants. Plants, like animals, can be resistant to parasites, and various strains resistant to certain nematodes have been developed.

FAMILY HETERODERIDAE

This important family of destructive plant parasites consists of many species belonging to three genera which can be identified according to the following key:[7]

1. Female a white saccate body with thin cuticle, eggs ejected into a mucoid mass about the posterior end; frequently gall-forming
   Meloidogyne Goeldi, 1887

   Female a tough, white saccate body, retaining most or all of eggs; not gall forming

2. Body becoming a brown cyst at maturity, vulva near terminus
   Heterodera Schmidt, 1871

   Body remaining white, vulva slightly posterior to middle of body
   Meloidodera Chitwood *et al.*, 1956

Meloidogyne is one of the many genera which typically forms galls, but in some species galls do not appear. The galls have given rise to the name "root-knot" nematodes for the group. Thousands of plants in a small area may be attacked resulting in wilting or death. Damage is done to many farm and garden plants including potatoes, peas, cereals, tomatoes, sugar beets, beans, clover, watermelon and decorative plants. Unfortunately, the presence of the worm parasites is not usually known until they occur in such large numbers that serious damage is well underway. *Meloidogyne marioni* (Fig. XV–13) is an example of one species that causes great damage among cultivated plants.

Eggs usually range from 38 to 90 microns in length depending on the species. The first larval molt occurs within the egg which hatches into worm-like larvae about 0.5 mm. long, with rounded heads and pointed tails. If these preparasitic larvae are in the soil they crawl about without feeding until they find a suitable plant, and then they penetrate large roots, rhizomes or tubers. These second-stage larvae use a piercing organ, or stylet, to penetrate the roots and to make their way to softer tissues near the center of the root. Here the worms molt three times, gradually increasing in size and in sexual dimorphism. The host reacts by forming giant cells on which the larvae feed. Hypertrophy of host tissue cells and the giant cells start the formation of the gall which is associated with disruption of the xylem. The whole infested area becomes distorted with the ball or knot of diseased tissue within which may be found all stages of the parasite from eggs to adults. Enlarged females become spherical or pear-shaped and may reproduce parthenogenetically. They may live in a gall or in other tissues. Young roots with heavy infestations may be covered with female worms which are attached to the host. At the posterior end of each worm is an egg mass in a gelatinous egg-sac. Thus, larval worms may be produced either within a plant, and migrate to other tissues, or may hatch in soil and attack other plants.

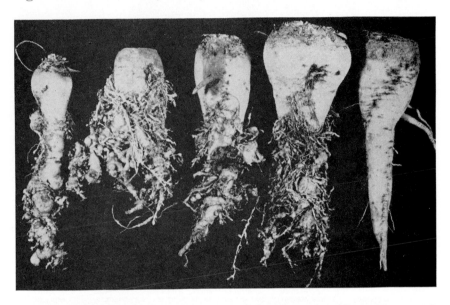

Fig. XV–13.—*Meloidogyne.* Root-knot nematode injury to sugar beets. Beet on right from soil treated with a nematocide. (Thomason and Lear, courtesy of Calif. Agriculture, University of California, Division of Agricultural Sciences.)

Heterodera is a genus of cyst formers. The female cuticle of these worms is transformed into a tough, brown, resistant cyst (Fig. XV–14) within which the eggs develop into larvae. Eggs average 46 × 100 microns. The first molt of the developing worm occurs within the egg. Larvae are liberated from the cyst and penetrate plant roots in which, after a series of molts, they mature. Some females swell and become lemon-shaped. The head and neck region remain embedded in host tissue while the rounded body, which becomes the brown cyst, is on the outside. The cyst "hatches" in one to severel years and the larvae enter tender plant roots. Infected plants die.

The potato root eelworm, or golden nematode, *Heterodera rostochiensis;* the sugar beet eelworm, *H. schachtii;* the cereal root eelworm, *H. major,* and the pea eelworm, *H. gottingiana,* are examples of plant nematodes of economic importance. The potato root eelworm causes widespread damage and is a typical example of the group. Males average a little over 1 mm. in length and are slender and worm-

Fig. XV–14.—*Heterodera*. Sugar-beet nematode cyst containing eggs. (Maggenti and Allen, courtesy of Calif. Agriculture, University of California, Division of Agricultural Sciences.)

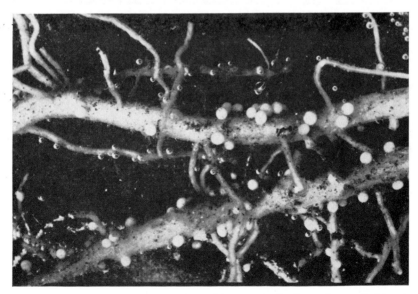

Fig. XV–15.—Immature females of the golden nematode *Heterodera rostochiensis* attached to potato roots. (Courtesy of W. T. Mai, Cornell University.)

like whereas the females become shortened and flask-shaped. There is a head-like projection and a sac-like body which is the "cyst." These cysts average about 0.6 mm. in diameter. Both males and females gradually become extruded to the root surface, and when development is complete the males usually leave the host plant and live an independent life in the soil. The mature sac-like females often remain attached to the plant by their head ends (Fig. XV–15). Mating occurs at this stage and the sac becomes filled with eggs. The females die and the sac turns dark in color, becomes tough and resistant, and is now a cyst, often containing several hundred eggs. Detached cysts remain in the soil ready to open under the right conditions, liberating the infective larvae which are about 450 microns long. Hatching depends on many factors but apparently the presence of other potato plants plays a role. There seems to be a diffusate from the roots of near-by potato plants which stimulates hatching. The life cycle normally requires from five to seven weeks and a single generation is produced each year.

The golden nematode can take up to 120,000 roentgens or more of radiation without being killed. The lethal dose for man is about 650 roentgens. The nematode can thus survive after being irradiated with a dose strong enough to kill 180 men. Some other plant nematodes can withstand doses higher than 600,000 roentgens. These facts suggest that after an atomic war nematodes may survive in abundance while other animals may all be dead.

Soil nematodes face many dangers besides desiccation and inability to find food or a proper host. Numerous species of soil fungi capture nematodes by producing adhesive "buttons" to which nematodes adhere. Others form mycelial rings in which the worms become enmeshed. In either case the fungi invade the captured worms and digest them, a process which takes about forty-eight hours.

Soil fumigants increase crop yield enormously by killing the nematodes, but, of course, their effectiveness is limited to those parasites which are in the soil.

For a detailed account of nematodes parasitic in plants see: Christie,[1] Krusberg,[5] and Thorne.[7]

BIBLIOGRAPHY

1. CHRISTIE, J. R., 1959. *Plant Nematodes.* Univ. Florida Agric. Expt. Sta., Gainesville. 256 pp.
2. HEWITT, W. B., RASKI, D. J., and GOHEEN, H. C., 1958. Nematode Vector of Soil-Borne Fanleaf Virus of Grapevines. Phytopath., *48*, 586–595.
3. HYMAN, L. H., 1951. *The Invertebrates: Acanthocephala, Aschelminthes, and Entoprocta. The Pseudocoelomate Bilateria.* Vol. III. McGraw-Hill Book Co., N. Y., 572 pp.
4. KAGAN, I. G., 1960. Trichinosis: A Review of Biologic, Serologic and Immunologic Aspects. J. Inf. Dis., *107*, 65–93.
5. KRUSBERG, L. R., 1962. Biology of Plant-Parasitic Nematodes. J. Parasitol., *48*, 826–829.
6. MYUGE, S. G., 1958. Trophical Characteristics of Potato Stem Nematodes. Abs. J. Referat. Zh. Biol., No. 1, 832. Orig. Pub: Izv. AN SSSR, Ser. biol. No. 3, 357–359.
7. THORNE, G., 1961. *Principles of Nematology.* McGraw-Hill Book Co., N. Y. 553 pp.

CHAPTER XVI

Phylum Arthropoda
Introduction, the Crustacea

MEMBERS of this phylum possess an exoskeleton with jointed appendages. The body is divided into a head, thorax and abdomen; the digestive tract is complete and the circulatory system forms a hemocoel which is the body cavity. The coelom is reduced. Respiration is accomplished by tracheae, gills, book lungs or body surface. Malpighian tubules serve as excretory organs in most species. The brain is dorsal whereas the main nerve cord is ventral in position. Paired ganglia usually occur in each somite, and eyes are simple or compound. Sexes are separate.

Some crickets puncture stems of raspberry plants and lay their eggs within the pith. Are these crickets more parasitic than those grasshoppers and crickets that simply chew the stems? No more forceful way to emphasize the difficulty of defining "parasite" can be found than to select a textbook on entomology and to read about the multitudinous methods by which insects have solved the problem of obtaining food. Among the most destructive plant pests are the chinchbugs, plantlice, mealybugs and other Hemiptera whose sucking mouthparts, extraordinarily rapid rate of reproduction, and general behavior combine to effect a devastating invasion of plants the world over. But are they not simply plant feeders instead of parasites? The ovipositor of the female of many leaf hoppers is adapted for lacerating plant tissues, and eggs are deposited in longitudinal rows on the stems or under the leaf sheath. Certainly this habit is as much a parasitic one as are the habits of lice. Is there any essential difference between a predator and a micropredator (e.g. a parasite)? Perhaps the word "essential" is the important one. Some general references are: Clausen,[5] Furman,[12] Gordon and Lavoipierre,[13] Herms,[15] Imms,[17] and Symes et al.[31]

Respiration in Insects

Both endoparasitic insects and free-living aquatic insects must be able to extract dissolved oxygen from the surrounding liquid or semiliquid medium, or to retain a connection with an atmospheric supply. Some of the most common devices employed by aquatic larvae, however, are not known to occur among those of endopara-

(384)

sitic habits. In parasitic forms with a closed tracheal system respiratory exchange occurs through a thin cuticle which covers a voluminous tracheal supply. Some early instars of parasitic insects are either atracheate or they have a tracheal system filled with fluid, requiring oxygen diffusion directly into the hemolymph. The paired, richly tracheated tail filaments of *Cryptochaetum* larvae (small flies, endoparasites of coccid hemipterans) and the blood filled caudal vesicle of braconid larvae (Hymenoptera) play important roles in respiration. In a few parasitic Hymenoptera and in most endoparasitic Diptera larvae, a connection exists between the open tracheal system of the parasite and the atmosphere. Examples are to be found among the Encyrtidae and minute Hymenoptera that frequently attack such insects as mealybugs and scales (Coccidae). The structure and behavior of the primary larval parasite are correlated with a respiratory modification of the egg shell—the aeroscopic plate or band.[20] This structure is a strip of modified chorion acting as an air-channel, and the larval spiracles are applied to the inner surface of the strip. The ovarian egg consists of two ovoid bodies connected by a narrow tube, and the entire contents of the egg remains in the posterior body when oviposition is completed. Larvae may possess spiracles, but all larvae may obtain oxygen from the hemolymph of the host by osmosis. Some larvae remain partly enclosed posteriorily by the shell so that the spiracles may gain contact with the air-bearing structures on the egg proper. Some parasitic larvae (conopid flies in adult bees and wasps) become attached to a tracheal trunk of their host. Other larvae (*e.g. Cryptochaetum*) perforate the body wall or trachea and thus place their spiracles in direct contact with the atmosphere. Evaginations of the proctodaeum, spine-like processes on or adjacent to the posterior spiracles, ribbon-like extensions of cocoons of ectoparasites, all illustrate the wide variety of ways in which parasitic insects have solved the problem of obtaining oxygen. A word of caution is needed here. Clausen[6] has pointed out, "In most instances the adaptations are assumed to have that function in the absence of any other apparent purpose, and though the assumption may be logical, yet there still remains the necessity for experimental work."

Reproduction

Most insects are *oviparous* but a few species reproduce by other ways than simply by laying eggs. The more common and interesting of these ways are described briefly below.

Viviparous insects produce larvae or nymphs instead of laying eggs. Sometimes the phenomenon is little more than a retention of the eggs until they hatch in the reproductive tract, but frequently it involves an elaborate modification of the morphology and physiology of the parent, and in such instances it may be called "pseudo-placental viviparity." Viviparity occurs in scattered representatives of many orders but it is particularly common among the partheno-

25

Parasitic wasps which drill a hole through the bark of trees and lay their eggs on caterpillars under the bark have what seems to be an amazing and mysterious ability to locate the caterpillar. Sound? vibration? odor? Something is there which the wasp detects. They do make mistakes, however, and some wasps must drill or probe several times to find the host. Even when the caterpillar is exposed and unprotected, a wasp will occasionally be led astray and lay its eggs on some worthless and unrewarding object.

In at least one instance, a larval fly has developed a special organ, like that of its host, to enable it to get out of the host's cocoon. The fly, *Systropus conopoides*, parasitizes the caterpillar of *Sibine non-aerensis*, remaining with its host until the cocoon is formed. When the fly has finished its preliminary development, it emerges from the coccon by drilling a hole by means of a special spine on its head, thus imitating the host pupa. This type of parallelism is called *homeopraxy*.

CLASS ISOPODA

(PILLBUGS, WOOD LICE)

These crustaceans possess bodies that are usually flattened dorsoventrally, without a carapace, with sessile eyes, and with a short abdomen whose segments are often partly fused. Each of the seven characteristically free segments of the thorax bears a pair of legs. Parasitic species are abundant and they tend to favor crustaceans and fishes as hosts. Most parasitic species have been found in ocean waters although a few freshwater forms have been described.

SUBORDER FLABELLIFERA

Cymothoidae is a family within which exists the whole range of gradations from actively swimming predatory species to parasites whose adult stages are permanently fixed to the host and incapable of locomotion. The free-swimming species may be exemplified by *Cirolano borealis* which possesses powerful biting jaws. The cirolanid isopods sometimes attack a cod, caught on a hook or otherwise at a disadvantage, and viciously gnaw their way into the body so that the fish is soon literally nothing but skin and bones. They have even been known to attack human beings. Other genera (e.g. *Aega*) of the family Cymothoidae have piercing and sucking mouth parts which enable the parasite to suck the blood of its host. The strong hooked claws on the anterior pairs of legs help the isopods to cling closely to the skin of their victim, but they are still able to leave the host and swim about in the water. After an ample meal the digestive canal of *Aega* becomes distended into a large bag of semisolid blood, and this mass, when removed and dried, is the "Peter's Stone" of old Icelandic folklore, to which magical and medicinal virtues were attributed. *Aega spongiophila* lives, not on fish as do other species of the genus, but within a sponge.

Cymothoa and *Nerocila* represent the genera of isopods which, as adults, cling to the gills or skin of their fish hosts by means of strong hook-claws that provide a firm purchase (Figs. XVI–1 and 2). Some species, parasitic on flying fish and on other fishes, cling to the tongue and almost prevent the unfortunate fish from closing its mouth. Another genus, *Ichthyoxenos*, occurs within cavities of its host skin, and each cavity encloses a male and a female parasite.

Livoneca convexa presumably begins its life cycle as a planktonic

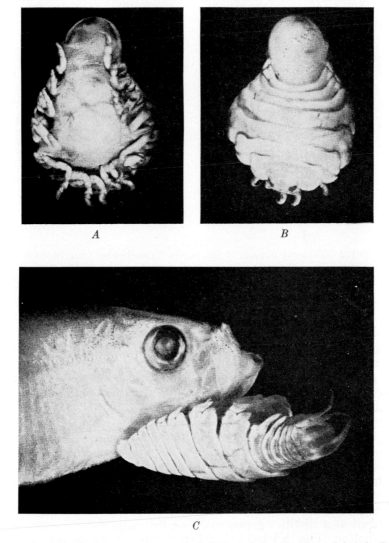

A   B

C

FIG. XVI–1.—Parasitic isopods. *A, B*, ventral and dorsal views of female *Riggia paranensis*. *C*, a marine sardine (*Clupea*) with an adult female *Nerocila orbignyi* clinging to its head. (Szidat, courtesy of Archiv f. Hydrobiologie.)

form.[22] Parasitic males enter gill chambers of the host fish (*Chloro-scombrus orqueta*), and females, probably commensal, enter the oral cavity of the same fish. Only the adult male shows evidence of causing direct damage.

Sexual dimorphism is the rule among all parasitic isopods, and the phenomenon of *protandrous hermaphroditism* occurs among the flabelliferans. This phenomenon starts when the parasite first attaches itself as a functional male to a host. Later the male becomes a female, develops a brood pouch, and produces viable eggs. Since both male and female are temporary parasites, sexual di-

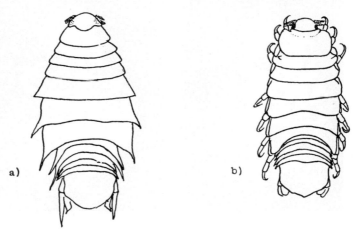

Fig. XVI–2.—Parasitic isopods of the family Cymothoidae from freshwater South American streams. *a*, *Nerocila orbignyi*, a sea form from the mouth of the La Plata river. *b*, *Livoneca symmetrica* from freshwater in British Guinea. (Szidat, courtesy of Archiv. f. Hydrobiologie.)

morphism cannot be attributed to the parasitic mode of life. The protandric male is not easily recognized, and a young sexually immature female has probably often been mistaken for the male. Any given species of cymothoid usually possesses a wide range of favored hosts, and it may also be found free in the plankton. Host specificity, therefore, is often not marked.

Gnathiidae, another family of flabelliferan isopods, also contains only temporary parasites, but, unlike those which are parasitic as adults, the gnathiids are parasites as larvae. These larvae are temporary dwellers on fishes, feeding exclusively on blood. Adult gnathiids may be found in plankton or in mud dredged from the bottom. Morphological differences among the larvae, adult male and adult female are so pronounced that each type was originally described as a distinct genus, such as, for example, *Praniza*, *Anceus* and *Gnathia* (Fig. XVI–3). Adults of this family do not feed, possessing neither a mouth nor a gut. The larvae attach themselves to the skin and gills of fishes and gorge themselves with blood. After three larval phases, each phase separated by a molt, the adult stage is reached. The male gnathiid uses its powerful mandibles for digging a burrow into the mud at intertidal levels, and into this burrow the male and female withdraw to end their lives in private.

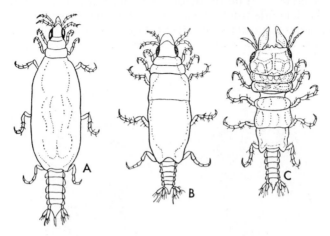

FIG. XVI–3.—*Gnathia maxillaris*. Sars. *A*, Larva; *B*, adult female; *C*, adult male (Sars). (Baer, *Ecology of Animal Parasites*, courtesy of The University of Illinois Press.)

SUBORDER EPICARIDEA

Contrary to the habits of the cymothoids and the gnathiids, which are temporary parasites at either the adult or the larval stages, the suborder Epicaridea consists of isopods parasitic in both larval and adult stages. This suborder is divided into two superfamilies, the Bopyrina and the Cryptoniscina, all of which are parasitic on crustacea.

Epicarids are particularly interesting because their life cycle involves two hosts, and because sexes are determined epigamically (*i.e.* after fertilization), depending on hostal environmental factors. See Baer[2] for details. The first epicarid larva resembles a small isopod, and possesses piercing and sucking mouth parts, and claw-like appendages with which it attaches itself to the surface of free-swimming copepods. This kind of larva is called an *epicaridium*, and while it remains upon its copepod host, it undergoes six successive molts and changes progressively into two distinct larval stages known as the *microniscus* and the *cryptoniscus* stages (Fig. XVI–4). Upon reaching the latter stage of development the parasite leaves its copepod host, proceeds to the sandy or muddy seabottom, and there it seeks a decapod crustacean, usually a crab, into whose branchial chamber or brood pouch it enters. Within this second host the parasitic cryptoniscus stage develops in one of two directions according to whether it belongs to the superfamily **Bopyrina** or to the superfamily **Cryptoniscina.**

If the cryptoniscus larva is a bopyrine it molts and thereby loses most of its pleopods, and is now known as a *bopyridium*. This larval stage initially always develops into a female; but successive larvae, either attached to the same host or to the female parasite, all become males. The question as to whether sex in parasitic isopods really depends upon the environment was answered by a series of experiments conducted by Reverberi and Pitotti[26] and by Reinhard[25]. *Stegophryxus hyptius*, a bopyrid ectoparasite on the abdo-

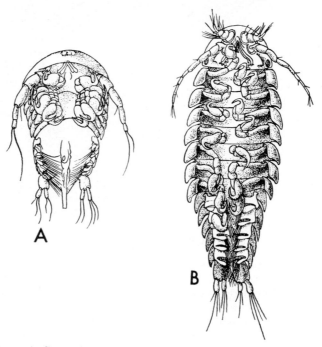

Fig. XVI–4.—*A, Cepon elegans*, microniscus larva. *B, Portunion kossmanni*, cryptoniscus larva. (Giard and Bonnier in Baer, *Ecology of Animal Parasites*, courtesy of University of Illinois Press.)

men of the hermit crab, *Pagurus longicarpus*, seeks the definitive host as a sexually undifferentiated and sexually undetermined cryptoniscus larva. Larvae that settle directly on the host develop into females, and those that attach themselves to a female bopyrid develop into males. Presumptive females, if removed from the host at an early stage and placed in the brood pouch of a female *Stegophryxus*, will change into males. Reverberi and Pitotti have successfully transformed the smaller of a pair of bopyrid females into a male by rearing the females *in vivo*, without their host crab. Sexual differentiation is, therefore, dependent upon environmental factors. Extra females or males on a host soon disappear, leaving only a single adult female paired with a single functional male (Fig. XVI–5).

Bopyrus squillarum lives in the gill cavity of the prawn, *Leander serratus*, and it causes a large swelling on one side of the host carapace. The parasite has a flat and distorted body, with an enormous mass of eggs on the ventral side of the female. The mouth parts form a short beak with which the parasite sucks the blood of its host. The

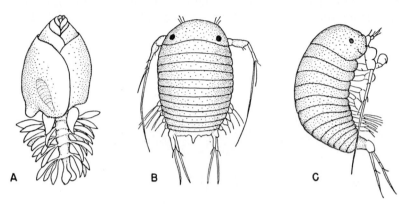

FIG. XVI–5.—Adult female and epicaridium larva of *Stegophryxus hyptius*. *A*, ventral view of adult female. The dwarf male, although not visible externally, is shown within the brood pouch by a dotted outline to indicate its position and relative size. × 5. *B*, The epicaridium or first larvae stage shown in dorsal view. × 120. *C*, Lateral view of epicaridium larvae. × 120. (Reinhard, courtesy of Biological Bulletin.)

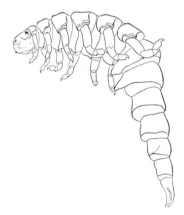

FIG. XVI–6.—*Pinnotherion vermiforme*, male, showing characteristic ventral curvature. (Atkins, courtesy of Proc. Zool. Soc. London.)

bopyrid isopods, especially those of the family Entoniscidae, frequently are the cause of a complete or partial atrophy of host gonads (Figs. XVI–6 and 7).

Most authorities believe that the entoniscids, while appearing to be internal parasites, are actually external, being surrounded by an invagination of the external chitinous covering of the host, and attached to its surface by thread-like chitinous tubes[1]. For example, the entoniscid *Pinnotherion vermiforme* occurs inside of the thorax and abdomen of the pea crab, *Pinnotheres pisum*—itself a parasite of the clam, *Mytilus edulus*. The male isopods have been found free in the body of the host, and hence they have been called true internal parasites[10], but they may have accidentally broken through the thin chitinous membrane from their normal position among the pleopods

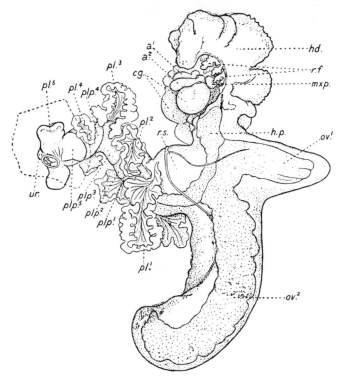

Fig. XVI–7.—*Pinnotherion vermiforme*, female. *a.*[1], vestige of right antennule; *a.*[2], vestige of right antenna; *cg.*, cephalogaster; *hd.*, hood-region of the brood-chamber; *h.p.*, hepato-pancreas; *mxp.*, maxilliped; *ov.*[1], *ov.*[2], anterior and posterior ventral processes of the gonad; *pl.*[1-5], right pleural lamellae; *plp.*[1-5], pleopods; *r.f.*, respiratory (?) folds; *r.s.*, position of the "receptaculum seminis," *ur.*, last abdominal somite. × 6.3. (Atkins, courtesy of Proc. Zool. Soc. London.)

of the female. The female entoniscid undergoes a pronounced morphological change, and the surface of its pleopods becomes corrugated and filled with numerous blood lacunae which serve in a respiratory function. In the same female the oostegites form a brood pouch, part of which appears as a hood around the head. Epicaridian larvae are expelled from this pouch through a secondary opening.

Probably all the parasitic isopods of the superfamily crypto-niscina are protandrous hermaphrodites. The males become mature in the cryptoniscan stage. The life history of this group starts in the same manner as that of the bopyrids, and it progresses similarly to the cryptoniscus larval stage. From here on the life history is markedly different. The larvae, after entering the branchial chamber or brood pouch of crabs become protandrous hermaphrodites of a delayed type since the males and females are morphologically distinct. An excess production of eggs causes the gravid female to undergo morphological and presumably physiological degeneration. Common among the degenerative changes is an asymmetrical disappearance of appendages from one side of the body. More drastic, however, is an atrophy of most internal organs of the female, leaving little more than a bulky sac packed full with eggs.

CLASS COPEPODA

(WATER "FLEAS")

A fine plankton net towed through almost any natural body of fresh or salt water soon collects multitudes of organisms consisting chiefly of minute crustaceans. The most abundant kinds of crustaceans in such hauls are usually copepods whose bodies furnish the major basic food supply for all larger aquatic animals. The best-known freshwater member of the class Copepoda is *Cyclops* (order **Cyclopoida,** Fig. XVI–8) which serves as the intermediate host for several helminth parasites of man and of other vertebrates. *Cyclops* is often called a "water flea."

Most copepods are free-living, but many are parasitic and, like so many other parasitic groups, they range in habits from the most casual and temporary contact with a host to a rigid and permanent attachment as adults or larvae within the host body. Most groups of aquatic animals (especially marine) may serve as hosts for at least one species of copepod during part of its life cycle. Echinoderms, annelids, ascidians, mollusks, arthropods, fishes and whales are universally invaded, and the parasite may appear practically identical with free-living species, or it may be so modified as an adult, that were it not for the larval stages, one would hardly be able to determine even the phylum to which the copepod belongs (Figs. XVI–10). Morphological simplification in copepods may sometimes be correlated with the distribution of their hosts in time, but such simplification seems to provide little assistance in the determination of the affinities of the parasites themselves.

Diagnostic features of copepods are as follows: free-living or parasitic, without compound eyes or carapace; with biramous or uniramous palps (or none) on the mandibles; typically six pairs of thoracic limbs, but none on the abdomen (*i.e.* posterior to the genital apertures); first pair of thoracic (invariably cephalo-thoracic) limbs always uniramous, sixth pair often uniramous, other pairs usually biramous; suctorial proboscis, common in parasitic species,

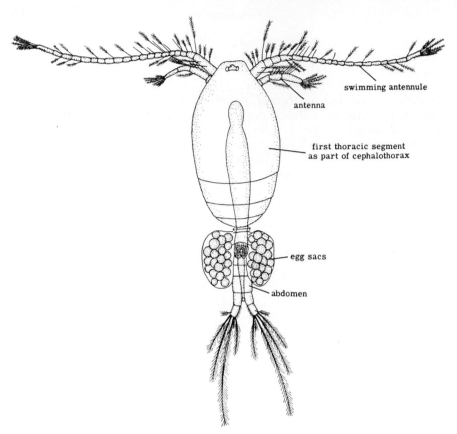

FIG. XVI–8.—*Cyclops.* (Bullough, *Practical Invertebrate Anatomy,* courtesy of The Macmillan Company.)

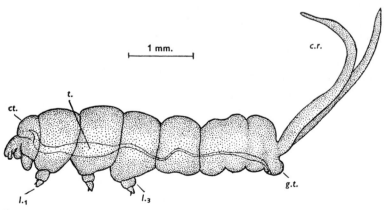

FIG. XVI–9.—Mature male parasite; side view, showing position of left re-productive organs.

FIGS. XVI–9, 10, 11, 12 are of *Cucumaricola notabilis,* a copepod parasite of the holothurian, *Cucumaria.* a^1, antennule; a^2, antenna; *c.r.,* caudal rami; *ct.,* cephalothorax; *g.t.,* genital tubercle; l_1, l_2, l_3, three trunk appendages; *mxp.,* maxilliped; *od.,* oviduct; *o.s.,* ovisac; *s.r.,* seminal receptacle; *s.p.* spatulate process; *t.,* testis. (Patterson, courtesy of Parasitology.)

(396)

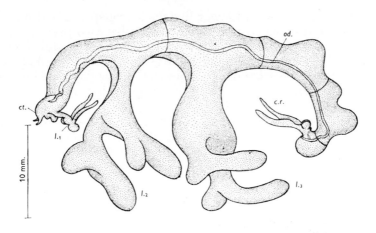

FIG. XVI–10.—Mature female; side view, with oviduct seen through translucent body wall. See legend above.

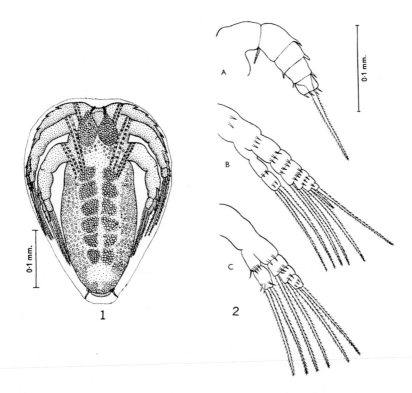

1

2

FIG. XVI–11.—*1*, Ventral view of nauplius larva seen through the egg membrane. *2*, Appendages of nauplius larva. *A*, antennule; *B*, antenna; *C*, mandible. See legend above.

formed by the upper and lower lips enclosing specialized mandibles; two pairs of antennae, one pair of mandibles, two pairs of maxillae and one pair of maxillipeds; head often greatly modified not only because of the specialized mouth parts, but because cephalic appendages (usually the second antennae) have become transformed into grappling organs.

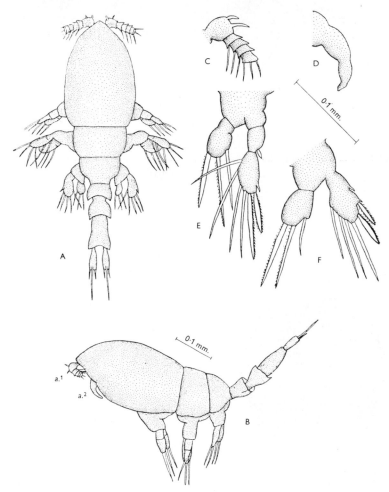

Fig. XVI–12.—First copepodid larva. *A*, dorsal view; *B*, side view; *C*, antennule; *D*, antenna; *E*, second trunk appendage; *F*, third trunk appendage. See legend above.

The sexes in copepods are nearly always separate. The male as a rule is much smaller than the female whose pair of ovisacs ("egg strings") is usually conspicuous. The female of *Chondracanthus merluccii* is 12,000 times larger than the male, but this sexual dimorphism is extreme. Hermaphroditism is rare. Most parasitic species appear to have several breeding seasons each year. In many instances (especially in some of the **Chondracanthidae** and **Lernaeopodidae**) the males are sessile on the females. In such cases the power of locomotion in the male is lost upon reaching maturity. In still others one act of copulation is apparently sufficient to fertilize the female for life, and the male then is not found in persistent association with the female. The embryos remain attached to the external opening of the oviducts, enclosed in the ovisac, until they hatch, a process often requiring several weeks. Nauplii larvae are, in the first stage, equipped with three pairs of appendages, one or more pairs of caudal setae (= balancers) and two distal antennulary setae (Figs. XVI–11 and 25). The three appendages represent the first and second antennae and the mandibles of the adult. Many parasitic forms hatch at a later stage, with more appendages.

Copepod larvae normally pass through six nauplius stages (the last three often called "metanauplius"), and five copepod stages, but abbreviated development may take place, especially in parasitic species.

Sample Genera of Parasitic Copepods

The family **Caligidae** (order **Caligoida**) is possibly the most widely distributed family of copepods parasitic on fishes, and it contains a larger number of genera (e.g. *Caligus* and *Lepeophtheirus*) and species than do other families. *Caligus* (Fig. XVI–13) is ectoparastic chiefly on fishes, with a suctorial proboscis; and it retains the power of swimming in the adult stage. This genus possesses two semicircular sucker-like organs on the frontal margin of the cephalic shield. *Caligus* does not always remain on one host.

Dinematura producta (similar in general appearance to *Caligus*), common on the great basking shark, has the same basic structure as does *Cyclops* but with many modifications related to a parasitic habit. Respiration in copepods is accomplished by a diffusion of gases through the body surface. Obviously then, the surface-volume ratio is of vital significance. *Dinematura* is about 2 cm. long, whereas *Cyclops* is only about 2 mm. long. The one, therefore, has a mass about 1000 times greater than that of the other, but if its shape were identical with that of *Cyclops*, the external surface of *Dinematura* would be increased only about 100 times. Even taking into account the relatively more sedentary existence of the parasitic species, there would not be sufficient surface for respiration. These considerations probably explain the existence, in *Dinematura*, of a number of flattened lobes projecting from the thoracic segments. The head of *Dinematura* possesses a median eye and short antennae armed with strong hooks used for clinging to the skin of the host. The mouth parts are adapted for piercing and sucking. The appendages used for swimming and the caudal fork with bristles are essentially similar in basic plan to those in *Cyclops*. The entire head is shaped like a shallow cup whose edges fit closely against the host skin, much like the fit of a limpet on a rock. This modification aids greatly in the

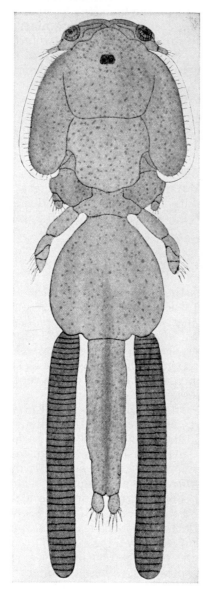

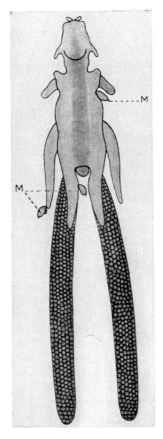

FIG. XVI–13.   FIG. XVI–14.

FIG. XVI–13.—*Caligus pelamydis* female, dorsal view.   × 22.5.   (Scott and Scott,
The British Parasitic Copepoda, The Ray Society, courtesy of B. H. Blackwell Ltd.)

FIG. XVI–14.—*Chondracanthus merluccii*, female, dorsal view, with attached males,
× 8.   (Scott and Scott, *The British Parasitic Copepoda*, The Ray Society, courtesy of
B. H. Blackwell Ltd.)

prevention of dislodgement by the pressure of water currents and waves. Trailing behind the body of the female is the pair of egg strings which may be as much as four times as long as the body.

Chondracanthus (order Cyclopoida) (Fig. XVI–14) is common on gills and in the mouths of various fishes. The female body of *C. gibbosus* within the gill cavity of the marine angler or fishing-"frog" (*Lophius piscatorius*) is extended into paired lobes which give it a curious irregular shape; and its appendages are greatly reduced. The mouth is flanked by sickle-shaped jaws, and the whole body may reach a length of about 2.5 cm. At the posterior end of the female body, just at the point where the egg masses are attached, a close inspection will reveal a minute, maggot-like object clinging by means of hook-like antennae. This object is the male which is attached, like a secondary parasite, to its enormously larger mate.

Lernaeocera, often called the "gill maggot" (Fig. XVI–15), is commonly seen attached to the gills of marine cod, and its bloated, S-shaped, blood-red body looks much more like a worm than it does a crustacean. The larval nauplius stage (unsegmented, 3 pairs of legs) proves its kinship with the arthropods. After a free-living period of growth, including several molts, the nauplius is transformed into a "cyclops" or "chalimus" stage when it becomes parasitic on the gills of certain flatfish (e.g. *Pleuronectes*) by means of suctorial mouth parts, accompanied by a reduction of its limbs. The chalimus attaches itself to gills of the host, first by the second antennae, then by a chitinous secretion that is extruded as a laterally flattened thread extending into the gill tissue. This stage is followed by a resumption of the power of movement when the parasite leaves its host and for a time lives a free-swimming, adult, sexually mature existence very similar to that of *Cyclops*. At this time fertilization of the eggs takes place, and the development of the male ceases. The female, however, now seeks a new host, generally a member of the cod family (*e.g. Gadus merlangus*), and again the gills are particularly attractive to the parasite. The anterior end of the female is buried into the host tissue, and it becomes curiously modified to form a branched anchor resembling short roots. The genital somites become greatly enlarged and vermiform, and the egg mass appears as a cluster of tightly coiled filaments. In proportion, the appendages of the thorax become minute and non-functioning.

Notodelphyidae (order Cyclopoida) is a family which consists of copepods almost universally inhabitants of the body cavities of tunicates. The group is a well-defined natural unit because of the preservation of fundamental characteristics in spite of a high degree of adaptive radiation. The family is characterized by the occurrence of a prehensilly modified articulated hook as the terminal member of the antennae, and the development of a brood sack enclosed within the body.[16] The life cycle probably involves five naupliar stages and six copepodid (subadult) stages. The second copepodid stage is the infective one, but the sequence of developmental events and possible metamorphosis in the life histories is al-

26

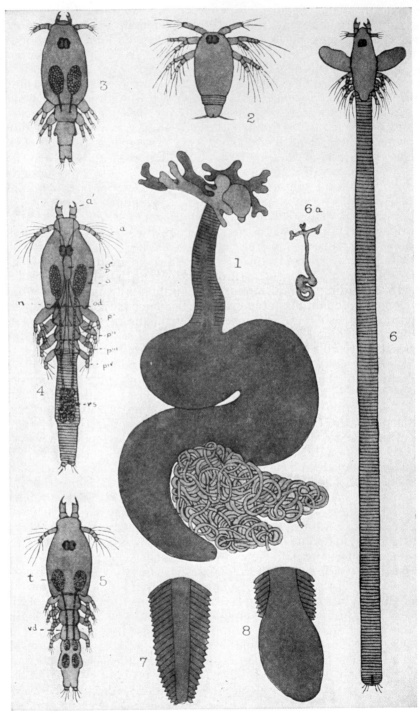

Fig. XVI–15.—*Legend on opposite page.*

most entirely unknown, and the mode of penetration has not been ascertained. Species whose appendages are the most reduced come from the more specialized habitats such as the genus found in the common cloaca of the systems of zooids of a compound ascidian. In another such form, there is an extreme degree of parasitic adaptation in the formation of a cyst within the ventral blood vessel of representatives of two genera of solitary tunicates.

Other symbiotic organisms commonly associated with notodelphyids in ascidians are: epizootic ciliates, sporozoa, hydroids, flatworms, nemerteans, nematodes, polychaetes, pinnotherid crabs, and, most commonly, other symbiotic copepods and amphipods. Illg[16] has described North American representatives of this copepod family; and concerning the interrelationships among the symbiotic organisms in tunicates, he notes that "the possibilities of complex cycles of nutritive relationships form one of the more obvious ecological corollaries of the biotic complex of ascidicolous organisms."

Xenocoeloma (order not definitely known), represents an extreme type of modification involving host tissue. This genus is parasitic on marine annelids, and the adult parasite is reduced to the hermaphroditic gonads plus some muscles. The mass is enclosed in a cylindrical outgrowth of the host epithelium which contains a gut-like prolongation of the host coelom (Fig. XVI–16). The life history is incompletely known, but the nauplius that emerges from the eggs resembles that of the monstrillids in the absence of digestive organs. The manner of access to the host has, unfortunately, never been observed.

The salmon gill-maggot, *Salmincola salmonea* (order Caligoida, family **Lernaeopodidae**), is a common and widespread copepod parasite of the Atlantic salmon (*Salmo salar*). The mature female parasite, when seen attached to a gill filament of its host, "somewhat resembles a gymnast hanging from a vertical bar.[11]" Attachment to the gill-filament is effected by means of a secreted "bulla" which is applied to the gill surface. A thin sheet of living gill tissue partly covers the bulla. A pair of prehensile maxillipeds lies behind an oral cone, and from the sides of the cephalon the maxillary "arms" (second maxillae) extend and converge on the bulla to which they are permanently fixed. The thorax bears no appendages. The paired egg sacs measure from 4 to 11 mm. in length. The life history of this

---

Fig. XVI–15.—*Lernaeocera branchialis*. *1*, Mature female side view, × 4. *2*, Newly hatched nauplius, × 51. *3*, Very young female, unfertilized, dorsal view, × 51½. *4*, Fertilized female, after leaving gills of flounder, dorsal view, × 27½. *5*, Mature male, dorsal view, × 28½. *6*, Fertilized female, "Pennell stage," just after attachment to gills of a Whiting, dorsal view, × 15¼. *6a*, A later stage than *6*, side view, natural size. *7*, Apex of the gill-ray of a flounder, × 18. *8*, Apex of the gill-ray of a flounder, showing malformation caused by young parasite, × 18. (Scott and Scott, *The British Copepoda*, The Ray Society, courtesy of B. H. Blackwell Ltd.)

copepod has been described by Friend[11] and will be used here to
exemplify the life history of the group. Figure XVI–17 presents a
diagram of the life-history, and Figures XVI–18, 19, 20 illustrate
details of external anatomy of various developmental stages of the
related genus *Achtheres*. During the first river phase of the fish, and
the first sea phase, totalling from two plus years to seven plus years,

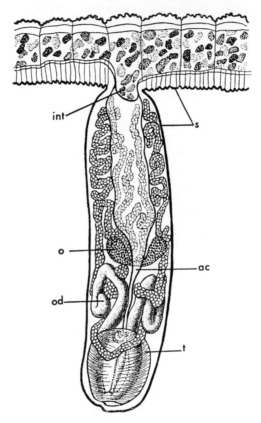

Fɪɢ, XVI–16.—*Xenocoeloma brumpti C* and *M*, section of the parasite and the annelid
host. *ac*, axial cavity formed by the host's coelom; *int*, host's gut; *od*, oviduct; *o*, ovary;
s, skin of both the host and the parasite; *t*, testis (Caullery and Mesnil in Baer, *Ecology
of Animal Parasites*, courtesy of University of Illinois Press.)

the salmon is not attacked by gill maggots, although it acquires sea-
lice. At the beginning of the second river phase the sea-lice are lost
and the maiden fish acquires larval gill-maggots which swim from
beneath the gill covers of other and older fish. In the fall the host
re-enters the sea, and during its sojourn (up to two years) in marine
waters its copepods thrive and grow but do not breed. When the
salmon re-enter the rivers their copepod parasites begin to breed.

The first copepodid larvae of *Salmincola salmonea* may live free for up to six days, but when they come in contact with the gills of a salmon they attach themselves "by means of a button and thread," and molt to become the second copepodid larvae. The next molt is followed by the sexually mature male or the first stage female, both of which may move freely over the gill surface, or they may attach themselves by means of chelate appendages. During this stage copulation takes place and the male disappears. Meanwhile the frontal gland in the female has been elaborating the attachment

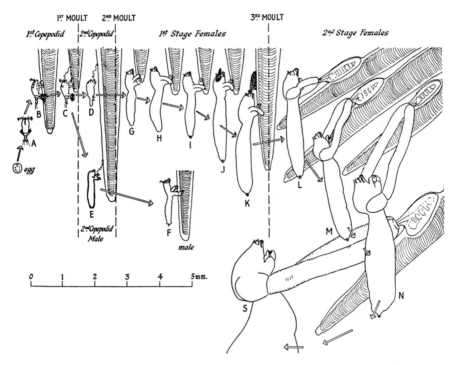

Fɪɢ. XVI–17.—Diagram of the life-history of the salmon gill-maggot. (Friend, courtesy of Trans. Royal Society of Edinburgh.)

bulla which is planted on the gill tissue in its final position. The female then molts and the distal ends of each second maxilla are forced as plugs into corresponding sockets in the bulla, and permanent attachment is achieved. The female then grows to mature size. Development to this stage requires about five or six months. One female may produce two or more generations of larvae.

Cucumaricola notabilis is a peculiar copepod which forms amorphous cysts within the coelom of the holothurian, *Cucumaria frauenfeldi.* Fertilized eggs and nauplius larvae, as well as adults, are contained within the cysts. There are two copepodid stages, the first an active swimming form and the second a quiescent form. Although this species is totally unlike any copepod known to parasitize either echinoderms or other types of hosts, and although it is of uncertain systematic position, being assigned[23] tentatively with the Chondracanthidae (order Cyclopoida), it is illustrated in Figures XVI–9 to 12 because of the interesting extreme amorphous condition of the female copepod.

Monstrillidae (order **Monstrilloida**) is an extraordinary family in that these copepods are free-living as adults but parasitic in the blood vessels of various polychaete worms, or in the body cavity of prosobranch snails during the intermediate stages. The nauplius of *Monstrilla* hatches without a mouth or gut, and it burrows into the body of its host, discards its chitinous exoskeleton and loses its limbs. By the time it reaches the host body cavity it consists only

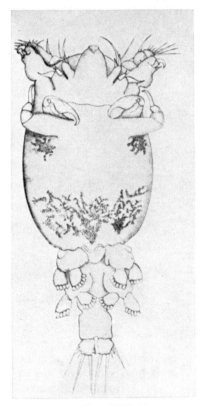

Fig. XVI–18.

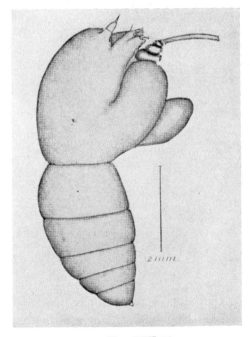

Fig. XVI–19.

Fig. XVI–18.—The free-swimming larva, first copepodid stage of *Achtheres*.
Ventral view of first copepodid larva, showing appendages. (Wilson, courtesy of Proc. U.S. Nat. Museum.)

Fig. XVI–19.—The second copepodid stage of *Achtheres*.
Side view of male larva. (Wilson, courtesy of Proc. U. S. Nat. Museum.)

of a naked mass of embryonic cells which then become surrounded
by a thin cuticle, and which develop a pair of long flexible processes
that apparently represent antennae.   The antennae absorb nutrients.   The food thus taken lasts during the entire remaining life
cycle throughout which there are no functional mouth parts.   The
mass of parasitic cells within the host gradually develops the organs
of the adult, which bores its way outside by means of rows of hook-

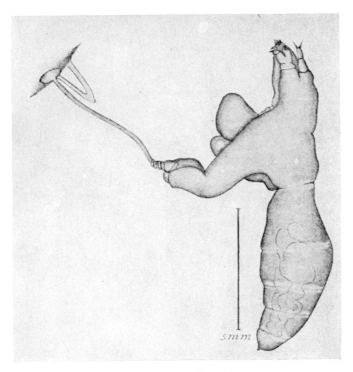

Fig. XVI–20.—Young adults of *Achtheres ambloplitis*.
Side view of sexually mature male, attached to spine of gill arch. (Wilson, courtesy of
Proc. U. S. Nat. Museum.)

like spines surrounding the pointed posterior end of the sac.   On
reaching the surface the enclosing membrane bursts and the adult
parasite is free, appearing similar to *Cyclops*.   The animal thus
passes its whole life cycle without a gut, and between the two
free-swimming stages, one at each end of its life, it exists as a bag of
parasitic cells absorbing nourishment from the internal fluids of its
host. See Figure XVI–21 of *Haemocera*.
    Further details about parasitic copepods may be found in works
by Calman,[4] Scott and Scott,[27] Gurney,[14] Wilson,[32] Baer,[2] and Lang.[19]

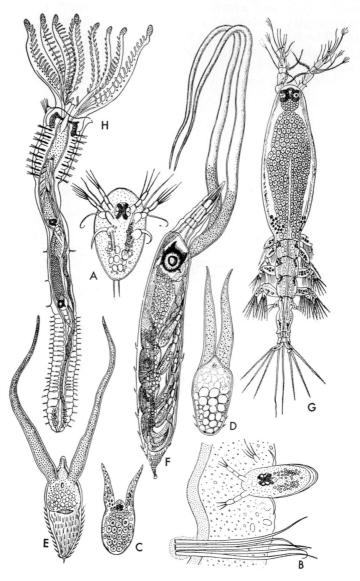

Fig. XVI–21.—*Haemocera danae* (Clap). *A*, Nauplius. *B*, Nauplius in the act of penetrating into the body of its host. *C–E*, Successive larval stages showing the development of the appendages and also of the spinous sheath enclosing the larva. *F*, Fully formed copepodid. *G*, Adult female copepod devoid of a mouth. *H.*, Annelid with two copepodid larvae in its coelomic cavity. (Malaquin in Baer, *Ecology of Animal Parasites*, courtesy of University of Illinois Press.)

CLASS BRANCHIURA

All modern European literature and most of the more up-to-date American references agree in referring this group, morphologically well differentiated from copepods, to a systematic category equivalent to that of copepods.[29]

Branchiurids are crustacea, temporarily parasitic on fishes, and they superficially resemble copepods, but differ from the latter in the possession of compound eyes, lateral carapace-like head-lobes fused to the sides of the first thoracic somite, an opening for genital

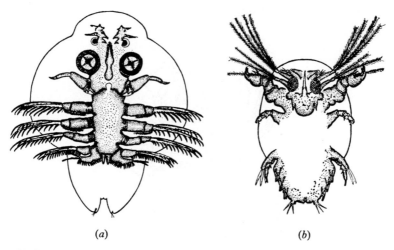

(a)   (b)

FIG. XVI–22.—*Argulus.* a, ventral view of the female. b, newly hatched larva. (Cameron, *Parasites and Parasitism,* courtesy of John Wiley and Son.)

products between the fourth pair of thoracic limbs, and a proximal overhang of some of the thoracic exopodites.   Other diagnostic features include an unsegmented, limbless, bilobed abdomen, and four pairs of biramous thoracic limbs.

Branchiurids are commonly called "carp lice," or "fish lice," and they are to be found on both fresh- and salt-water fishes.   The females deposit their eggs on stones, bits of wood and on other objects, and the larvae resemble adults.   The most common genus, *Argulus* (Fig. XVI–22), has a pair of suckers situated on the maxillae, and a poison spine in front of the proboscis.   It clings to the skin and gills, and appears to have little host preference.   Growth and development of *Argulus* take place most effectively in water whose pH is 4 to 9.[30]

CLASS AMPHIPODA

Although many amphipods are associated in a casual manner with marine invertebrates, few species are parasitic.   Some members of

the family Gammaridae have suctorial mouth parts and they lead
a semi-parasitic existence. A number of forms burrow into other
animals in order to obtain food, such as *Phronima sedentaria* (family
Phronimidae) in colonies of tunicates, but the relationship is one of
predation. *Hyperia galba* appears to be a true parasite of jellyfish.[7]
The class Amphipoda is characterized as follows: body often laterally
compressed, absence of a carapace, abdomen flexed ventrally between the third and fourth somites, telson usually distinct, usually
marine. The most common species are those called "sand fleas."

The class Amphipoda may be divided into the following suborders
of which the first is the largest: **Gammaridea, Hyperiidea, Ingol-
fiellidea,** and **Caprellidea.**

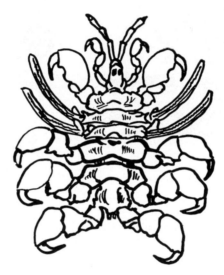

Fig. XVI–23.—*Cyamus ceti.* The whale louse. (Bate and Westwood, *A History of
British Sessile-eyed Crustacea,* courtesy of John Von Voorst.)

Parasitic Caprellids

Cyamidae is a family which contains five genera of amphipods
found on various Cetacea. These semiparasites have dorsoventrally
flattened bodies, reduced abdomens, claws on their legs, and they
burrow into the skins of their hosts. *Cyamus,* the whale "louse"
(Fig. XVI–23) is the best known, and it has a wide geographic range.
Only a few reports have been made on cyamids of the small, toothed
cetaceans commonly known as dolphins and porpoises, and additional collections from these mammals are needed. One recent
collection was of *Syncyamus* (Fig. XVI–24) from the blow-hole
and angle of the jaw of a dolphin from Panama Bay. Cyamid
mouth parts are not adapted for sucking blood; instead, the animals
appear to live by gnawing the skins of their hosts. The amphipods

are unique among crustacean parasites in being unable to swim at any period of their life history. The young settle down near their parents, and masses of individuals of all sizes may be seen clinging closely together on the skin of their host, often intermingled with barnacles. Other genera are *Paracyamus*, *Platycyamus* and *Isocyamus*. For further details see Bowman[3] and Margolis.[21]

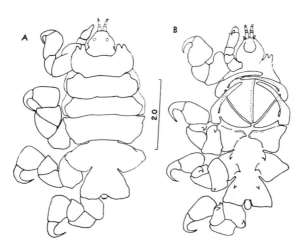

Fig. XVI–24.—*Syncyamus pseudorcae.* A, Female, dorsal; B, Female, ventral. (Bowman, courtesy of Bull. Marine Sci. of the Gulf and Caribbean.)

CLASS CIRRIPEDIA

(BARNACLES)

Barnacles are among the most highly modified crustaceans, and they abound in marine waters attached to rocks, pilings, shells of other animals, or on almost any other solid surface that provides a firm purchase. Like so many other sessile animals, barnacles, with few exceptions, are hermaphroditic, and their bodies are enclosed in a calcareous shell composed of plates which commonly overlap or are fused to furnish a formidable bulwark against pounding waves or grazing predators. Charles Darwin's two volumes[8] on barnacles are classic standard reference works. Two other general references of particular value to students are Pilsbry[24] and Krüger.[18]

Cirripedia are crustaceans without compound eyes in the adult; with a carapace (except in rare instances) as a mantle over the trunk; with typically six pairs of biramous thoracic limbs and usually a mandibular palp which is never biramous. A free-swimming nauplius larva (Fig. XVI–25) hatches from the cirriped egg, and, after a feeding period of a few days, it molts several times and changes into a *cypris* larva (resembling an ostracod) with a bivalve shell. The shell valves, unlike those of an ostracod, are united along both the dorsal and ventral surfaces (Fig. XVI–26). The larval barnacles possess the typical crustacean features of chitinous, jointed, two-branched appendages heavily fringed with bristles. After about a week or more the cypris larva settles to the bottom on a solid object and becomes attached by the antennae at the head end with the aid

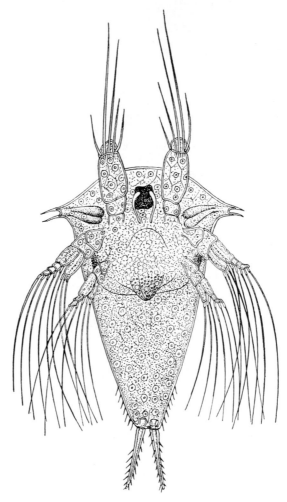

Fig. XVI–25.—*Sacculina carcini*, nauplius larva. (Delage in Baer, *Ecology of Animal Parasites*, courtesy of University of Illinois Press.)

of a cement gland. By a series of remarkable changes the adult stage is reached and the animal is permanently situtated, "standing on its head", spending its life in reproduction and in sweeping food and water into its shell by means of its lacy appendages, which reach out like a delicate casting net.

The species of barnacles range in habits from completely free-living to casual commensalism to extreme pathogenic parasitism. Many forms illustrate phoresis in which host specificity is pronounced, as in those species which are attached only to gorgonian corals, decapods, starfish, sharks, or whales.

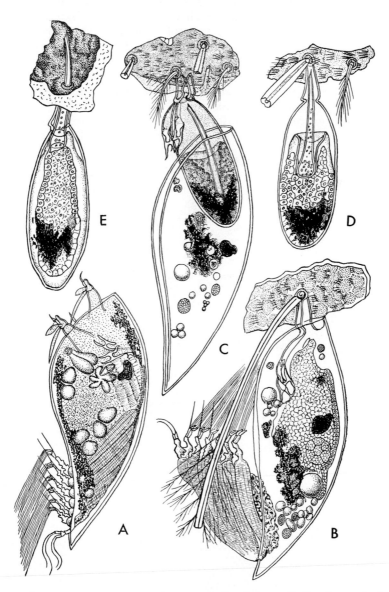

FIG. XVI–26.—*Sacculina carcini* Thomps. *A*, Cypris larva. *B*, Cypris attached to its host by its antennae and shedding its locomotory appendages. *C*, Kentrogon larva. *D–E*, Stages of penetration of the kentrogon into the crab. (Delage in Baer, *The Ecology of Animal Parasites*, courtesy of University of Illinois Press.)

Examples of commensal cirripeds are: *Chelonibia* which has developed a branched system of roots that penetrate into manatees and into the bone of the plastron of marine turtles; *Coronula, Tubicinella, Cryptolepas,* and *Xenobalanus* whose calcareous shell plates grow into the skin of whales; and *Anelasma squalicola* (Fig. XVI–27) partly buried in the skin of sharks. In the latter species a pear-shaped portion is embellished with branched, root-like appendages that apparently secrete an enzymatic substance that dissolves the surrounding muscle tissues of the host. *Rhizolepas annellidicola* is another parasitic barnacle which is anchored to its host (the annelid, *Laetmonica producta*) by a system of foot-like appendages. Two other examples are *Platylepas* on turtles, manatees and sea snakes, and *Alepas* on various medusae.

The most extremely modified parasitic cirripeds belong to the order **Rhizocephala** whose members live on or within the bodies of

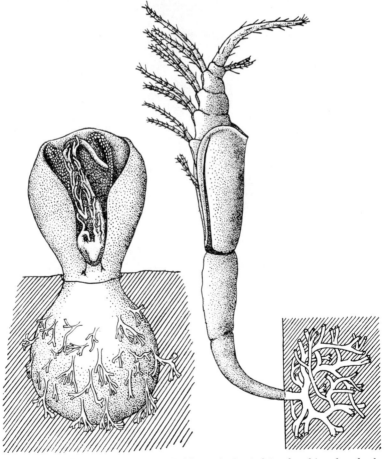

Fig. XVI–27.—*Anelasma squalicola* (left) partly buried in the skin of a shark; and *Rhizolepas annellidicola* (right) attached to an annelid host. (Baer, *Ecology of Animal Parasites,* courtesy of University of Illinois Press.)

other crustacea, mostly decapods. The larval stages appear identical with those of free-living barnacles but there is no trace of a mouth or gut in the parasites. The adult rhizocephalid possesses neither appendages nor segmentation, and it is anchored to the host by a stalk from which roots proceed into the host tissues. The best-known Rhizocephala are *Sacculina carcini* and *Triangulus munidae*. The remarkable life history of *Sacculina* starts with a *nauplius* possessing the characteristic frontal horns of cirriped nauplii.[9] The *cypris* larva of *Sacculina* is active after dark and it attaches itself by its antennae to a crab, at the base of a bristle. Soon after attachment the whole trunk with its muscles and appendages is thrown off and a new cuticle is formed under the old one. The body of the parasite becomes an amorphous cellular mass within the two valves of the cypris. From this mass the *kentrogon* larva is developed, and by means of a short dart-like tube that pierces the integument of the host the kentrogon (a mass of embryonic cells) flows into the body of the crab. The parasitic embryonic cells are carried by the host circulation to the ventral surface of the gut where they begin to multiply and spread out in all directions as root-like branches. A rounded cellular mass (the future *sacculina externa*) containing the rudiments of genital organs and a ganglion, now appears at the base of the root system, and the parasite migrates to a spot on the ventral side of the crab near the single diverticulum of the gut. At this point the parasite makes a hole through the host integument, and the external portion of the barnacle is thrust through this hole, and it grows into the hermaphroditic adult. The *sacculina interna* continues to grow and it may permeate almost the entire body of the host (Fig. XVI–28). A "sacculinized" crab may live with its barnacle parasite for at least two years, and it may become infected with two or more individuals. The crab, however, ceases to molt and its metabolism, particularly that relating to sexual development and activity, is profoundly modified. See p. 535 for a discussion of the effects of this parasite on the sex determination of the hosts.

Thompsonia, parasitic on crabs, hermit crabs, and other decapods, becomes so extremely modified as to resemble a fungus in both appearance and function. Like *Sacculina*, the parasitic rootlets are diffused throughout the host tissue, but in *Thompsonia* these rootlets give off sacs which attain an external position at a molt of the host. The sacs contain nothing but ova which ripen (probably by parthenogenesis) into cypris larvae.

Rhizocephala have been reported from freshwater. *Sacculina gregaria* in the crab, *Eriocheir japonicus*, travels with its host from brackish water to freshwater, but this parasite is able to reproduce only when the crab returns to brackish water to incubate its eggs and shed its larvae. Rhizocephala apparently are tolerant of a variety of different hosts, thus demonstrating a lack of close host specificity. For further details of parasitic barnacles see Baer,[2] and Smith[28].

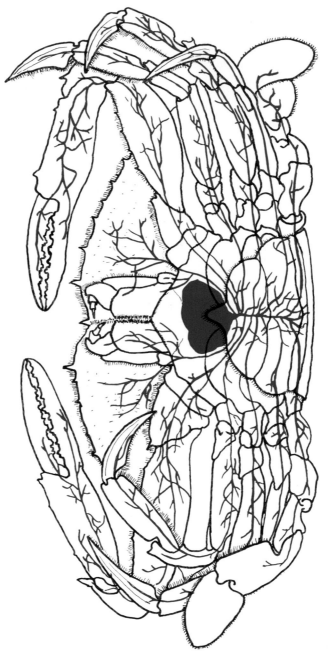

FIG. XVI-28. —The root-like branches of *Sacculina* permeating the body of its crab host. (Original.)

BIBLIOGRAPHY

1. ATKINS, D., 1933. *Pinnotherion vermiforme* Giard and Bonnier, an Entoniscid Infecting *Pinnotheres pisum*. Proc. Zool. Soc. London, 1933, Part II, 319–363.
2. BAER, J. G., 1951. *Ecology of Animal Parasites*. Univ. Illinois Press. 224 pp.
3. BOWMAN, T. E., 1955. A New Genus and Species of Whale-Louse (Amphipoda: Cyamidae) from the False Killer Whale. Bull. Mar. Sci. Gulf Caribbean, *5*, 315–320.
4. CALMAN, W. T., 1911. *The Life of Crustacea*. 289 pp. Methuen & Co. London.
5. CLAUSEN, C. P., 1940. *Entomophagus Insects*. McGraw-Hill Book Co., N. Y. and London. 688 pp.
6. CLAUSEN, C. P., 1950. Respiratory Adaptations in the Immature Stages of Parasitic Insects. Arthropoda, *I*, 197–224.
7. DAHL, E., 1959. The Amphipod, *Hyperia galba*, an Ectoparasite of the Jelly-fish, *Cyanea capillata*. Nature, *183* (4677), 1749.
8. DARWIN, C., 1851 and 1854. *A Monograph on the Sub-class Cirripedia, with Figures of all the Species*. Vol. 1 (1851) 400 pp., Vol. 2 (1854) 684 pp. Ray Society, London.
9. DAY, J. H., 1935. The Life-History of *Sacculina*. Quart. J. Micros. Sci., *77*, 549–583.
10. DRACH, P., 1941. Nouvelle Conception sur les Rapports Éthologiques des Entonisciens et de Leurs Hôtes. Critique de la Théorie Classique Ectoparasitaire. C. R. Acad. Sci., *213*, 80–82.
11. FRIEND, G. F., 1941. The Life-History and Ecology of the Salmon Gill-Maggot *Salmincola salmonea* (L) (Copepod Crustacean). Trans. Roy. Soc. Edinburgh, *60*, 503–541.
12. FURMAN, D. P., 1961. *Manual of Medical Entomology*. The National Press, Palto Alto, California. 122 pp.
13. GORDON, R. M. and LAVOIPIERRE, M. M. J., 1962. *Entomology for Students of Medicine*. Blackwell Sci. Publ., Oxford, 353 pp.
14. GURNEY, R., 1931–33. *British Fresh-Water Copepoda*. Vol 1, 1931, 238 pp.; Vol. 2, 1932, 336 pp.; Vol. 3, 1933, 384 pp. The Ray Society, London.
15. HERMS, W. B., 1961. *Medical Entomology*. 5th ed. Rev. by M. T. James. Macmillan Co., N. Y., 616 pp.
16. ILLG, PAUL, 1958. North American Copepods of the Family Notodelphyidae. Proc. U. S. Nat. Mus., *107*, 463–649.
17. IMMS, A. D., 1957. *A General Textbook of Entomology*. Methuen & Co. Ltd. London. 886 pp.
18. KRÜGER, P., 1940. *Cirripedia*. In Bronn, H. G., *Klassen und Ordnungen des Tierreichs*.Leipzig, *5*, 1–560.
19. LANG, K., 1948. Copepoda "Notodelphyoida" from the Swedish West-Coast with an Outline on the Systematics of the Copepods. Ark. Zool., *40A*, 1–36.
20. MAPLE, J. D., 1947. The Eggs and First Instar Larvae of Encyrtidae and their Morphological Adaptation for Respiration. Univ. Calif. Pub. Ent., *8*, 25–122.
21. MARGOLIS, LEO., 1955. Notes on the Morphology, Taxonomy, and Synonomy of Several Species of Whale-lice (Cyamidae: Amphipoda). J. Fish. Res. Bd. Canada, *12*, 121–133.
22. MENZIES, R. J., BOWMAN, T. E., and ALVERSON, F. G., 1955. Studies of the Biology of the Fish Parasite *Livoneca convexa* Richardson (Crustacea, Isopoda, Cymothoidae). Wasman J. Biol., *13*, 277–295.
23. PATERSON, N. F., 1958. External Features and Life Cycle of *Cucumaricola notabilis* nov. gen. et sp., a Copepod Parasite of the Holothurian, *Cucumaria*. Parasitol., *48*, 269–290.
24. PILSBRY, H. A., 1907 and 1916. The Sessil Barnacles (Cirripedia) Contained in the Collections of the U. S. National Meusum; Including a Monograph of the American Species. U. S. Nat. Muc. Bull., *60*, (1907) and *93*, (1916).
25. REINHARD, E. G., 1949. Experiments on the Determination and Differentiation of Sex in the Bopyrid *Stegophryxus hyptius* Thompson. Biol. Bull., *96*, 17–31.
26. REVERBERI, G., and PITOTTI, M., 1942. Il Ciclo Biologico e la Determinazione Fenotipica del Sesso di *Ione Thoracica* Montagu. Bopiride Barassita di *Callianassa laticauda* Otto. Pubb. Staz. Zool. Napoli, *19*, 111–184.

27. SCOTT, T., and SCOTT, A., 1913. *The British Parasitic Copepoda.* Vol. I. *Copepoda Parasitic on Fishes.* V. II. Plates (72 plates). The Ray Society. Dulau & Co., London. 252 pp.
28. SMITH, G., 1906. Rhizocephala. Fauna und Flora des Golfes von Neapel., *29*, 1–122.
29. SNODGRASS, R. E., 1950. Comparative Studies on the Jaws of Mandibulate Arthropods. Smithson. Misc. Coll., *116*, 1–85.
30. STAMMER, J. VON., 1959. Beiträge Zur Morphologie, Biologie und Bekämpfung der Karpfenläuse. Zeit. f. Parasitenk., *19*, 135–208.
31. SYMES, C. B., THOMPSON, R. C. M., and BUSVINE, J. R., 1962. Insect Control in Public Health. Elsevier Pub. Co., Amsterdam & New York, 227 pp.
32. WILSON, C. B., 1902–1924. (Numerous papers on North American copepods) Proc. U. S. Nat. Museum, *25* through *64*.

CHAPTER XVII

Phylum Arthropoda, Class Insecta I

LICE

IN 1842 Henry Denny, working on lice, wrote, "In the progress of this work, however, the author has had to contend with repeated rebukes from his friends for entering upon the illustration of a tribe of insects whose very name was sufficient to create feelings of disgust." Such feelings for lice have inspired the application of the terms "cooties," "crabs," and "vermin" for these tiny insect pests of the skin. "Plant lice," "book lice," "bark lice," "dust lice," and "louse flies" are also insects, but not closely related to true parasitic lice. Also, the crustacean "fish lice" and "wood lice" add to the confusion of common names. Most beginning students of parasitology hear a great deal about lice, but see only a few preserved specimens. A careful examination of a bird's feathers, or a quick combing of a mammal's fur with a fine-toothed comb will generally reward the searcher with numerous lice as well as with other arthropod ectoparasites. When present in large numbers lice may cause an intolerable itch, or they may be the vectors of serious disease.

All lice are parasitic on the surfaces of birds and mammals. In temperate climates lice are most numerous during February and March, and least numerous between June and August. Reasons for this kind of seasonal variation in numbers are not well understood. The lice are divided into the order **Anoplura,** which contains species whose mouth parts are adapted for sucking the blood and tissue fluids of mammals—hence often called "sucking lice"; and the order **Mallophaga,** containing the lice whose mouth parts are adapted for chewing epithelial structures on the skins of their hosts. The chewing habit has given rise to the term "biting lice" for the Mallophaga, but they do not actually bite. The classification used here is that devised by Hopkins.[10a]

The Mallophaga have broad heads, at least as broad as the thorax, wheras the Anoplura have heads that are narrower than the thorax (Compare figures XVII–2 and 4). Another readily distinguishable feature is the presence in the Mallophaga and the absence in the Anoplura of pigmented, heavily chitinized mandibles.

All lice are wingless, have dorsoventrally flattened bodies, short antennae with three to five segments, and reduced or absent eyes.

The thorax, indistinctly segmented, bears one pair of spiracles. The short legs possess tarsi whose claws are used for grasping feathers or hair. The abdomen, always without cerci, generally bears six pairs of spiracles. Unlike most arthropod parasites, all lice spend their entire lives on the bodies of their hosts, and infestation from one host to another is accomplished by direct contact. For this reason host specificity is relatively well marked (see p. 638). Lice eggs, known as "nits," are attached by the female to the feathers or hairs of the host (Fig. XVII–1).

An interesting method of emergence of the nymph from the egg of the pigeon chewing louse, *Columbicola columbae*, was described

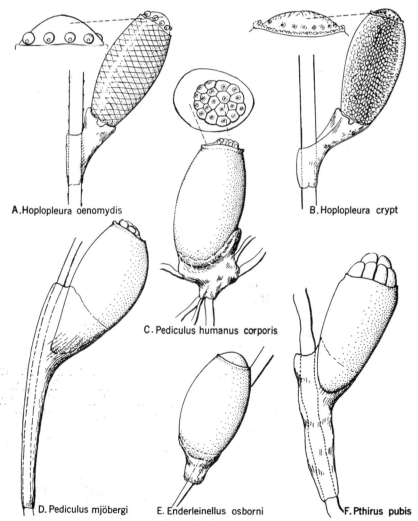

A. Hoplopleura oenomydis   B. Hoplopleura crypt

C. Pediculus humanus corporis

D. Pediculus mjöbergi   E. Enderleinellus osborni   F. Pthirus pubis

Fig. XVII–1.—Eggs of lice. (Ferris, The Sucking Lice. *Memoirs of the Pacific Coast Entomol. Soc.*, Calif. Acad. Sci., San Francisco.)

by Rothschild and Clay.[21]   The egg cap (operculum) is provided
with small pores through which air may pass to the inside.   The
nymph within the egg, when ready to leave, swallows air which
passes through the digestive tract and is forced to the bottom of
the egg.   The air pressure thus accumulated gradually thrusts the
nymph up against the operculum which is pushed open by the head
of the nymph.   The human louse larva, *Pediculus humanus,* is said
to emerge in the same manner, but other lice and the bed bug, *Cimex
lectularius,* and certain fleas open their eggs either by the use of
hatching spines on the head of the larva, or by pressure caused by an
enlarged head distended with amniotic fluid which has been swallowed by the larva.

Both Anoplura and Mallophaga possess a relatively simple life
cycle without metamorphosis.   The first nymph, which develops
within the egg, is structurally similar to the adult, differing chiefly
in its smaller size, absence of color and underdeveloped sex organs.
Four nymphal instars, each separated by a molt (ecdysis) precede
the adult stage.   In *Columbicola* each stage lasts six or seven days,
and between each molt the body becomes successively larger and
darker in color.   After the third and final molt the nymph becomes
either a male or a female sexually mature adult.   In many species the
female, which is almost always larger than the male, far outnumbers
the latter.   Sometimes the male of a species is rare, or has never been
found.   Although parthenogenesis is known to occur in at least one
species of mammalian louse, the rarity or apparent absence of males
may be attributed to their death immediately after mating.

Many lice, particularly those whose diet is chiefly keratin, possess
within their bodies symbiotic intracellular bacteria which presumably aid in the digestion of food.   The bacteria pass from louse to
louse by way of the eggs.   Similar bacteria are found in ticks, mites,
bed bugs, and in some blood-sucking Diptera.   The bacteria possibly
play a role in host specificity, being unable to cope with "strange"
blood if the louse gets on the wrong host.

ORDER MALLOPHAGA

This order contains about 2,600 known species of lice, primarily
parasitic on birds, but also on dogs, cats, horses, cattle, goats, sheep,
and other mammals.   The Mallophaga have not been convicted as
effective carriers of disease-producing microorganisms.   Feather
lice range in size from the minute males of *Goniocotes* which scarcely
reach 1 mm. in length, to the large hawk-infesting *Laemobotkrion*
which attains a length up to about 10 mm.   The mouth parts,
adapted for chewing epithelial materials, may have severe effects
on the hosts.   Literature on the diet and digestive processes of
members of this order has been reviewed by Waterhouse.[26a]   He
notes that lice eat the protecting sheaths of growing feathers,
feather-fiber, down, skin-scurf, scabs, blood, their own eggs and
cast skins, and probably also mucus and sebaceous matter.   The

lice on birds apparently can digest keratin (see note above on symbiotic bacteria). Some species on mammals ingest hair, and it is possible that these species chew off pieces from the sides in somewhat the same manner as does a beaver when it fells a tree. However, mammalian Mallophaga probably prefer a diet resembling that of many of the species parasitic on birds (*e.g.* epidermal scales,

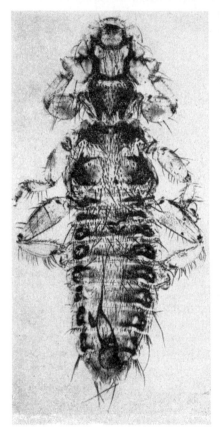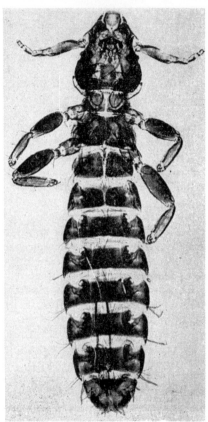

Fig. XVII–2.—The two main types of feather lice. *Left,* Amblycera. *Right,* Ischnocera (Rothschild and Clay, *Fleas, Flukes and Cuckoos* courtesy of Wm. Collins Sons and Co. Ltd. London.)

skin-scurf, wool-wax). Although they possess chewing mouth parts, some species of Mallophaga regularly feed on the freshly-drawn blood of their hosts. For example, *Menacanthus stramineus,* the body-louse of poultry, actively feeds on its host's blood, but other species prefer blood clots. It should also be noted that some species of Mallophaga parasitic on birds possess piercing mouth parts, and that they feed, as do the Anopleura, on the blood and tissue fluids of their hosts. One genus, *Piagetiella,* has selected the throat-pouches of pelicans and cormorants as a preferred place to live.

According to Eichler[8] it is possible that certain birds attempt to rid themselves of lice by picking up ants and placing them on their feathers or by perching on an ant hill with wings outstretched. It is presumed that ants eat lice, but this presumption has been questioned. Another interesting idea is that the birds eat ants, and the resulting formic acid in the bird discourages the lice. We do know that practically all mammals that eat ants are nearly free from lice. Scratching by the host undoubtedly helps to rid the animal of fleas, but the effectiveness of this habit against lice is questionable. However, Eichler counted 20,000 lice on the skin of one dog which, due to a defect, could not scratch itself. Damage to feathers caused by lice is probably very light, but it is difficult to separate damage caused by lice from that caused by feather mites. Although the Mallophaga are not effective carriers of human disease, one species (*Trichodectes canis*) acts as the intermediate host for a dog tapeworm, and the genus *Dennyus* on swifts serves as the intermediate host of a filaria (*Filaria cypseli*).

The order Mallophaga is divided into the three superfamilies **Amblycera, Ischnocera,** and **Rhynchophthirina.** The latter is sometimes considered as a separate suborder, and it is represented by only one species, *Haematomyzus elephantis*, parasitic on African and Indian elephants. The other two superfamilies (Fig. XVII–2) will be described briefly.

SUPERFAMILY AMBLYCERA

Species of lice belonging to this superfamily are parasitic on both birds and mammals, and they include the feather, shaft and body lice of poultry, and a number of pests on guinea pigs and other rodents. They may be distinguished by the antennae which are almost always composed of four segments, the third being stalked (Fig. XVII–3). The antennae always lie in a ventral groove on each side, and they may or may not project beyond the side of the head. The maxillary palps, sometimes absent, may also project beyond the sides of the head in preserved specimens, and may, therefore, be mistaken for antennae. The mandible chewing motion is in a horizontal plane. The ninth and tenth segments of the abdomen are fused.

Examples of the superfamily Amblycera are as follows:

Menopon gallinae (= *M. pallidum*) is often called the shaft louse of fowl. The female is about 2 mm. long and it lays its eggs in clusters on the feathers (Fig. XVII–3).

Menacanthus (= *Eomenacanthus*) *stramineus* (= *M. biseriatum*) is the yellow body louse of fowl and turkeys. The female is 3.3 mm. long and it prefers the skin to feathers. It may be seriously injurious to adult fowl. One chicken may be infested with more than 6,000 lice of several species (Fig. XVII–4).

Heterodoxus contains species which occur on dogs (in warm countries only, not in Europe), kangaroos and wallabies.

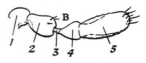

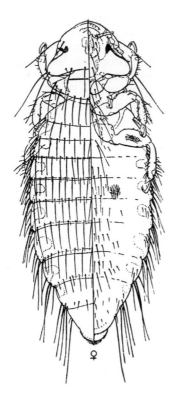

Fig. XVII–3.—*Menopon gallinae*, female. Note that the antenna (B) of this species, unlike that of most Amblycera, has five segments. (Lapage, G., *Veterinary Parasitology*, courtesy of Oliver and Boyd Ltd.)

SUPERFAMILY ISCHNOCERA

Lice belonging to this superfamily are commonly found on cattle, equines, goats, sheep, dogs, cats, and also on fowl and other birds. The lice can be distinguished by their easily visible filiform antennae composed of from three to five segments (Fig. XVII–2). There are no maxillary palps. The first and second, and the ninth and tenth segments of the abdomen are fused, and the eleventh segment may not be visible.

Examples of the superfamily Ischnocera are as follows.

Damalinia (= *Bovicola*) is found on cattle, sheep, goats, deer, other two-toed ruminants and horses. *D. bovis* (= *Trichodectes bovis*) is called the red louse of cattle. It is the most widely distributed louse on cattle in Britain, and is also common in North America. The lice in winter are found at the base of the tail, on the shoulders and along the back, unless there is a very heavy infestation in which case the lice may be found all over the host body. The irritation caused by these active pests may be severe, and the infested cattle

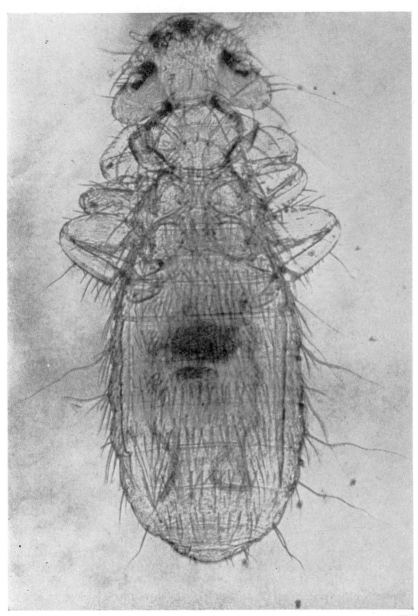

FIG. XVII–4.—*Menacanthus* (=*Eomenacanthus*) *stramineus*. The yellow body-louse of the fowl. (Lapage, G., *Veterinary Parasitology*, courtesy of Oliver and Boyd Ltd.)

often try to rid themselves of the lice by biting the skin and rubbing themselves against tree trunks, fence posts and rocks.

Trichodectes contains species found on dogs, martins, weasels, badgers, skunks, and other small mammals. The female is almost 2 mm. long, and it may serve as the vector of the larval stage of a dog cestode (Fig. XVII–5).

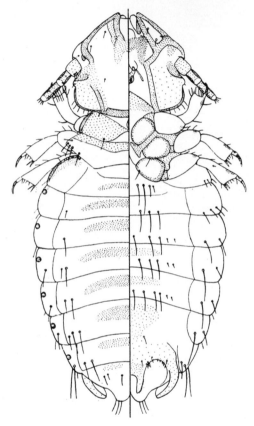

Fig. XVII–5.—*Trichodectes mustilae* female. (Bedford, courtesy of Onderstepoort J. Veter. Sci. and Animal Industry.)

Cuclotogaster (=*Lipeurus*) *heterographus* is found on the skin and feathers of the head and neck of fowl, partridge and other birds. It is often called the fowl head louse, and it may be seriously injurious. The female is about 2.45 mm. long, and its eggs are laid singly on the feathers (Fig. XVII–6).

ORDER ANOPLURA (= SIPHUNCULATA)

About 250 species of sucking lice have been described, and they are all parasitic on mammals. In addition to their characteristic

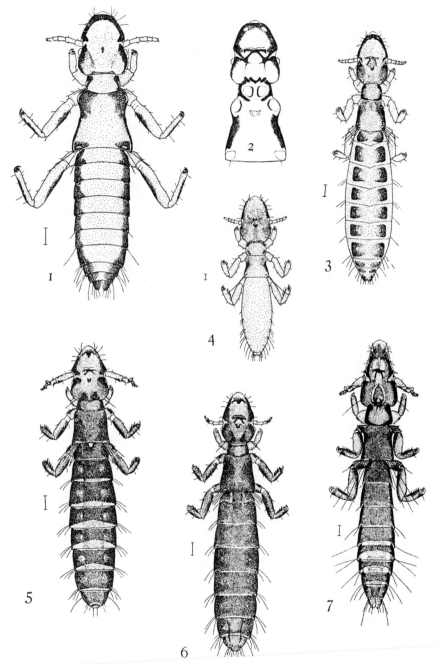

FIG. XVII–6.—*Cuclotogaster* (=*Lipeurus*), various species.   (Kellogg, courtesy of
Leland Stanford Jr. Univ. Publ.)

piercing mouth parts, the lice can be distinguished by their antennae which are usually composed of five segments, always visible, and by the small, fused thorax. The eyes are reduced or absent, and the third pair of legs, often broad and flattened, is usually the largest. Each tarsus has only one claw. The single pair of thoracic spiracles opens on the dorsal side of the mesothorax. The six pairs of abdominal spiracles are arranged as those of the Mallophaga. Only seven of the nine abdominal segments are visible externally. The mouth parts, adapted for piercing and sucking, are retracted into the head when not in use, thereby obviating the need for a proboscis.

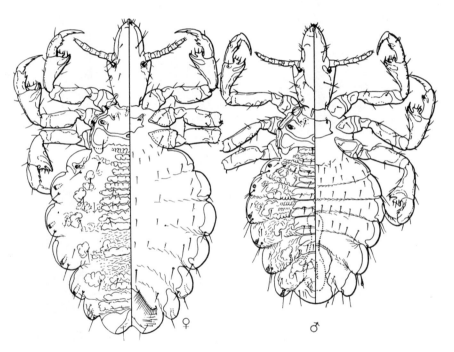

Fig. XVII-7.—*Haematopinus suis.* (Ferris, *The Sucking Lice*, courtesy of The Pacific Coast Entomological Society.)

The family **Linoganathidae** contains *Linognathus vituli*, the bluish-black, long nosed cattle louse. Its first pair of legs is much smaller than the others. The family **Neolinognathidae** contains only two species, parasitic only on elephant-shrews in East and South Africa. The genus is *Neolinognathus*. The family **Haemato-pinidae** contains *Haematopinus suis*, the largest of all lice to be is found on farm stock. The female is 4 to 6 mm. long, and the male 3.4 to 4.75 mm. long. It is the only species of louse that infects the domestic pig (Fig. XVII-7).

Human lice. The family **Pediculidae** contains the human head louse and the body louse of the genus *Pediculus*, and the human

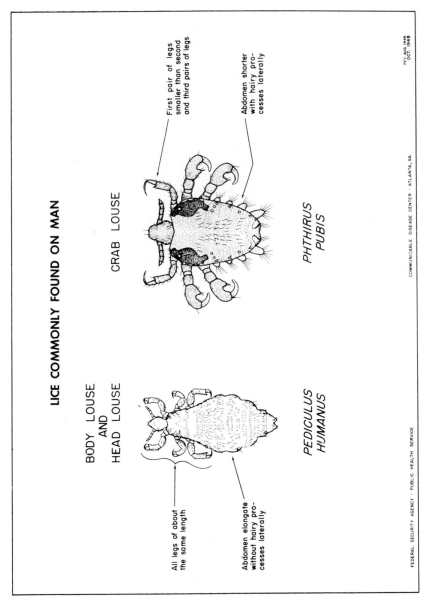

Fig. XVII-8.—Lice commonly found on man.

pubic or crablouse belonging to the genus *Phthirus* (Fig. XVII–8). *Pediculus humanus* occurs in two forms, the head louse, *P. humanus*, and the body louse, *P. humanus humanus* (= *P. humanus corporis*). The two look very much alike. A typical head louse and a typical body louse are rather easily distinguished, but they overlap in appearances and movements. Head lice average approximately 2.4 mm. long and are slightly smaller than body lice. Body lice, however, are seldom if ever found on the head, whereas head lice may be found on the body. The lice are adapted for clinging to hairs, but the body lice have found refuge in the clothing with which man has compensated for his nudity. Head lice and body lice can interbreed and produce fertile offspring which may possess characters intermediate between the two parents.

Copulation between a male and female human louse begins when the male crawls underneath the female, approaching her from behind. When the tips of their abdomens unite the female rears up to a vertical position, lifting the male with her. The two lice then return to a horizontal position and remain united for from thirty minutes to several hours. The female may lay up to 300 eggs during her life which, under optimum conditions, lasts about a month. The oval eggs, or nits, are laid singly, and they measure about 0.8 by 0.3 mm. At 30° C. the eggs hatch in eight or nine days and the young nymph is 1 mm. long. Adult lice can suck up as much as 1 mg. of blood at a time, but probably they prefer to take smaller quantities at frequent intervals. At 30° C. they can survive only about three days of starvation. Experiments have shown that lice can move at a rate of 9 inches (23 cm.) per minute. They prefer a temperature of 29° to 30° C., and they avoid, when possible, any change in humidity. Their immediate past experience conditions the response to environmental changes—hence different individuals often exhibit different responses. Movement toward dark areas is chiefly a response to directed light received by the horizontally placed eyes. See Wigglesworth[28] for details on the sensory physiology of *Pediculus humanus*.

Phthirus is a genus which possesses a wide thorax that constitutes most of the body; and the coxae are far apart at the margins of the thorax. *P. pubis* (Fig. XVII–8) frequents the pubic hairs and perianal regions of man, but it may wander to other parts of the body, including the head. It is smaller and much broader than the other two human lice, and its legs have the appearance of being attached to the edge of the somewhat flattened body. The forelegs are slender with long fine claws whereas the middle and hind legs are thick, with thick claws. The adult seems to be unable to survive for longer than a day when removed from its host, and its total span of life is about one month. Although transmission from person to person is accomplished by close contact, it is a grave injustice to assume that sexual contact is the only mode of transfer.

The Effect of Sucking Lice on Their Hosts

Haematopinus suis probably transmits the virus of swine fever, and lice in general probably carry tularemia and leishmaniasis. *Polyplax spinulosa* of black and brown rats transmits the rickettsia that causes typhus. Nevertheless, the sucking lice are not known to be of any great importance as vectors of domestic and wild animal diseases. They may be called host irritants, and because they often increase rapidly in numbers they frequently are the cause of scratching, restlessness, biting, loss of sleep, and interruption of feeding. During the biting process the saliva injected into the wound prevents the host's blood from coagulating as it is sucked through the slim mouth parts. It is the reaction of the host cells to the louse saliva that causes the symptoms of irritation. Lice seem never to be satisfied for long with one meal, but go on feeding all the time. Blood exuding and clotting at the sites of the bites may form a fertile location for the growth of bacteria, or an effective attractant for flies whose larvae may cause serious malady (see p. 491).

In man, *Pediculus humanus* can transmit impetigo, trachoma and cholera by simple mechanical contamination, and this louse is the normal vector of exanthematous typhus caused by *Rickettsia prowazeki*, of trench fever caused by *R. quintana*, and of louse-borne relapsing fever caused by *Spirochaeta recurrentis*. The rickettsia that are ingested by the louse with its blood meal multiply in its gut cells which eventually burst, thus liberating large numbers of these parasitic bodies into the louse feces. Man acquires typhus by rubbing infected louse feces into an abrasion of the skin. The infected louse dies in about ten days after acquiring the cellular parasites because of its ruptured gut cells. Hans Zinsser's book, *Rats, Lice and History*[29] gives a vivid picture of the manner in which lice and typhus fever have influenced the history of mankind.

Trench fever became widely prevalent during World War I, and has since disappeared. The spirochaetes of relapsing fever penetrate the louse gut and multiply within the fluid of the body cavity. They remain in this fluid until the louse host is crushed, at which time the spirochaetes escape and may enter a human host through an abrasion of the skin. Obviously the habit of "popping" lice with the finger nails, and the disgusting practice of biting lice to kill them is seriously hazardous if relapsing fever is prevalent.

Head lice are frequently a serious problem among urban children, but much more rare among adults. Body lice are largely confined to those adults and children who do not change their underwear frequently. Conditions of crowding, especially during sleeping hours, are particularly conducive to the spread of lice. For these reasons such groups as destitute people, refugees, vagrants, prisoners, and armies provide fertile fields for lice populations. A chronicler contemporary of the well-known church dignitary St. Thomas à Becket has written that on the morning after the churchman was murdered his vestments were removed, and the hair-cloth underwear was so infested with lice that they "boiled over" as the cloth was stripped from the cold body.

Control of all lice depends on good feeding and sound management if livestock are involved, and the judicious use of appropriate dips and dusts. DDT, toxaphene, chlordane, gamma BHC (benzene hexachloride), phenothiazine, sodium fluoroscilicate, gammexane, rotenone and derris are among those most frequently used with success.

Primary defense against human lice involves personal cleanliness of body and clothing. It is well to remember that even in civilized communities there are always some chronically lousy individuals whose feeble efforts at personal cleanliness are ineffectual, or who have ceased to worry about their condition and who passively offer their parasites to every passerby.

ORDER HEMIPTERA

(BUGS)

SUBORDER HOMOPTERA

Plant bugs and their relatives are predominantly phytophagous (plant feeders) with piercing and suctorial mouth parts. A considerable number of species show a strong tendency toward entomophagy, and in a number of instances plant feeding has been abandoned entirely and the predatory role is obligatory. Here, again, the delicate line separating a predator from a parasite defies discovery. The bugs typically possess two pairs of wings, the anterior pair being most often of a harder consistency than the posterior pair. The slender, segmented beak constitutes the most easily recognizable feature of bugs. Palpi are atrophied, and the labium is in the form of a dorsally-grooved sheath receiving two pairs of bristle-like stylets (modified mandibles and maxillae) (Fig. XVII–9). Metamorphosis is usually incomplete.

Probably no other group of insects is so directly concerned with the welfare of man because of the vast amount of injury to plants brought about directly and indirectly by thousands of species of bugs. Chinch-bugs, leaf-hoppers, plant lice, cotton stainers, white flies, tea blight bugs, scale insects, and mealy bugs are among the most destructive. Many bugs are the insect vectors of virus diseases of plants, and some transmit protozoal diseases (*e.g.* Chagas' disease, see p. 54) to man and animals. The extraordinarily rapid rate of reproduction occurring in many members of the Homoptera constitutes a cardinal factor bearing upon the devastation for which these insects are responsible. Only a few of the parasites of plants will be mentioned because the subject of plant pathology, especially as it involves the insects, is so vast that it requires many volumes, and a special course of study, to do it justice. For this reason, and because of precedent, the animal parasites of plants have not been used in the traditional course in "Parasitology". Nevertheless, these parasites are excellent examples of the state of parasitism; they are easy to obtain, and they lend themselves readily to a study of basic principles.

Psyllidae is a family of "jumping plant lice" which frequently become serious parasites of fruit trees (pears, apples) and other

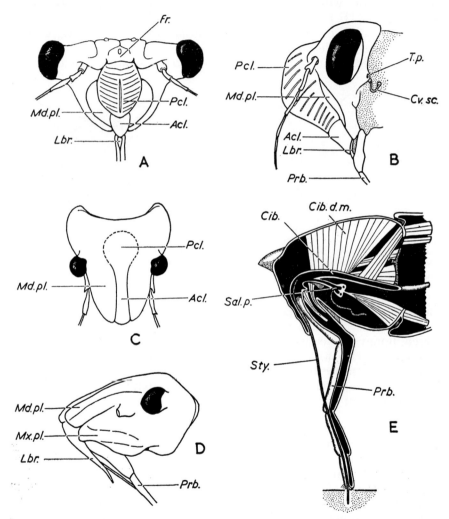

Fig. XVII–9.—Head and mouthparts of *Hemiptera. A, B,* Frontal and lateral views of *Magiciada septendecim* (after Snodgrass, 1935). *C, D,* The same of a Pentatomid, *Euschistus variolarius* (after Snodgrass, 1935). *E,* Section of head of *Graphosoma italicum* in feeding position (after Weber, 1930).

Acl, anteclypeus; *cib,* cibarium; *cib.d.m.,* cibarial dilator muscles; *Cv.sc.,* cervical sclerae; *Fr.,* frons; *Lbr.,* labrum; *Md.pl.,* mandibular plate; *Mx.pl.,* maxillary plate; *Pcl.,* postclypeus; *Prb.,* proboscis (labium); *Sal.p.,* salivary pump; *Sty,* stylets. (Imms, A *General Textbook of Entomology,* courtesy of E. P. Dutton and Co.)

plants. Nymphs, and sometimes also adults of the genus *Psylla* (Fig. XVII–10) damage the blossoms and stunt the shoots, and they often produce gall-like malformations. Nymphs of many species secrete large amounts of a white, waxy substance. The potato or tomato psyllid, *Paratrioza cockerelli*, transmits a virus disease to potatoes, tomatoes, peppers, and eggplants.

Aleyrodidae consists of the minute white flies, resembling tiny moths, whose wings are dusted with a mealy, white, powdery wax (Fig. XVII–11). The adults are usually observed while they are actively feeding on leaves, but the immature instar young, except the first, are sessile, and they look like scales. A conspicuous and characteristic organ, present in both larval and adult stages is the

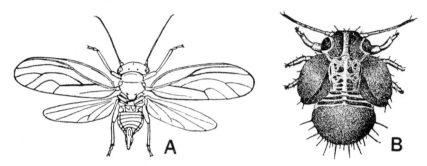

FIG. XVII–10.—*A, Psylla mali* (after Carpenter). *B, Psylla pyricola*, nymph in last instar (after Stingerland). All enlarged. (Imms, A *General Textbook of Entomology*, courtesy of E. P. Dutton and Co.)

vasiform orifice which opens on the dorsal surface of the last abdominal segment. Within the orifice is a tongue-shaped organ upon which honeydew collects from the anus. Whiteflies are abundant throughout the world, especially in the tropics and subtropics. They are parasitic on citrus trees, tomatoes, cucumbers and other plants. Damage results from the process of sucking sap from leaves. For details on the whiteflies see Quaintance and Baker,[20] and Sampson.[22]

Aphididae includes the aphids or plant lice (Fig. XVII–12). These familiar soft-bodied insects are frequently found in large numbers consisting of individuals in all stages of development sucking the sap from young shoots or leaves of plants. Diagnostic morphological features of these insects are the cornicles or "honey tubes" situated at the posterior end of the abdomen. The cornicles are the channels from glands which secrete a waxy fluid that acts as a protection against predaceous enemies. Honeydew is emitted through the anus. The antennae are relatively long; the front wings are considerably larger than the hind wings, and when at rest they are generally held vertically above the body.

The life cycle of many aphids is unusual and complex, and the physiological mechanisms underlying host-alternation, parthenogene-

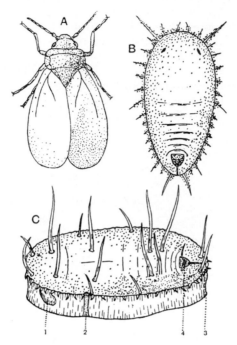

FIG. XVII–11.—The white fly *Trialeurodes vaporariorum*. *A*, imago × 50. *B*, larva in first instar × 150. *C*, puparium × 65.

1, adult eye; *2*, thoracic breathing fold; *3*, caudal breathing fold; *4*, vasiform orifice. (Lloyd, Ann. App. Biol. 9, in Imms, *A General Textbook of Entomology*, courtesy of E. P. Dutton and Co.)

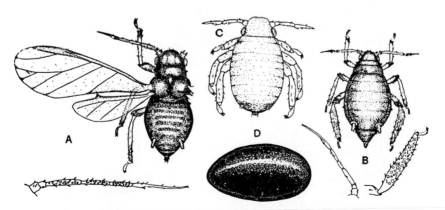

FIG. XVII–12.—*Aphis fabae*. *E*, male; *F*, oosporous female; *G*, fundatrix, 1st instar; *H*, egg. The antennae are also shown under higher magnification, together with the tarsus in *F*. (From original drawings by J. Davidson in Imms, *A General Textbook of Entomology*, courtesy of E. P. Dutton and Co.)

sis and polymorphism are not clearly understood. Undoubtedly seasonal changes in the physiology of the growing host plant are at least partly responsible for the complexities of the cycle. They commonly cause a curling or wilting of the food plant, and they frequently serve as vectors of a number of important virus and fungus plant diseases. For details see Börner,[5] Gillette and Palmer,[10] Smith,[23] Theobald,[24] Kennedy and Stroyan[15] and Imms.[12]

The superfamily **Coccoidea** includes the familiar "mealy-bugs" (e.g. *Pseudococcus*) and "scale insects", all of which are

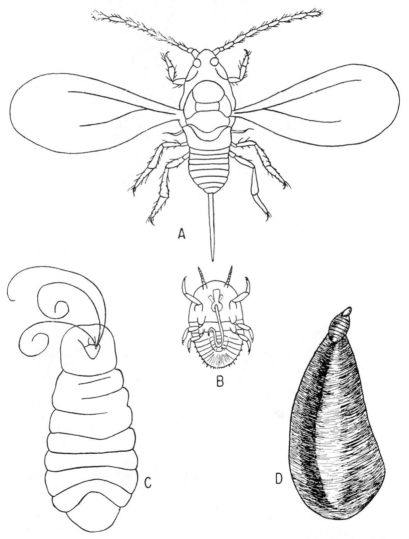

FIG. XVII–13.—The oystershell scale, *Lepidosaphes ulmi* (Linn.). *A*, adult male. *B*, newly hatched young, or crawler; *C*, adult female; *D*, scale of female. (Redrawn from various sources. Borror and Delong, *An Introduction to the Study of Insects*, courtesy of Rinehart and Co.)

characterized by the more or less degenerate, wingless females with obscure segmentation and often atrophied legs and antennae. The males have a single pair of wings or, rarely, they are wingless, and, lacking mouth parts, they do not feed. The males look like small gnats with a style-like process at the end of the abdomen (Fig. XVII–13).

Like the aphids, many coccoidea secrete honeydew which renders them attractive to ants; and many secrete a powdery or clear wax or lac. These secretions have been used by man for centuries in the preparation of shellac and candle wax. The life histories of this family have not been studied extensively, but they include partheno-genesis, oviparity, and viviparity. The first instar nymphs are provided with functional legs, and their mobility ensures dispersal of the species.

A great many species of the coccoidea are injurious parasites of cultivated and other plants. Some species prefer only one kind of host (e.g. *Cryptococcus fagi* on *Fagus sylvaticus*) whereas others appear to have little host preference. *Lepidosaphes ulmi*, for example, is known to infest about 130 widely separated species of plants. The San José scale (*Quadraspidiotus perniciosus*) on deciduous fruits, and the red scale (*Aonidiella aurantii* and *Chrysomphalus ficus*) on citrus trees are fine examples of coccoidea whose feeding habits and general biology result in serious damage to their hosts. Some mealybugs are vectors of virus diseases (Ferris[9]).

SUBORDER HETEROPTERA

The **Reduviidae** consists of bugs whose 3000 or so described species exhibit a wide range of variation in form. The subfamily Triato-minae contains bugs of medium size to large, and usually of a black or brownish color, but sometimes with bright red or yellow markings (Fig. XVII–14). The head is characteristically long, narrow, and with a neck-like portion immediately behind the eyes. The rostrum (beak) is three-segmented and bent sharply back under the head when at rest, and the antennae are filiform and are inserted on the sides of the head between the eyes and tip of the snout. The abdomen is often widened at its middle, exposing the margins of the segments lateral to the folded wings. The wings of Heteroptera are generally placed, when at rest, so as to reveal a conspicuous triangular area immediately posterior to the thorax. The reduviids commonly live on the blood of other insects, but a few triatomids ("assassin bugs") attack higher animals, including man. *Rhodnius prolixus* and species of *Triatoma* and of *Panstrongylus* are the natural vectors for *Trypanosoma cruzi*, the causative agent of Chagas' disease, a frequently-fatal form of human trypanosomiasis (see p. 54). Many species of assassin bugs will inflict a painful bite if carelessly handled, and severe allergic symptoms occasionally occur. The bugs are regularly found in nests or burrows of rodents or other host animals. For details of these bloodsucking bugs see Buxton,[6] and Usinger.[25,26]

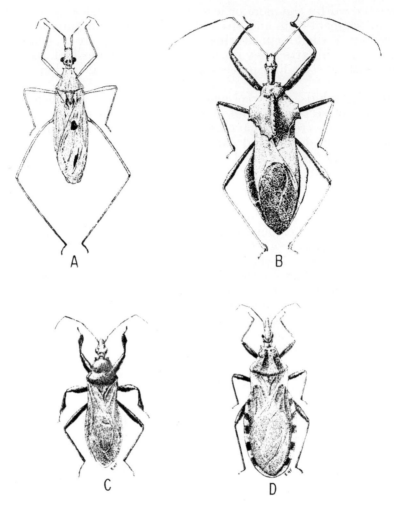

Fig. XVII–14.—Assassin bugs. *A Narvesus carolinensis* Stal. × 2; *B*, the wheel bug, *Arilus cristatus* (Linn.), × 1½; *C*, *Melanolestes picipes* (Herrich-Schaeffer), × 2. *D*, a blood-sucking conenose, *Triatoma sanguisuga* (Leconte), × 2. (Courtesy of Froeschner and the American Midland Naturalist.)

The **Cimicidae** consists of bedbugs parasitic on birds and mammals. Characteristic morphological features (Fig. XVII–15) are an oval, flattened body about 4 mm. long without wings, and covered with many hair-like spines. The compound eyes are conspicuous, but ocelli are absent; the rostrum lies in a ventral groove, and the tarsi are three-jointed. The thorax consists of three segments: an anterior large prothorax extending forward on either side of the head; a mesothorax whose visible portion is a small triangle; and a metathorax hidden from view dorsally by two small pads which are rudimentary forewings.

Members of the genus *Cimex* are associated with birds, bats, man and other mammals, and have a world-wide distribution. The bat bedbug is *C. pilosellus*. In New Guinea man is attacked by *Leptocimex boueti*; the nests of martins may harbor *Oeciacus hirundinis*[18a]; and in North and Central America *Haematosiphon modorus* is a parasite of poultry.

The two most common bedbugs which attack man and which are found the world over, are *Cimex lectularius* of temperate climates, and *C. hemipterus* of tropical countries. Both species, colored dark mahogany or bright chestnut, hide in cracks, crevices, or under rugs by day, and emerge at night to feed on human blood. The sucking beak contains two stylets designed for piercing the

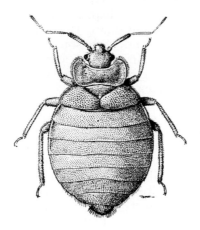

Fig. XVII–15.—Male bedbug. (*The Bed-Bug,* courtesy of British Museum Natural History Economic Series No. 5, 1954.)

skin. After puncturing the host skin the bug pumps saliva into the wound through the salivary tube, and then sucks up a mixture of the saliva and host blood. The saliva probably prevents coagulation of blood, and it is responsible for the irritating effects of the bite. Nymphs also feed on blood, and when the bug has finished feeding it usually pauses a moment, then runs away as fast as possible. The bugs are able to endure long fasts, and some have been kept alive without food for over a year.

Bedbugs are generally considered as loathsome creatures because of their nocturnal, stealthy attacks and because of their peculiar pungent odor. One of the earliest references in English to these pests is that of Humphrey Lloyd who translated the following statement made by Pope John XXI in the sixteenth century. "Small stynkinge wormes which live in paper and wod, called Cimices."

Before the female bedbug can lay fertile eggs, she must not only mate but she must feed. The pearly white, slightly curved, opetculated eggs are normally laid on rough surfaces like those found in crevices and behind wallpaper. A quick-drying cement fastens each egg (about 1 mm. long) securely to the surface of the material on which it is deposited. Upon hatching, after six to ten days, the nymphs, about the size of a pinhead, appear very similar to the adult, and immediately seek shelter. There are five molts before the adult stage is reached. For details on the ecology of bedbugs see Johnson.[14]

Bedbugs and Disease.—Bedbugs are not responsible for the transmission, as natural vectors, of disease. Mechanical transmission of infections by means of contaminated feet of the insects may take place, and leptospirosis is known to be transmitted from guinea pig to guinea pig by the bite of bedbugs; but, in spite of some conflicting accounts and persistent suspicion, no clear evidence has been presented for bedbugs being more than harmless pests of mankind. McKenny-Huges and Johnson,[18] however, have called attention to the fact that "in infested areas it is often possible to pick out children from buggy homes by their pasty faces, listless appearance and general lack of energy. It can be argued that the house in which bugs are tolerated will also be the home of malnutrition, dirt and other causes of physical infirmity. Such causes cannot be held solely responsible, and sleepless nights with constant irriation due to the injection of the minute doses of bedbug saliva into the blood are likely to contribute largely to the ill-health of children and even of certain adults. Some fortunate people are not affected by the bites of bedbugs; others gain immunity after repeated biting; whilst others, less fortunate, are always susceptible."

Bedbug control is basically a matter of cleanliness. For heavy infestations the liberal application of a 5 per cent DDT spray in kerosene is most effective. One per cent lindane is also satisfactory. The spray should cover infected furniture, mattresses, wall surfaces and floors.

ORDER LEPIDOPTERA

(MOTHS AND BUTTERFLIES)

The vast majority of butterflies and moths are entirely free-living, feeding on plant materials, but in one family, the **Epipyropidae** comprising minute moths, the entomophagous habit reaches its highest development among all Lepidoptera. Some of these moths are obligate external parasites attacking principally Homoptera of the family Fulgoridae (leaf-eaters). All species of these parasites are limited to a single host during larval development. Instances of true parasitism by members of other lepidopterous families are exceedingly rare. In a typical example of a parasitic moth the female deposits numbers of eggs upon the foliage of the food plant of the host. Young larvae wander about in search of a host, and when it is found, they attach themselves to the host body with their heads directed caudally, and feed upon its secretions. The mandibles of the parasite become embedded in an aperture in the integument of the host abdomen, but the effects of parasitism upon the host appear to be slight. The family **Cyclotornidae** also includes parasites; the first instar larvae of *Cyclotorna* (in Australasia) parasitize Homoptera, whereas the second instar larvae live in ants' nests. For details of this group see Clausen[7] and Balduf.[2]

ORDER SIPHONAPTERA (Also Called APHANIPTERA)

(FLEAS)

Over 1,300 species of fleas have been described, and undoubtedly there are many more not yet discovered by man. The adults only are parasitic, and they, like the lice, are restricted to birds and mammals on whose blood they feed. Fleas have bodies that are laterally compressed, and the first segment, the coxa, of each leg is large, aiding in the jumping ability for which fleas are justly famous. Most of us may recall how difficult it is to catch a flea. This difficulty is the result of the small size of the flea, its laterally compressed and slippery body, the backward directed spines, and the strong, active legs tipped with claws. These characteristics enable fleas to jump from one host to another and to move easily between hairs and feathers. The compact structure of a flea is adapted

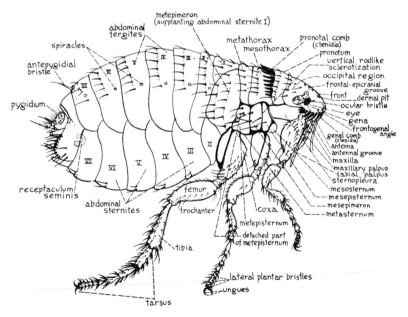

FIG. XVII–16.—*Ctenocephalides felis*, the cat flea, adult female. (Dept. of Health Education and Welfare, Public Health Service, Atlanta, Ga.)

phenomenon of a complex social organization among ants, bees and wasps has captured the attention of everyone who has even a mild interest in the kaleidoscopic life of the insect world. The highly evolved condition which parasitism has reached in the order has been independently acquired among species belonging to diverse super-families. Even in the suborder Symphyta, which includes all of the more primitive members of the order, there are some species which are parasites, as larvae, of plants.

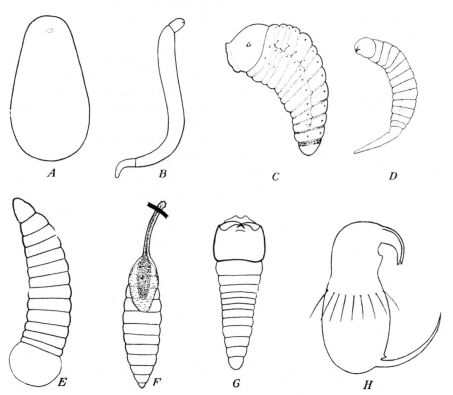

Fig. XVII–23.—First-instar larval forms of some parasitic Hymenoptera. *A*, sacci-form; *B*, asexual; *C*, hymenopteriform; *D*, caudate; *E*, vesiculate; *F*, encyrtiform; *G*, mandibulate; *H*, teleaform. (Clausen, *Entomophagous Insects*, courtesy of McGraw-Hill Book Co.)

The order consists chiefly of ants, bees, wasps, sawflies, and ichneumon flies. Parasitism is prominently displayed by members of the order, and insects are favored as hosts. Diagnostic features of the order include two pairs of membranous wings interlocked by means of hooklets; mouthparts adapted for biting, sucking or lapping; an abdomen usually constricted at its base and its first segment fused with the metathorax; an ovipositor modified for piercing, sawing or cutting; larvae often legless; pupae commonly in cocoons; metamorphosis complete.

The phenomenon of *polyembryony* (production of two or more embryos from a single egg) occurs in some of the parasitic Hymenoptera. During this process an egg, laid in the egg of a host insect, produces polar bodies which, instead of being discarded, become centers of cytoplasm surrounded by a membrane called a *trophamnion*. The whole embryonic mass of parasitic tissue divides to form a number of morulae, each of which becomes an embryo. In this manner within a single host a brood of from 2 to about 3,000 parasites may be produced. Here the cost of the lives of hundreds or thousands of larval parasites is the life of one host—a bargain indeed!

Typical parasitic hymenopteran insects are entomophagus (insect-eating) and parasitic only during the larval stages. There is a great variety in the manner and place of oviposition by the female, ranging from the common internal placement of the egg within the body of the host to its deposition on foliage or in plant tissue far removed from the animal host. Upon hatching, the parasitic larvae (Figs. XVII–23 and 24) feed upon the host which is usually itself a larva or an egg and is thereby destroyed. The fact that any given larva may be either ecto- or endoparasitic, according to the species of the host on which it feeds, indicates that the nature of the host is responsible for the behavior of the larva. The larvae of *Onchophanes lanceolator*, for example, is ectoparasitic on the caterpillars of *Cacoecia sorbiana*, but endoparasitic in caterpillars of other genera of Lepidoptera. Another wasp larva may be found attached to spiders. Insect parasites may pupate inside the host, on its outer surface, or even entirely apart from it. Details of the processes of host selection, site selection for oviposition, and placement of the egg on or in the host body vary immensely, but one example will be outlined to emphasize the complexity of the habits of parasitic Hymenoptera. This example is *Tiphia*, described on page 460.

Some of the larger or more important groups of parasitic Hymenoptera will be described and illustrated below. Examples have been selected more or less at random to indicate the diversity of the parasitic mode of life as adopted by these insects. The system of classification and the factual information is taken largely from Imms.[12] All of the examples belong to the suborder Apocrita which includes the vast majority of the Hymenoptera, and which is characterized by a deeply constricted abdomen between the first abdominal segment (propodeum) and the second, and by larvae without legs. The common custom of dividing the Apocrita into the *Parasitica* and the *Aculeata* (stinging forms) appears too artificial to continue, because both groups contain many exceptions, and because there is no clear biological distinction between them. Instead, a series of twenty-one superfamilies is recognized, and six of these will be mentioned.

Venom. Parasitic Hymenoptera often kill or paralyze their hosts prior to oviposition, but some species apparently never inject venom into the host. The host reaction to the venom may be im-

29

mediate or it may be delayed for several minutes. Very little is
known about the venom of parasitic hymenopteran insects, but
Beard[3] calculated that the venom of the wasp *Bracon hebetor* diluted
to 1 part in 200,000,000 parts of the host hemolymph was sufficient
to cause permanent paralysis. The site of action in the host appears
to be the neuromuscular junction.

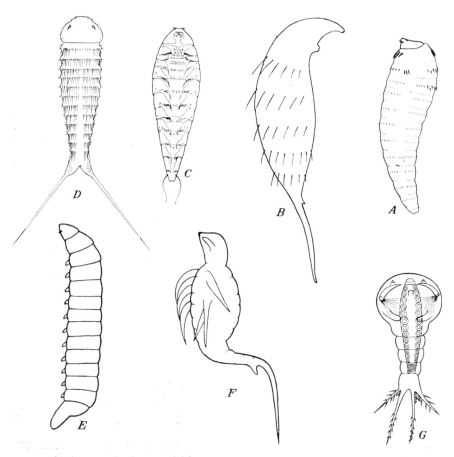

Fig. XVII–24.—First-instar larval forms some of parasitic Hymenoptera. *A*, micro-
type; *B*, mymariform; *C*, planidium; *D*, agriotypiform; *E*, polypodeiform; *F*, eucoili-
form; *G*, cyclopiform. (Clausen, *Entomophagous Insects*, courtesy of McGraw-Hill Book
Co.)

SUPERFAMILY ICHNEUMONOIDEA

Ichneumon flies (Fig. XVII–25) are predominantly parasites of Lepidoptera, but many of them use as hosts the Hymenoptera, Coleoptera, Diptera, Arachnida, and a few other arthropods. Most species of the parasites are probably seldom restricted
to any individual species of host, and in their behavior the ichneu-

mons are among the most highly evolved of all solitary insects. Most of them are internal parasites of the immature stages of their hosts. The presence of a caudal tail on the newly-hatched ichneumon larva of many species is a prominent feature. The head in the young larva is large and often strongly sclerotized, but older larvae (third instar) generally become maggot-like with reduced heads. Fully fed, mature larvae construct silken cocoons. Adults commonly display remarkably long ovipositors, that of *Thalessa* reaching up to fifteen cm. (six inches) in length.

Braconid wasps (Fig. XVII–26), like the ichneumonids, select

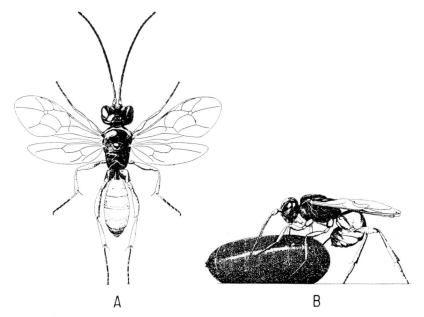

A   B

FIG. XVII–25.—A hyperparasitic ichneumon, *Phygadeuon subfuscus* Cresson (Gelinae). *A*, adult male; *B*, female ovipositing in puparium of host. The host of this ichneumon is a tachinid fly, *Paradexodes epilachnae* Aldrich, which is parasitic on the Mexican bean beetle, *Epilachna varivestis* Mulsant. (Courtesy of U.S.D.A.)

FIG. XVII–26.—A female braconid (*Lysiphlebus testaceipes*) ovipositing in an aphid. (Clausen, *Entomophagous Insects*, courtesy of McGraw-Hill Book Co.)

a wide variety of hosts, but the Lepidoptera are the most commonly parasitized. The braconids are closely similar in both structure and habits to the ichneumonids. The well-studied *Apanteles glomeratus* is a common parasite of the larva of *Pieris* (Lepidoptera) which may support 150 parasites. Mature larval parasites (or parasitoids, see p. 15) gnaw their way through the skin of their host and then produce a mass of sulphur-yellow cocoons irregularly heaped together. The genus *Rogas* is a wide-spread parasite of the tent caterpillar, *Malacosoma*, in North America. Little, if any, host preference is shown by these parasites for the different species of *Malacosoma*.

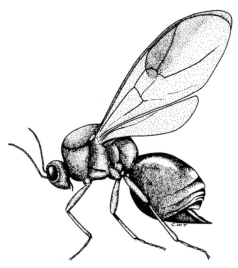

Fig. XVII–27.—A gall wasp. *Diplolepis rosae* (Linn.). This species develops in the mossy rose gall. (Borror and DeLong, *An Introduction to the Study of Insects*, courtesy of Rinehart & Co.)

SUPERFAMILY CYNIPOIDEA

Gall wasps (Fig. XVII–27) are small, often minute, darkly colored insects which lay eggs in plant tissues, mainly on oaks, thereby producing swollen galls around the developing larvae. Males are rare, parthenogenesis common, and the pedicel-equipped eggs hatch into legless larvae which do not spin a cocoon. The parasites gain shelter and nutrition from the galls, or are inquilines in them. The forms of galls produced by these insects are almost endless and they may occur in all parts of the plant from the roots to the flowers. An explanation of the phenomenon of gall-formation has not yet been made to the satisfaction of botanists or entomologists. All that can be said at the present time is that galls are produced as the result of reactions of the cambium and other meristematic plant tissues in response to the stimuli induced by the presence of the living larval parasite. In addition to the insects that actually

produce a gall, the latter is frequently the abode of Diptera, Coleoptera, Lepidoptera and other Hymenoptera.

SUPERFAMILY CHALCIDOIDEA

Chalcid wasps are small insects with elbowed antennae, and
they probably comprise the largest group in the order Hymenoptera.
The bulk of the species are either parasites or hyperparasites of
other insects, and they are of great economic value in the biological
control of insect pests (see p. 580). Some larvae infest the seeds
or stems of plants, others are hyperparasites of other insects which,

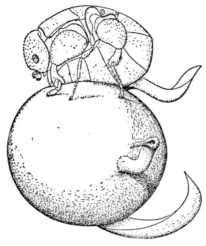

Fig. XVII–28.—Male *Blastophaga psenes* fertilizing the female, the latter within a
galled flower of the fig. (Imms, *A General Textbook of Entomology*, courtesy of E. P.
Dutton and Co.)

in their turn, destroy insect species harmful to man. The orders
most frequently parasitized are Lepidoptera, Homoptera, Diptera
and Coleoptera. Enormous numbers of eggs and larvae of Lepidoptera succumb to attacks by chalcid wasps but the pupal stage
is rarely invaded. The Coccoidae (Hemiptera), often called "scale
insects" or "mealy bugs", are the most universally attacked of any
group of insects. For a general account of the biology of the group
see Clausen.[7]

Among the most remarkable chalcids are the "fig insects" (family
Agaontidae) which maintain a symbiotic relationship with various
species of *Ficus*. The best known species is *Blastophaga psenes*
(Fig. XVII–28) which is a symbiont of the fruit of *Ficus carcia*. In
the words of Imms, "the eggs of this Chalcid are laid in the ovaries
of the caprifig and give rise to galls therein. The male imago emerges
first and, on finding a gall containing a female, commences to gnaw
a hole through the wall of the ovary and fertilizes the female while
the latter is still *in situ*. The female leaves the receptacle through

the opening at its apex, and, laden with adherent pollen, flies to a neighboring fruit. If the latter be in the right condition she seeks the opening and gains admission into the interior of the receptacle, where she commences oviposition. Should the caprifig, from which she has emerged, be suspended in a tree of the Smyrna variety she enters a fruit of the latter, but subsequently discovers that she has selected a wrong host, since the flowers are of such a shape that they do not permit oviposition within them. After wandering about for a while, she usually crawls out of the receptacle and incidentally pollinates the flowers. Most of the males die without ever leaving the receptacles in which their development took place. *B. psenes*, while in the fig, sometimes becomes the host of another wasp (*Philotrypesis*) which may be called a "cleptoparasite".[16]

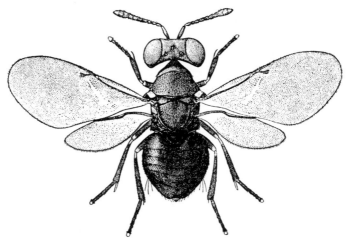

Fig. XVII–29.—A typical chalcid, *Blastothrix sericea*, female: magnified. (Imms, *A General Textbook of Entomology*, courtesy of E. P. Dutton and Co.)

Hardly a single order of insects is immune from attack by members of the family **Encyrtidae.** *Blastothrix* (Fig. XVII–29) has been studied extensively. In the Family Trichogrammatidae the genus *Trichogramma* (Fig. XVII–30), which usually parasitizes the eggs of Lepidoptera (as many as twenty individuals may develop within one egg) has been used extensively in connection with biological control. *T. minutum* alone has been found to attack more than 150 host species representing seven orders of insects. The family Pteromalidae is one of the most common, and the majority of species in this family are external gregarious parasites of lepidopterous larvae and pupae (Fig. XVII–31). Among the Aphelinidae, *Eretmocerus serius* has been used effectively for the biological control of "white flies" (Hemiptera). This parasite (Fig. XVII–32) has the unusual habit of being ectophagous during the first and a portion of the second stage, and then entering the body of its host when the latter becomes a pupa.

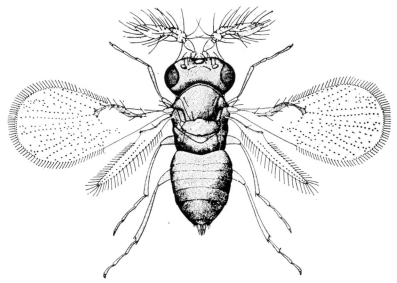

Fig. XVII–30.—The adult male of *Trichogramma minutum*. (Clausen, *Entomophagous Insects*, courtesy of McGraw-Hill Book Co.)

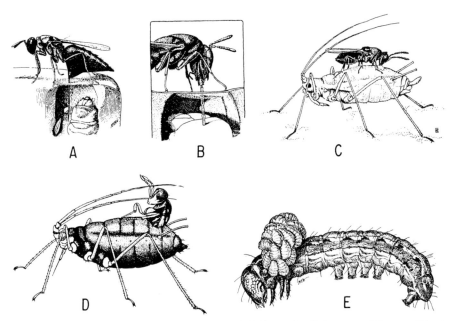

Fig. XVII–31.—Feeding and emerging chalcids. *A, Habrocytus* (Pteromalidae) ovipositing; *B, Habrocytus* feeding at the tube made by her ovipositor; *C, Zahropalus inquisitor* (Howard) (Encyrtidae) feeding at an oviposition puncture made in the abdomen of an aphid; *D*, adult of *Aphelinus jucundus* Gahan (Eulophidae) emerging from an aphid; *E*, a colony of *Euplectrus* larvae (Eulophidae) feeding on a caterpillar (*A* and *B*, courtesy of Fulton and the Entomological Society of America; *C* and *D* courtesy of Griswold and Entomological Society of America; *E*, courtesy of U.S.D.A.)

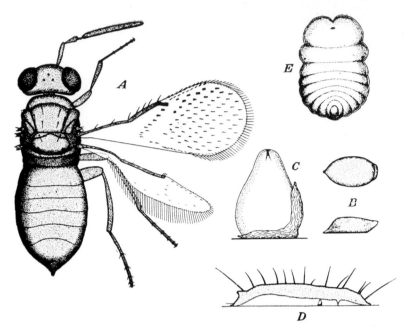

FIG. XVII–32.—Developmental stages of *Eretmocerus serius*. *A*, the adult male; *B*, the egg, dorsal and lateral views; *C*, the first-instar larva; *D*, host larva with first-instar larva beneath the body; *E*, the mature larva. (Clausen, *Entomophagous Insects*, courtesy of McGraw-Hill Book Co.)

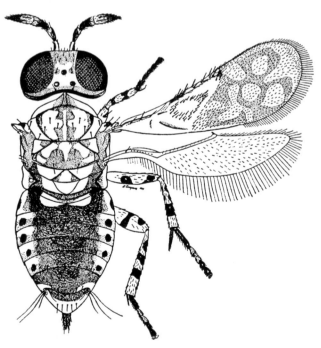

FIG. XVII–33.—*Marietta carnesi*, female. A hyperparasite of the primary parasite of a scale insect. (Compere, courtesy of Univ. Calif. Publ. Entomol)

(458)

Marietta carnesi (Fig. XVII–33) is a tiny aphelinid wasp, a little over a millimeter long, which parasitizes another wasp, *Comperiella bifasciata*, which is parasitic in a scale insect. The first wasp is thus a hyperparasite on the primary parasite of the scale insect.

SUPERFAMILY PROCTOTRUPOIDEA (=SERPHOIDEA)

All the members of this superfamily are parasitic, some on eggs of other insects, some on larvae and pupae; some are hyperparasites and a few are inquilines. The majority of species develops cocoons but in the aphid-infesting forms the body of the host protects the pupa. *Platygaster dryomyiae* (Fig. XVII–34) exhibits polyembryony. *Mantibaria* (= *Riela*) *manticida* exhibits an exceptionally advanced

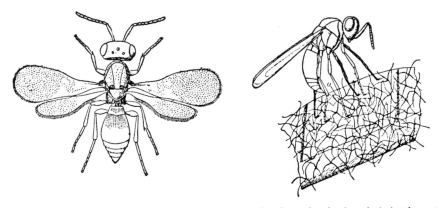

Fig. XVII–34.—*Platygaster dryomyiae*, female. On the right the female is in the act of oviposition in an egg *O*, of *Dryomyia* (Cecidomyidae). (Imms, *General Textbook of Entomology*, courtesy of E. P. Dutton and Co.)

type of parasitism. It is the only known case of an adult hymenopteran insect that feeds on the blood of its host. Development takes place within the egg mass of the praying mantis, *Mantis religiosa*. After the adult parasites settle down on the adults of the host, the female parasite gnaws through the chitinous veins at the base of the wings of the mantis. Here the parasites cast off their wings and lead ectoparasitic lives at about the only spot where the parasite can escape being brushed off by the formidable front legs of the mantis. If the mantis is a female and has commenced oviposition, the adult parasite migrates to the genital region to lay its eggs in the host ootheca while the latter is being formed. Parasites that settle upon the male mantis perish with their hosts.

SUPERFAMILY SCOLIOIDEA

Vespoid wasps belong to an extensive group including some of the most primitive members of the stinging forms, as well as some of the largest of the Hymenoptera. Many of these wasps are parasitic, usually on coleopterous larvae. The vespoid wasps, generally large, hairy, and dark in color, are ectoparasites of larval scarabaeid beetles. Their bodies are often marked with spots or bands of yellow or red, and their wings frequently display a metallic iridescence.

Tiphiidae is the dominant family of hymenopteran parasites attacking scarabaeid beetle grubs in the soil. They are solitary wasps which develop as external parasites, usually upon the final larval instar of the host. The genus *Tiphia* (Fig. XVII–35) is the most cosmopolitan and the most common of the family, and the adult female commences its parasitic activities by burrowing into

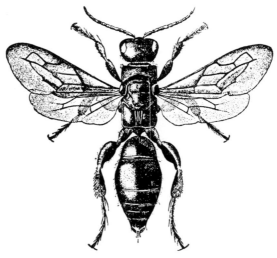

Fig. XVII–35.—*Tiphia transversa*, female vespoid wasp. (Imms, *A General Textbook of Entomology*, courtesy of E. P. Dutton and Co.)

the soil to gain access to the cell occupied by the grub. The following account is taken from Clausen,[7] and it describes the behavior of *T. popilliavora*. As soon as the female wasp finds a grub, "she first crawls over the dorsum of the body from the rear, then curls the abdomen down and around the side, and inserts the sting in the venter of the thorax, usually between the first two segments. This stinging is repeated until the grub is quiescent. She then turns to the abdomen and commences an extensive kneading of the ventral surface with the mandibles, beginning with the first segment and continuing for its length. When this is complete, she grasps the lateral margin with the mandibles and coils the body transversely over the dorsum and to the ventral surface, forming almost a complete circle. The tip of the abdomen is applied to the groove between the fifth and sixth abdominal segments, near the margin, and is rhythmically moved backward and forward for several minutes, thus broadening the groove and possibly rasping away a portion of the integument to permit of more ready penetration by the larva.

In the course of this preparation, any egg or young larva that may be present as a result of an earlier oviposition is rubbed off or broken. The egg is finally extruded and is firmly attached by a mucilaginous material. It lies transversely in the groove, with the anterior pole directed toward the median ventral line of the host body. The wasp may then quit the body or remain for a period of feeding, as has already been described. The grub recovers from the effects of the sting in twenty to forty minutes."

SUPERFAMILY APOIDEA

Social and solitary bees are best known through the voluminous literature on the honeybee, one of the best understood of all insects. Of the numerous parasitic genera of the family Apidae the largest is probably *Nomada* whose members are similar to wasps in appearance, and are usually black and yellow in color, with almost bare bodies. Species of this genus are usually parasitic on different species of *Andrena*, the common solitary bee of the Holarctic region, and on other genera of bees. Linsley and MacSwain[17] have described in detail the habits of *Nomada*.

ORDER COLEOPTERA

(BEETLES)

Over a quarter of a million species of beetles have been described, and a great many more are undoubtedly yet to be found by man. The order contains a relatively small number of parasitic forms most of which are ectoparasites. Probably the most distinctive feature of beetles is the elytra or front wing. Most beetles have four wings, but the front pair is thickened, leathery or hard and brittle, and it serves as a protective sheath over the longer and membranous hind wings which are the only ones normally used for flight. The elytra generally meet in a straight line down the middle of the back.

Staphylinidae comprises the rove beetles. Adults are recognized by their slender bodies, short elytra, and by their habit of elevating the abdomen when disturbed. Only a few species of this family are true parasites, the best known being in the genera *Coprochara*, *Aleochara*, and *Baryodma*. The larvae of these beetles live within the puparium of Diptera, but they are obligate external parasites upon the pupae.

Ripiphoridae is a family which comprises a few hundred species all parasitic as larvae in the larvae of the Hymenoptera, cockroaches and a few other insects. The adult beetles are conspicuous with their streamlined bodies, comb-like or fibrous antennae of the males, and varied color patterns (Fig. XVII–36). The triungulinids (first instar larvae, Fig. XVII–37) of all species are equipped with a caudal sucker, and they are able to assume an erect position with their legs free for grabbing on to passing insects or other objects. Each

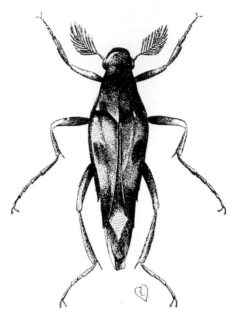

Fig. XVII–36.—The adult female of *Macrosaigon pectinatus*, a ripiphorid bettle. (Clausen *Entomophagous Insects*, courtesy of McGraw-Hill Book Co.)

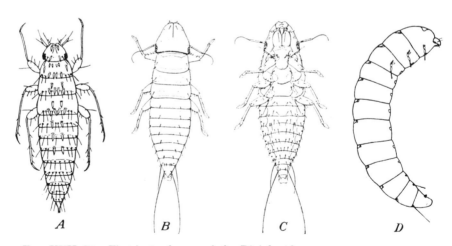

Fig. XVII–37.—First-instar larvae of the Ripiphoridae.
A, *Ripidius denisi* Chob. (after Chobaut); B and C, *Macrosaigon flabellatum* F., dorsal and ventral views, before feeding; D, the same at the completion of the endoparasitic phase, immediately before the first molt, showing the extreme distention of the body and the wide separation of the segmental plates. (Grandi in Clausen, *Entophagous Insects*, courtesy of McGraw-Hill Book Co.)

larval instar is markedly different from the others, a condition known as hypermetamorphosis. *Metoecus paradoxus*, common in Europe, is a parasite of the larvae of wasps (*Vespa* spp.). Only a portion of the first stage is passed internally, just beneath the skin, and the second larval stage of the parasite is found as a collar encircling the neck of the host.

Meloidae is a very large family whose members are called blister beetles or oil beetles. The long-legged, soft bodied adults have a strongly deflected head and often reduced elytra, or no wings at all. The larvae, as in the case of the family Rhipiphoridae described above, exhibit hypermetamorphosis (Fig. XVII–38). Although the

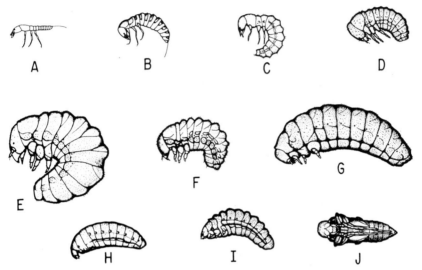

Fig. XVII–38.—Larval and pupal instars of the black blister beetle, *Epicauta penn-sylvanica* (DeGeer), showing hypermetamorphosis. *A*, newly hatched first instar, or triungulin; *B*, fully fed first instar; *C*, second instar; *D*, third instar; *E*, fourth instar; *F*, newly molted fifth instar; *G*, gorged fifth instar; *H*, sixth instar (coarctate larva or pseudopupa); *I*, seventh instar; *J*, pupa. (Courtesy of Horsfall and the Arkansas Agricultural Experiment Station.)

adult meloidids are entirely plant feeders, the larvae are parasitic or predaceous, the parasitic species preferring the cells of various bees of the families Megachlidae and Andrenidae as their transient homes. In the majority of cases the relationship between the beetle larva and the bee larva is not one of true parasitism. The parasite generally consumes the egg of the host, then remains to feed upon the food mass stored in the cell by the parent bee. Many species of these beetles are predators on the egg pods of locusts. An example of a species that attacks bees is *Tricrania sanguinipennis*. Another example is *Sitaris muralis* which attacks bees of the genus *An-throphora*. Eggs of the parasite are deposited near the nest of the bees in August, and the newly hatched triungulinids hibernate until the following spring when the more successful individuals attach themselves to the hairy bodies of the bees. *Anthophora* constructs cells in the ground, and when the female bee deposits an egg in a honey-filled cell, a triungulid slips off her body, alights on the egg, and thereby becomes imprisoned in the sealed-up cell where it eats the egg and honey, moults several times and becomes an adult plant-feeding beetle.

ORDER STREPSIPTERA
(TWISTED-WINGED PARASITES OR STYLOPIDS)

Stylopids are small, endoparasitic insects that exhibit a striking sexual dimorphism in the adult stage. The males have branched antennae, large protruding eyes, club-like structures (halteres) instead of fore wings, and large hind wings. The females are wingless and normally they remain in the host enclosed in a puparium which protrudes slightly from the body of the host. A few females leave the host and have a larviform structure with a terminal gonophore. Only about 300 species are known, and these species have commonly been placed within the order Coleoptera. All species, so far as is known, complete their larval development within the body of the host in a manner similar to that of the beetle *Ripidius* in cockroaches (see p. 461). The first instar larvae of stylopids bear a striking resemblance to those of the Ripiphoridae (Coleoptera, see p. 462). The minute adult males are not encountered by collectors nearly as often as are the females, and many species have consequently been described on the basis of one sex only. In common parlance, insects harboring these parasites are said to be "stylopized."

Although a few records of Orthoptera and Hemiptera as hosts to the Strepsiptera are known, the preferred hosts are members of the Homoptera (chiefly Auchenorrhyncha) and of the Hymenoptera (chiefly Vespoidea, Sphecoidea and Apoidea). The following account of the biology and habits of these parasites is based upon *Xenos vesparum*, a parasite of wasps and bees (see Imms[12] and Clausen[7]). The male lives only a few hours after emerging from the host, but the female remains permanently endoparasitic with its cephalothorax protruding through the body wall of the wasp or bee. Copulation takes place by the male alighting on the host and inserting the aedeagus (penis plus lateral structures) into the aperature of the brood canal of the female. Larvae hatch within the brood canal of the female and issue in large numbers, sometimes several thousand, through the genital canals. Larvae eventually emerge through the brood canal, and they remain as active creatures upon the body of the host until opportunity is afforded for escape. The first instar larvae are known as triungulinids (Fig. XVII–39). The larvae probably leave the first or "maternal" host when the latter are closely associated with others on flowers or in the nest. By simple attachment to adult wasps or bees the larval parasites are transported to larval hosts, within which they speedily burrow through the body wall and take up lodgings in body spaces between the organs, pushing them out of position. Absorption of nutrients from the host blood results in growth of the parasite, and after the seventh instar the parasitic larva works its way outward and protrudes from the body wall of the host which is by now in the pupal stage of development. The male parasite now undergoes pupation, and soon the winged insect is liberated (Fig. XVII–40). The female

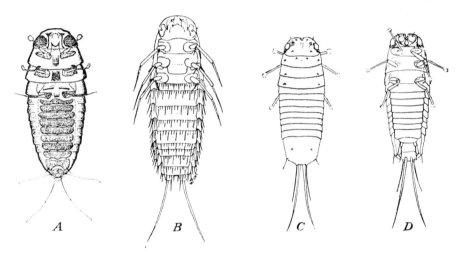

Fig. XVII–39.—First-instar larvae of the Strepsiptera. (Clausen, *Entomophagous Insects* courtesy of McGraw-Hill Book Co.)

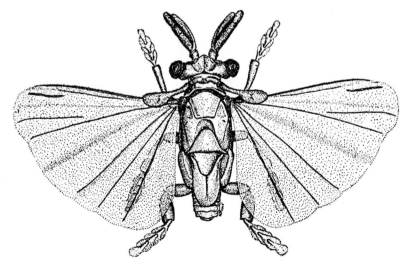

Fig. XVII-40.—*Stylops shannoni*, male, enlarged. (Imms, *General Textbook of Entomology* courtesy of E. P. Dutton and Co.)

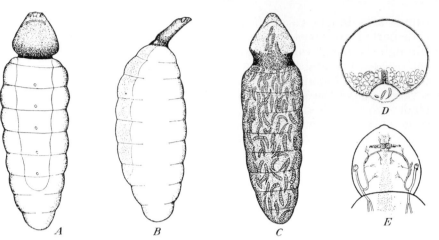

Fig. XVII–41.—Adult females of the Strepsiptera, with details. *A, Stylops melittae* Kirby, showing the genital openings on the cephalothorax and the brood chamber; *B*, the same lateral view; *C*, a gravid female of *Halictophagus curtisii* Dale, showing fully developed trungulinids distributed throughout the body; *D*, a diagrammatic cross section through the fourth abdominal segment of *S. melittae*, showing the outer portion of the genital canal and several triungulinids in the brood chamber; *E*, cephalothorax of *Xenos vesparum* Rossi, dorsal view, showing the single pair of spiracles, the anterior commissure and the longitudinal tracheal trunks, which divide in the first thoracic segment. (*Redrawn after Nassanov*, 1892, '93 in Clausen, *Entomophagous Insects*, courtesy of McGraw-Hill Book Co.)

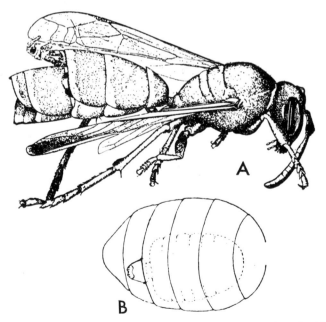

Fig. XVII–42.—*A, Polistes gallicus*, with a male *Xenos vesparum* (a stylopid) hatching from the puparium. *B*, Abdomen of *Andrena vaga*, with adult female of *Stylops* sp. (Baer, *Ecology of Animal Parasites*, courtesy University of Illinois Press.)

(Fig. XVII–41) becomes a white grub-like creature remaining within the host.

The effects of stylopids on their hosts vary considerably depending on numbers of parasites within one host, length of time which the parasites spend within the host, seasonal and other considerations (Fig. XVII–42). Generally, however, marked changes in the growth and development of the host occur, including pronounced alterations of the secondary sexual characters.[27] Much confusion has arisen from the description of "new" species of stylopized wasps and bees. For further details see Bohart[4] and Pierce.[19]

BIBLIOGRAPHY

1. Anonymous, 1949. *Fleas as a Menace to Man and Domestic Animals. Their Life-History, Habits and Control.* 6th ed., British Mus. Nat. Hist. Econ. Ser. 3. London. 18 pp.

2. BALDUF, W. V., 1938. The Rise of Entomophagy Among Lepidoptera. Amer. Nat., *72*, 358–379.

3. BEARD, R. L., 1952. The Toxicology of Habrobracon Venom: a Study of a Natural Insecticide. Bull. Conn. Agric. Exp. Sta., *562*, 1–27.

4. BOHART, R. M., 1941. A Revision of the Strepsiptera with Special Reference to the Species of North America. Univ. Calif. Pub. Ent., *7*, 91–160.

5. BÖRNER, C., 1952. Europae Centralis Aphides. Die Blattläuse Mitteleuropas. Namen, Synonyme, Wirtspflanzen, Generationszyklen. Schrift. Thüring. Land. Heilpflanz. Weimar, *4*, (3), 484 pp.

6. BUXTON, P. A., 1930. The Biology of a Bloodsucking Bug, *Rhodnius prolixus*. Trans. Entomol. Soc. London, *78*, 227–236.

7. CLAUSEN, C. P., 1940. *Entomophagus Insects.* McGraw-Hill Book Co., N. Y. and London. 688 pp.

8. EICHLER, W., 1938. "Einemsen" und verwandte Handlungen. Stettiner Entom. Zeitung, *99*, 299–302.

9. FERRIS, G. F., 1937–1953. *An Atlas of the Scale Insects of North America.* Stanford, California. *1*, 1–136; *2*, 137–268; *3*, 269–384; *4*, 285–448; *5*, 1–278, 108 figs.; *6*, 279–506, 85 figs.

10. GILLETTE, C. P. and PALMER, M. A., 1931–1936. The Aphidae of Colorado. Pts. I–III. Ann. Ent. Soc. Amer., *24*, 827–934; *25*, 369–496; *27*, 133–255; *29*, 729–748.

10a. HOPKINS, G. H. E., 1949. The Host-Associations of the Lice of Mammals. Proc. Zool. Soc. London, *119*, 387–604.

11. HUBBARD, C. A., 1947. *Fleas of Western North America. Their Relation to the Public Health.* Iowa State Coll. Press. 533 pp.

12. IMMS, A. D., 1957. *A General Textbook of Entomology.* Methuen & Co. Ltd. London. 886 pp.

13. JELLISON, W. L., 1959. Fleas and Disease. Ann. Rev. Entomol., *4*, 389–414.

14. JOHNSON, C. G., 1942. The Ecology of the Bedbug, *Cimex lectularius* L. in Britain. J. Hyg., *41*, 345–461.

15. KENNEDY, J. S. and STROYAN, H. L. G., 1959. Biology of Aphids. Ann. Rev. Entomol., *4*, 139–160.

16. KUTTAMATHIATHU, J. J., 1958. The Biology of *Philotrypesis caricae* (L.), Parasite of *Blastophaga psenes* (L.) (Chalcidoidea: Parasitic Hymenoptera). Proc. XVth Internat. Congr. Zool., London, p. 662–664.

17. LINSLEY, E. G. and MacSWAIN, J. W., 1955. The Habits of *Nomada opacella* Timberlake with Notes on Other Species (Hymenoptera: Anthophoridae). The Wasmann J. Biol., *13*, 253–276.

18. McKENNY-HUGES, A. W. and JOHNSON, C. G., 1954. *The Bedbug. Its Habits and Life History and How to Deal With It.* Brit. Mus. Nat. Hist. Econ. Ser., *5*, London. 18 pp.

18a. MEYERS, L. E., 1928. The American Swallow Bug, *Oeciacus vicarius* Horvath (Hemiptera, Cimicidae). Parasitol., *20*, 159–172.

19. PIERCE, W. D., 1909. A Monographic Revision of the Twisted Wniged Insects Comprising the Order Strepsiptera Kirby. Bull. U. S. Nat. Mus., *66*, 232 pp.

20. QUAINTANCE, A. L. and BAKER, A. C., 1917. A Contribution to Our Knowledge of the White-flies of the Subfamily Aleyrodinae (Aleyrodidae). Proc. U. S. Nat. Mus., *51*, 335–445.

21. ROTHSCHILD, M. and CLAY, T., 1952. *Fleas, Flukes and Cuckoos. A Study of Bird Parasites.* Collins, London. 305 pp.

22. SAMPSON, W. W., 1943. A Generic Synopsis of the Hemipterous Superfamily Aleyrodoidea. Ent. Amer., *23*, 173–223.

23. SMITH, L. M., 1937. Growth, Reproduction, Feeding and Wing Development of the Mealy Plum Aphid in Relation to Climatic Factors. J. Agric. Res., *54*, 345–364.

24. THEOBALD, F. V., 1926–1929. *The Plant-lice or Aphididae of Great Britain.* Ashford & London, *1*, 372 pp; *2*, 411 pp; *3*, 364 pp.

25. USINGER, R. L., 1939. Descriptions of New Triatominae with a Key to Genera (Hemiptera, Reduviidae). Univ. Calif. Pub. Entomol., *7*, 33–56.

26. USINGER, R. L., 1944. The Triatominae of North and Central America and the West Indies and their Public Health Significance. Public Health Bull., *288*, 83 pp.

26a. WATERHOUSE, D. F., 1953. Studies on the Digestion of Wool by Insects. IX. Some Features of Digestion in Chewing Lice (Mallophaga) from Bird and Mammalian Hosts. Aust. J. Biol. Sci., Melbourne, *6*, 257–275.

27. WHEELER, W. M., 1910. The Effects of Parasitic and Other Kinds of Castration in Insects. J. Exp. Zool., *8*, 377–438.

28. WIGGLESWORTH, V. B., 1941. The Sensory Physiology of the Human Louse *Pediculus humanus corporis* De Geer (Anoplura). Parasitol., *33*, 67–109.

29. ZINSSER, H., 1935. *Rats, Lice and History*; Being a Study in Biography, Which, After Twelve Preliminary Chapters Indispensable for the Preparation of the Lay Reader, Deals with the Life History of Typhus Fever. Little, Brown & Co. Boston. 301 pp.

CHAPTER XVIII

Phylum Arthropoda
Class Insecta II
Order Diptera

(FLIES)

INJURIOUS insects cost the United States approximately four billion dollars a year. This sum includes losses due to such activities of insects as damage to livestock, crops, buildings, and stored products, and to various control measures. Much of this tremendous loss is caused directly or indirectly by parasitic insects and a significant amount of the damage is done by flies, gnats, mosquitoes and other members of the order Diptera. Of the many orders of insects this one possesses the greatest number of parasitic forms. Although some flies are parasitic as adults, most of the parasitic species have freeliving adults whereas their larval stages live in invertebrate or vertebrate hosts. Since so many flies deposit their eggs in decaying organic matter, it is not surprising that some of them have developed the habit of depositing eggs in fetid wounds of other animals. The developing larvae, or maggots, then have an opportunity to penetrate deeper into the bodies of their hosts. For an account of feeding habits of blood-sucking arthropods see Weitz.[6]

Structure

Insects belonging to the order Diptera are characterized by the possession of only one pair of wings, hence the name *diptera* which means "two wings." Immediately behind the wings occur a pair of club-shaped organs called "halteres." These organs are considered to be vestigial wings. The three body divisions, head, thorax, and abdomen, which characterize insects, are especially marked in the Diptera. The adult head usually possesses prominent eyes and a pair of antennae (Fig. XVIII–1). The thorax supports legs and wings. The wings are membranous and may be smooth, hairy or, as in the mosquitoes, may possess scales. Venation of the wings is an important diagnostic feature (Fig. XVIII–2). The abdomen is usually distinctly segmented and bears the genitalia at its

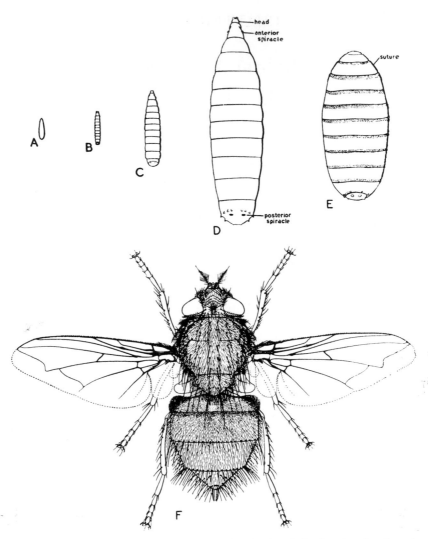

Fig. XVIII–1.—*Calliphora erythrocephala.* The blue bottle fly showing the character-istic appearance of *A*, the egg; *B*, the first stage larve; *C*, the second stage larva; *D*, the third stage larva; *E*, the puparium; *F*, the adult or imago. (Smart, *Insects of Medical Importance*, courtesy of British Museum, London.)

posterior end. Some of the major taxonomic details for flies are
illustrated in figure XVIII–3. The life cycles of Diptera usually
involve the egg, larva, pupa, and adult. The egg may hatch within
the body of the female but most dipterous insects lay eggs. Larvae
of flies are called maggots and, like other larvae, they undergo a
series of molts while growing.

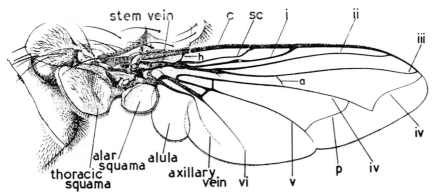

Fig. XVIII–2.—Right wing of *Calliphora erythrocephala*. *a*, cross vein; *c*, costa; *sc*,
subcosta; *p*, posterior cross vein. Longitudinal veins numbered by Roman numerals.
(Smart, *Insects of Medical Importance*, courtesy of British Museum, London.)

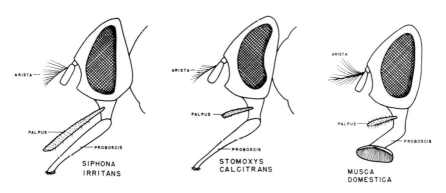

Fig. XVIII–3.—Taxonomic details of flies. (Federal Security Agency.)

Families of Diptera

Only families containing the more important parasites of man
or of animals will be discussed. The student may consult any
modern text on entomology for a more complete presentation.[3,4]
The following families are considered here: Culicidae, Simuliidae,
Tabanidae, Oestridae, Tachinidae (= Larvaevoridae), Calliphoridae,
Sarcophagidae, Muscidae, Hippoboscidae and Psychodidae. All
of these families, except the last, are illustrated in Figure XVIII–4.

Family Culicidae. Mosquitoes transmit such serious diseases as human and avian malaria, dengue fever, yellow fever, fowl pox, elephantiasis, and other forms of filariasis. Thus it is not surprising that, on the basis of weight alone, the literature on mosquitoes is staggering.

At least 2,000 species of mosquitoes occur in the world and they may be found in almost every country. These insects (Fig. XVIII–5)

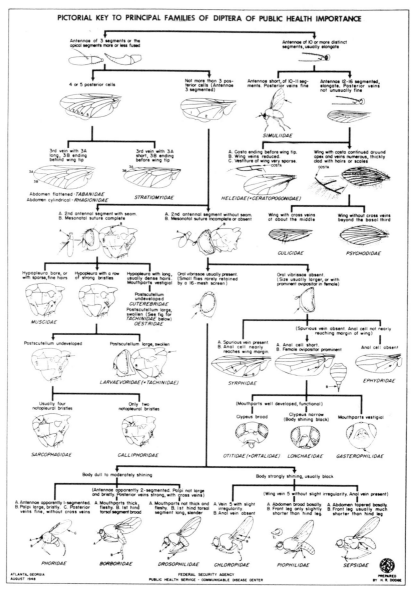

Fig. XVIII–4.—Pictorial key to principal families of diptera of public health importance. (Federal Security Agency.)

are characterized by slender bodies and long legs. The mouth parts of adult females form a blood-sucking proboscis (Fig. XVIII–8 and 9). The antennae of the male tend to be bushier and thus more prominent than those of the female. Mosquitoes in general may be distinguished from similar flies by their wing venation. Of especial value is the presence of two bifurcated veins toward the apex of each wing. These divided veins are separated by a single vein (Fig. XVIII–5). The veins are covered with scales.

Recognition of the various genera and species of mosquitoes is of such great importance to the medical parasitologist that space is given below to pictorial keys and other illustrations. These keys

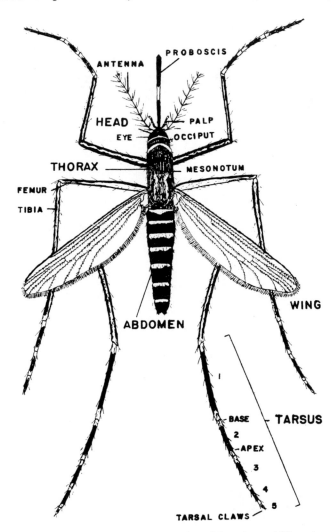

FIG. XVIII–5.—*Culex tarsalis,* adult. (Owen, *The Mosquitoes of Wyoming,* courtesy of Univ. Wyoming Pub.)

are self-explanatory and should be of considerable aid in the identification of the common forms, especially those found in the United States.

The life cycle of mosquitoes involves the usual egg, larva, pupa and adult stages; and the larvae and pupae live in water. Eggs, about a millimeter in length, are laid by members of the genus *Culex* in groups on the surface of water. These eggs adhere together

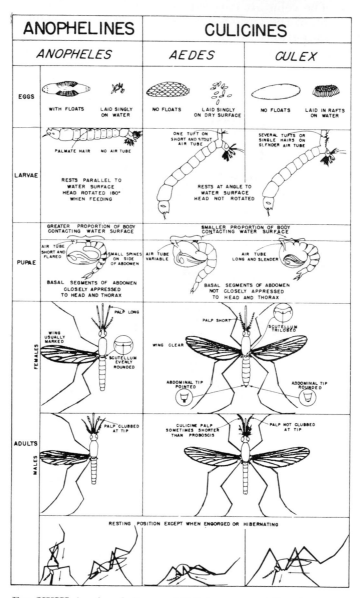

Fig. XVIII-6.—Anophelines and Culicines, comparative characters.
(United States Public Health Service.)

in the form of tiny rafts. Members of the genus *Anopheles* deposit their eggs singly without gluing them together and they remain afloat by virtue of lateral air chambers (see illustration in key, Fig. XVIII–6. Upon hatching, the larvae swim about and search for food (*e.g.* minute algae). They are sometimes called "wrigglers" because of the way they move through the water. Larvae come to the surface periodically and obtain air through breather tubes or siphons, a habit which leads to their destruction at the hands of zealous antimalarial workers (see below). The young insects grow and molt four times and after the last molt they become pupae. A pupa is shaped like a comma with a very large head equipped with siphons. The pupae are so active they are called "tumblers." They do not feed, but during the few days of their existence the adult structures develop. When they molt the pupae come to the surface of the water, thus permitting the winged adults to take up their aerial and terrestrial life. After mating, the male soon dies but the female lives during the winter in a dormant condition in protected places like sheds, barns and abandoned houses. The sperm within her body remain viable, ready to fertilize the eggs which appear in the spring.

Mosquitoes are probably best known for transmitting *Plasmodium*, the causative organism of malaria. The life cycle of this protozoan parasite is described in Chapter V, p. 117. Man is usually more interested in what this parasite does to himself than he is in how the parasite affects the mosquito. The protozoa undergo greater changes in the mosquito than they do in man, suggesting that the mosquito reacts more violently than does man to plasmodial infection. Mosquitoes, however, are probably better adapted to the parasite than is man, but we know relatively little about the adjustments a mosquito has to make. It should be noted that even some anopheline mosquitoes, which are the normal vectors of *Plasmodium* do not become infected even after a meal of parasitized human blood. This fact is not surprising, because some people are also refractory to infection, but our knowledge of parasite-host relations between *Plasmodium* and mosquitoes is limited.

Enemies of mosquitoes are legion. These insects may be parasitized by other sporozoa (microsporidia, coccidia) as well as by gregarines (*Lankesteria, Caulleryella*), flagellates (*Herpetomonas, Crithidia*), ciliates (*Lambornella, Glaucoma*), trematodes (*Agamodistomum, Pneumocoeces* larvae), filaria, mites (Hydrachnidae) and blood-sucking midges. As if these internal and external parasites were not enough, mosquitoes have many larger natural enemies to plague them. Larval stages are attacked by water beetles, by voracious dragonfly larvae and by salamanders, frogs, and fish. Adult mosquitoes are eaten by wasps and predacious flies, spiders, lizards, birds, and bats.

Destruction of immature mosquitoes can be accomplished by adding oil to the water in which they live. This technique prevents them from obtaining oxygen because they cannot pierce the firm

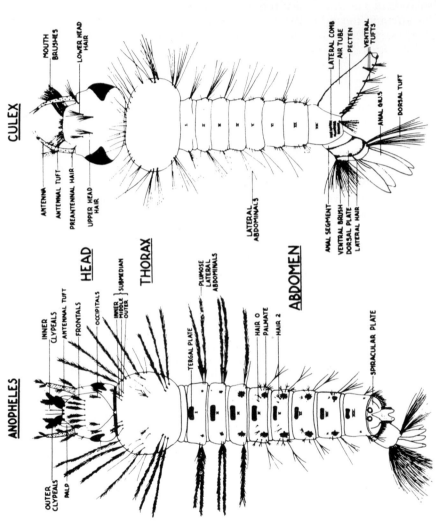

Fig. XVIII-7. — Comparative characters of *Anopheles* and *Culex* larvae. (United States Public Health Service.)

surface layer of oil with their delicate breathing tubes. The chief destructive effect, however, is due to volatile toxic substances in most oils used (*e.g.* kerosene, diesel fuel). Various larvicides such as copper sulfate, Paris green or naphthalene may also be added to the water to kill larvae and pupae. Students should remember that these chemicals may also kill desirable organisms. Insect sprays containing DDT, pyrethrum, lindane, or any of a number of other chemicals are effective against adult mosquitoes.

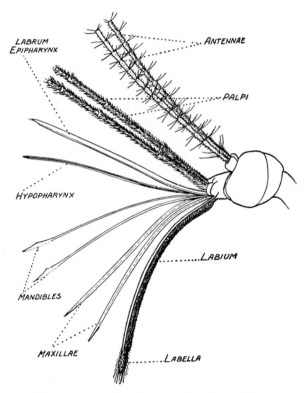

Fig. XVIII–8.—Mouth parts of female mosquito, (*Anopheles quadrimaculatus*) dissected out of the sheath. Note that the mandibles have finely serrated, blade-like lips for cutting and that the maxillae have pointed chitinous lips with fewer and coarser serrations than the mandibles. The proboscis is made up of all parts labeled except the antennae and palpi. (Fox, *Insects and Disease of Man*, courtesy of the Blakiston Company.)

Elimination of breeding places is a highly recommended method of mosquito control. Swampy areas may be drained and filled, and such containers as cisterns or small vessels may be emptied or covered.

Family Simuliidae. The family Simuliidae is world-wide in distribution and it includes small insects called blackflies or buffalo gnats. The immature stages of these flies are aquatic, normally preferring running water. Both larvae and pupae are attached to rocks

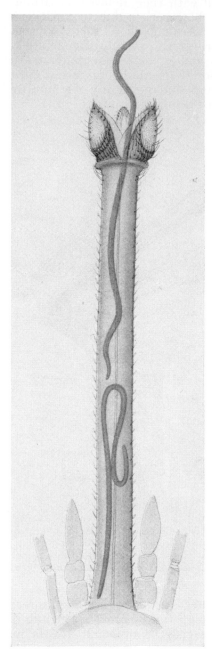

Fig. XVIII–9.—Mature larva of *Wuchereria bancrofti* escaping from the proboscis of the mosquito *Culex fatigans*. (Francis, courtesy of United States Public Health Service Hygienic Laboratory Bull. No. 117.)

or to plants under water. Adults are hump-backed (Fig. XVIII-10) hence the name "buffalo gnat." They sometimes occur in enormous swarms, especially near water; and they cause considerable annoyance to livestock and man by their vicious bites. Some species will gather in tremendous numbers on domestic mammals and on birds. The flies may cause such an annoyance to poultry that the birds may leave their nests. Aggressive female insects sometimes get under the wings of young birds and suck so much blood that the birds die.

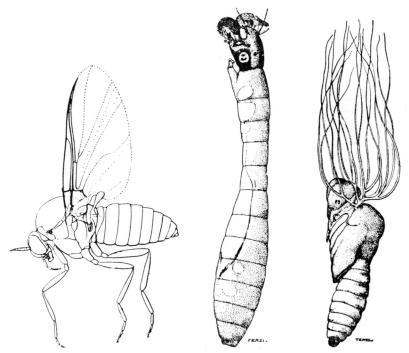

Fig. XVIII–10.—*Simulium*, a black fly. Left figure, a side view of adult. Middle, a larva; right, a pupa. (Smart, *Insects of Medical Importance*, courtesy of British Museum.)

Danger from the gnats is not only due to loss of blood and possibly bacterial infection of bitten areas, but also to the toxic saliva of the insect, and to parasites which the fly might transmit.

The major parasite which simuliid flies carry is the roundworm, *Onchocerca volvulus* (p. 358) which infects man in some of the warmer countries such as Africa, Central America, and Mexico. The flies may also transmit tularemia and the protozoan parasite, *Leucocytozoon*. The latter organism is a blood inhabitant of birds, especially of turkeys and ducks. The name indicates that this parasite, inhabits white blood cells. There is evidence, however, that the host cells are erythrocytes which are quickly altered and superficially resemble leucocytes (p. 114). *Leucocytozoon simondi* is found in the peripheral blood of ducks while *L. smithi* is a similar parasite of turkeys. Common insect vectors are *Simulium nigroparvum*, *S. venustum* and *S. occidentale*. The flies attach themselves to the necks of the birds and feed for two to three minutes before flying away. The use of insecticides and other control measures against the fly are only partially effective.

Family Tabanidae. Tabanidae is another family of flies whose females suck blood. These insects are considerably larger than the Simuliidae and are known as horse flies, deer flies, or clegs (Fig.

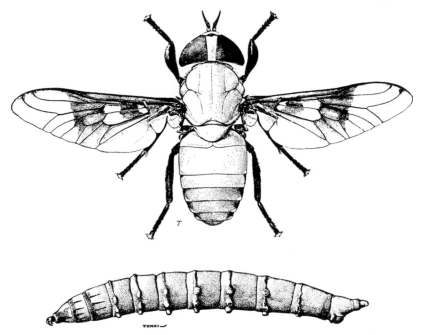

FIG. XVIII–11.—*Tabanus latipes* with its larva. (Smart, *Insects of Medical Importance*, courtesy of British Museum.)

XVIII–11). They are stout flies, each with a broadly triangular head, most of which is composed of eyes. Immature stages are typically aquatic, or to be found in wet earth, a habit which accounts for the presence of the adults near freshwater or marshy areas. Many species, however, may fly several miles from their breeding places. As with many other groups of flies, the males feed on plant juices and pollen. Sexes may be distinguished by the distance between the eyes, as seen from above. Male eyes are close together or *holoptic*, whereas the female eyes are distinctly separated or *dichoptic*. Genera important to the parasitologist are *Tabanus* and *Chrysops*.

Various species of *Tabanus* transmit the flagellate blood parasite, *Trypanosoma evansi*, which causes the disease *surra* in horses, cattle, dogs, elephants and in other animals (p. 55). Members of this genus of flies also carry *anthrax* and *tularemia* to man and animals.

Tularemia is also transmitted by *Chrysops* which, in addition, may carry the filarial worm, *Loa loa* (p. 361). Different species of the genus *Chrysops* feed at different times of the day. *C. silacea* and *C. dimidiata* do most of their biting during the morning and then later in the afternoon; *C. langi* and *C. centurionis* do the bulk of their biting in the evening at sunset.

Family Psychodidae. The subfamily with which we are specially interested is the Phlebotominae or *sandflies* which have piercing mouth parts and are vectors of leishmaniasis (p. 58). A few of the important species which transmit *Leishmania* to man and other vertebrates are *Phlebotomus argentipes*, *P. papatasii*, *P.*

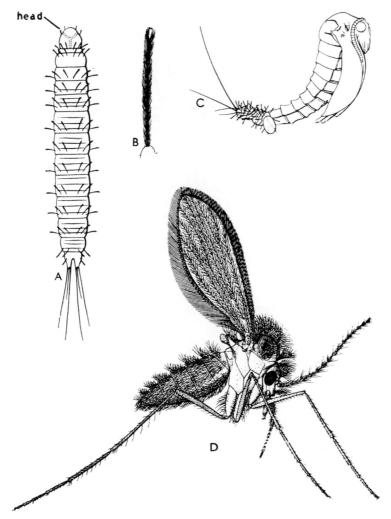

Fig. XVIII–12.—Larva, pupa and adult female of *Phlebotomus papatasii*. (Smart, *Insect of Medical Importance*, courtesy of British Museum.)

perniciosus, P. sergenti, P. chinensis, P. longipalpis and *P. inter-medius.*

Sandflies (Fig. XVIII–12) may be found during the day in pro-tected moist places such as caves, burrows or other holes in the ground, sheds, crevices or in loose piles of humid material. Eggs are laid in the soil or in other material which is shady and moist, and the larvae develop in three to four days. After feeding for about two weeks they change into the pupal stage which lasts another week. The entire life cycle takes one to three months depending on the temperature. The female sucks blood at night, especially at times when there is no wind since these insects are extremely weak fliers.

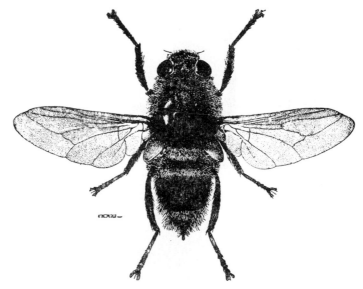

Fig. XVIII–13.—*Hypoderma bovis*, the ox-warble, adult. (Smart, *Insects of Medica Importance*, courtesy of British Museum.)

Family Oestridae. Warble flies are so called because their larvae usually lie under the skin of their hosts and cause a swelling known as a "warble." The flies have been placed in the family Oestridae by some workers and in the family Hypodermatidae by others.

The best-known members of this group are the ox warble, *Hypoderma bovis* (Fig. XVIII–13), a stout hairy fly which looks a little like a bee, and a similar species, *H. lineatum*, the heelfly. The adult heelfly is hairy, black and yellow, and several times larger than a housefly. *H. lineatum* has no mouth parts and cannot sting; hence it is unable to do any direct harm to cattle. In the spring each female fly lays hundreds of eggs on the leg or body hairs of cattle. In a few days the eggs hatch into tiny, white spiny larvae which crawl down the hairs and burrow through the skin. For several months the larvae wander around the intestines, liver, heart, muscles, or other organs, apparently enjoying the protection and warmth of their host. Some of them spend many weeks in the connective tissues of the esophagus. When the worst of the winter is over they migrate to the back and produce small swellings or warbles in the skin. They make a tiny hole in the skin for air and they increase in size to about 25 mm. in length. During this period they turn dark brown. In the spring or summer, the grubs, or maggots, emerge through the holes and drop to the ground and pupate. They crawl under loose soil or trash, and after two to seven weeks, depending on the temperature, the adult flies emerge.

One hundred millions to three hundred millions of dollars are lost annually in the United States because of damage to hides and irritation and annoyance to cattle. The animals get "off their feed," lose weight, and are generally unthrifty. Milk production diminishes. The holes in the skin make the hide unfit for high quality leather.

No specific drug is available which can be fed to cattle and which is completely effective against this parasite. In some areas of the United States (*e.g.* Wyoming), however, administering of an insecticide orally with a balling gun in the fall of the year has proven to be reasonably successful. Lindane, aldrin, and dieldrin show promise. Many insecticides have been used to kill the larvae in the skin. These drugs are applied as washes, drips, or sprays. Rotenone is one of the best. Most farmers simply press the grubs out of the warbles.

Dermatobia hominis, a somewhat similar fly, though not so hairy, may occur as a maggot in the skin of man in Central and South America. This warblefly is about 12 mm. in length. The non-biting females attach their eggs to the bodies of mosquitoes (*Janthinsoma lutzi*) or to other flying insects. The eggs thus get a free ride to a new host. When the mosquitoes alight to feed on man or on other warm-blooded animals, the warblefly eggs hatch and the larvae penetrate the skin of their new host.

Oestris ovis (Fig. XVIII–14) is a fly which, instead of laying eggs, deposits its larvae or maggots in the nostrils of sheep, goats and a few other mammals such as deer. The maggots crawl into the nasal passages, and, during the next few weeks, they molt twice. When fully grown, and about 25 mm. long, they come out of the nose, drop to the ground and pupate. From the pupa the adult fly emerges. It is also called a gadfly or nasalfly.

This fly may attack shepherds or other persons who have recently eaten goat's milk products and whose breath smells of such food as cheese. The fly deposits its larvae in the shepherd's nostrils, on his lips or even on his eyes, and sometimes it causes considerable damage.

The names *botfly* and *warblefly* are used somewhat interchangeably. Thus *Gasterophilus intestinalis* (Fig. XVIII–15) may be called a horse bot or warblefly. The adult of this botfly also looks a

31

little like a bee. It attaches its eggs to hairs on the legs or bodies of horses. As soon as the eggs become infective, the larvae pop out when they are brushed by the moist, warm lips of the horse. These larvae are spiny and they become attached to the horse's lips or tongue and thus are easily swallowed. They may, however, burrow through the mucous membranes of the mouth and make their way to the stomach through various tissues. The larvae attach themselves to the lining of the stomach, sometimes in such large numbers that this membrane is almost covered with them. After some

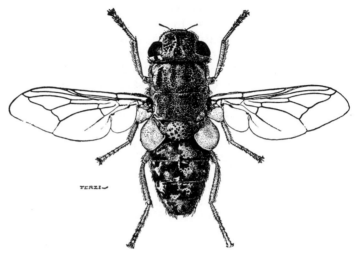

FIG. XVIII–14.—*Oestrus ovis*, the adult sheep nostril fly. (Smart, *Insects of Medical Importance*, courtesy of British Museum.)

months of maturing, the maggots pass from the host's body with feces, drop to the ground and pupate. Adult flies emerge from the pupae and when they start laying eggs the life cycle is complete.

Family Tachinidae. The family Tachinidae contains may species of flies, all of which are parasitic on insects or other arthropods (*e.g.* terrestrial isopods). Some of the tachinids look like houseflies and some appear more like bees or wasps, but most of them possess long bristles on the tips of their abdomens. A tachinid normally deposits its eggs on the body of its host (*e.g.* larvae of butterflies or beetles), and larvae burrow inside to eat. The larva literally eats itself out of house and home, killing its host. When mature, the fly crawls out of the host and pupates on the ground. Some tachinids lay their eggs on foliage and when the larvae emerge they crawl on and into a host, or they are infective after being swallowed by the host. For comments on the evolution of the tachinids see page 681.

Some flies parasitize grasshoppers. Both nymphal and adult grasshoppers (*Chortophaga viridifasciata*) in Tennessee have been

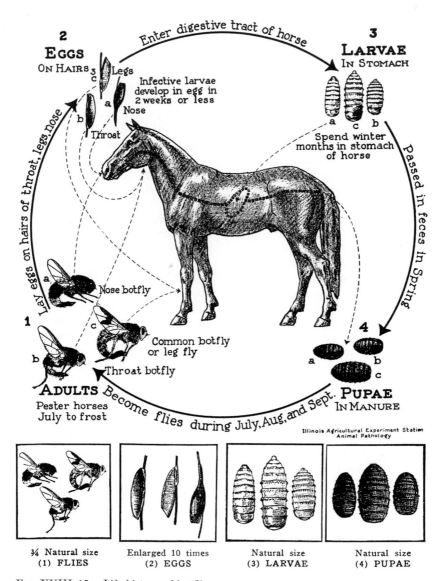

¾ Natural size — (1) FLIES

Enlarged 10 times — (2) EGGS

Natural size — (3) LARVAE

Natural size — (4) PUPAE

FIG. XVIII–15.—Life history of botflies.

1, Flies pester horses from July to frost, laying their eggs on the hairs of the nose, throat, and legs. *2,* In the *eggs* larvae develop in two weeks or less and enter the digestive tract. *3, Larvae* spend the winter months in the stomach, where they are a drain on the animal; in the spring they pass out in the manure. *4,* In the ground *pupae* develop from the larvae. During July to September these pupae become flies, which start the life cycle all over again. (Thorp and Graham, courtesy of University of Illinois College Agriculture.)

found to be inhabited by the tachinid fly, *Ceracia dentata*, and by the sarcophagid, *Sarcophaga hunteri*.[1] The parasites occur as larval stages either free in the hemocoel of the host or, as they get older, attached to tracheal trunks, an air sac or abdominal spiracles. As if the difficulties in reaching maturity for *C. dentata* are not enough, these parasitic flies may themsleves be parasitized (hyperparasitism) by a hymenopteran (*Brachymeria tegularis*) which may occur within the puparia of the flies.

Family Calliphoridae. Blowflies may look somewhat like houseflies but the former are often a little larger and frequently are metallic green or blue in color. They have the habit of laying their eggs on organic masses such as dead animals, excrement, open sores or exposed cooked or uncooked food. The eggs hatch into maggots which proceed to eat the material around them.

Occasionally, infested meat is cooked for the dinner table, but the infestation has passed unnoticed until, upon carving the meat, the dead maggots fall out upon the plate, much to the disgust and distaste of the diners.

The genus *Calliphora* includes the bluebottle flies whose larvae are commonly found in decaying meat. Eggs are also laid in exposed foul wounds of man and animals. The maggots eat only the putrid tissues in the wound. Occasionally live *Calliphora* maggots are swallowed in cooked meat, and rarely they pass through the body. The emergence of these maggots from the intestine accounts for some of the reported cases of myiasis in man. The term *myiasis* refers to the presence of parasitic maggots in or on man or animals (see p. 491). *Lucilia sericata* and *Phormia regina* are two species whose larvae have been used by physicians to clean wounds and to treat such diseases as osteomyelitis in man. *Lucilia* is the genus of the greenbottle fly; *L. sericata* is the sheep maggotfly.

Lucilia bufonivora lays its eggs on the back of a toad or other amphibian.[2] The eggs hatch within a day, apparently due to the chemical nature of the skin glands. The tiny larvae crawl to the head region and on the surface of the eye. By blinking its eyes, the toad carries the maggots to the lacrimal ducts which lead to the nasal cavity. Here the larvae molt and form the second stage which actively feeds on host tissues and eventually destroys the cartilaginous nasal septum. When mature, the larvae drop out of this enlarged nasal cavity and pupate in the ground.

Chrysomyia bezziana is a green blowfly which seems to have a preference for wounds and body spaces of man and of wild and domestic animals. The larvae (Fig. XVIII–16) may be found in the nose, eyes, ears, alimentary canal, urinary passages, genital organs or tiny cuts or sores in the skin. The eggs may even be laid in the pierced ear lobes of women. At first the small maggots are not noticed but when they grow to a centimeter or more in length and begin to burrow through the skin near the wound, they may produce a tumor of considerable size, especially if many worms are present. This species is found in the Philippines, India, and Africa. Maggots of the clusterfly, *Pollenia rudis*, crawl from eggs in the soil to earthworms (*Allolphophora chlorotica*) and enter the openings of the male sex ducts. After a dormant period of eight months the larvae feed and grow and destroy much of their host's tissues. After several molts the mature larvae leave the earthworm host and pupate in the ground.

Callitroga hominivorax is a bluish blowfly about twice the size of a housefly. It lays its eggs in neat rows on the edges of wounds of mammals, especially on fresh cuts. The eggs hatch in a day or less into maggots which feed on living flesh. These maggots are called "screwworms." The wound attended by screwworms has a foul

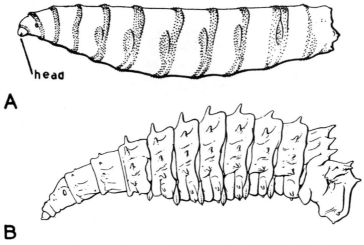

Fig. XVIII–16.—*Chrysomyia bezziana. A*, The mature third stage larva. × 8. *B*, The mature third stage larva of *C. albiceps*, × 8. (Smart, *Insects of Medical Importance*, courtesy of British Museum.)

odor. In about a week the maggots drop to the ground and pupate in the soil. In another week, if the weather is warm, adults emerge. In still another week or less new eggs, about 200 in a batch, are deposited on the edge of a cut, sore, navel of new born animals, or on some other abrasion. This screwworm is an obligatory parasite of warm-blooded animals and is responsible for twenty million dollars worth of damage annually to United States livestock. Untreated animals usually die. General control involves doing all that is possible to prevent cuts and scratches on livestock. A new method of control consists of releasing laboratory reared sterilized male flies in an infected area. Females do not mate a second time, so those which happen to mate with sterile males cannot reproduce. This trick played on unsuspecting females has resulted in a significant reduction in screwworm infection in relatively isolated areas. Chloroform, benzol and various mixtures of other medicants are used in treatment.

Other blowflies, principally *Phormia regina* the black blowfly, *Callitroga macellaria* the secondary screwworm fly, and *Phaenicia sericata* the greenbottle fly, possess larvae which are called fleece-worms. They attack the hair of sheep and goats and also enter wounds. Eggs are usually deposited on soiled fleece or on old or new sores. In addition to injuring the quality of fleece and aggravating wounds they may carry the germs of anthrax, plague, undulant fever, tularemia and of enteric diseases.

The tumbufly of Africa, *Cordylobia anthropophaga* (Fig. XVIII–17), measures about 10 mm. in length and is yellowish brown in color.

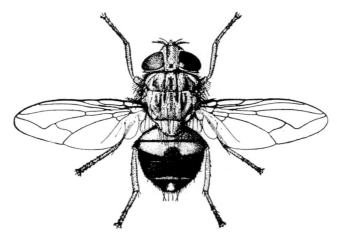

FIG. XVIII–17.—*Cordylobia anthropophaga*, the tumbufly, female, × 4. (Smart, *Insects of Medical Importance*, courtesy of British Museum.)

Eggs are deposited on the ground where they hatch. When the appropriate host (man and other mammals) lies on the ground, larvae burrow through the skin into their new home; and as a larva grows it produces a boil-like swelling in the skin which has a small hole at the top of the boil. Through the hole the maggot breathes and discharges its waste. When mature, the maggot emerges through the hole, drops to the ground and pupates.

Family Sarcophagidae. The family Sarcophagidae contains the fleshflies. These insects are sometimes placed with blowflies in the family Metopiidae. Fleshflies are rather large, grey insects with longitudinal black stripes on the dorsal surface of the thorax (Fig. XVIII–18). Notice the checkered appearance of the abdomen. Like the blowflies, the fleshflies are scavengers and the larvae may be found in wounds, carrion, sores or body cavities of man and animals. Unlike the blowflies, most of the fleshflies do not lay eggs but are larviparous. The genus *Sarcophaga* is world-wide in distribution. The genus *Wohlfahrtia* contains species which parasitize man and animals, thus causing myiasis in these hosts. A larva of *Wohlfahrtia magnifica* has even been found in the cavity of an infected tooth.

Family Muscidae. The family Muscidae is well known for furnishing man with some of his most serious insect parasites. They include the tsetse fly, *Glossina* (Fig. XVIII–19), carrier of the causative organisms of African sleeping sickness (p. 53, 54); the stablefly, *Stomoxys calcitrans*, which can transmit (mechanically) the causative organism of oriental sore (p. 58); the hornfly, *Lyperosia* (= *Diphona*) *irritans*, which often creates serious losses in livestock by attacking newly dehorned animals. Other flies of this family attacking livestock are *Haematobia* and the common housefly, *Musca domestica*.

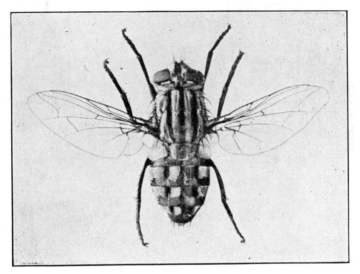

Fig. XVIII–18.—*Sarcophaga hemorrhoidalis*, female. A fleshfly. (Mönnig in *Veterinary Helminthology and Entomology*, courtesy of Bailliere, Tindall and Cox.)

The latter is not a biting species but it may act as a mechanical carrier of disease such as dysentery, cholera, anthrax, typhoid fever, and yaws. It may also transmit worms. The roundworm, *Habronema muscae*, is a parasite in the intestine of horses. Embryos of the worm leave the body of a horse in feces and enter the bodies of fly larvae. When the flies mature the worms have reached their final larval stage, and they mature in the horse when flies are swallowed.

PUPIPARIA

(A SECTION OF THE SUBORDER CYCLORRHAPHA)

Pupiparia are peculiar looking flies which are ectoparasitic on birds and mammals. They are blood-sucking and are called louse flies, bat flies, tick flies, lice flies or keds. They usually are

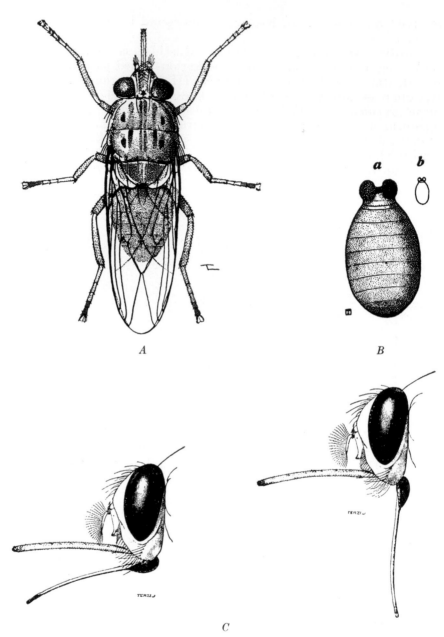

A

B

C

Fig. XVIII–19.—A tsetse fly. *A, Glossina longipennis* in the resting attitude assumed by the living fly. Note the position of the wings, × 4 (after Austen). *B,* Puparium of tsetse fly. *a,* enlarged; *b,* natural size. The posterior end is towards the top of page. (After Austen from Castellani and Chambers). *C,* Head of species of *Glossina* showing how the proboscis with its bulb-shaped base is lowered from the palpi for the act of feeding. The palpi are not inserted into the wound but remain horizontal as the piercing proboscis is sunk into the skin (Castellani and Chambers. Smart, *Insects of Medical Importance,* courtesy of British Museum.)

wingless, flattened diptera which can be found on the bodies of animals or in bird nests or bat roosts. Some of them (*Stenopteryx* and *Crataerhina*) possess wings. Wild animals are attacked as well as horses, sheep, and other domestic forms. That ectoparasitic flies are found on bats is not surprising when one considers the probability that ancestral flies deposited their eggs in bat droppings. From this start the association undoubtedly became progressively closer until today there are such forms as the completely wingless pupiparous species, *Nycteribia biarticulata*, which at first glance looks more like a louse than it does a fly. The pupiparia belong to several families.

Family Hippoboscidae. The family Hippoboscidae includes the more common species of Pupiparia. An important member of the family is the sheep ked or "sheep tick," *Melophagus ovinus*, a wingless, leathery flattened insect (Fig. XVIII–20) which is hardly

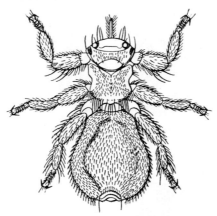

Fig. XVIII–20.—*Melophagus ovinus*, the sheep ked. × 4. (Smart, *Insects of Medical Importance*, courtesy of British Museum.)

recognizable as a fly. It is about 6 mm. long and, like other pupiparia does not lay eggs but gives birth to larvae already advanced to almost the pupal stage.

Pseudolynchia maura, another hippoboscid, is a louse fly which lives on pigeons. In addition to causing annoyance to the birds, this ectoparasite carries an endoparasite of birds, the malarial-like blood parasite, *Haemoproteus*.

Myiasis. Myiasis is the term given to an infection of a host by fly larvae, especially maggots (Fig. XVIII–21). Several examples have already been given. Many species of maggots may occasionally be found in man or animals. Those species which occur in the intestine produce intestinal myiasis, whereas those in the genital organs or urinary tract produce urinogenital myiasis. Some maggots occur only in wounds and sores, especially foul and suppurating sores, whereas others actually get into living flesh, producing boils or weals in the skin or, as we have seen, preferring the chambers of the nose, mouth, eyes, or ears.[5]

Intestinal myiasis is usually caused accidentally by contaminated food or drink. Fly eggs or maggots may occur on over-ripe fruit, raw meats, cheese, salads, dried fish, dirty water, or milk. Urinogenital myiasis is usually also accidental. Flies may lay their eggs on the exposed and unclean pubic area. Some of the genera of flies involved in accidental myiasis are *Calliphora, Musca, Fannia, Stomoxys, Drosophila, Sepsis,* and *Tipula.*

Flies which deposit their eggs in or near foul wounds and whose larvae thus have an opportunity to invade the wound belong mainly

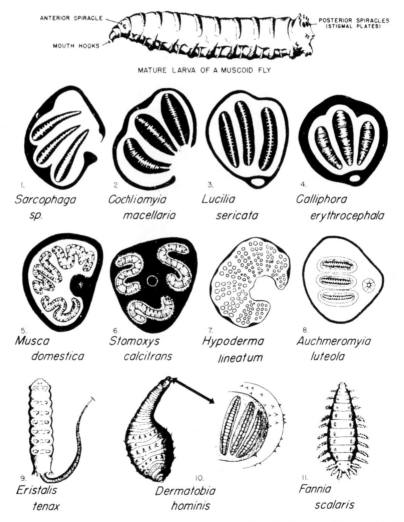

ANTERIOR SPIRACLE

MOUTH HOOKS

POSTERIOR SPIRACLES (STIGMAL PLATES)

MATURE LARVA OF A MUSCOID FLY

1. *Sarcophaga sp.*

2. *Cochliomyia macellaria*

3. *Lucilia sericata*

4. *Calliphora erythrocephala*

5. *Musca domestica*

6. *Stomoxys calcitrans*

7. *Hypoderma lineatum*

8. *Auchmeromyia luteola*

9. *Eristalis tenax*

10. *Dermatobia hominis*

11. *Fannia scalaris*

FIG. XVIII–21 —Key characters of myiasis-producing fly larvae. Figures 1 to 8 are stigmal plates. (Federal Security Agency.)

to the following genera, *Sarcophaga, Phormia, Callitroga,* and *Chrysomyia.*

Identification of many of these maggots is difficult. One of the common diagnostic characters is the nature of the posterior spiracles. Figure XVIII–21 illustrates these spiracles as they appear in the larvae of some myiasis-producing flies.

Invertebrates have their share of parasitic fly larvae. Some Hymenoptera may contain maggots which actually attach their spiracular openings to the host trachea in order to breathe. The snail, *Helicella vergata,* may become so infested with fly maggots that the parasites kill their host and eat practically all of the dead tissues.

BIBLIOGRAPHY

1. AMAND, E. ST. and CLOYD, W. J., 1954. Parasitism of the Grasshopper, *Chortophaga viridifasciata* (Degeer) (Orthoptera: Locustidae), by Dipterous Larvae. J. Parasitol., *40,* 83–87.
2. BAER, J. G., 1951. *The Ecology of Animal Parasites.* Univ. Ill. Press. Urbana, Ill. U.S.A. 224 pp.
3. HERMS, W. B., 1961. *Medical Entomology.* 5th ed. Rev. by M. T. James. Macmillan Co. N. Y., 616 pp.
4. IMMS, A. D., 1957. *A General Textbook of Entomology. Including the Anatomy, Physiology, Development and Classification of Insects.* 9th ed. rev. by O. W. Richards and R. G. Davies. Methuen & Co. London. 886 pp.
5. JAMES, M. T., 1947. *The Flies that Cause Myiasis in Man.* Dept. Agric. Misc. Publ., No. 631. Wash., D.C.
6. WEITZ, B., 1960. Feeding Habits of Bloodsucking Arthropods. Exper. Parasitol., *9,* 63–82.

CHAPTER XIX

Phylum Arthropoda
Class Arachnoidea (= Arachnida)
Class Pentastomida

ORDER ACARINA

(MITES AND TICKS)

ACARINA abound almost everywhere, but, except for ticks which are large enough to be easily recognized, they are little known to biologists in general. A handful of soil is likely to contain several to thousands of specimens. All ticks, however, and certain mites, are parasitic on or in terrestrial vertebrates during at least one stage in their life cycles. They may be the direct causative agents of disease, or they may transmit pathogenic microorganisms, or they may serve as reservoirs of infection. Hundreds of species live on or in plants, often causing serious damage. The feathers of birds and the hairs and skin of mammals are favorite habitats, while internal organs of both vertebrates and invertebrates are frequently invaded by mites. Fourteen pounds of ticks were once removed from the skin of one horse in three days, and as many ticks were still left on the suffering animal. Freshwater ponds, streams, rivers, and the oceans all have their mite faunas. The Acarina are not small enough to be handled like protozoa, yet they are too small to be treated like insects, and they are not soft-bodied enough to be studied like worms. For these reasons they require special techniques for their collection and preparation for study.

Most acarologists, entomologists and zoologists consider the Acarrina to be an order of the Class Arachnida. The group, however, is sometimes listed as a subclass, or even as a separate class, of arthropods. The mites and ticks are readily separated from other arachnids by the possession of a distinct gnathosoma (an anterior capitulum bearing mouth parts) and by the absence of a clearly recognizable division between the cephalothorax and abdomen. The phylogeny of the Acarina is obscure, and most authorities on the group consider it to be polyphyletic in origin.[4,13]

Morphology

An outer cuticle covers a single layer of epithelial cells and sclerotized layers which the cells secrete. The whole integument is membranous or leathery, and sometimes has hard plates or shields. Special structures such as glands, setae and sensory organs are derived from integumentary cells. Figure XIX–1 illustrates details of the external anatomy.

Mouth parts consist of a pair of chelicerae which usually terminate in small pincers (chelae) possessing a dorsal, fixed digit and a

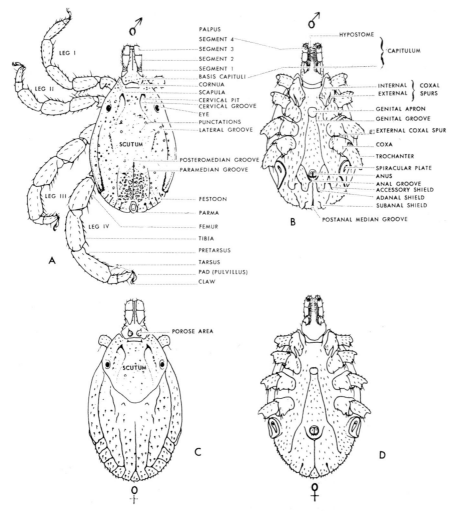

FIG. XIX–1.—Key morphological characters. Hypothetical male ♂ and female ticks, ♀ family Ixodidae. *A* and *B*, ♂ male dorsal and ventral views; *C* and *D*, female, ♀ dorsal and ventral views. (Hoogstraal, *African Ixodoidea*, U.S. Naval Medical Res. Unit No. 3, Cairo.)

ventral, movable digit; and in a pair of pedipalps (or palpi) usually consisting of four to six segments, sometimes modified as a thumb and claw.   The majority of Acarina possess three pairs of walking legs as larvae and four pairs as adults.   These legs are usually divided into six segments which terminate in well-developed claws.   Of primary importance to the systematics of the group are the anatomical features of the respiratory system.   The suborders are established largely upon the basis of the numbers and location of the stomata (= spiracles or openings of trachea).

Many of the larger mites rather closely resemble the ticks, but mites are usually small forms in which the hypostome is hidden and unarmed, whereas ticks are larger forms in which the hypostome is exposed and armed with teeth or hooks.   Two or more simple eyes may be present, but they never occur on the capitulum.   The foregut is subdivided into a buccal cavity, a pharynx or pumping organ and an esophagus.   The midgut is a thin-walled stomach, and the hindgut terminates in a sacculate rectum.   Although there is a single-chambered heart in some forms of ticks, in most Acarina the circulatory system consists only of colorless blood.   Two external spiracles (stomata) are generally visible, and they lead to long convoluted tracheae.   There is a single gonad in each sex, and the spermatozoa, in the form of spermatophores, are introduced into the vagina by the male capitulum, there being no penial organ.

The two groups of Acarina may be differentiated as follows.

Ticks	*Mites*
1. Body clothed with short hairs or bare.	1. Body clothed with long hairs.
2. Hypostome exposed and possessing teeth.	2. Hypostome hidden and unarmed.
3. Larger forms, all macroscopic.	3. Usually small forms, many microscopic.
4. Body texture leathery in appearance.	4. Body texture membranous in appearance.
5. Pedipalps prominent and segmented.	5. Pedipalps almost lacking in some forms.
6. Chelicerae heavily chitinized, bearing strong cutting teeth at their distal ends.	6. Chelicerae reduced to blades or rods.

TICKS

SUBORDER IXODIDES
FAMILIES ARGASIDAE AND IXODIDAE

About 800 different species of ticks occur in the world.   The life cycle begins with *eggs* in masses deposited by the female on the ground, in cracks and crevices in houses, or in nests and burrows of animals.   Favorable conditions include moisture, abundant vegetation and numerous hosts.   Female ticks may lay as many as 30,000 eggs. The six-legged *larvae*, often called "seed ticks" (Fig. XIX–2), which hatch from the eggs must find a host and begin feeding on blood. After molting, the larvae become *nymphs* which have eight legs but no genital opening. Nymphs also molt after feeding, and become *adults*. The female increases greatly in size after feeding, often reaching four times its original adult length, and increasing from 1 to 450 mg. in weight. The male, however, is enclosed in a nonelastic integument which prevents much increase in size

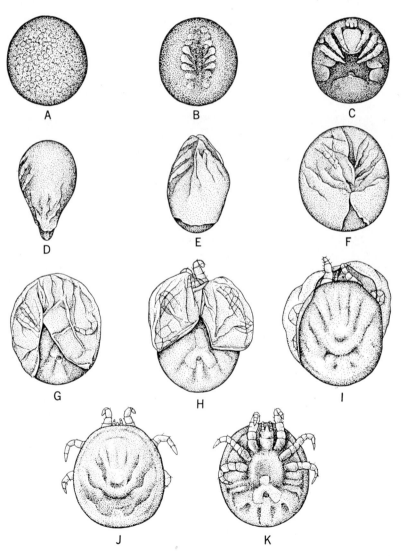

Fig. XIX–2.—*Ornithodoros moubata* egg and larva. (Hoogstraal, *African Ixodoidea*, United States Naval Medical Research Unit, No. 3 Cairo.)

during feeding. Ordinarily the parasites climb on to a host and feed between molts (Fig. XIX–3), and drop to the ground and molt or deposit eggs. The complete life cycle may require from a few weeks to two years, and it varies considerably among the numerous species of ticks. See Figure XIX–4 for a key to genera.

After a meal of blood the female tick is ready for copulation and oviposition. Both sexes are blood suckers. It has been estimated that as many as 200 pounds of blood may be withdrawn from a large host animal by ticks in one season.[12] The spermatophores are introduced into the vagina by the capitulum of the male. Hard ticks usually lay from 2,000 to 8,000 eggs after a pre-ovipositional period of from three to twenty-four days (*e.g.* for *Dermacentor variabilis*). The time of oviposition varies from two to six weeks. Soft ticks lay fewer eggs (100 to 200) in several batches following successive blood meals.

FIG. XIX–3.—*Acanthodactylus* lizard infested with nymphs of *Hyalomma*. (Hoogstraal and Kaiser, courtesy of Ann. Entom. Soc. Amer.)

Adult ticks may withstand starvation for several years, and, as Rothschild and Clay[18] have said they, "are the great exponents of the gentle art of waiting." In addition to waiting for food, both sexes may wait many months for a mate, and may remain together in copulation for over a week. Ticks are intermittent parasites of mammals, birds and reptiles, usually spending most of their lives on the ground where they seek the shade. They often crawl up onto bushes or other vegetation and wait for any suitable host to come along. The majority of the ixodids (Fig. XIX–4) in the immature stages parasitize different hosts from those preferred during the adult stage. *Dermacentor andersoni*, (= *D. venustus*) for example, may be found as nymphs and larvae on rodents, and as adults on sheep and man. On the other hand, the larvae of *Boophilus annulatus* become attached to cattle and remain on these hosts until the adult tick is ready to lay eggs.

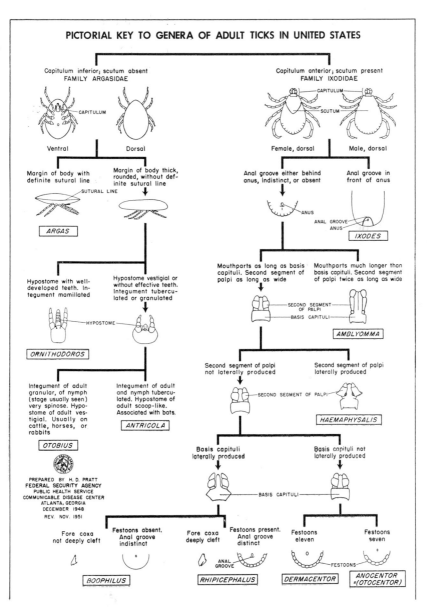

Fig. XIX–4,

Tick-borne Diseases

The several disorders and diseases of vertebrates traceable to ticks may be divided into two groups as follows (See Arthur[1]).

A. *Local inflammatory and traumatic damage at the site of attachment* may be a mild inflammation and itching, or it may be far more serious, such as the invasion of the auditory canal by the spinose ear tick, *Otobius megnini*, causing edema, hemorrhage, thickening of the stratum corneum and partial deafness. The sharply toothed chelicerae cut an opening into the epidermis, then the recurved teeth of the hypostome serve as effective anchoring organs. Such an invasion of the auditory canal is common in cattle. Salivary fluid from the tick prevents coagulation of the host blood as it is sucked through a tubular stylet within the mouth cavity. Adults of this tick do not feed at all. The genus *Amblyomma* may be found on man, other mammals, birds and reptiles. *A. maculatum* sometimes occurs in enormous numbers on such ground-feeding birds as meadow larks, and it is also a serious parasite of livestock, attacking the inner surface of the outer ear.

B. *Systemic damage* may result in tick paralysis or in a less severe form of sensitization reaction to a toxic substance secreted by the

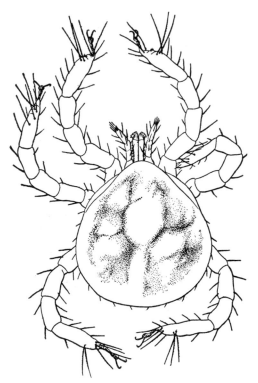

Fig. XIX–5.—*Argas americanus.* Six-legged stage. (Hassall, United States Department of Agriculture.)

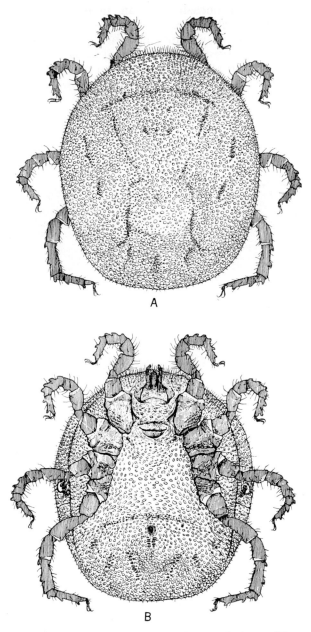

A

B

FIG. XIX–6.—*Ornithodoros moubata*, dorsal and ventral views. (Hoogstraal, *African Ixodiodea*, United States Naval Medical Research Unit, No. 3, Cairo.)

salivary glands of the tick. Tick paralysis is commonly found in domestic animals and occasionally in man, especially children. About twelve ixodid ticks have been implicated (e.g. *Dermacentor andersoni*). The toxic substance, possibly elaborated by the tick ovaries or ova, causes a progressive ascending flaccid motor paralysis, elevation of temperature, impairment of respiration, speech and swallowing, and occasionally death due to respiratory or cardiac paralysis. Treatment of man involves complete removal of the ticks.

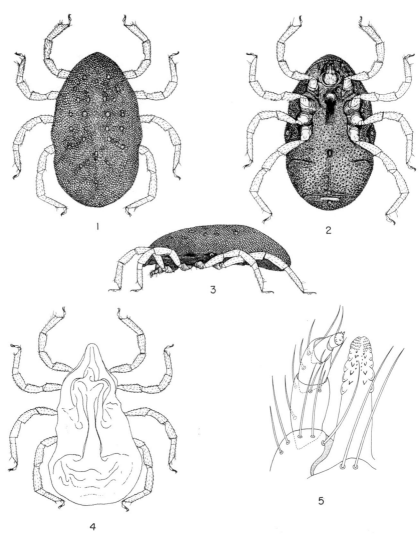

Fig. XIX–7.—*Ornithodoros salahi* from the Egyptian fruit bat *Rousettus egyptiacus*. *1*, Male engorged, dorsal; *2*, Male engorged, ventral; *3*, Male engorged, lateral; *4*, Male emaciated, dead, dry; *5*, Male hypostome and palp, ventral. (Hoogstraal, courtesy of J. Parasitology.)

In addition to A and B above, ticks frequently serve as vectors of diseases caused by viruses, rickettsias, bacteria, and protozoa.[19a] Among the viral diseases transmitted by ticks are tick fever of sheep, and lymphocytic choriomeningitis of rodents. Rabies of many mammals in the U.S.S.R. has been reported as being transmitted by ticks, possibly by *Argas persicus.*

Relapsing fever of vertebrates, caused by spirochaetes (*Borellia*) has been described from many areas over the world. Transovarial passage of *Borellia* occurs through several generations of ticks.

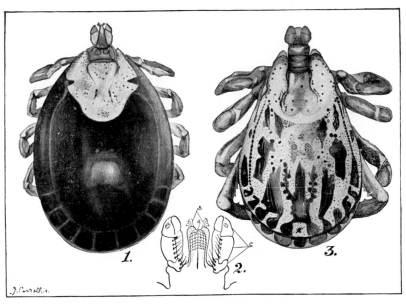

Fig. XIX–8.—*Dermacentor andersoni.* *1*, dorsal view of female; *2*, head showing hypostome (*a*) chelicerae (*b*) and palp (*c*); *3*, dorsal view of male. Enlarged. (Stitt's *Diagnostics and Treatment of Tropical Diseases*, courtesy of the Blakiston Division, McGraw-Hill Book Co.)

Tick-borne strains of *Borellia* are commonly transmitted to birds by the genus *Argas* (Fig. XIX–5), and to mammals by the genus *Ornithodoros* (Figs. XIX–6 and 7). This tick (*Ornithodoros*) possesses a remarkable ability to survive under conditions of starvation and low humidity. It averages about 8 mm. in length. A thin layer of wax in the epicuticle greatly reduces water loss, and the ability to close the spiracles and to extract water from moist air assists the tick in its regulation of water balance. Relapsing fever in man is characterized by recurrent febrile paroxysms, and three or four such attacks recur at intervals of about a week until immunity is established. The mortality rate is about 4 per cent. Except for the relatively few instances where ticks invade human residences, human relapsing fever results from man's intrusion upon the natural habitat of the tick and its host. At least thirteen different species of *Ornithodoros* are known to be vectors of various species of the spirochaete, *Borellia*, throughout the world. Relapsing fever may also be transmitted by mites.

Texas cattle fever (= red water, splenic fever, Mexican fever) is widely distributed among cattle in Europe, Africa, the Philippines and North, Central and South America. Theobald Smith was the first worker experimentally to incriminate ticks as vectors of disease. He and Kilbourne[19] described the causative agent, the protozoan *Babesia bigemina*, and they discovered the surprising fact that the parasites are carried from the infected mother tick to her offspring

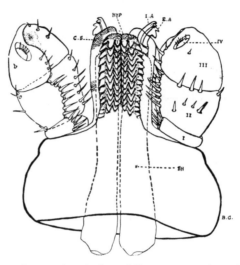

FIG. XIX–9.—Ventral view of capitulum of *Demacentor andersoni*. *BC*, bases capitulum; *C.S.*, cheliceral or mandibular sheath; *E.A.*, external article of chelicera; *IA*, internal article of chelicera; *HYP*. hypostome; *SH*, shaft of chelicera; *I, II, III, IV*, segments of palp. (Matheson's, *Medical Entomology*, courtesy of Charles C Thomas.)

through the eggs. The parasites multiply within the red blood cells of cattle, and within tissues of the tick. *Boophilus annulatus* in North and South America and in Europe, *Rhipicephalus appendiculatus* in tropical Africa, and other species of ticks are common vectors. The protozoan genus *Babesia* causes other diseases commonly known as "piroplasmosis" in domestic animals.

Tularemia is caused by a plague-like bacterium, *Pasteurella tularensis*, and its symptoms are similar to those of typhoid fever. It is found in mammals, birds and man, but is most common in rabbits and ground squirrels. The disease is characterized by an ulcer localized at the site of inoculation, and it is transmitted through the bite or fecal contamination of *Dermacentor andersoni* (Figs. XIX–8 and 9), *D. variablilis*, and *Haemaphysalis leporispalustris*. The bacterium may pass from one generation of tick to another through the ovaries. The disease may be acquired by man by simply

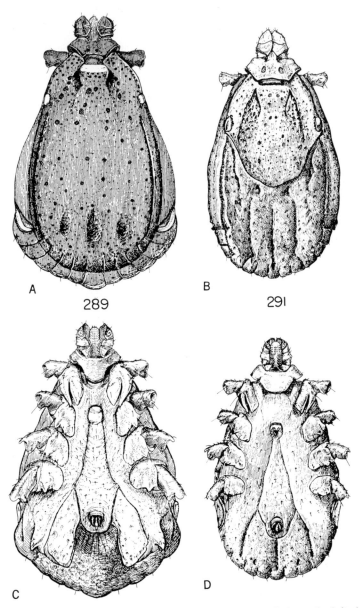

A 289 B 291

C D

FIG. XIX–10.—*Rhipicephalus sanguineus sanguineus*. The male is on the left, female on the right. (Hoogstraal, *African Ixodoidea*, United States Naval Medical Research Unit No. 3, Cairo.)

handling diseased animals or their infected ticks. It is seldom fatal. Other tick-borne bacterial diseases of mammals are anthrax, erysipeloid and brucellosis. Fishes in the U.S.S.R. have been reported to acquire brucellosis through ticks.

American (Rocky Mountain) spotted fever, caused by *Rickettsia rickettsii*, is an acute febrile disease of wild rodents transmissible to man and laboratory animals. It is uncommon in the Rocky Mountain regions of Canada and the United States, but more common in eastern United States, and in various parts of Central and South America. The disease is transmitted by several species of ticks, especially *Dermacentor andersoni* which during its immature stages is a parasite of rodents, but as an adult is found on larger mammals including man. After an incubation period of from five to ten days a chill and rise in temperature is followed by a rash over the face and trunk. Both male, female, and immature ticks may infest man.

Other tick-borne rickettsial diseases are: heartwater disease of sheep, goats and cattle; hemoglobinuric fever of domestic animals; and anaplasmosis of domestic animals. Although dogs frequently are infested with ticks, cats rarely have them. The brown dog tick, *Rhipicephalus sanguineus* (Fig. XIX–10), is one of the most common. Other ticks to be found on dogs include *Dermacentor andersoni*, *D. variabilis*, *Amblyomma maculatum* and *Ixodes scapularis*.

MITES

Mites abound in soil, humus, stored food, marine and fresh water, and as parasites of plants and animals. Between 15,000 and 20,000 species are common in nests of birds and other small animals.[17] Mites vary in size from less than 0.5 to about 2.0 mm. As a group they are free-living, but the family Laelaptidae contains the largest number of parasitic genera whose members are mostly lymph feeders as larvae or nymphs, and blood feeders (haematophagous) as adults. The life cycle from *egg* to *larva* (6-legged) to *nymph* (8-legged) to *adult* is completed in from about eight days to more than four weeks. Mites feed on decaying organic matter or on the tissues of dead or living organisms. Some species use insects as a means of transportation as well as a source of food. Mites are most numerous in temperate zones. Parasitic species generally exhibit highly specialized structures such as enormous clawlike processes on the first pair of legs, used for grasping hairs of the host. Other species are adapted for such habitats as under the scales of snakes (the snake mite, *Ophionyssus natricis*); on the skin and feathers of birds where one genus, *Harpyrynchus*, lives in the feather follicles which become enlarged to form tumors; or within the lungs of snakes (family Entonyssidae). A family of mites allied to the latter (family Pneumonyssidae) contains free-living and parasitic forms, and one species may be found encapsulated in the bronchi or lungs of some Old

World monkeys. Other mites may be found in the nasal passages of sea lions, in breathing tubes of domestic fowl, and in numerous other locations on or within the host. For a general account see Hughes.[11]

Non-burrowing species, called *psoroptic* mites, pierce the skin, cause inflammation, exudations, itching and scab formation. For these reasons they are known as scab mites, and they cause *scabies*. A second group, the *sarcoptic* mites, consists of species which burrow into the skin and cause sarcoptic mange. The word *mange* is used rather loosely to include the effects of both types of mites. An infestation of mites is termed *acariasis*, and when the infestation is in the skin, producing channels in which eggs are deposited, the term *sarcoptic acariasis* is used (*e.g.* as in human scabies caused by *Sarcoptes scabiei*). When mites deposit their eggs at the base of the host hairs or on the skin, producing scabs, the term *psoroptic acariasis* is used (*e.g.* as in sheep scab caused by *Psoroptes communis* var. *ovis*).

Bird mites may become beneficial as well as harmful.[6] A group (Cheyletidae) of "de-lousing" mites on birds prey on feather mites (Analgesidae) and possibly also on the eggs of feather lice (Mallophaga), and thereby destroy these ectoparasites and relieve the bird hosts of at least a portion of their misery.

Invertebrates may also be infested with these parasites. For example, mites (*Unionicola*) have been found on mussels (*Anodonta*). Other species infest amphipods.

Mite-Borne Diseases

Itch and Mange Mites (Sarcoptoidea). — Numerous species of mites occasionally infest man but *Sarcoptes scabiei* is responsible for human scabies. This species is so similar to forms of the same genus which infest dogs, cats, rabbits, foxes, pigs, horses and cattle that all of them are commonly considered as biological races (see p. 653) of one species. *S. scabiei* (Fig. XIX–11) lives in cutaneous burrows where the gravid female deposits one to a few oval eggs daily for from four to five weeks. Six-legged larvae produce lateral tunnels or they start new ones. Cutaneous lesions begin to develop in a few days after initial infestation, but the characteristic intense itching does not start until a month or so. The microscopic fecal pellets from the parasites are responsible for vesiculation and associated pruritus. Infestations similar to those just described for man are common on domestic animals. Scaly-leg mites on poultry cause lifting of the scales and a swollen condition of the shank with deformity and encrustation.

Scab mites which cause psoroptic acariasis differ from the itch mites in possessing long, slender legs, all four pairs of which extend beyond the margin of the elongate body (Fig. XIX–12). The best known of these mites is *Psoroptes equi* var. *ovis* of sheep. Other varieties of this species infest cattle, horses and goats, and one species

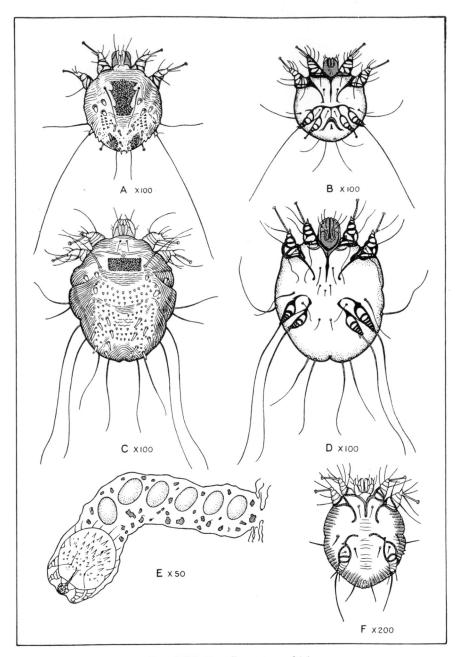

FIG. XIX–11.—*Sarcoptes scabiei.*

A, male, dorsal view; *B,* male, ventral view; *C,* female, dorsal view; *D,* female, ventral view; *E,* female with eggs in burrow; *F,* hexapod larva, ventral view. (*A* to *D,* redrawn from Munro, *E,* redrawn from Banks; *F,* redrawn from Blanchard. (Belding, *Textbook of Clinical Parasitology,* courtesy of Appleton-Century-Crofts Inc.)

causes ear canker in rabbits. The mites are to be found on the surface of the body among the scabs at the base of the hairs, and generally in areas most thickly covered with hair. *Otodectes cynotis,* which closely resembles *Psoroptes,* is responsible for a common ear infestation of dogs, foxes and cats.

The myocoptic mange mite, *Myocoptes musculinus* (Fig. XIX–13), is a widespread hair-clasping parasite of white or brown laboratory mice. It sometimes causes considerable trouble, especially where mice are kept for long-term experiments in crowded cages.

Oribatid mites (Fig. XIX–14) commonly serve as intermediate hosts of tapeworms belonging to the order Cyclophyllidea. The

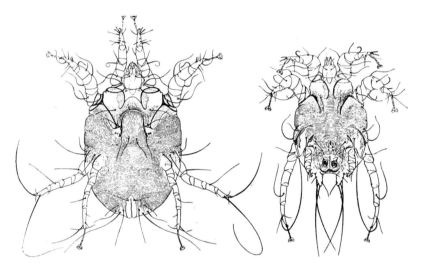

FIG. XIX–12.—*Psoroptes equi.* Left, ventral view of female. Right, ventral view of male. (Baker, Evans, Gould, Hull, and Keegan, *A Manual of Parasitic Mites of Medical or Economic Importance,* courtesy of National Pest Control Assoc. Inc.)

worms *Moniezia expansa* of sheep, *Bertiella studeri* of primates, *Cittotaenia ctenoides* and *C. denticulata* of rabbits, *Anoplocephala perfoliata, A. magna,* and *Paranoplocephala mamillana* of equines, *Moniezia benedeni* of ruminants, *Thysaniezia giardi* of sheep and goats, and others are well-known examples.

Chiggers and Harvest Mites (Trombidoidea).—Larval stages (chiggers) of the families Trombidiidae and Trombiculidae are parasitic, whereas the postlarval stages are predators usually on soil arthropods. The larval trombidiids are parasitic on arthropods, and the trombiculid chiggers are parasites of a great many kinds of vertebrates, even fishes, but especially of mammals (for details see Wharton and Fuller[21]). The larvae of the family Trombidiidae frequently cause an intense, intolerable itch on the skin of man and animals. These mites are bright red or orange in color (hence the common name "red bug"), just visible to the naked eye, and they

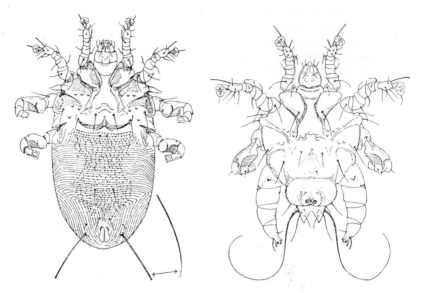

Fig. XIX–13.—*Myocoptes musculinus*. Left, ventral view of female. Right, ventral view of male. (Baker, Evans, Gould, Hull, and Keegan, *A Manual of Parasitic Mites of Medical or Economic Importance*, courtesy of National Pest Control Assoc. Inc.)

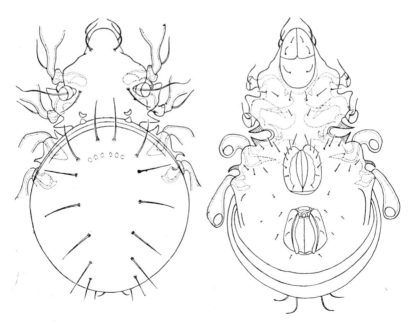

Fig. XIX–14.—An oribatid mite, *Metabelba papillipes*, female. Left, dorsal view; right, ventral view. Legs removed. (Baker, Evans, Gould, Hull, and Keegan, *A Manual of Parasitic Mites of Medical or Economic Importance*, courtesy of National Pest Control Assoc. Inc.)

live as adults in grassy and bushy terrain frequented by domesticated animals or wild rodents. The six-legged larvae are parasites that, contrary to popular belief, do not burrow into the skin. The adult body is divided into an anterior portion (cephalothorax), bearing the mouth parts and the two anterior pairs of legs, and a larger posterior portion bearing the two posterior pairs of legs (Fig. XIX–15). The eggs are deposited singly or in small clusters on the moist ground, most frequently in damp places well covered with vegetation, and in six days the fully developed larva hatches.

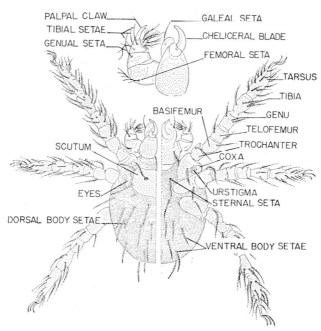

Fig. XIX–15.—*Trombicula alfreddugesi*. Dorsal and ventral views of larva to illustrate external morphological characters. (Baker, Evans, Gould, Hull, and Keegan, *A Manual of Parasitic Mites of Medical or Economic Importance*, courtesy of National Pest Control Assoc. Inc.)

The larva attaches itself to a vertebrate host and remains on its skin for from a few days to a month. Saliva from the parasite dissolves a minute spot of the skin, and a tubular structure is formed. This structure, called a stylostome, is almost as long as the body of the mite, and it becomes filled with semi-digested tissue debris on which the parasite feeds. *Eutrombicula* and *Trombicula* are the most common genera.

Scrub typhus (= *mite typhus*) in the Far East is transmitted by the larvae of species of the genus *Trombicula*, and is caused by *Rickettsia tsutsugamushi*. Various rodents serve as reservoirs of the disease which in man may have a high mortality rate.[2] On epidemiological grounds the mites are suspected of transmitting epidemic hemorrhagic fever, a virus disease in Korea, Manchuria and Siberia.[20]

False spider mites (Tenuipalpidae or Phytoptipalpidae) contain a number of species of economic importance (*e.g.* species of the genus *Brevipalpus* on citrus and ornamentals in many parts of the world) which commonly feed on the lower surfaces of leaves. Some species feed on bark, and others on flower heads; a few form plant galls. The needle-like cheliceral stylets of these mites pierce the epidermis, the chlorophyll of the plant host is lost, and the plant tissues acquire a silvery appearance that later becomes rusty (for details of these mites see Pritchard and Baker[16]).

Predaceous Mites (Tarsonemoidea). — The family Pediculoididae contains the North American "grain itch" mite, *Pediculoides ventricosus*, which feeds on larvae of insects that infest wheat and other grains, and also on the larvae of other insects, many of which are harmful (*e.g.* the cotton-boll weevil). These soft-bodied mites frequently swarm over the surface of the human body and burrow superficially into the skin, but unlike the Sarcoptidae, they soon leave the skin.

Parasitoid Mites (Parasitoidea). — The bloodsucking mites belonging to the family Dermanyssidae (= Macronyssidae) are parasites of reptiles, birds, and mammals, and they frequent nests and burrows. The "red mite" or "roost mite" or "chicken mite" (*Dermanyssus gallinae*) of poultry, and the "tropical rat mite,"

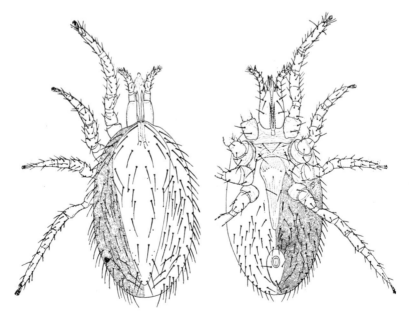

FIG. XIX–16.—*Ornithonyssus bacoti*. Left, dorsal view of female. Right, ventral view of female. (Baker, Evans, Gould, Hull, and Keegan, *A Manual of Parasitic Mites of Medical or Economic Importance,* courtesy of National Pest Control Assoc. Inc.)

Ornithonyssus (= *Bdellonyssus*) *bacoti*[4] (Fig. XIX–16) are examples of animal pests that are also injurious to man. The genus *Bdellonyssus* is concerned with the transmission of certain rickettsial and virus diseases of man. *Dermanyssus gallinae* is a common parasite of pigeons, chickens, sparrows and other birds. Roost mites may be so abundant as to cause severe anemia and even death to young birds. After feeding they leave the host and hide in crevices.[10]

Nasal mites belonging to the genus *Sternostoma* are primarily parasitic in the nasal cavities of birds. Some species, such as *S.*

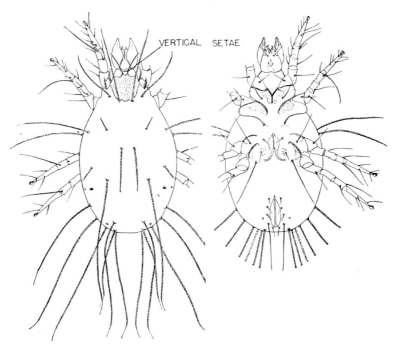

Fig. XIX–17.—*Tyrophagus lintneri*. Left, dorsal view of female. Right, ventral view of female. (Baker, Evans, Gould, Hull, and Keegan, *A Manual of Parasitic Mites of Medical or Economic Importance*, courtesy of National Pest Control Assoc. Inc.)

tracheacolum, the canary lung mite, is an internal parasite of the trachea, air sacs, and bronchi of the lungs, but not in the nasal cavities.

Food Mites (Tyroglyphoidea). — "Grocer's itch," "copra itch," "miller's itch," "cottonseed itch," "barley itch" are some of the common names given to human infestations of very tiny mites belonging to the family Tyroglyphidae (= Acaridae) or to the family Glycyphagidae. These mites (Fig. XIX–17) feed upon and develop rapidly in such foods as grain, cheese, dried meat, dried fruit, insect collections, stored seeds, as well as such materials as stuffing in furniture. Literally millions of them may appear in a few days. Persons handling infected stored food products may be attacked temporarily by the mites and experience severe dermatitis. It has been found that contact with the living mites is unnecessary to produce the symptoms because they appear as readily after infested material is rubbed on the skin, or after dust from it is blown on the skin, or even after the dust is inhaled. Hence the bodies or excretions of the mites are toxic, although allergy also plays a part in the production of symptoms.

Follicular Mites (Dermodicoidea).—A worm-like mite, infesting hair follicles and sebaceous glands of various mammals is known as *Demodex folliculorum*. It has an elongated abdomen and

Fig. XIX–18.—*Demodex canis.* Ventral view of female. (Baker, Evans, Gould, Hull, and Keegan, *A Manual of Parasitic Mites of Medical or Economic Importance,* courtesy of National Pest Control Assoc. Inc.)

stumpy legs, and may sometimes be found in clusters of 200 or more. Although infestation of human skin is common, particularly on the scalp and face, it is generally harmless, but in dogs the mites (Fig. XIX–18) produce a severe type of mange, and in hogs and cattle they may be the cause of skin tubercles.

For details on parasitic mites of medical and economic importance see Baker *et al.,*[3] and for a discussion of acaricides see March[14] and Traub.[19a]

The Treatment of Tick and Mite Infestations

Specific acaricides are characterized by the lack of, or low, toxicity to insects and to mammals, but virtually nothing is known about the primary mode of action of these compounds. There appears to be a relatively high susceptibility of the larval stage to the acaricides. Most studies of this problem have dealt primarily with phytophagous mites, but the usual recommendations for control of parasitic mites and ticks suggest chlorinated hydrocarbon insecticides rather than the more specific acaricides. Ticks have become highly resistant to DDT, BHC, toxaphene and to other chemicals in South Africa and Australia. Among the many chemicals used are lindane, benzyl benzoate emulsion, tetraethylthiuram monosulfide, chlordane, lime-sulfur, nicotine sulfate, and benzene hexachloride (BHC). For details of this problem see March[14] and Lindquist and Knipling.[13]

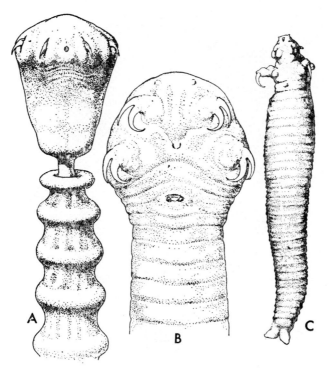

Fig. XIX–19.—*A*, Anterior extremity of *Armillifer annulatus*. *B*, Head of *Leiperia gracilis*. *C*, Entire specimen of *Raillietiella mabuiae*. (Baer, *Ecology of Animal Parasites*, courtesy of University of Illinois Press.)

CLASS PENTASTOMIDA

(TONGUE WORMS)

Members of this group of bloodsucking, strictly endoparasitic arthropods are parasites of mammals, birds, reptiles and fishes. They are legless and worm-like, but near the mouth are two pairs of hollow, curved, retractile hooklets which are rudimentary appendages (Fig. XIX–19). The immature stages (Fig. XIX–20)

33

are mite-like in appearance, with two or three pairs of legs. Adult pentastomids feed on blood and mucosal cells in the mouth, esophagus or respiratory passages of their hosts.

Relatively little is known of life histories and general biology of these worms, although some life cycles in the genus *Linguatula* have been fairly well understood for many years. In most genera, such as *Armillifer* (Fig. XIX–21), *Sambonia*, *Raillietiella*, *Porocephalus*, *Linguatula* and *Megadrepanoides*, a life cycle involving two

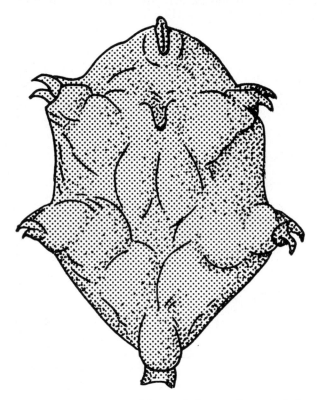

FIG. XIX–20.—Newly hatched larva of *Porocephalus crotali*, ventral view. (Modified from Penn, courtesy of J. Parasitol.)

vertebrate hosts would be expected because the adult parasites normally occur in carnivorous lizards or snakes. These hosts regularly feed on smaller reptiles, amphibians and mammals in which larval pentastomids have been found. For example, adults of *Porocephalus crotali* live in the lung cavities of crotaline snakes, especially of those species of rattlesnakes (*Crotalus*) which range along the western parts of North, Central and South America.[5] The parasite eggs which reach the outside through the snake sputum are readily ingested by muskrats, opossums, bats, armadillos, raccoons, and other mammals, in which they hatch in the small intestine. Larvae

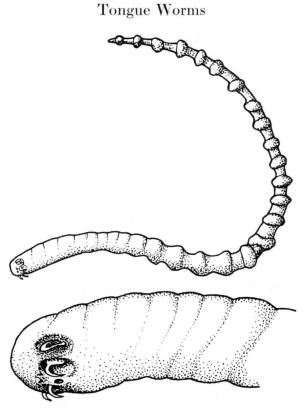

FIG. XIX–21.—*Armillifer* sp. from the lung of a python in Indonesia. Bottom, enlarged view of head. Top, entire specimen. The preserved worm was 72 mm. long. (Original.)

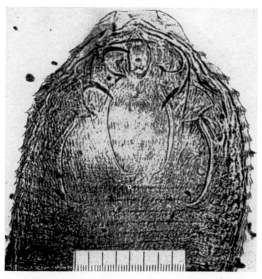

FIG. XIX–22.—*Linguatula serrata*. Head end. Each division of the scale represents 10 microns. (Sprehn, courtesy of Parasitologische Schriftenr.)

migrate to the viscera (*e.g.* lungs and liver) where they become encapsulated in the tissues and where, in about three months, they develop into nymphs. If the nymph-infected tissue of the mammal is ingested by an appropriate snake, the nymphs migrate up the esophagus into the tracheae and lungs where they become adult pentastomids. See Heymons,[7,8] and Penn[15] for details.

Linguatula serrata (Fig. XIX–22) is one of the best-known species of this group. The adult female is tongue-shaped, 100 to 130 mm. long and up to 10 mm. wide, whereas the male is about 20 mm. long and 3 to 4 mm. wide. Eggs containing embryos with rudimentary legs are deposited in the nasal passages and frontal sinuses of mammals (commonly dogs) and are discharged in nasal secretions. Upon reaching water or moist vegetation embryonation is com-

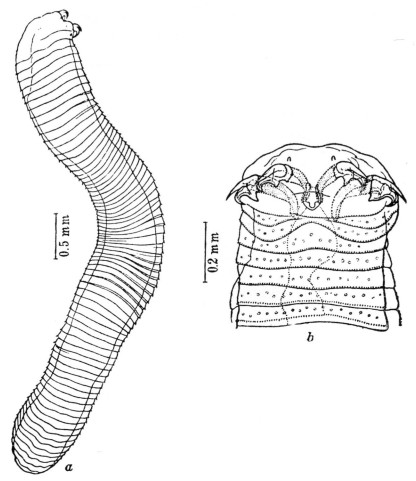

FIG. XIX–23.—*Pentastomum solaris.* *a,* entire worm, lateral view; *b,* anterior end, ventral view. From the lungs of a crocodile. (Tubangui and Masilungan, courtesy of Philippine J. Sci.)

pleted, and if the eggs are ingested by the intermediate host (*e.g.* cattle, goats, sheep, rabbits, rats, man) hatching occurs in the digestive tract, and the larvae migrate through the intestinal wall and become lodged in the liver, mesenteric nodes and other viscera. After a number of molts, requiring a period of from five to six months, the nymph stage is attained. Nymphs lie encapsulated with the host tissue, and they are the infective stage for carnivorous animals which feed on the herbivorous intermediate hosts. Although the general belief is that nymphs are digested out of their capsules and immediately migrate to the nasal passages of the definitive host, there is evidence[9] that instead the nymphs quickly leave their cysts after the death of the intermediate host, and cling to the mucous membrane of the mouth of the carnivorous host. *L. rhinaria* is a common parasite of livestock, and it is a facultative parasite of man in both adult and nymphal stages. This species also occurs in rats, dogs, and in such experimental animals as guinea pigs. In the genera *Linguatula*, *Pentastomum* (Fig. XIX–23), *Sebekia* and *Leiperia* each hook is double in both pairs.

BIBLIOGRAPHY

1. ARTHUR, DON R., 1961. *Ticks and Disease.* Pergamon Press, London. 1961. Harper & Row, N. Y., 1962. 461 pp.
2. AUDY, J. R., 1956 (1958). The Role of Mite Vectors in the Natural History of Scrub Typhus. Proc. Tenth Internat. Congr. Entom., *3*, 639–649.
3. BAKER, E., EVANS, T., GOULD, D., HULL, W., and KEEGAN, H., 1956. *A Manual of Parasitic Mites of Medical or Economic Importance.* National Pest Control Assoc. Inc., N. Y. 170 pp.
4. BAKER, E. W. and WHARTON, G. W., 1952. *An Introduction to Acarology.* Macmillan Co., N. Y. 465 pp.
5. ESSLINGER, J. H., 1962. Development of *Porocephalus crotali* (Humboldt, 1808) (Pentastomida) in Experimental Intermediate Hosts. J. Parasitol., *48*, 452–458.
6. FAIN, A. and HYLAND, K. E., 1962. The Mites Parasitic in the Lungs of Birds. The Variability of *Sternostoma tracheacolum* Lawrence, 1948 in Domestic and Wild Birds. Parasitol., *52*, 401–424.
7. HEYMONS, R., 1935. Pentastomida. In Bronn's *Kl. Ord. Tier.*, 5 (4) vol. 1, 268 pp.
8. HEYMONS, R. and VITZTHUM, H. G., 1936. Beiträge zur Systematik der Pentastomiden. Z. Parasitenk., *8*, 1–103.
9. HOBMAIER, A. and HOBMAIER, M., 1940. On the Life Cycle of *Linguatula rhinaria*. Am. J. Trop. Med., *20*, 199–210.
10. HOLLANDER, W. F., 1956. Acarids of Domestic Pigeons. Trans. Amer. Micros. Soc., *75*, 461–480.
11. HUGHES, T. E., 1959. *Mites or the Acari.* The Athlone Press. Bristol, England. 225 pp.
12. HUNTER, W. D. and HOOKER, W. A., 1907. Information Concerning the North American Fever Tick. Washington, D.C., Dept. Agric., in Bur. Entomol. Bull., No. 72. 87 pp.
13. LINDQUIST, A. W. and KNIPLING, E. F., 1957. Recent Advances in Veterinary Entomology. Ann. Rev. Entomol., *2*, 181–202.
14. MARCH, R. B., 1958. The Chemistry and Action of Acaricides. Ann. Rev. Entomol., *3*, 355–376.
15. PENN, G. H., JR., 1942. The Life History of *Porocephalus crotali*, a Parasite of the Louisiana Muskrat. J. Parasitol., *28*, 277–283.
16. PRITCHARD, A. E. and BAKER, E. W., 1958. The False Spider Mites (Acarina: Tenuipalpidae). Univ. Calif. Publ. Entom., *14*, 175–274.

17. RADFORD, C. D., 1950. The Mites (Acarina) Parasitic on Mammals, Birds and Reptiles. Parasitol., *50*, 366–394.
18. ROTHSCHILD, M. and CLAY, T., 1952. *Fleas, Flukes & Cuckoos.* Collins, 304 pp.
19. SMITH, T. and KILBOURNE, F. L., 1893. Investigations into the Nature, Causation, and Prevention of Texas or Southern Cattle Fever. Bureau Anim. Indust., Washington, D.C.
19a.TRAUB, R., 1962. Some Considerations of Mites and Ticks as Vectors of Human Disease. p. 123–134, In: Maramorosch, K. (ed.), *Biological Transmission of Disease Agents.* Academic Press, New York & London, 192 pp.
20. TRAUB, R., HERTIG, M. LAWRENCE, W. H., and HARRISS, T. T., 1954. Potential Vectors and Reservoirs of Hemorrhagic Fever in Korea. Amer. J. Hyg., *59*, 291–305.
21. WHARTON, G. W. and FULLER, H. S., 1952. A Manual of the Chiggers. Mem. Ent. Soc. Wash., *4*, 1–173.

CHAPTER XX

Miscellaneous Phyla

PORIFERA

SPONGES are rarely parasitic. One species, *Cliona celata*, bores into the shells of mollusks. This species may reduce oyster shell substance by as much as 40 per cent by this tunneling. The activity of the sponge may cause a break through the inner shell layer. These breaks are repaired if the water is warm (above 7° C). If the water is cold the hole remains unrepaired. The adductor and hinge muscles may also be damaged.

COELENTERATA

Peachia sp. and *Edwardsia* sp. are sea anemones whose larval stages become parasitic (inquinilism) on the surface of the body or in the gastrovascular cavity of other anemones (medusae) or in ctenophores. The parasites maintain their position by sucker-like adaptations of their mouths, and they feed on particles of food carried by a current created by ciliary action of the host.

Hydrichthys is a hydroid which lives as a colony on the body of fishes and, occasionally, on crustacea. The parasite has lost its tentacles and each polyp feeds on the blood and tissues of the host which has been injured by the root-like outgrowths, or stolons, sent into the host flesh by the parasite.[4,10]

The medusa stage of coelenterates may also be parasitic. *Mnestra* lives attached to the throat of the snail *Phyllirhoe*. The medusa is specialized in structure, having lost most of its tentacles, and it appears to destroy the tissue of its host.

CTENOPHORA

Gastrodes parasiticum (Fig. XX–1) is a ctenophore whose young stage is parasitic (commensal) in the mantle of the tunicate, *Salpa fusiformis*. The ctenophore is a flattened organism about 1 mm. in diameter, round in outline with a concave oral surface and an arched aboral surface. The larvae of these ctenophores are of the planula type, thus suggesting a relation to the Coelenterata. The larval *Gastrodes* develops characteristic ctenophore rows of ciliated "combs,"

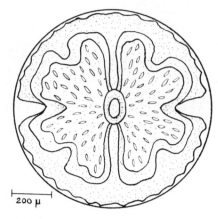

200 μ

Fig. XX–1.—*Gastrodes parasiticum*, a parasitic ctenophore of a tunicate. (Original.)

statocysts, tentacles and gastrovascular system. The parasite leaves its host, matures as a free-living organism, and produces planula larvae which enter new hosts.[5]

MESOZOA

Mesozoa are highly specialized parasites of marine invertebrates. Some authorities classify them as a separate phylum while others consider them as a class under the phylum Platyhelminthes. The phylogenetic origin of the group is obscure and it is even possible that the two major groups (Dicyemida and Orthonectida) are diphyletic, that is, they are not closely related. Certainly the group is controversial, and whether one places it in a separate phylum or not depends partly on whether the simplicity of the Mesozoa is considered "degenerate" or progressively specialized. The following

---

Fig. XX–2.—*Dicyema sullivani*, a mesozoan parasite of *Octopus bimaculatus*.

All figures made with the aid of a camera lucida from preparations fixed in Bouin's fluid and stained with Ehrlich's acid hematoxylin.

Fig. 1.—Nematogen containing vermiform larvae in various stages of development. The axial cell nucleus and two small accessory nuclei present in the axial cell are hatched to distinguish them from the somatic cell nuclei.

Fig. 2.—Anterior end of a nematogen in side view, showing the calotte (polar cap) and parapolar cells.

Fig. 3.—Anterior end of a nematogen in dorsal view.

Fig. 4 and 5.—Very young emerged nematogens prior to the formation of vermiform larvae.

Figs. 6 and 7.—Vermiform larvae still inclosed in the axial cells of their parent nematogens.

Note the spiral twist of the calotte, and the four axoblasts already present in the axial cell. One of the larvae has 31 somatic cells, the other 33. (McConnaughey, courtesy of J. Parasitol.)

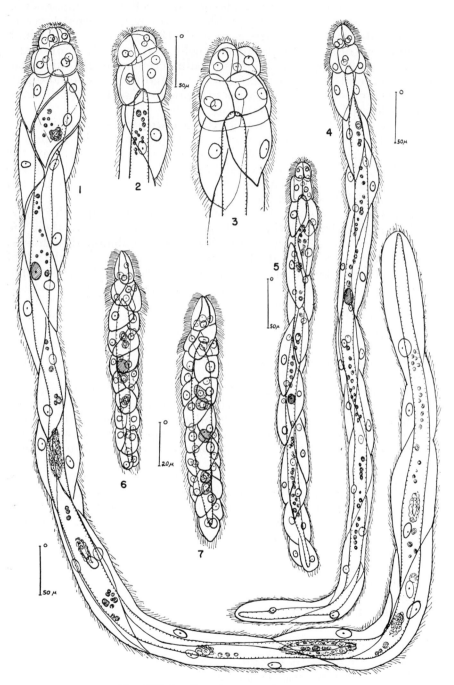

FIG. XX–2.—*Legend on opposite page.*

general characteristics identify the group: cellular endoparasites, radial symmetry (with some notable exceptions), external layer of ciliated cells which serve digestive and other functions and which surround one or several reproductive cells, body usually minute and worm-like, but may reach 4 or more millimeters in length, life cycle involving an alternation of sexual and asexual generation, no digestive tract, reproduction by means of agametes (authorities disagree on questions of sexual reproduction).

It is clear that the Mesozoa is a little-known group of parasites and is one which deserves much study. For details on the anatomy, life history and systematic relations of this group of organisms the student is referred to the several papers of Henri Nouvel,[11] and to Stunkard[13] and McConnaughey.[8,9] See also Hyman[5] for a general discussion and a bibliography.

All of the Mesozoa can be placed in two main groups, the Dicyemida and the Orthonectida. These two groups differ in their life cycles. Dicyemida live in the renal organs of cephalopod mollusks. For the most part they are host-specific. Much of the detail of their structure and life history has to be worked out. The adults are of two types: the *nematogens*, which bear vermiform embryos; and the *rhombogens*, which produce free-swimming ciliated (infusoriform) larvae. These larvae grow within the rhombogens, are released, and escape from the host. The larvae mature and either develop within themselves a generation of nematogens or they develop into rhombogens. The manner of infection of new hosts by rhombogens is obscure.

Dicyema sullivani (Fig. XX–2) is a parasite of the nephridia of *Octopus bimaculatus* from southern California and lower California. The adult worm (nematogen) is slender and averages from $\frac{3}{4}$ to $1\frac{1}{2}$ mm. long, whereas the vermiform larvae, which develop within the parent nematogen, reach a length of 100 microns before escaping from the parent.

Orthonectids possess free-swimming sexual stages which penetrate the host and then liberate germinal cells. These germinative elements enter host cells and multiply by polyembryony, comparable to the asexual method of trematode development in snails. Members of a typical genus, *Rhopalura*, live in cavities and tissues of flatworms, nemerteans, brittlestars, annelids and a clam.

Classification of the Mesozoa is difficult because the group has long been the dumping ground for organisms whose exact position in taxonomy is obscure. Although authorities differ, there is general agreement on the validity of the following groups:

Phylum Mesozoa

　　Order Dicyemida (= Rhombozoa)
　　　　Genus *Dicyema* (e.g. *D. sullivani* from the kidneys of *Octopus bimaculatus*)
　　　　Genus *Pseudodicyema* (e.g. *P. truncatum* from the kidneys of cuttlefish, *Sepia*)

Genus *Dicyemennea* (e.g. *D. californica* from the kidneys of *Octopus bimaculatus*)

The following two genera are sometimes placed in a separate group—Heterocyemida.

Genus *Conocyema* (e.g. *C. polymorpha* from the kidneys of *Octopus vulgaris*)

Genus *Mycrocyema* (e.g. *M. vespa* from the kidneys of *Sepia officinalis*)

Order Orthonectida

Genus *Rhopalura* (e.g. *R. ophiocomae* from the kidneys of a brittlestar)

Genus *Stoecharthrum* (e.g. *S. giardi* from polychaete worms of the genus *Scoloplos*)

NEMERTEA (=RHYNCHOCOELA)

Almost all nemertians (ribbon worms or proboscis worms) are free-living, bottom-dwelling, marine animals whose soft bodies are equipped with a conspicuous proboscis. A few commensal species have been described. *Nemertopsis actinophila* is a slender form which lives beneath the pedal disk of sea anemones. *Carcinonemertes* (1 to 70 mm. long) may be found on the gills and on egg masses of crabs. Some species of *Tetrastemma* live in the branchial cavity of tunicates. *Gononemertes parasitica* is a commensal species to be found on crustaceans.[7]

ROTIFERA

Rotifers are dioecious, microscopic animals that are abundant in fresh water, brackish water and moist soil. A few species live in the ocean, and a few are parasites. A ciliary organ (corona) is located at the anterior end of the body; the pharynx is provided with movable jaws (mastax); and typical flame-bulb protonephridia are present. Male rotifers are generally much smaller than females, and are rarely seen.

Seison moves about like a leech on the gills of the crustacean, *Nebalia*. *Pleurotrocha* may be found on colonial vorticellids (protozoa), *Daphnia*, *Cyclops*, insect larvae and *Hydra*. Various species of *Proales* invade the heliozoan, *Acanthocystis*, pond snails, the tips of filaments of the alga, *Vaucheria*, and *Volvox*. *Albertia* is a worm-like, transparent rotifer that lives in the coelom of earthworms and other annelids.

In parasitic rotifers the head, corona and mastax tend to be reduced. For details see Budde,[3] Hyman,[6] Bartoš,[2] and Rees.[12]

ANNELIDA

Commensalism among annelids is relatively common but pathogenic parasitism is rare. It is sometimes difficult, however, to distinguish between the two types of relationships. Leech-like oligo-chaetes (*Branchiobdella* and *Bdellobrillus*) are found attached to the gills of crayfishes and are undoubtedly commensals. *Ichthyotomus sanguinarius*, on the other hand, is a blood-sucking parasite attached to the fins of the eel, *Myrus vulgaris*, and to other fishes. The attachment organ involves two protrusible stylets which articulate with one another. The worm reaches 10 mm. in length and is dorso-ventrally flattened. It is a neotenic larva, becoming sexually mature when only 2 mm. long. *Histriobdella* is another neotenic poly-chaete found in the branchial chambers of the European and Nor-wegian lobsters. This annelid is probably a commensal. *Stratiodrilus*, another genus which becomes sexually mature while in the young stage, is found on freshwater crayfishes in Australia, Madagascar and South America.

Myzostomids are polychaetes which often inhabit crinoids. The worms are so modified in shape that they are almost unrecognizable as annelids. They are dorsoventrally flattened, protandrous her-maphrodites, becoming first males then females. Some species bur-row into their hosts and form cysts within which a male and a female are sometimes found. *Myzostomum pulvinar* occurs in the intestine of a crinoid, while *Protomyzostomum polynephris* lives in the coelomic cavity of the ophiuroid, *Gorgonocephalus*. *P. nephris* feeds on the genital glands of the ophiuroid and causes partial castration of the host. Some mysoztomids are so firmly attached to the surface of crinoids they leave permanent scars.

Oligochaetes are rarely parasitic. One species, *Friderica parasitica*, lives on another oligochaete, an earthworm. This parasite possesses a centrally located sucker, and the posterior half of its body is flat-tened. *Schmardaella lutzi* is an oligochaete which lives in the ureters of South American tree frogs. A transparent oligochaete, *Pelma-todrilus planariformis*, is a flattened species whose host is an earth-worm in Jamaica. The parasite lives on the surface of the worm.

Some of the polychaete parasites are lumbrinerid-like worms belonging to the superfamily Eunicea. Some invade other members of the same superfamily and they sometimes grow so large they are tremendous in proportion to their hosts. All of these lumbrinerid-like parasitic polychaetes belong to the family Arabellidae or at least show affinities to this family. The parasites have been found in members of the following polychaete families: Eunicidae, Onuphidae, Syllidae and Terebellidae; and in echiuroids (Bonellia). The parasites usually invade the body cavity or vascular system, normally while the host worms are in early developmental stages. Such parasites include *Drilonereis benedicti* in *Onuphis magna*; *Oligognathus parasiticus* in *Bonellia viridis* and *Haematocleptes tere-belloides* in *Terebellides stroemii*. One species, *Haplosyllis cephalata*, attaches itself by its pharynx to the cirri of an eunicid worm. This method of attachment by the pharynx is also seen with the ecto-parasitic *Parasitosyllis* which lives on other polychaetes and on nemerteans.

Leeches are not normally considered to be parasites. They are predators, sucking blood from their "hosts" (prey). A few species, however (*e.g.* some of the rhynchobdellids), become sedentary and never leave their hosts, a habit which is suggestive of parasitism.[1,7a]

MOLLUSCA

Few mollusks become parasites. As with other groups, it is sometimes difficult to decide whether an organism is a commensal or a harmful parasite. The clam, *Entovalva mirabilis*, is an internal parasite of a synaptid (a holothurian). Other species of the same genus of clams may be found in other synaptids. Some commensal clams live on or in sea urchins, sipunculids, crustacea, and other inverte-

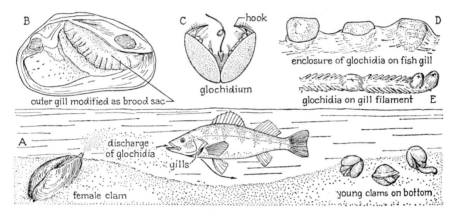

Fig. XX–3.—Life cycle of glochidia. (Storer's *General Zoology*, courtesy of McGraw-Hill.)

brates. These mollusks belong to several genera (*e.g. Modiolaria, Montacuta* and *Lepton*) and they may injure their hosts, but the relationships are not well understood.

Glochidia are larval members of the clam family Unionidae. They belong to several genera and species of unionid parasites of fish. The young freshwater clams are discharged in vast numbers from the mother clam and become attached to the gills and body surface of various fishes. These glochidia (Fig. XX–3) possess two small valves which aid in attachment with a pincer-like action. The host epidermis grows over the parasite. Later, host tissue breaks down, and within the chamber thus formed each young clam metamorphoses. It then breaks out of the chamber, drops to the sand and matures into an adult clam.

Specific glochidia occur on fishes inhabiting the same biotope as that of the adult clam, but the segregation is ecological because experimentally the glochidia can be induced to fix themselves to many different kinds of living supports, and, in nature, the speed of the fish and level at which it swims influences the fixation of the larval clam.

Parasitic snails belong to the prosobranchiate gastropods. Some of them become greatly modified in shape. *Odostomia* (Fig. XX–4) is a type which has lost its radula and parasitizes mussels, pectens and oysters. *Odostomia eulimoides* (family Pyramidellidae) attacks oysters causing malformations of the edge of the shell of the host. The parasite then forms small pockets in the shell and penetrates

Fig. XX–4.—*Odostomia scalaris* with proboscides inserted between the valves of a clam. (Baer, *Ecology of Animal Parasites*, courtesy of University of Illinois Press.)

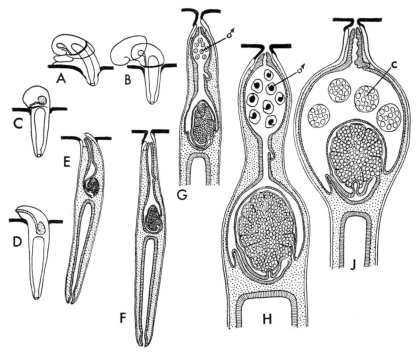

Fig. XX–5.—Supposed mode of entrance of *Entocolax* into its host. (Baer, *Ecology of Animal Parasites*, courtesy of University of Illinois Press.)

toward the adductor muscle. The margin of the shell becomes thickened and the adductor muscle becomes covered with shell deposits. Sand gets into the host and may cause suffocation and death. As many as seven parasitic snails have been found in one oyster. Various other genera parasitize sea urchins, sea stars, brittle stars and holothurians. Sample genera are: *Megadenus*, *Thyonicola*, *Entocolax* (Fig. XX–5) and *Comenteroxenos* (all in the body cavity of holothurians), and *Eulima*, *Stylifer* and *Thyca* (in other echinoderms). *Gasterosiphon deimatis* is a species which has lost its intestine but feeds on the blood of its host, a holothurian, by inserting its proboscis-like esophagus into a host blood vessel and taking blood into its stomach.[1,14]

BIBLIOGRAPHY

1. BAER, J. G., 1951. *Ecology of Animal Parasites.* Univ. Ill. Press. 224 pp.
2. BARTOŠ, E., 1957. Die Rädertier der Kiemenhöhle der Süsswasserkrabbe (*Potamon potamon*). Věst. Cesk. Spol. Zool., *21*, 376–380.
3. BUDDE, E., 1925. Die Parasitischen Rädertiere mit besondere Berücksichtigung der in der Umgegend von Minden I. W. beobachteten Arten. Zs. Morphol. Ökol. Tiere Berlin, *3*, 706–784.
4. GUDGER, E. W., 1928. Association Between Sessile Colonial Hydroids and Fishes. Ann. Mag. Nat. Hist. (ser. 10), *1*, 17–48.
5. HYMAN, L. H., 1940. *The Invertebrates: Protozoa through Ctenophora.* Vol. 1, McGraw-Hill Book Co., New York. 726 pp.
6. HYMAN, L. H., 1951. *The Invertebrates/ Acanthocephala, Aschelminthes, and Entoprocta. The Pseudocoelomate Bilateria.* Vol. III. McGraw-Hill Book Co., N. Y. 572 pp.
7. HYMAN, L. H., 1959. *The Invertebrates: Smaller Coelomate Groups.* Vol. V. McGraw-Hill Book Co., 783 pp.
7a. MANN, K. H., 1962. *Leeches (Hirudinea) Their Structure, Physiology, Ecology and Embryology. With an Appendix on the Systematics of Marine Leeches*, by E. W. Knight-Jones. (Internat. Ser. of Monogr. on Pure & Applied Biology, Zool. Division) Oxford, and New York, Pergamon Press. 201 pp.
8. McCONNAUGHEY, B. H., 1949. *Dicyema sullivani* A New Mesozoan From Lower California. J. Parasitol., *35*, 122–124.
9. McCONNAUGHEY, B. H., 1949. Mesozoa of the Family Dicyemidae from California. Univ. Calif. Pub. Zool., *55*, 1–34.
10. MIYASHITA, Y., 1941. Occurrence of a New *Hydrichthys* in the Pacific Coast of Japan. Annot. Zool. Janonenses, *20*, 151–153.
11. NOUVEL, H., 1933. Recherches sur la cytologie la physiologie et la biologie des Dicyemides. Ann. Inst. Océanogr., *13*, 165–255.
12. REES, B., 1960. *Albertia vermicularis* (Rotifera) Parasitic in the Earthworm *Allolobophora caliginosa*. Parasitol., *50*, 61–66.
13. STUNKARD, H. W., 1954. The Life-history and Systematic Relations of the Mesozoa. Quart. Rev. Biol., *29*(3): 230–244.
14. TIKASINGH, E. S., 1961. A New Genus and Two New Species of Endoparasitic Gastropods from Puget Sound, Washington. J. Parasitol., *47*, 268–272.

CHAPTER XXI

Effects of Parasitism on the Host

INTRODUCTION

The effects of parasitism on the host are intimately related to the effects of the host on the parasite. The two organisms involved in the partnership react on each other. Some of these reactions, such as special growths, are easily seen, but most of them induce only slight changes in body form or behavior, or they are of a purely biochemical nature.

Effects of parasitism on the host depend on many factors. Age, diet, genetic factors and susceptibility of the host are important examples; and obviously so are the size, number and virulence of the parasites, and their motility, migration and method of feeding. The organ or organs in which parasites live are of major significance. Among the miscellaneous effects are malnutrition, destruction of tissues, pressure effects, reduced resistance to bacterial or viral infections, introduction of these microbes, interference with other parasites, production of toxins and, possibly, allergic conditions. Combinations of these factors may be responsible for the fact that the rate of metamorphosis, in insects for example, may be increased or may be decreased by the presence of parasites. The host increases in weight when infected with certain parasites. This interesting reaction occurs in mice with spargana, *Tribolium* with *Nosema* and in rats and mice with *Trypanosoma lewisi* and *T. duttoni*.

The effect of a parasite, at least in one case, may be dependent on the presence or absence of a single substance. This case involves *Entamoeba invadens*. The ameba is a natural non-pathogenic parasite of herbivorous turtles which furnish particulate carbohydrate in their intestine.[20] The amebas require small particles of starch in order to encyst. Encystment is a necessary stage in their life cycle. In snakes, however, no particles of starch are present because snakes are carnivorous. The amebas are apparently unable to utilize dissolved food in the lumen of the gut; hence, in these hosts they invade the intestinal mucosa and feed on secretions of the intestinal epithelium, producing 100 per cent fatality among snakes infected experimentally.

Effects of a host in counteracting internal parasites may be of a mechanical nature, such as phagocytosis or the use of a covering layer of the pigment melanin around the parasite; or the effects may be more strictly chemical in nature, such as the action of antibodies. The toxin "ascaron" has been isolated from the common roundworm *Ascaris* by Japanese workers. This toxin causes allergic symptoms in man, especially children, and it may be the toxin responsible for pathological changes in the central nervous system. Parasitic worms and protozoa are frequently the cause of serious allergic conditions, and their toxins may even be conveyed through maternal milk to infants. Parasites may also contribute to avitaminosis of the host by hampering resorption of vitamins from the alimentary tract, or by using the vitamins themselves. *Dibothriocephalus latus*, for example, will absorb almost half of an oral dose of vitamin B_{12} in a human intestine.

General Tissue Reactions

Direct destruction of host tissue by mechanical or chemical activities of the parasite is obviously related to host reaction. If a parasite produces a chemical substance which destroys host tissue, the destruction is not a host reaction; but if, in addition, inflammation occurs, the host is reacting to the parasite. Mechanical or chemical destruction of host tissue by the parasite is closely related to immunity reactions of the host. The first place to look for localized reactions is, of course, at the spot of attachment or lodging. One has only to pick off a firmly attached parasite to see at least mild inflammation of host tissue. The inflammatory reaction may progress to a swelling or to tissue degeneration, or cancerous-type growths may occur.

The cockroach, *Blatella germanica*, serves as the intermediate host of several parasites, among them being the tapeworm, *Hymenolepis diminuta*, and the larva of the nematode, *Physaloptera hispida*. The latter worm lies in a cyst, and it is responsible for a sequence of host tissue reactions in the wall of the cockroach colon involving hypertrophy of nuclei, fibrosis at the sides of the parasitized zone, and the rupture of the muscle layer surrounding the cyst.

Mechanical pressure of parasites may set up inflammation, cause the formation of connective tissue, rupture host tissues, produce hemorrhages, or initiate a variety of other reactions. Pressure effects may be the direct or indirect result of single parasites in a small space, as occurs when a young ascarid crowds into a minute blood vessel. Single, but greatly enlarged, parasites, such as certain bladder worms in various organs, may bring about similar effects. Large numbers of parasites such as adult nematode worms in lymph vessels may evoke serious mechanical damage.

Host reaction to eggs of the tapeworm, *Taenia mustelae*, has been reported in detail.[11] When two field mice were fed worm eggs, the mice succumbed within the first two weeks from excessive liver damage and internal hemorrhage. In other mice cestodes began to appear after eight days. The young tapeworms increased in size and then ruptured the liver capsule. Many of the worms migrated

34

elsewhere. Some appeared subcutaneously, producing hemorrhage, some were found in the thymus, and others caused a severe hemorrhage into the peritoneal cavity. By the seventeenth day of development the mice had produced isolation membranes around some of the larvae. This tendency of a host to wall off a parasite, to separate itself from a foreign body from which it is otherwise unable to get away, is a general one and is widespread. When it occurs in the reaction of a host to infection with *Trichinella spiralis* larvae in muscles, calcium salts may be produced by the host and deposited in parasite tissues, thus calcifying the annoying organisms. If response by the host is not adequate, and the concentration of parasites is sufficiently high, the host may, of course, die. The biochemical aspects of these relationships are complex and not clearly understood, but certainly some adjustment to a parasite must be made or the host is in danger. Trichinosis may be so severe in swine that death of the host occurs as early as seven to ten days after infection. The numbers of infected hogs which die, however, are extremely few. Even the numbers of infected hogs which show symptoms are far less than 1 per cent.

The heterophyid fluke, *Cryptocotyle lingua*, in the gut of terns and dogs may cause a pronounced reaction on the part of the host.[34] The worms live between the villi and in the lumen of the intestine. "They denude the epithelium, produce a copius exudation of mucus, cause pressure atrophy, necrosis, a sloughing of tissue, hyperemia, infiltration of eosinophils and plasma cells, and hyperplasia of the fixed tissue elements." The injury is mainly mechanical and if the host does not die, a "self-cure" seems to take place. This result suggests an immunity reaction. From the medical point of view one can be glib about such pathogenic effects of parasites on their hosts. From the basic biochemical point of view, however, little is known of the true relationship between the physiological activities of the parasite and the reaction of host tissues. It is easy to observe that a certain organ is damaged, but it is extremely difficult to say with certainty what reaction or reactions caused the damage.

Severe thickening of blood vessels of any infected organ obviously may interfere with the normal functioning of that organ. Blood flow may be impeded when heart worms are present in large numbers in dogs. Worms in the brain may cause mental disturbances in man. Liver function may become abnormal if this organ is heavily infected with flukes. Other metabolic disturbances caused by parasites include biochemical changes in the host serum and physiological disturbances (*e.g.* increase in fat). For example, *Sacculina*, the peculiar, branched, thread-like parasite of crabs, is probably toxic to its host as is indicated by the results of injection of parasite extracts into crabs. Paralysis and death usually occur. When *Sacculina* grows into internal organs the crab ceases to molt. This reaction may be associated with the increase of the lipoid content of the hemolymph in the infected crab. These reactions indicate that the parasite exerts a general injurious effect on the host.

Age resistance against parasites is common (see p. 575). Usually the older the host the more the resistance. Part of the explanation for this fact is associated with immunity reactions but other factors undoubtedly play a role. A change in diet may be significant. For example, a decrease in carbohydrate with a corresponding increase in protein intake will, in some cases, protect the host against intestinal parasites. Often this change in diet occurs in man. There is also evidence that older vertebrate hosts have more duodenal goblet cells than do younger hosts, and that these cells are associated with resistance in older animals. The contained mucus apparently has an inhibitory effect on some parasites. In some animals, however, there is an increase in susceptibility to parasites as the host becomes older. The topographical localization of worms within the intestine varies with the species but is constant for any one species whether other worms are present or not. A change in the metabolic rate of the intestinal mucosa undoubtedly plays a role in the degree of success attained by the parasite in establishing itself in this type of habitat.

Effect On Nutrition

Loss of food due to the nutrient needs of parasites is usually not a serious problem for the host. Many parasites even make partial compensation for this loss. They may incompletely oxidize their food so that they excrete partially oxidized substances. These substances are frequently utilized by the host. Thus the host ingests the food, digests it, "feeds" some of it to parasites which derive energy from partial breakdown of the digested material, and which excrete the rest to be used completely by the host. As is discussed briefly in Chapter 23, page 587, the rumen of cattle and of other ruminants contains many ciliates. It is reasonable to suppose that the host benefits not only by digesting the vast numbers of protozoa which die, but also by utilizing some of the intermediate breakdown products of cellulose (p. 589).

The popular notion that a person with worms is constantly hungry is not borne out by fact. Intestinal worms may eat the food that their host swallows, but two or three worms consume a negligible fraction of any one host meal. Malnutrition, however, is a common associate of parasites in general. This condition is due to many factors other than actual robbery of food by parasites. The symptom is often spoken of as "off its feed" and is common with worm infections in domestic animals. A few parasites will usually do no harm, nor do they normally produce observable effects on the host. When an animal suffers malnutrition due to parasitic infection, it is usually the result of a long-standing disease or of an unusually heavy infection, or both.

The malarial parasite and the roundworm, _Ascaris_, are good examples of organisms which may cause malnutrition in man. This condition is due to a reduction of effective protein supplies in the host by vomiting, anorexia, diarrhea or liver damage; and to increased protein requirements, due to feeding of the parasite, protein destruction and the building up of antibodies from a protein base.[21] Protein deficiency impairs normal metabolism of the liver, hence the effect of many parasites on the host is reflected in liver abnormalities such as fatty degeneration. In addition to malaria, kala-azar and schistosomiasis are diseases which involve this type of liver impairment in man.

Blood Changes

When the white-footed mouse (*Peromyscus*) is infected with the flagellate, *Trypanosoma cruzi*, there occurs an increase in the numbers of large lymphocytes; a decrease in the numbers of eosinophilic leukocytes; enlargement of the spleen, bronchial, lumbar and inguinal lymph nodes; hyperplasia of the lymphoblasts and lymphocytes of the follicles in the spleen; myeloid metaplasia in the spleen, and other reactions.[35] A disturbance in the blood picture of their hosts may also follow worm infection. Nodular worms, hookworms and stomach worms in calves cause a decrease in erythrocytes and an increase in leukocyte count. Microfilariae of *Loa loa* in the insect, *Chrysops*, become situated in polynuclear cells. A breakdown of host cell walls occurs, and the area becomes a filarial syncytium within which the parasites undergo metamorphosis to the infective stage. *Onchocerca volvulus* in the fly, *Simulium*, appears to develop in the same manner but in thoracic fibers.

Much of the pathology described above is due to direct destruction of host tissue by mechanical or chemical means and it should be emphasized again that this type of phenomenon must not be confused with true reactions of the host.

Anemia

The loss of red blood cells resulting in anemia is a common effect of parasitism. One of the best known examples is anemia due to the presence of hookworms in the intestine. This type is the result of removal of blood due to the feeding habits of the worm, and it can be simulated by simply withdrawing blood at intervals from the patient. In a healthy host the condition can usually be remedied by iron therapy. In man the erythrocytic count may drop below 2,000,000 per cubic millimeter (from about 5,000,000) and the hemoglobin may drop below 30 per cent of normal. This decrease results in "... a severe pallor, extreme languor and indisposition to play or work, popularly interpreted as laziness; a flabbiness and tenderness of the muscles; breathlessness after slight exertion; enlargement and palpitation of the heart, with weak and irregular pulse; edema, making the face puffy and the abdomen 'pot-bellied'; a fishlike stare in the eyes; reduced perspiration; more or less irregular fever, and heartburn, flatulence, and abdominal discomfort. The appetite is capricious, and frequently there is an abnormal craving for coarse 'scratchy' substances such as soil, chalk, and wood."[7]   In addition to these reactions, the removal from the body of the protein and iron may be particularly serious during pregnancy.

Anemia may also be due to the failure of the blood-forming organs to function normally or to receive appropriate constituents for the formation of normal blood cells.   The fish tapeworm, *Dibothrio-cephalus latus*, apparently causes this type of pernicious anemia in its human host.

Protozoan parasites may also produce an anemia in their host. The malarial organism, *Plasmodium*, the sleeping sickness parasite, *Trypanosoma*, the causative agent of cattle piroplasmosis, *Babesia*, and various coccidia all evoke this response.   Red cells may be destroyed by occupancy, but where no mechanical destruction is possible the effect is probably due in part to lytic substances.   It is best, however, to think of the entire body of the host as reacting to parasites in the blood.   This approach emphasizes the complexity of the problem and indicates the involvement of other organs, such as the spleen, and other processes such as production of acidosis, anoxia, phagocytosis, vascular endothelial changes, temperature effects, and antibody formation.

Influence On Sexual Processes Of Host

The shrimp, *Leander serrifer*, is parasitized by either of two species of the isopod bopyrids, *Bopyrus squillarum* and *Diplophyrus jordani*.[36] These parasites obtain their food by sucking blood.   Breeding characters of the shrimp are normal so long as the parasites remain on the host.   If the parasites are removed or fall off, however, the breeding characters disappear completely from the pleopods at the next molting.   But if the parasites occupy the branchial chamber of the shrimp, the breeding characters never develop.   Thus, under the right conditions, the parasites are apparently able to inhibit normal sexual behavior of the host.

Certain hermit crabs parasitized by some of the rhizocephalids (e.g. *Sacculina*) show some degree of sex reversal.   Some males are feminized, as is indicated by altered appendages, but some are not. The parasitized female crabs seem to be more resistant since they do not take on male characteristics.   Possibly the parasites produce a toxin which inhibits normal development of male characters. Certainly the gonads of a host are sometimes altered enough to prevent the production of normal gametes.   *Sacculina* in a male crab may die before the host testes have completely degenerated. The crab is often able to recover, but then may produce both sperm and ova, thus becoming hermaphroditic.[22]

Parasitic castration may be caused by two different sorts of animal associations.   On the one hand the parasites may live within the gonads, causing a direct castration due to more or less complete atrophy of these organs.   On the other hand, an indirect alteration of gonads and of the secondary sexual characters may take place, leading to complete castration or to the production of individuals more or less intersexual in appearance. See Reinhard[22] and Hartnoll.[13]

Direct destruction of the gonads occurs when the warble fly, *Cuterebra emasculator*, infests the chipmunk, *Tamias listeri*.[5] Many trematode larvae destroy the hermaphroditic or unisexual glands of the snails they infect. The trematode, *Distomum megastomum*, may obliterate the gonads of the crab, *Portunus depurator*. Tapeworm larvae may bring about castration of fish gonads.[30] Some mermithid nematodes parasitize female midges (chironomids) and bring about a certain amount of sex reversal. Male characters may appear in the insects, and in extreme cases the ovaries are replaced by testes.

A holotrich ciliate lives in the testes of starfishes (*Asterias rubens*) in the Plymouth area of the United States Atlantic coast. The parasites are especially abundant in well-fed medium-sized starfishes in which they occur in up to 28 per cent of the males during March to April. The effect of the protozoa on the host is a breakdown of all the germinal tissue in the testes. Most of the starfishes suffer complete castration. Marine copepods may also become castrated by a parasitic dinoflagellate.

Parasitic worms may become castrated by their own parasitic protozoa. To be a parasite and a host at the same time apparently presents fearful problems. The tapeworm, *Catenotaenia dentritica*, which lives in a squirrel, is parasitized by a haplosporidian, *Urosporidium charletyi*, which brings about castration of its worm host. The common sheep tapeworm, *Moniezia expansa*, is sometimes so parasitized by the microsporidian, *Nosema helminthorum*, that not only the gonads but all other tissues of the worm are infected. Hyperparasitism of worms leading to possible castration has also been noted with microsporidia in the fish acanthocephalid, *Echinorhynchus*; with the flagellate, *Giardia muris*, in the fluke, *Echinostoma revolutum*, from a mouse; and in several species of microsporidia in other trematodes and cestodes.

Indirect parasitic castration is much more common than is direct destruction of the gonads. The parasitic isopods of the suborder Epicaridea are all parasitic on prawns and crabs, and they commonly cause a degeneration of the gonads of their hosts. The isopod, *Liriopsis pygmaea*, parasitic on the barnacle, *Peltogaster curvatus*, (itself attached to hermit crabs), feeds during its young stages on the host juices. The epicarid apparently diverts food from the ovary which consequently degenerates.

Among the many other examples of a crustacean host being castrated or sterilized by a parasitic crustacean is the hermit crab, *Pagurus longicarpus*. This crab may be burdened with two species of isopods, a bopyrid, *Stegophryxus hyptius* (Fig. XVI–5), p. 392, and an entoniscid, *Paguritherium alatum*. The bopyrid lives attached to the abdomen of its host whereas the entoniscid lives within the hemocoel. Usually the crab is not parasitized by both of these organisms at the same time. *Sleyophryxus* seems to have little effect on its host but *Paguritherium* brings about complete castration of the female crab, and practically complete atrophy of the gonads of the male crab.[23]

Strepsipteran insects (Figs. XVII–40 and 41, pp. 465–466) are small peculiar forms whose larvae are endoparasitic in various members of the insect orders Hymenoptera and Homoptera. One result of this parasitism is atrophied ovaries in the female host and sterility in the male. External genitalia and secondary sexual characteristics may also be altered. Plague-carrying fleas on rodents may be castrated by a nematode, *Heterotylenchus pavlovskii*.[16a]

Castration of vertebrate hosts by parasites apparently rarely occurs. There are sexual differences, however, in reaction to worm parasites. Female hamsters are more resistant to the roundworm, *Nippostrongylus brasiliensis*, than are male hamsters, but this sexual difference is absent in rats which are hosts to the same worms.

Several theories have been developed to explain the effects of parasitism on the sexual development of the host. These theories include the production of toxic substances (mentioned above), interference with general nutrition, interference with fat metabolism, hormone changes, or mechanical destruction of gonad tissues. A clue to the specific causes of parastic castration may be found in a study of morphogenic effects produced by the gonads through hormonal influences. If the eye stalks of the prawn (*Leander serratus*) are removed, not only does a reaction in the chromatophores occur, but also a rapid development of the ovary, and eggs are produced out of season. Obviously an endocrine gland in the stalk directly or indirectly acts on the growth of the ovary. If a parasite modifies the hormonal balance of its host, the genital glands and secondary sexual characters of that host clearly may become altered.

One of the best suggestions to explain these effects of parasitism, is that, in a manner not yet understood, the parasite upsets the balance between male and female potentialities which are presumably present in all animals.

A suggestion has been made that the words "parasitic castration" are inappropriate when discussing the effect on invertebrates because in such hosts secondary sexual characteristics are apparently independent of the gonads. The implied effect of such castration on these characters, therefore, is nil.[3] It would seem appropriate, however, to use the phrase to indicate destruction or alteration of gonad tissues by parasites without reference to any further effect on the structure or behavior of the host.

Immunity—General

Immunity should not be confused with other types of resistance to a parasite. Resistance is often non-specific, and it may be due to many factors such as size of host, general health or age or sex of host, diet, external environment, hereditary factors, hibernation, action of digestive juices, or even callouses on the host's feet. Thus many conditions unrelated to the presence of the parasite may prevent infection.

The first comprehensive studies of immunity reactions were made with bacterial infections. A natural step from these studies to like considerations of other parasitic infections has been taken by many investigators. A surprisingly large mass of literature has been written on this problem and to cover all of these researches would be far beyond the scope of this book. Attention will be drawn to the development of this field of parasitology, and to some recent investigations, to give the student some conception of the scope and complexity of the problem.

Among the most important and persistent unanswered questions about parasite-host relationships are those that deal with the exact biochemical explanation of the ability of the parasite to feed and grow within a host environment that may be biochemically hostile. One attempt at such an explanation was that by Lewis,[19] called the *Balance Hypothesis*. It is outlined below.

The normal host metabolites, such as vitamins, amino acids and organic acids, generally supply all the types of food required by a parasite. The kinds and quantities of these metabolites vary not only from host to host, but within one host at different times. Hence the environment of the parasite is constantly changing, and the resistance and susceptibility of the host is also changing. These host metabolites, if favorable to the growth of the parasites, may determine the innate susceptibility of the host. There is thus a balance in the host between the metabolic substances that inhibit and those that promote the growth of the parasite.

This balance hypothesis gains validity on the basis of the known occurrence in both plant and animal hosts, of inhibitors caused by nutrients which are present in metabolic concentrations. The retention of a parasite may, therefore, be explained without recourse to special agents such as antibodies, antibiotic substances, phagocytes, enzymes, toxins or other barriers.

A comparable hypothesis to the one just outlined is that proposed by Garber,[12] and called the *Nutrition-Inhibition Hypothesis* of pathogenicity. The two host environments which most directly affect the fate of an invading parasite are the nutritional environment and the inhibitory environment. Each of these two environments may be either ineffective or adequate. Thus there are four possible combinations which range from deficient nutrition-effective inhibition to adequate nutrition-ineffective inhibition. Only the latter combination results in virulence. The others result in avirulence, but the parasites might, nevertheless, persist. Enzymatic, morphological, and antigenic characteristics of the parasite introduce complications into this otherwise simple scheme.

In all such hypotheses based upon the presence or absence of food, the test lies in examining, in complete biochemical detail, the definitive nutrition of a parasite and the relevant content of its environment within the host. Such exhaustive tests have rarely been made.

Immunity reactions against parasites are undoubtedly basically the same as those against bacterial or virus infections. The host produces antibodies against chemical substances produced by the parasite. The mechanisms probably involve many factors and are undoubtedly the chief reasons why there is such a phenomenon as host specificity. Parasitic adaptation may depend on the specific absorption of a layer of host serum protein which helps protect the parasite against antibody. Some natural immunity is due to purely mechanical factors such as the small size of very young animals, which fact precludes the establishment of fairly large parasites.

Intestinal parasites generally do not elicit demonstrable antibody formation. As was mentioned above, tissue parasites, especially blood inhabiting forms, probably all do, at least to some extent. The more intimate the relation between host and parasite, the more antibody production is to be expected. Amebas living in lesions in the intestinal mucosa do not evoke as much antibody formation as do amebas living in the liver. See Stauber[25] for a discussion of immunity and intracellular protozoa.

The kinetics of the rise and fall of serum antibody, the interplay of synthesis and of the metabolic decay of antibody, and the role of different organs in producing changes in the titer (standard strength) of serum antibody were reported by Taliaferro[28] in a study of the formation of antisheep hemolysins in the rabbit. Although it is hazardous to generalize from the results of one type of experimentation on one or two species of animals, a brief review of Taliaferro's results gives an idea of what might be operative between a parasite and its host. The antigens used were sheep red blood cells and boiled stromata which were carefully prepared and injected in measured amounts into the veins of rabbits. After a latent period, the rise and fall of antibody in the rabbit followed a discontinuous curve when plotted. The indicated changes of titer were the consequence of the interplay of changing rates of formation of the antibody by different organs or tissues, and were also due to antibody decay. At first the spleen produced the most antibody but soon it diminished in quantity, whereas nonsplenic sources produced less at first but continued to be active over a much longer period of time. After repeated injections of antigen, different effects were produced on different organs. There was, for example, a cessation in antibody production by the spleen.

Immunity and Protozoa

Immunity to the pathogenic effects of *Entamoeba histolytica* infection is a condition which undoubtedly exists. It is, however, little understood and cannot be predicted. Most people apparently have a natural immunity to this organism, and it rarely causes much if any trouble for the host. We must not forget that this lack of pathogenicity may be due to some factor in the parasite and not to resistance of the host. Also, resistance of the host may be due to local conditions such as congestion, stasis, or ulcers at the point of attack rather than to true immunological agents. However, various experiments show that man, monkeys, and kittens probably give an immunological response to an amebic antigen. The lack of definite acquired immunity to this parasite may be due to its production of lipid haptens rather than of the strongly antigenic carbohydrate haptens as occur in bacteria.

As long ago as 1914 aqueous antigens were prepared from the feces of infected cats or from the pus of a liver abscess of man, and positive complement fixation reactions were obtained with serum from five human cases of amebic dysentery, and with serum from three cats experimentally infected from man. Normal feces reacted negatively. Later, cats were successfully infected rectally with *Entamoeba histolytica* obtained from an acute human case. Serum from normal cats or from cats infected for less time than a week gave negative precipitation tests. Ulcer scrapings extracted with Coca's fluid were used.

A precipitin test for human malaria was unsuccessfully sought by Taliaferro.[26] He did get encouraging results by using antigen material from heavily infected placentas. With better technique a dependable precipitin test for the diagnosis of this disease seemed possible. Taliaferro[27] carried his experiments to birds and he found that large quantities of the malarial parasite, *Plasmodium relictum*, injected intravenously into a bird during the exoerythrocytic period of infection are killed in from fifteen minutes to a few hours. Thus there must have been some antibody in the blood of the bird. His attempts to transfer this antibody passively failed. At the same time Craig[9,10] made an important report on complement fixation in amebiasis. He found that there were hemolytic, cytolytic and complement-binding substances in absolute alcohol extracts of 48-hour-old cultures of *Entamoeba histolytica*. The amebas were grown on Boeck-Drobohlav's medium. Hemolytic properties were destroyed by heating to $80°$ C for one hour. Although the hemolytic agent was not an exotoxin and was not specific for human red blood corpuscles, being equally hemolytic to rabbit and guinea pig erythrocytes, the complement fixing substance was specific for *Entamoeba histolytica*. Craig examined the stools of 225 persons. The serum from 24 infected and 2 uninfected persons gave positive complement fixation. He concluded that complement fixation occurs not only in dysentery patients, but in mild cases and carriers. It does not occur in infections with *Entamoeba coli*, *Endolimax nana*, *Iodamoeba bütschlii*, *Trichomonas hominis* or *Chilomastix mesnili*, nor in various other diseases, including syphilis, unless *E. histolytica* is also present. Because of the technical difficulties in carrying out the test, he was inclined to withhold judgment on the practical significance of the reaction. At the present time there is serious doubt about the reliability of the test for routine diagnostic procedure.

If amebas have become established within an organ such as the liver, other reactions may occur in addition to whatever antibodies are produced. The host does not seem to attack the parasite directly by phagocytosis, but relies more on circumscription or blocking the area by tissue exudates and perhaps by fibrin which surrounds the ulcers containing the amebas. The general body responses to inflammation apparently create conditions unsuitable for the amebas.

Filtered saline extracts of *Trypanosoma brucei* or *T. equiperdum* used as test antigens, resulted in positive fixation tests with serum from 25 horses having dourine, and negative tests with 25 normal horses.[34a] Extensive investigations have confirmed the test as certain and specific in diagnosing dourine.[31, 32, 33] A hemolytic system of sheep red blood corpuscles(5 per cent), hemolytic rabbit serum and complement from normal guinea pigs has been used successfully to obtain 79.5 per cent positive results from 200 suspected cases of Chagas disease.[17] The antigen was prepared with the spleen of a puppy infected with *Trypanosoma cruzi*. Immune serum in animals experimentally infected with various species of *Trypanosoma* has been definitely established. The action of the serum may be on the basis of antibodies such as opsonins or lysins or on reproduction-inhibiting antibodies. Trypanocidal properties from an immune serum have been removed by adsorption with *T. lewisi*, leaving the reproduction-inhibiting property.[28] The *in vivo* manifestations of these two properties are strikingly different, and one may be formed independently of the other. Taliaferro has named the reproduction-inhibiting property *ablastin*, a new type of antibody. Immune serum from rabbits immunized with *T. lewisi* contained only the trypanocidal property and not the reproduction-inhibiting one.

Acquired immunity has been found to occur in many protozoal infections. Young rats may acquire immunity to *Toxoplasma gondii* by receiving antibodies either through the placenta or through their mother's milk or both. Acquired immunity has been demonstrated in Texas cattle fever and in oriental sore. In the former disease it is caused by a low grade or latent infection with *Babesia* (= *Piroplasma*) *bigemina*, whereas immunity to oriental sore has been shown to follow supposedly complete recovery from a primary infection with *Leishmania tropica*. Vaccine treatment has been successful. Artificial immunity to oriental sore was practiced long before the etiological agent was known. Natives of the Near East usually inoculate material from a sore on an unexposed part of the body to prevent the occurrence of a sore with its resulting scar on the face.

The entire community in a certain mining area in India (Singhbhum District) is probably continuously infected with malaria. In young children there is usually a period of acute infection lasting for two years followed by a stage of immunity which lasts throughout childhood into adult life. In adult life 50 per cent still show infection by microscopic examination. Lysins and reproduction-inhibiting antibodies undoubtedly exert a direct effect on the course of infection.

Resistance to trypanosome infection in fishes is sometimes related to social behavior.[2] During experiments on the effect of temperature upon resistance of freshwater fishes to infection by these flagellates, it was found that behavior patterns modified the temperature effects. Tench, perch and goldfish were studied, and these fishes behaved according to a "peck dominance" type of organization in which each fish had its place in the society. The numbers of trypanosomes in the blood of the fishes were not only correlated with the temperature of the water, but also with the feeding activity of the fishes. This feeding activity was associated with the social position of the fish and with its territorial behavior. There was evidence that the production of antibodies by the fish against the flagellates may be controlled by this social position indicating that the immunity was not the direct effect of temperature. As a rule, the most dominant fish in the tank rid themselves of trypanosomes most quickly.

Bird plasmodia apparently enjoy a greater freedom from host interference than do trypanosomes. Reproducing-inhibiting antibodies are apparently absent in bird malaria, and phagocytic activity on the part of the host does not exterminate the parasites. Consequently, the parasites may persist for years.

Phagocytosis is limited to the macrophages in human malarial infections.[6] The entire parasite-erythrocyte combination, rather than the isolated merozoites, is phagocytosed in all stages of development. Phagocytosis by the macrophages occurs as early as four hours following infection. Thereafter it occurs constantly during the entire acute period. The first distinct evidence of the activation of macrophage-producing cells appears eighteen hours after infection. The height of this activation is coincident with the crisis of infection (eighth or tenth day). Phagocytosis is well initiated within fifteen minutes after superinfection, and within twenty-four to forty-eight hours this process has so successfully removed the parasites that they can no longer be found in the peripheral blood. Although the activity of the mesenchyme appears to decline, it is still effective 654 days after initial infection. Thus the mechanism of immunity to superinfection is primarily cellular, and it consists of an increased rate of phagocytosis by the cells of the reticuloendothelial system, especially by those of the spleen and liver. Not only is there an increase in the number of phagocytic cells, but also a greatly increased rate of phagocytosis by the individual phagocytes.

The problem of diagnosis of parasitic diseases by means of serological reactions has been studied for many years with varying results. One of the earliest diseases thus investigated was coccidiosis. Interest was initiated when it was discovered that Wassermann tests on normal rabbits sometimes gave positive results. The explanation suggested was that coccidiosis caused this reaction. Numerous investigators took up the study of complement fixation tests on normal rabbits and on those infected with coccidia. Some of the investigators reported significant results and recommended the test for general use. Others, however, found the test unreliable. Bachman[1] experimentally infected rabbits with *Eimeria perforans* and *E. stiedae* and he noted that precipitation tests were uniformly negative. A definite specific response to coccidia was shown by the results of 932 benzoin flocculation tests on 66 rabbits five weeks to four years old. The flocculation of the sera of the rabbits infected with *Eimeria* was distinctly increased over the flocculation of normal serum. Bachman concluded that the attempts to demonstrate antibody response in rabbits experimentally infected with coccidia were not entirely conclusive, and that there was no indication of a physio-chemical change taking place in the sera of such infected animals. Other investigators reported that the immune responses of rabbits to an acute infection of *Eimeria stiedae* are similar to those evoked by an acute bacterial infection in which recovery confers immunity to another infection.[14]

Intradermal injections of oocysts of *Eimeria caviae* into guinea pigs which have recovered from infection with this parasite clearly demonstrate a cutaneous hypersensitivity.[15] This reaction is manifested by the appearance, in approximately forty-eight hours, of an inflamed area surrounding the point of infection, plus swelling, induration, and somewhat later, by central necrosis.

Serological reactions obviously cannot be used as the only method of diagnosing coccidiosis in rabbits. We must return to the original method of identification of cysts in the feces. However, with improved technique and standardization of method, there will probably be developed a serological process suitable for final diagnosis.

Natural immunity to coccidiosis in chickens has been investigated by a number of workers in order to attempt a control of the disease among the poultry farms. Commercially reared fowls usually possess a high degree of resistance, if not immunity, but they may develop fatal coccidiosis after maturity. Cage-reared fowls usually remain susceptible, but a high degree of resistance or immunity may be developed regularly by experimental inoculation. Young commercially-raised chicks probably attain their resistance by the occasional ingestion of oocysts from infected soil. Immunity to the several species of coccidia in some chicks is apparently definite and specific. Similar immunity in guinea pigs infected with *Eimeria caviae* develops, and degenerate forms of this parasite appear in partially immune animals. Hypersensitivity to coccidial proteins exists and it may be produced by parental infection. Quantitative studies were made on oocyst reproduction by *E. miyairii* during immunization of rats belonging to different strains.[4] The results indicated that susceptibility of rats to coccidiosis has a genetic basis. The serum apparently contained no inhibiting principle capable of decreasing the numerical increase of the parasites of the rat into which they were injected.

Natural immunity to coccidial infection has thus been definitely established, although some of the attempts to demonstrate it have failed. Unquestionably a resistance of some sort is set up on the part of the host in all coccidial infections, and it will be merely a matter of time before the resistance can be experimentally established for each species.

Immunity and Helminths

Immunological studies of helminth infections have shown that worms, too, evoke immune responses in the host. Worms in tissues produce greater effects than do lumen parasites. The nematode, *Heterakis spumosa*, lives in the colon of the rat, and larval worms invade the body by penetrating intestinal mucosa. As a result of the secretions or excretions of the invading worms, the host develops antibodies (precipitins). This reaction is apparently due to the metabolites which are poured out of the larval stages during tissue migration.[24] Immunity may be transferred experimentally from one host to another. Several workers have incubated parasitic worms in normal serum and then injected this serum into a host animal which thus becomes protected against the parasite. Probably metabolites from the cultured worms cause antibody formation in the host. One technique for determining the presence of immune bodies in host serum is to place a drop or two of the serum on a slide, add some of the parasites (*e.g.* nematode larvae), protect them with a sealed cover glass and incubate. Immune serum is indicated by the formation of precipitins in any of the physiological openings of the worms. In larval nematodes these openings would be the buccal cavity, anal pore and excretory pore.

The esophagi of hookworms contain a substance which has a proteolytic action. It is possible to dissect the esophagi from these worms, grind them in saline with a tissue grinder, and extract the enzyme. When this enzyme from the dog hookworm, *Ancylostoma caninum*, is injected into dogs these animals become at least partially immune to a challenge infection with hookworm. This immunity is indicated by the fact that a second infection is light, the worms being fewer in number and smaller than in a first infection. The experiment indicates that antibodies which may act as antienzymes are formed in hosts as a response to substances which possess enzymatic activity in the secretions and excretions of worms. Immunity results from the inhibition of enzymatic activity in the parasite.[29]

Immune reactions to the oncospheres of tapeworms seem to be somewhat similar to those reactions to nematodes. An oncosphere is the name given to the young tapeworm which hatches from the egg. It possesses three pairs of hooks which help it to penetrate the intestinal epithelium of the host. Several workers have studied host reaction to this parasite and they have found that, in general, the oncospheres penetrate rapidly, and within a few days they develop into the cysticercoid or other stage in host tissues. Apparently the host reacts to this infection by changing in some way the intestinal epithelium or by producing some substance in the intestine which reacts with the larvae from a second infection. This immunity reaction is usually successful in preventing a second infection. Most oncospheres from a second infection are not able to penetrate the intestinal epithelium. If they are successful they soon die, indicating a second wall of defense on the part of the host. Possibly some parasites are able to maintain themselves within their host by changing their antigenic structure from time to time and thus escape the host antibodies which would otherwise destroy them.

Immunity to *Hymenolepis nana* in rats occurs after egg infection but not directly after infection with cysticercoids. This difference is understandable because egg infection leads to the tissue phase of the parasite while cysticercoid infection (indirect) leads to the adult phase in the gut. Antibodies may be produced against this tapeworm.[16] If rabbits are immunized by injections of homogenates of adult *H. nana*, then bled, and the serum collected, this serum is strongly sensitized against the worms. If an adult *H. nana* is placed in such serum it immediately becomes unusually active and withdraws its rostellum. After a few hours a precipitation occurs on the worm, beginning with the anterior end and progressing posteriorly along the strobila. A certain amount of natural immunity is undoubtedly possessed by some hosts against some worm parasites.

In dual infections of mice and rats with *Hymenolepis nana* and *H. diminuta* the *H. nana* are much more successful in maintaining themselves. The immunogenic tissue phase of the *H. nana* elicits an inhibitory reaction to infectivity and growth of the nonimmunogenic *H. diminuta*. The host reaction which develops against *H. nana* proves to be just as strong against *H. diminuta*. There seem to be large numbers of common antigens among helminths. Antibodies get into the lumen of the host gut from sloughed and disintegrated mucosa cells and also by passing through cell membranes.[16]

It is possible that complimentary genetic systems have developed in some animal parasites and their hosts which involve the specific reaction of one gene in the parasite with one gene in the host, giving a common phenotype of resistance or susceptibility. Such a genetic relation has developed between the flax rust and its host.

Relation of Animal Parasites to Bacterial and Viral Infections

Bacterial or viral infections often accompany general lowering of vitality which brings about reduced resistance to infections. This relation is little understood and it is frequently described in vague terms, but it is undoubtedly associated with the lack of ability to form antibodies against the bacteria. Obviously if the overall efficiency of man or of animals is reduced, the ability to ward off infections is also reduced. This reduced resistance to bacterial invasion may result from heavy or long-standing parasitic infection (*e.g.* with hookworms).

Introduction of infective bacteria or viruses is always a possibility when there is injury to host tissue by animal parasites. Ectoparasites are notorious offenders in this regard. They can bite or pierce the skin or mucous membranes, and thus destroy the host's first line of defense against bacterial infection. Larval flesh flies have been known to eat away part of the mucous membranes of the nasal passageways of man which thereafter become infected with bacteria, resulting in death of the host. Such flies may develop in any body opening and pave the way for more serious trouble.

The spread of bacterial diseases by parasitic worms is a subject which has received little investigation. Unquestionably, helminths play an important role in the transmission of certain bacterial and viral diseases although the occurrence is probably rare.[20a] The intestinal mucosa of man and of other animals is often pierced or otherwise damaged by worms, so the possibility of bacteria entering a wound is obvious. Larval worms and other parasites (see above) that penetrate the skin likewise provide an opportunity for the inoculation of bacteria. The host normally organizes its defense mechanisms to prevent the bacteria from going deeper into the body. A curious reaction has been observed between body fluids of parasitic worms and surrounding bacteria. The body cavity fluids of some helminths show a bacteriostatic action but only on those species of bacteria foreign to the vertebrate host.

BIBLIOGRAPHY

1. BACHMAN, G., 1930. Immunity in Experimental Coccidiosis of Rabbits. Am. Jour. Hyg., *12*, 641.
2. BARROW, JAMES H., 1955. Social Behavior in Freshwater Fish and its Effect on Resistance to Trypanosomes. Proc. Nat. Acad. Sci., *41*, 676–679.
3. BAER, J. G., 1951. *Ecology of Animal Parasites*, The Univ. of Illinois Press, Urbana. 224 pp.
4. BECKER, E. and HALL, P., 1932. Quantitative Studies on Oocyst Production by *Eimeria miyairii* During Immunization of Rats Belonging to Different Strains (abstract). J. Parasitol. Urbana., *19*, 159.
5. BENNETT, G. F., 1955. Studies on *Cuterebra emasculator* Fitch 1856 (Diptera: Cuterebridae) and a Discussion of the Status of the Genus *Cephenemyia* Ltr. 1818. Canad. J. Zool., *33*, 75–98.
6. CANNON, P. and TALIAFERRO, W., 1931. Avian Malaria Acquired Immunity. J. Prev. Med., *5*, 37–64.
7. CHANDLER, A. C. and READ, C. R., 1961. *Introduction to Parasitology*. 10th ed. John Wiley & Sons, New York and London. 822 pp.
8. COLE, W. H., 1955. *Some Physiological Aspects and Consequences of Parasitism*. Rutgers U. Press. New Brunswick, N. J. 90 pp.
9. CRAIG, C., 1927. Observations upon the Hemolytic, Cytolytic and Complement-binding Properties of Extracts of *E. histolytica*. Am. Jour. Trop. Med., *7*, 225–240.
10. CRAIG, C., 1928. Observations upon Complement Fixation in Infections with E. *histolytica*. Proc. Nat. Acad. Sci., *14*, 520–526.
11. FREEMAN, REINO S., 1956. Life history Studies on *Taenia mustelae* Gmelin, 1790 and the Taxonomy of Certain Taenioid Cestodes from Mustelidae. Canad. J. Zool., *34*, 219–242.
12. GARBER, E. D., 1956. A Nutrition-Inhibition Hypothesis of Pathogenicity. Amer. Nat., *90*, 183–194.
13. HARTNOLL, R. G., 1962. Parasitic Castration of *Macropodia longirostris* (Fabricius) by a Sacculinid. Crustaceana, *4*, 295–300.
14. HEIST, C. E. and MOORE, T. D., 1959. Serological and Immunological Studies of Coccidiosis of Rabbits. J. Protozool., *6* (supplement), 7.

15. HENRY, D. P., 1932. Coccidiosis of the Guinea Pig. U.C. Pub. Zool., *37*, 211–268.
16. HEYNEMAN, D. and WELSH, J. F., 1956. *In vitro* Study of *Hymenolepis nana* Rabbit Antiserum Against Eggs, Cysticercoids, and Adult Stages of That Parasite. J. Parasitol., *42*, (Sect. 2), 31.
16a. KUROCHKIN, YU.V., 1961. *Heterotylenchus pavlovskii*, sp. n., a Nematode Castrating Plague-Carrying Fleas. Doklady Akad. Nauk USSR (Transl. by AIBS, Washington, D.C.), *135*, 952–954.
17. LACORTE, J., 1927. A Reaccoo do Desvio do complemento na Molestra di Chagos. Men. Inst. Oswaldo Cruz., *20*, 197–224.
18. LARSH, J. E., JR. and HENDRICKS, J. R., 1949. The Probable Explanation for the Difference in the Localization of Adult *Trichinella spiralis* in Young and Old Mice, J. Parasitol., *35*, 101–106.
19. LEWIS, R. W., 1953. The Balance Hypothesis of Parasitism. Amer. Naturalist, *87*, 273–281.
20. MEEROVITCH, E., 1957. On the Relation of the Biology of *Entamoeba invadens* to its Pathogenicity in Snakes (abstract). J. Parasitol., *43*, (Sect. 2), 41.
20a. PHILIP, C. B., 1962. Helminths as Carriers of Microbial Disease Agents of Man and Animals. p. 159–169, In: Maramorosch, K. (ed.), *Biological Transmission of Disease Agents*. Academic Press, New York & London, 192 pp.
21. PLATT, B. S., 1956. Protein Malnutrition. British Postgraduate Medical Federation, *Lectures on the Scientific Basis of Medicine*, Vol. 4, chap. IX. Athlone Press, London.
22. REINHARD, E. G., 1956. Parasitic Castration of Crustacea. Exper. Parasitol., *5*, 79–107.
23. REINHARD, E. G. and BUCKERIDGE, SISTER, F. W., 1950. The Effect of Parasitism by an Entoniscid on the Secondary Sex Characters of *Pagurus longicarpus*. J. Parasitol., *36*, 131–138.
24. SMITH, P. E., 1953. Life History and Host-Parasite Relations of *Heterakis spumosa*, a Nematode Parasite in the Colon of the Rat. Amer. J. Hyg., *57*, 194–221.
25. STAUBER, L. A., 1963. Some Aspects of Immunity to Intracellular Protozoan Parasites. J., *Parasitol.*, *49*, 3–11.
26. TALIAFERRO, W., 1927a. A Precipitin Test in Human Malaria. J. Parasitol., *13*, 216.
27. TALIAFERRO, W. H., 1927b. Immunity to Super Infection with *Plasmodium relictum* in the Canary. J. Parasitol., *13* (3), 217.
28. TALIAFERRO, W., 1932. Trypanocidal and Reproduction-Inhibiting Antibodies to *Trypanosoma lewisi* in Rats and Rabbits. Am. J. Hyg., *16*, 32–84.
29. THORSON, R. E., 1956. The Stimulation of Acquired Immunity in Dogs by Injections of Extracts of the Esophagus of Adult Hookworms. J. Parasitol., *42*, 501–504.
30. WARDLE, R. A. and MCLEOD, J. A., 1952. *The Zoology of Tapeworms*. The University of Minnesota Press, Minneapolis, Minnesota. 870 pp.
31. WATSON, E., 1914. The Serum Test for Dourine. Rep. Vet. Director Gen., Canada, for yrs., ending March 31, Appendix, *19*, 111–115.
32. WATSON, E., 1915. Dourine and the Complement Fixation Test. Parasitol., *8*, 156–183.
33. WATSON, E., 1920. *Dourine in Canada, 1904–1920. History, Research, and Suppression.* Canada, Dept. Agric. Health of Animals Branch. 43 pp.
34. WILLEY, C. H. and STUNKARD, H. W., 1942. Studies on Pathology and Resistance in Terns and Dogs Infected With the Heterophyid Trematode *Cryptocotyle lingua*. Trans. Amer. Micros. Soc. LXI, 236–253.
34a. WINKLER and WYSCHELESSKY, S., 1911. Die Agglutination, Präzipitation und Komplement-bindung als Hilfsmittel zum Nachweiss der Trypanosomenerkrankheiten, im besonderen der Beschälseuche. Berlin. Tierarztl. Wchnschr., *27*, 933–936.
35. WOOD, S. F., 1937. Cytological Variations in the Blood and Blood-Forming Organs of White-footed Mice Experimentally infected with *Trypanosoma cruzi*. Univ. Calif. Pub. Zool., *41*, 389–418.
36. YOSHIDA, M., 1952. On the Breeding Character of the Shrimp, *Leander serrifer*, Parasitized by Bopyrids. Annot. Zool. Japonenses, *25*, 362–365.

CHAPTER XXII

Effects of Parasitism on the Parasite

INTRODUCTION

MUCH has been written about the effects of parasites on their hosts, but relatively little is known of the effects of the hosts on their parasites. A parasite may make its host ill, but does the host make the parasite ill? The reciprocal nature of the parasite-host relation should be kept in mind constantly when we consider the following discussion on the effects of parasitism on the parasite.

Since the relationship between a host and its parasite is reciprocal, one can expect both partners to be modified because they live together. Even if the parasite kills the host, the latter is sometimes able to leave its mark on the parasite, or, as Salt[29] has said, is able to "bequeath to its parasite an important and sometimes striking legacy of morphological, physiological and behavioristic characters."

As we have seen in the preceding chapter, a host may modify its tissues and alter its metabolism during its adjustment to the parasite. Failure to adjust properly often results in weakness, incapacities or disease, but the adjustment of the parasite to its host is even more marked. The parasite has the problem of maintaining its basic organization, yet retaining enough flexibility to adapt itself to changing conditions in its new surroundings. This adjustment is a delicate process, a critical balance which is in a state of continuous flux. No wonder the parasite is so often not suited to life in a host other than the one to which it has become accustomed. A thorough understanding of the physiological aspect of the parasite-host relation cannot be realized until a careful study is made of the biochemical natures of the specific parasite and particular host under consideration.

The over-all result of parasitism, so far as the parasite is concerned, is a life of ease without much effort. As was mentioned in an earlier chapter, parasites obtain "free board and lodging" with abundant food, and some freedom from competition and from predators. The general effect on the parasite, however, is an increase in the structure and function of those systems associated with reproduction and attachment, but at the same time a simplification of the sensory and locomotor systems. One example of these changes is the modification of organs of locomotion into organs of attachment.[3]

In general we find a trend of modification, a sort of direction of evolution, which varies in character among the groups of parasites. Nematodes, for example, tend to increase in size. To be impressed

(548)

with this trend, one has but to compare the sizes of free-living nematode worms which are found in soil or water with the average size of the animal parasitic forms. Trematodes, on the other hand, have not responded to parasitism with such a pronounced increase in size but they have undergone a greater increase in complexity.

When a parasite inhabits two or more different types of hosts in its life cycle the effect on the parasite is different in each host, and when one host harbors several different kinds of parasites the effect of the host generally differs with each type of parasite.

Adaptation of a parasite to its host, with the concomitant adjustment of the host, are the main factors in successful parasitism. This adjustment evolves slowly and it may require hundreds of thousands of years. Man has probably been parasitized by the malarial parasite, *Plasmodium*, for as long as there has been a human race, but the parasite has not yet become completely adapted to man. Its present degree of success is maintained partly by enormous reproductive output to meet the fantastic odds against the completion of a normal cycle by any one zygote. That it has a long way to go before becoming well adapted to its host is probably indicated by the severity of the host reaction. After all these thousands of years there are still about 200,000,000 cases of malaria annually in the world with about 1 per cent mortality. A well adapted parasite causes little harm to its host. Obviously the internal parasite remains alive only so long as its host lives.

Prosperous parasitism requires certain essentials for maintenance within the body of the host. (1) Entry into the host must be comparatively easy. Many parasites accomplish this all-important first step passively by being swallowed as a cyst or egg. Active entry usually demands the development of special organs such as histolytic glands. (2) A parasite must be able to stay within the particular organ or organs to which it has become adapted. For the larger parasites this requirement is often met by the development of mechanical devices such as suckers or hooks. (3) The basic bodily processes common to all living things must be allowed to function. That is, the parasite must find within its new habitat all the necessary factors for such processes as respiration, assimilation, growth, and reproduction. (4) The parasite must be able to counteract the defense mechanisms of its host and the adverse consequences of numerous other results of a hostile environment. Some of these deterrents to successful parasitism are host enzymes, foreign proteins, hormones, toxic substances, phagocytes, antibodies and change in osmotic and pH conditions of the surrounding medium.

PHYSICAL ADAPTATIONS

Parasites have developed a fascinating variety of organs for maintaining themselves within or on their hosts. It would require an entire book to describe in detail all the different behavior techniques and the hooks, suckers, holdfasts, spines, teeth, adhesive secretions, scales, lips, papillae, setae, alae, flagella, pseudopodia, and other structures employed for this purpose. Some of the common ones and a few of the more unusual or bizarre modifications will be described to illustrate the wide range of such adaptations which specific habitats within or on hosts apparently require.

Suckers and suction cups are common in many types of parasites. Even among the protozoa there may be found structures which are at least suggestive of such organs. The flagellate, *Giardia* (Fig. III–16, p. 62), has a sucker-like ventral surface which apparently helps the organism to maintain itself on the mucosal surface of its host or on fecal particles. One or more suckers are characteristic of tapeworms and flukes. These organs range from the single, cup-shaped type to be seen on the anterior end of the Chinese liver fluke, *Opisthorchis sinensis*, to large multiple-foliated forms on certain tapeworms. The monogenetic flukes cling to their hosts while they browse on mucus, blood or tissue, and the attachment is maintained by various modifications of the anterior and posterior parts of the body. The monogene posterior region, especially, is modified into different types of holdfasts or *haptors* (Fig. VII–4, p. 164). The simplest haptor is just a broad ventral outgrowth of the body, but in other flukes this ventral surface is divided by raised, muscular, radial septa into a number of parts, each of which exhibits individual suctorial action. Suckers on parasitic crustacea often occur. The carp louse (*Argulus*) possesses suckers formed by modified second maxillae. These branchiurids attach themselves to the skin or gill chambers of freshwater and marine fishes. A parasitic copepod (*Caligus*) has a pair of suckers at the bases of the first antennae.

Certain of the xiphidiocercariae possess within the oral sucker a gland of amorphous appearance which opens through pores on the dorsal surface. It is called a *virgula* and it appears late in the development of the cercaria and disappears after the parasite has penetrated its host. The virgula has an adhesive property which is used during the penetration process and it also discharges a mucoid material that envelops the larva as this parasite migrates through the host. This material may be a protection against injurious chemicals within the host body.[12]

Parasitic worms may possess rings or rows of hooks in addition to suckers. In many tapeworms there is a single ring of hooks at the anterior end. Others possess several such rings. Even young larval tapeworms usually possess hooks. They develop in the larva before the parasite has hatched from the egg. Three pairs of hooks, which give rise to the name *hexacanth larvae*, are characteristic. The acanthocephalid proboscis (Fig. XII–1, p. 289) is heavily armed with many rows of hooks. One of these worms, *Macracanthorhynchus hirudinaceus* is a common worm in the intestine of hogs, but representatives of the phylum are abundant in all vertebrate groups (see p. 293).

Other mechanical anchoring systems have been developed by many parasites. Parasitic copepods are notorious for attaining bizarre shapes. One of them becomes anchored in the skin and flesh of fishes with a shaft protruding to the outside. The common name of this parasite is, appropriately, the "anchor worm" (*Lernea carassii*). Some parasitic copepods have lost or modified so many of their structures that they are almost unrecognizable as copepods (Fig. XVI–10, p. 397). The unsegmented, distorted, limbless animals can be identified mainly by their larval stages. Even some of the protozoa possess remarkably complex structures for holding themselves to the host. Thus, among the gregarines we find *epimerites* which are extensions of the bodies thrust into host tissues (Fig. V–I, p. 98).

Adaptations by loss of organs or of functions are drastic features of the lives of many parasites. This loss has a profound effect on the parasite, and it probably renders the parasite more host-specific. A loss of the intestine has occurred in the thorny-headed acanthocephalid of hogs mentioned above. There is even a gutless parasitic snail (*Thyonicola serrata*) which lives in a sea cucumber. An even more drastic loss of organs occurs in *Sacculina*, described on previous pages of this book. This barnacle has become plant-like in general appearance (Fig. XVI–28, p. 416), and the adult has lost its alimentary canal, its appendages, and its segmentation. The body of the parasite is a sac-like structure from which branched processes extend throughout the host crab. These processes serve as anchoring devices as well as feeding organs (see p. 415).

Modification of insect and arachnid bodies for maintaining themselves on their hosts are especially noteworthy. Lice, fleas, and bedbugs are wingless. To maintain their position, however, they must be able to cling to host hairs or feathers or scales, so usually they have developed strong, large claws. In some ticks, mites and lice the claws are shaped in such a manner that they closely fit the hairs of their hosts.

Some parasites require pronounced modifications only in the immature stages. Warble and botflies find it necessary to provide some means of anchoring their eggs to the hairs of their hosts. Eggs of the warble fly of cattle are attached by means of a stalk near the base of the hair. When the larvae emerge they burrow into the skin. The eggs of the botfly of horses are attached to the outer ends of the hair, without stalks. This position of attachment is undoubtedly related to the necessity of rapid transit of the larva from the egg to the mouth of the horse. Transition has to occur during the moment the host brushes its hair with its lips. The rapid hatching of the egg is easily demonstrated in the laboratory. Simply clip a few egg-ladened hairs from a horse and place them in a shallow dish under a microscope. Add warm water and, if the eggs are ready to hatch, the opercula will pop open and the larvae will be ejected within a fraction of a second.

Loss of physiological characters is as important as loss of morphological characters. The worm, *Ascaris*, for example, has lost the cytochrome—cytochrome-oxidase system, and many enzymes of the tricarboxylic acid cycle. This worm has also lost the mechanism for the metabolism of arginine phosphate. Obviously any loss of this nature must be accompanied by the loss of the need for the end-products of these reactions or by the development of a method of obtaining the needed substances from the host or from other associated organisms.

PHYSIOLOGICAL ADAPTATIONS

The size of the host may affect the proportions of parts of the bodies of its insect parasites. Thus in *Trichogramma*, one of the chalcid wasps which parasitizes a moth, modifications of the wings and antennal bristles are a response to the size of the host. Since modification of certain parts of insect parasites or even a sufficient discrepancy in size between males and females might prevent copulation, the host could be responsible for a reproductive barrier between male and female parasites. We know relatively little about the physiological processes which take place in an insect parasite as it seeks its host. The olfactory sense plays a role, but there appears to be a distinct difference in the manner in which a host attracts a male insect and the manner in which it attracts a female insect of the same species. Of course, the difference may lie with the insects and not with the host. Some hymenoptera females, which are able to deposit either fertilized or unfertilized eggs "at will" in a host larva, apparently are induced, by unknown means, to deposit fertilized eggs in the larger hosts. In this direct manner the host may have an effect on the sex ratio of its parasites. Age is related to size, and we have already noted that the effect of parasites on the host is conditioned by the age of the host, but the age of the host also influences the size of some of its parasites. The tapeworm *Hymenolepis diminuta*, for example, varies in size with the age of the rat in which it lives, becoming larger in older rats. The basis for the difference in worm size, however, is difficult to establish since rats of different ages differ themselves in size and in many other developmental characteristics. See page 575 for a consideration of host age in relation to parasite numbers.

Physiological processes of the parasite may differ markedly from those of the host, and profound changes may take place in a parasite as it adjusts to living within its environment. Glycolytic enzymes of parasites and of hosts, for example, may differ in various ways: (1) in kinetic properties, *e.g.* affinity for substrates; (2) in substrate specificity; (3) in immunochemical properties; and (4) in reaction with chemotherapeutic agents.[23]

One of the requirements for a parasitic mode of life is an ability to adjust to the oxygen variations which occur within a host. Although most if not all parasites use oxygen as the hydrogen acceptor when it is available, other substances are used widely. The ability of a normally anaerobic parasite to oxidize sugar completely in the presence of oxygen is known as the *Pasteur effect*. This effect has been demonstrated for many worms. In general, most worms show little Pasteur effect but the nematodes, *Eustrongylides ignotus* and *Litomosoides carinii*, show marked effect. As oxygen requirements are studied it becomes increasingly evident that probably there are no truly obligate anaerobe animal parasites.

When the host's normal reactions are weakened, or otherwise altered, its pathogenic parasites may increase in numbers. Such a cause and effect relationship has been induced experimentally by placing mice under the influence of alcohol. The development of the malarial parasite (*Plasmodium berghei*) in the blood of these mice was subsequently advanced. Some people like to justify drinking by claiming that the alcohol kills any "bugs" that may be present in the body. The experiment with mice would seem to indicate just the reverse.

The strong reciprocal influence between a host and its parasites is clearly illustrated when a population of parasites (*e.g.* protozoa) is passed repeatedly through experimental hosts. Such passage may, on the one hand, enhance the virulence of the parasite and kill its hosts, or, if the host is an "unnatural one" the virulence of the parasite may be reduced. For other examples of reciprocal influences see the chapter on general ecology of parasitism, especially size relationships (p. 574), host age and parasite numbers (p. 575), movements and hibernation (p. 573), parasitocoenosis (p. 582) and symbiotic cleaning (p. 594).

Sporozoites of the coccidian, *Eimeria necatrix*, introduced into chickens are taken up or engulfed by macrophages which carry the sporozoites into the intestinal gland epithelium.[33] Such transport of parasites by macrophages is common, but in this case the parasites are unharmed, and they are liberated by the degeneration of macrophage cells—a sort of taxi service to the preferred site of infection, but upon reaching its destination the taxi falls apart to discharge its passengers. The parasite is obviously protected against the normal destructive processes of the macrophages. It is illogical to think that the host protects the parasite, so one must assume that the parasite produces some substance which protects itself. Van Doornick and Becker[33] reported that about 72 per cent of the sporozoites in the lamina propria (a thin layer of connective tissue just under the mucous membrane of the gut) were engulfed within eighteen hours, and the authors suggested that this engulfment may be a necessary part of the life cycle of the parasite.

Host Diet

In the numerous studies that have been made on the effect of the host's diet on the well-being of the parasite there exist many different opinions, but one might conclude that a deficiency in the host diet has the effect of rendering the host more vulnerable to parasitic infections. Whatever the cause, when certain essentials are reduced or omitted, the overall resistance of the host to the parasite decreases. This observation applies particularly to intestinal parasites and it implies that the intestinal environment becomes more favorable to the parasite during periods of malnutrition. It would seem that a healthy host is generally more free from parasites than is an unhealthy one. Although a moderately unhealthy host often harbors increased numbers of parasites, a definitely ill host is often in too poor condition even to support its parasites.

The kind of nutritive material ingested by larval *Trichogramma* affects the development of wings in the male parasite. Those wasps that feed on moth eggs (the normal host), generally develop into winged adults, whereas those that feed on alderfly eggs (abnormal hosts) develop almost exclusively into wingless adults.

In regions of South America where human malnutrition is prevalent, chronic malaria is common, whereas in other regions where malnutrition is virtually absent, malaria is present but rarely in a chronic form. A series of experiments on the diet relationships of canaries and various species of *Plasmodium* have been conducted to help solve this problem.[2] Most of the birds on poor diets had more severe primary attacks of malaria than did the controls. In general, these primary attacks were characterized by greater numbers of parasites, higher parasite peaks (the greatest number of parasites per 10,000 erythrocytes counted in a single day during an infection), longer patent periods, and more severe symptoms. The mortality rate was highest and relapses occurred only in birds on deficient diets. Immunity was greatly reduced or entirely absent in a number of nutritionally deficient birds.

Experiments on the effect of a rice-seed diet on parasitism of canaries with *Plasmodium relictum* were also carried out by Brooke.[2] The birds were placed on a diet of progressively smaller amounts of the stock mixture, and they were given as much freshly boiled polished rice as they would eat. The canaries ate the rice with no objection, but the amounts varied per individual bird. The normal seed intake was reduced to about 70 per cent. Control birds were maintained on an enriched diet. During the study, the experimental birds showed ruffled feathers and a loss of weight prior to inoculation with parasites on the twentieth day. Due to the high carbohydrate intake, a vitamin B_1 deficiency was suspected, so thiamine was added to the drinking water after the sixteenth day. After twenty days the birds on the two diets were each inoculated with approximately 20,000,000 parasites. One of the control birds soon died, the other experienced a relatively mild infection and then it died. On the basis of autopsy findings Brooke suggested that the cause of the death of the two control birds was not due to malaria. One bird on the reduced diet had 18 per cent more parasites than did the control bird, and a 75 per cent higher parasite peak. The results indicated that *P. relictum* in canaries possibly is inhibited in growth and reproduction in a host that is maintained on an adequate or enriched diet. One should be cautious, however, about drawing conclusions from experiments on a small number of animals.

Experiments of the sort just described may be misleading in several ways. If the omission of certain substances in the host diet does not appear to affect a parasite, the negative response is not necessarily an indication that the parasite does not require that substance. The parasite may be independent of its host's diet as a source of that substance. The suggestion has been made that the average *Ascaridia galli*, a roundworm living in the intestine of chickens, does not need vitamin A, B-complex, or D. This suggestion was based on the fact that alteration of the host diet does not seem to affect the nematode. It would be safer to conclude only that the nematode may not be dependent on its host for these vitamins.

A diet consisting largely of milk or milk sugar has an adverse effect on intestinal helminth and protozoan fauna. There is no evidence that the milk directly injures the worms, and probably the effect is due to an alteration of the environment. A diet rich in lactose changes the intestinal emptying time and alters such reactions as oxidation-reduction potential, pH and the synthesis of vitamins by intestinal microorganisms. As yet we are not familiar enough with the biochemistry of parasites to understand fully the effects of these changes on intestinal parasites. Certainly we cannot assume that the nature of the metabolism of vitamins or of any other substance is necessarily the same in the parasite as in the host.

The types of carbohydrates in the host diet have a gross effect on the size of the rat tapeworm, *Hymenolepis diminuta*.[24] Tapeworms in rats which receive starch as the sole carbohydrate are much larger than those in rats which receive only dextrose or sucrose. The reasons for this difference are still obscure but they may be associated with differences in availability of carbohydrate to the parasite, with effects of different carbohydrates on the bacterial flora of the gut (and, therefore, an indirect effect on the worms), or with different effects on the physiology of rat and worm. Starvation of a rat will cause a reduction in the weight of its tapeworms and, curiously enough, will increase the ability of the parasite to utilize glucose. Starvation of a hamster will cause a reduction in weight of its tapeworms, but will not increase the worm's ability to utilize glucose. Tapeworms of the dogfish shark also lose weight when their host is starved and this loss can be prevented by the oral administration of starch. This effect of starvation on the weight of intestinal tapeworms would hardly justify starving a man in an effort to rid him of worms. The nature and quantity of the host dietary carbohydrate also has a definite effect on the growth and egg production of many worm parasites.

The diet of an animal is of major importance in determining the kinds and numbers of its worm parasites that utilize intermediate hosts. For example, fish that feed on animal plankton have an entirely different parasite fauna from the fauna in fish whose diet consists of algae.

Surrounding Fluids

The chemistry of the surrounding medium has a profound influence on a parasite. Obviously, if the chemical composition of the surrounding medium is antagonistic, the parasite is apt to die. It is surprising, however, how resistant some parasites can be to changes in their chemical environment. Blood was drawn from the hearts of chickens infected with *Plasmodium gallinaceum* and then it was defibrinated and placed in feeding tubes about 7.5 to 10 cm. long by 1.5 cm. in diameter.[8] The tubes were covered with membranes, prepared from gut sausage casing, which were relaxed in water and alcohol. Mosquitoes (*Aëdes aegypti*) were allowed to feed upon the blood in these tubes for from thirty to forty-five minutes, and the tubes were agitated at about five-minute intervals to prevent the interference of sedimentation with the number of gametocytes ingested by the insects. In some of the blood cell suspensions various concentrations of saline were substituted for serum. Within a range of 0.7 per cent to 1.15 per cent saline there was no significant difference in the intensity of infection. The intensity was slightly lowered at 0.85 per cent but was materially lowered at 1.3 per cent. The osmotic pressure of the host blood obviously affected the behavior of the parasite. The mean infection rate determined by this method of *in vitro* feeding was similar to that induced by bird feeding. Again we must use caution in interpreting the results. As Eyles[8] has pointed out, when considering the relationship between a mosquito and the plasmodium it carries, the vertebrate host cannot be ignored. There are factors in the blood of the vertebrate host which influence the subsequent infection in the mosquito.

Why is an intestinal parasite not digested by the enzymes of its host? This question is frequently asked by students. A common answer is that the living parasite produces "antienzymes." Undoubtedly part of the answer to the question lies in those processes which prevent an animal from digesting its own intestinal mucosa. There is, however, no real evidence for the existence of antienzymes in parasites. Certainly the nature of the outer covering of worms plays an important role in preventing them from being attacked by host enzymes. This cuticle is probably composed of a polymerized mucoprotein, the molecules of which may be protected from proteolytic enzymes by a shell of glycogen molecules. The cuticular cortex of living nematodes is not digested by pepsin or trypsin, although the under layers are readily dissolved by these enzymes. When a worm dies it is quickly digested, indicating that death is accompanied by changes in the cortex which permit penetration of the digestive enzymes. In the case of protozoa, we have to fall back on the postulation of some kind of "inhibitor" being produced by the parasites as at least part of the answer.

The effects of host alimentary canal secretions on its parasites have received little attention. If a parasite produces a substance which stimulates the production of host intestinal secretions, these secretions may have an important regulating effect on the parasite. We know that certain materials (such as fatty acids) produced as end-products of helminth metabolism may increase host intestinal secretions, but their effects, in turn, on the parasite are yet to be understood. The problem is one which deserves careful study and one which is undoubtedly of considerable significance in the parasite-host relationship. We know little about the variations of secretory activity from one site in the intestine to another. Bile salts secreted by the liver are resorbed chiefly in the ileum, but apparently not at all in the duodenum. Thus parasites such as *Giardia, Ascaris* and *Trichostrongylus* find in the duodenum a markedly different biochemical environment than obtains in other parts of the gut.

The stomach of sheep apparently produces a substance which causes parasitic larval nematodes to secrete a fluid (hormone?) which, in turn, causes the worms to molt.[27] Also, a host stimulus appears to induce eggs of *Ascaris* and *Ascaridia* to secrete a fluid ("hatching fluid") which causes the eggs to hatch. The stimulus for experimentally hatching eggs of *Ascaridia galli* depends upon the concentration of undissolved carbonic acid, dissolved carbon dioxide, the pH and the oxygen reduction potential.[25,26]

Such studies emphasize again the necessity for studying the host and its parasites as a biological unit. This unit not only involves the host as the environment of the parasites, but it involves the external environment of the host as well. The internal environment of the host obviously includes its parasites. Parasitologists and ecologists must labor together for many years before most of the details of the environmental factors which influence parasitism are readily understood (see Chapter XXIII).

Hormones

The effect of various hormones of the host on parasites of the digestive tract is being studied by many investigators, and only a beginning has been made on an understanding of the relationships involved. As might be expected, some of the information is conflicting. In mildly hyperthyroid chickens, for example, the roundworm, *Ascaridia galli*, attains significantly greater lengths than do worms from normal and mildly hypothyroid birds. But the reverse condition has been reported for the worm, *Heterakis gallinae*, which attains a greater length in mildly hypothyroid hosts. Possibly the two worms behave differently toward the hormone thyroxin, and possibly different research techniques led to different results. We cannot assume that because one species of intestinal worm is found to react in a certain manner to a hormone, another species of worm in essentially the same environment will react in a similar manner. Many experiments will have to be made under varying and controlled conditions before we can draw general conclusions.

The effect of thyroxin on the cysticercoids of the tapeworm,

Hymenolepis nana, of mice throws some light on this problem. If mice are given daily 3 mg. of thyroid extract by mouth for a month prior to infection, a slightly higher percentage of these cysticercoids will develop than is usual in normal or hypothyroid animals. It would seem that, in general, a decrease in thyroxin production on the part of the host would favor at least those parasites in its intestine which rely heavily on carbohydrates as a source of food. Thyroxin has a stimulating effect on the absorption in the intestine of carbohydrates and fats. It follows that hypothyroidism slows the rate of absorption of these foods and thus makes more of them available to helminths or to any other organisms which might use them.

A most remarkable effect of host hormones on parasites was suggested by Szidat.[32] He found a trematode (*Genarchella genarchella*) in snails of the species *Littoridina australis* living in a lagoon near Buenos Aires. The unusual thing about the fluke was that its entire life cycle could be completed within the snail. Thus the first intermediate host is the only essential one while the true final host, the fish, *Salminus maxillosus*, has become unnecessary. The cercaria stage is suppressed and there is no second intermediate host. The rediae produce metacercariae which mature and lay numerous eggs containing miracidia, within the rediae. Szidat suggested that when the original fish host became adapted to fresh water, in a former epoch, it produced excess hormones from the thyroid gland and from the hypophysis. The action of these hormones might have been responsible for the shortening of the life cycle of the parasite.

Even protozoa of invertebrates apparently are influenced by host hormones. Our knowledge of the hormones of invertebrates is limited but there is evidence of the presence of sex hormones, growth hormones, neurohormones, and perhaps many others. Since hormones are non-specific, we might look for the same types of reactions in parasites of invertebrates as those we observe in parasites of vertebrates. We know, for example, that glandular changes in termites and in woodroaches have a direct bearing on the life cycles of their flagellates (p. 584), but we know little more than that. The field is wide open for research.

Of all hormones studied in relation to parasitism, none has received as much attention as have the sex hormones. As might be expected, not all of the results are in agreement.

Sexual differences between hosts and concurrent differences among their parasites have been studied only rarely. One such study of lice on the meadow vole and on the deer mouse showed that the rate of infestation of voles was significantly lower in females than in males, but that no such difference was apparent in the mice. Also, the average numbers of lice and the increase in infestation rate with host age were significantly greater in male voles than in females.[5] Obviously the male vole provides a more favorable environment for the growth and development of lice, but the reasons for such differences are not clear. Stahl[31] found that only in young mice, during the third to tenth week after experimental infection with *Aspiculuris tetraptera*, was there a heavier burden of worms in male hosts. The male rat is more susceptible to infection with the nematode, *Nematospiroides dubius*, than is the female, but hormones are not necessarily involved.[7] Much experimental work must be done on this and related problems before answers can be formulated.

The effect of sex hormones on the growth rate and numbers of the nematode, *Ascaridia galli*, in chicks was studied by Sadun.[28] Fifty-eight chicks were divided into three groups: group I males, group II females, and group III males and females serving as controls. When the chicks were four days old, members of group I were given the male hormone testosterone propionate, and members of group II were given the female hormone estradiol benzoate. When the chicks were nine days old all 58 were inoculated with 500 worm eggs each. The worms in male chicks grew somewhat faster in hormone treated hosts, especially during the first ten or twelve days . The difference subsequently became less pronounced or disappeared completely. Worms in treated female chicks seemed to grow a little more slowly than usual. The total number of worms in both treated groups, however, decreased. Sadun concluded that a moderate dose of homologous sex hormones increased the resistance of chickens to *Ascaridia galli* as measured by the number of worms present.

Hymenolepis diminuta, the common tapeworm of rats, has also been the subject of much experimentation on the effects of hormones of the host on the parasite. An elaborate series of experiments on the growth of this worm in normal and in castrated male and female rats was performed by Addis.[1] The rats were maintained on complete diets and on diets with certain deficiencies. Some of the animals on each type of diet were given sex hormones while others were not. Adult, immature, pregnant and non-pregnant rats were used. Growth of the tapeworms was normal in male rats which were kept on a vitamin-deficient diet, but in female rats, also kept on a vitamin-deficient diet, the tapeworms were stunted in growth. Castration of male rats, whether kept on a vitamin-deficient diet or not, stunted the growth of the tapeworms. Normal growth of the worms could be restored by injecting or feeding testosterone or progesterone. When female rats were castrated (spayed) there was no effect on the worms, but when the female rats were kept on a vitamin-deficient diet the growth of the tapeworms was stunted in both castrated and noncastrated rats. Injection of male sex hormone into castrated female rats on a vitamin-deficient diet caused a slight improvement in growth of the worms. Injection of male sex hormones into normal females on a vitamin-deficient diet did not improve growth of the tapeworms. The only definite conclusion which Addis presented was that the worms were dependent on testosterone or progesterone for normal growth in male rats. Results like these are hazardous to interpret without a great deal more corroborative research.

Castration of the rat host causes a decline in the rate of synthesis of glycogen from sodium pyruvate and glucose in *Hymenolepis diminuta.* Host fasting, on the other hand, accelerates the rate of synthesis of glycogen from glucose but not from pyruvate. The significance of these types of reactions may be argued but they serve to point out an area of challenging and productive research.[6]

When the testes are removed from a mammal one of the results is a deposition of fat in various tissues of the body. If a castrated rat harbors the tapeworm, *Hymenolepis diminuta,* fat is also deposited in the tissues of the worm. This occurrence is difficult to explain but it might be related to a blocking effect on protein synthesis. Additional effects of castration of the host on this tapeworm are: lowered ability to become established in the gut, reduced transamination (the reversible transfer of amino groups in amino acids), and lowered carbohydrate synthesis as noted above. These effects indicate a general reduction in the level of metabolism.

Another indication of the relationship between the sex hormones of the host and the life of the parasite is seen in *Schistosoma mansoni* in mice. These blood flukes are especially interesting because they are bisexual. A group of castrated male albino mice was infected with the flukes, while a group of uncastrated mice was similarly infected as controls. Nine weeks later all the mice were sacrificed and a count was made of the adult parasites found. There was a significant reduction in the number of male *Schistosoma* only in the castrated hosts, indicating a beneficial effect of male sex hormones of the host on the male parasites. In another study of worms in mice it was noticed that male mice harbored twice as many pin worms as did female mice. Whether this difference was due to sex hormones or to other factors is unknown.

Several studies have indicated that the resistance of male hosts (*e.g.* rats,[7] frogs[13]) to helminths is increased after the experimental administration of the female hormone estradiol. Quite a different kind of relationship from those mentioned above has been reported for the mosquito, *Anopheles quadrimaculatus,* and the nematode larvae of *Dirofilaria immitis.*[35] If the mosquito is decapitated immediately after it has fed on an infected dog, the normal metamorphosis and growth of the nematode takes place. Thus the "interruption of the gonadotropic hormone cycle in these mosquitoes, as observed by the failure of their ovarian development, does not interfere with the development of the parasite."

Sex and Sexual Cycles of Parasites

A relation between the sexual cycles of an animal and its intestinal organisms has been noted in the wood-feeding roach, *Cryptocercus.*[21] This insect is host to symbiotic intestinal protozoa. If part of the brain (pars intercerebralis) is removed from the roach before the beginning of the molting period, the sexual cycles of the insect are entirely suppressed. If the portion of the brain is removed during the molting period, those cycles which have not completed gametogenesis are usually blocked. In roaches whose sexual cycles have been thus blocked the symbiotic intestinal protozoa usually degenerate. Control of molting is apparently more directly a function of the hormone *ecdysone* produced by the prothoracic gland. During each molting period of the cockroach the intestinal flagellates undergo sexual cycles, but normally not at other times. If, however, ecdysone is injected into adult insects which lack prothoracic glands and also into intermolt nymphal hosts, gametogenesis is induced in the flagellates.

The flagellate, *Barbulanympha*, is one of many that lives in the gut of *Cryptocercus*, and normally it begins its gametogenesis from twenty-five to thirty days before the molting of the host. If this parasite is transferred to a defaunated nymph fifteen days before the insect is ready to molt, the flagellate will not start gametogenesis, and it will die. If *Trichonympha*, another roach parasite, is transferred in like manner to another defaunated host, the flagellate will begin its sexual cycle at its usual time which, in this case, is only five to six days before molting of the host begins. This evidence indicates again that the host is responsible for initiating the sexual cycles of its parasitic flagellates. There is also evidence that not only does the host start the cycles but that it controls these cycles during their courses of development.[4]

The sex of some parasitic isopods is apparently determined by the host. In *Ione thoracica* the first bopyridium larva to become attached to a crab is always a female, whereas all the rest are always males. Thus the larvae are ambipotent. Just what causes the parasites to develop into one sex at one time and the other sex at another time is still a mystery. See page 388 for a more detailed discussion of parasitic isopods.

INTRACELLULAR PARASITES

If a parasite lives within a cell of its host, this environment must certainly have profound effects on the parasite. Intracellular parasites undergo a change during their residence in a cell and this change is reflected in their subsequent behavior. Chicks of various fowl can be infected with bird malaria by the intravenous inoculation of either the sporozoites or erythrocytic stages of such parasites as *Plasmodium gallinaceum*, *P. lophurae*, *P. fallax*, and *P. cathemerium*. The tissue stage of the parasite is normally found in the endothelial cells. Logic dictates that when sporozoites are injected into the blood stream they proceed at once into such cells. In the bird hosts, however, they first enter the reticular cells of the splenic Malpighian body.[10] Here they multiply, emerge from the cells and then, via the blood stream, go to and enter various endothelial cells. Since they do not enter endothelial cells when first injected, one can assume that they become changed as a result of their residence in splenic cells. No one knows just what causes this change but the antibodies of the host undoubtedly play a part. Whatever the biochemical nature of the change, the result is a different type of parasite which is now able to enter and live in new types of host cells.

BEHAVIOR OF HOST

The behavior of the host may have a pronounced effect on the behavior of the parasite, as has been suggested, at least indirectly, many times on the previous pages of this book. For example, when practically all stages of a tick are found on one host (*e.g.* the castor bean tick, *Ixodes ricinus*), the host generally has no fixed habitat. On the other hand, ticks parasitizing hosts which usually remain in one place can stay on the ground or vegetation for long periods of time, and they still find a host when they need one. A curious sexual difference is shown by the fact that both male and female ticks are apt to be found on wandering hosts but only the females are steady boarders on hosts with more fixed habits.

Mixed colonies of termites can be established after thoroughly chilling the insects in a refrigerator.[7a] Under these conditions *Kalotermes jouteli* has demonstrated resistance to infection with flagellates from *K. schwarzi*, but the reciprocal cross may be successful. Apparently, behavior of the termite hosts rather than resistance to transfaunation is operative.

Stress and Parasitism

Stress causes many reactions including an alteration in the hormonal balance of a host. This imbalance may decrease inflammation of tissues and weaken other resisting mechanisms. Stress is thus undoubtedly a factor in parasitism because anything that lowers host resistance is apt to favor the establishment of parasites. The sensitive periods of parasite development are particularly subject to the effects of stress on the host.

Cortisone is being used experimentally to determine its possible influence on the relation between host and parasite. Several investigators have reported increased susceptibility of mice to intestinal worms as a result of feeding or injecting cortisone. Mice which are usually resistant to infection with the roundworm, *Strongyloides ratti*, can become infected if given daily doses of cortisone. This response might be anticipated when one remembers that bacterial infections are followed by the production of adrenocorticotrophic hormone (ACTH) from the pituitary gland, and consequent release of adrenal glucocorticoids which diminish normal inflammatory responses of the host. In a recent study[14] cortisone at a dose of 75 mg. per kg. of body weight significantly increased susceptibility of worm-free mice to infection with the pinworm, *Aspicularis tetraptera*. Cortisone also has a profound effect on resistance of experimental mice to the tapeworm, *Taenia taeniaeformis*. The drug makes refractory hosts highly susceptible but it must be given to the laboratory animals before the twelfth day of infection.[22] Even ectoparasites may benefit from host stress, or at least from the injection of the host with ACTH or cortisone. In an experiment with lambs, daily injections of ACTH for one month broke down resistance which had developed against keds (Fig. XVIII–20 p. 491). Similar results occurred after cortisone injection. It was concluded that physiological or environmental stress, such as pregnancy or undernourishment, can affect the basic annual ked population cycle.[18] As one might expect, all experiments do not lead to the same conclusions. Working with the rat, Villarejos found that cortisone did not increase susceptibility to amebiasis.[34] Many more studies of the effect of cortisone should be made.

Population density, sexual cycles, changes in the blood picture, antibody formation, metabolism of basic foodstuffs, tissue damage and many other body activities and reactions are intimately related to stress, and, therefore, they may influence the parasite burden. Trichomoniasis may be predominately due to emotional stress.[15,16] Acute amebiasis in kittens is probably due more to psycho-physical responses to stress than to infection with the parasite *per se*.[11] Parasites may aggravate pathogenic conditions due to non-parasitic factors. Injurious effects of partial starvation and low environmental temperature on mice, for example, may be more serious if the animals are infected with *Trypanosoma duttoni*,[30] and infectious bronchitis in chickens may be more serious if ascarids are also present.[9]

Preliminary work on stress and its relation to the flagellate, *Trichomonas*, in the cecum of ground squirrels has shown that there is a direct correlation between the numbers of these protozoan parasites and the degree of stress to which the hosts are subjected.[19,20] Stress factors being studied include hunger, temperature, mechanical irritation, crowding, darkness, light and fighting. Curiously enough, caging the squirrels, without subjecting them to additional stress seems to have as much influence on the flagellate numbers as do most of the planned stress factors. Fighting among the squirrels was specially effective in promoting an increase in numbers of cecal flagellates. Murie[17] (personal communication) has reported significant increase in numbers of two unidentified cecal protozoa in mice in cold-exposed and high density groups.

This field is wide open for research and holds considerable promise.

BIBLIOGRAPHY

1. ADDIS, J. C., 1946. Experiments on the Relations Between Sex Hormones and the Growth of Tapeworms (*Hymenolepis diminuta*) in Rats. J. Parasitol., *32*, 574–580.
2. BROOKE, M. M., 1945. Effect of Dietary Changes Upon Avian Malaria. Am. J. Hyg., *41(1)*, 81–108.
3. CAULLERY, M., 1952. *Parasitism and Symbiosis* (English translation). Sidgwick & Jackson, London. 340 pp.
4. CLEVELAND, L. R. and NUTTING, W. L., 1955. Suppression of Sexual Cycles and Death of the Protozoa of Cryptocercus Resulting From Change of Hosts During Molting Period. J. Exp. Zool., *130(3)*, 485–514.

36

5. COOK, E. F. and BEER, J. R., 1958. A Study of Louse Populations on the Meadow Vole and Deer Mouse. Ecology, 39, 645–659.
6. DAUGHERTY, J. W., 1956. The Effect of Host Castration and Fasting on the Rate of Glycogenesis in *Hymenolepis diminuta*. J. Parasitol., 42(1), 17–20.
7. DOBSON, C., 1961. Certain Aspects of the Host-Parasite Relationship of *Nematospiroides dubius* (Baylis) II. The Effect of Sex on Experimental Infections in the Rat (an Abnormal Host). Parasitology, 51, 499–510.
7a. DROPKIN, V. H., 1946. The Use of Mixed Colonies of Termites in the Study of Host-Symbiont Relations. J. Parasitol., 32, 247–251.
8. EYLES, D. E., 1952. Studies on *P. gallinaceum*. II: Factors in the Blood of Vertebrate Host Influencing Mosquito Infection. Amer. Jour. Hyg. 55(2), 276–296. 1952. (Illus.)
9. FOSTER, A. O., 1960. Parasitological Speculations and Patterns. J. Parasitol., 46, 1–9.
10. HUFF, C. G., 1953. Changes in Host-cell Preferences in Malarial Parasites and their Relation to Splenic Reticular Cells. Naval Med. Research Inst., 11, 987–992.
11. JOSEPHINE, M. A., 1958. Experimental Studies on *Entamoeba histolytica* in Kittens. Amer. J. Trop. Med. and Hyg., 7, 158–164.
12. KRUIDENIER, F. J., 1951. The Formation and Function of Mucoids in Virgulate Cercaria Including a Study of the Virgulate Organ. Am. Midl. Nat., 46, 660–683.
13. LEES, E. and BASS, L., 1960. Sex Hormones as a Possible Factor Influencing the Level of Parasitization in Frogs. Nature, 188, (4757), 1207–1208.
14. MATHIES, A. W., JR., 1962. Certain Aspects of the Host-Parasite Relationship of *Aspiculuris tetraptera*, a Mouse Pinworm. III. Effect of Cortisone. J. Parasitol., 48, 244–248.
15. McEWEN, D. C., 1960. Common Factors in *Trichomonas* Vaginitis. Gynaecologia, 149, (Suppl. ¾), 63–69.
16. MOORE, S. F. and SIMPSON, J. W., 1956. The Emotional Component in *Trichomonas* Vaginitis. Amer. J. Obst. and Gyn., 68, 947.
17. MURIE, MARTIN, 1963. Personal communication on increase in cecal protozoa in mice exposed to cold.
18. NELSON, W. A., 1962. Development in Sheep of Resistance to the Ked *Melophogus ovinus* (L). II. Effects of Adrenocorticotrophic Hormone and Cortisone. Exp. Parasitol, 12, 45–51.
19. NOBLE, G. A., 1961. Stress and Parasitism. I. A. Preliminary Investigation of the Effects oi Stress on Ground Squirrels and Their Parasites. Exp. Parasitol., 11, 63–67.
20. NOBLE, G. A., 1962. Stress and Parasitism II. Effect of Crowding and Fighting Among Ground Squirrels on Their Coccidia and Trichomonads. Exp. Parasitol., 12, 368–371.
21. NUTTING, W. L. and CLEVELAND, L. R., 1958. Effects of Glandular Extirpations on *Cryptocercus* and the Sexual Cycles of its Protozoa. Jour. Exp. Zool., 137(1), 13–38.
22. OLIVER, L., 1962. Studies on Natural Resistance to *Taenia taeniaeformis* in Mice. II. The Effect of Cortisone. J. Parasitol., 48, 758–762.
23. READ, C. P., 1961. The Carbohydrate Metabolism of Worms. In: *Comparative Physiology of Carbohydrate Metabolism in Heterothermic Animals*. Martin, A. W., (ed.) Univ. Wash. Press. Seattle. 144 pp.
24. READ, C. P. and ROTHMAN, A. H., 1957. The Role of Carbohydrates in the Biology of Cestodes. I. The Effect of Dietary Carbohydrate Quality on the Size of *Hymenolepis diminuta*. Exp. Parasitol. 6(1), 1–7.
25. ROGERS, W. P., 1958. Physiology of the Hatching of Eggs of *Ascaris lumbricoides*. Nature, 181, 1410–1411.
26. ROGERS, W. P., 1962. *The Nature of Parasitism. The Relationship of Some Metazoan Parasites to Their Hosts*. Academic Press, New York and London, 287 pp.
27. ROGERS, W. P. and SOMMERVILLE, R. I., 1957. Physiology of Exsheathment in Nematodes and its Relation to Parasitism. Nature, 179, 619–621.
28. SADUN, E. H., 1951. Gonadal Hormones in Experimental *Ascaridia galli* Infections in Chickens. Exper. Parasitol., 1, 70–82.
29. SALT, G., 1941. The Effects of Hosts upon their Insect Parasites. Biol. Rev., 14, 239–264.

30. SHEPPE, W. A. and ADAMS, J. R., 1957. The Pathogenic Effect of *Trypanosoma duttoni* in Hosts Under Stress Conditions. J. Parasitol., *43*, 55–59.
31. STAHL, W., 1961. Influence of Age and Sex on the Susceptibility of Albino Mice to Infection with *Aspiculuris tetraptera*. J. Parasitol., *47*, 939–941.
32. SZIDAT, L., 1956. Über den Entwicklunszyklus mit progentischen Larvenstadien (Cercariaeen) von *Genarchella genarchella* Travassos 1928 (Trematoda, Hemiuridae). Tropen. & Parasit., *7*, 132–153.
33. VAN DOORNICK, W. M. and BECKER, E. R., 1956. Penetration and Invasion of the Intestinal Mucosa of the Chicken by the Sporozoites of *Eimeria necatrix*. J. Protozool., *3*, Suppl., 2 (Abstract).
34. VILLAREJOS, V. M., 1962. Cortisone and Experimental Amebiasis in the Rat. J. Parasitol. *48*, 194.
35. YOELI, M., UPMANIS, R. S. and MOST, H., 1962. Studies on Filariasis. II. The Relation Between Hormonal Activities of the Adult Mosquito and the Growth of *Dirofilaria immitis*. Exper. Parasitol., *12*, 125–127.

CHAPTER XXIII

Ecology of Parasitism. I. General

INTRODUCTION

THE concepts of ecology in the study of parasitology frequently have been ignored, but they are essential to the understanding of parasitism. Ecology is the basis for much of the discussion of such problems as invasion of the host, reactions of host and of parasites, chemistry of parasitism, parasite-host specificity and evolution of parasites and their hosts.

In this chapter we shall emphasize the general principles of ecology through a consideration of parasite communities and their immediate environments. Examples of parasites and their hosts will be selected from among both aquatic and land habitats because of the marked environmental differences between animals and plants that live on land as compared with those that live in water. Some of these differences are: (1) a much greater temperature fluctuation on land; (2) the limiting nature of moisture on land; (3) the relatively constant content of oxygen and of carbon dioxide in air as compared with water; (4) the discontinuous nature of land, thereby creating geographic barriers; and (5) the nature of the substrate or soil which is itself a highly developed ecological system.

Early works on the ecology of parasitism dealt with the epidemiology of human disease in the tropics. Recent works have focused the attention of parasitologists on the necessity of an ecological approach to all studies in parasitology if a broad and accurate understanding of parasitism is to be attained. May,[53,54] for example, has said that disease is "that alteration of human tissues that jeopardizes their survival *in a given environment.*" Academician E. N. Pavlovskii[61] has emphasized the "doctrine of nidality" which may be stated as follows (from Audy,[7]), "A disease itself tends to have a natural habitat in the same way as a species: many diseases, and especially the zoonoses, have natural habitats in well-defined ecosystems where pathogens, vectors, and natural hosts form associations or biocenoses within which the pathogen circulates; therefore, a landscape is an epidemiological factor because its characteristics are those of the local ecosystem (hence Pavlovskii's term 'landscape epidemiology')." Audy himself is concerned with the diseases of particular populations of hosts, and his approach "is to consider a host-species A (and its own specially modified environment) as the habitat and food supply of a large array of parasitic and commensal organisms, a number of which may cause disease in individuals of A in suitable circumstances. The whole assemblage makes up a parasite-pattern characteristic of A, and differing from that of species B largely because B and A (*i*) have genetically different constitutions, (*ii*) usually occupy different niches, so that each is exposed to a different milieu and to different 'occupational' hazards, and (*iii*) may belong to different biocenoses." Such an approach makes clear Audy's statement that "symptomatic disease due to an infective agent is a special response which the agent may rarely produce."[5] Baer[9] has said that "parasites are subject to the same general laws that govern all free-living organisms. The latter, however, are adapted in various ways to widely different biotopes whereas parasites have adapted themselves to a very specialized, and consequently limited, environment. The association of the parasite with its host is also a problem of ecology and all the more interesting in that, in many cases, it is possible to furnish indisputable evidence that such associations originated several thousands of centuries ago." Ecological field studies which involve groups of hosts and their parasites become much more profitable than the same studies which ignore the parasites. The biologist who is not a parasitologist is not accustomed to using parasites as "ecological labels" which provide an abundance of information about the habits and habitats of their hosts—information waiting to be tapped (Audy[8]). See also.[6,19,20,40]

POPULATIONS AND COMMUNITIES

A biotic community is a unit of various organisms loosely held together by the interdependence of its members. A *population* is a smaller, more intimately associated group within the community. Whereas each individual has its own characteristics, communities and populations have additional characteristics as the result of the aggregate. A group of parasites such as microfilariae in blood, trichina in muscle, or amebas in the gut, may behave as a population whose cohesion is largely dependent upon mechanical rather than chemical factors. The community concept, however, has not been studied in detail by many parasitologists. One might consider the parasites in an organ of the host as a community quite apart from the host—the latter being the external environment of the community. But since the host is a living organism as intimately associated with its parasites as the latter are with themselves, the host and its parasites should be studied as a community of organisms. The more important characteristics of a population as distinct from those of an individual are: density, birth rate, biotic potential (=maximum reproductive power), death rate, age distribution, dispersion and growth form.

Thus the student should develop a community concept when studying parasitology. When a parasite is studied by itself, apart from its environment, only a part, and often a small part, of its total biology can be understood. The community principle in ecological theory emphasizes the orderly manner in which diverse organisms usually live together. In other words, "as the community goes, so goes the organism." The modern approach to parasitology envisages an ecological complex formed by the parasite, the vector, the host and various features of the host's environment. But this complex is far more than the sum of its parts. It is something new and forever changing.

THE ECOLOGICAL NICHE

The "habitat" is the place where an organism lives, such as the intestine, but the "ecological niche" is the organism's position or status within the habitat, and it results from the organism's structural adaptations, physiological responses, and specific behavior. The niche depends on where the organism lives *and* on what it does. The niche of a parasite cannot be described accurately until one knows details of the mutual interactions between abiotic and biotic environments, numbers of individuals, and the effects of interaction of the parasites among themselves and with their hosts. Two species rarely occupy the same ecological niche, but if two species with the same requirements find themselves in the same niche, competition will tend to force one of them to be eliminated. Species which are phylogenetically closely related normally do not occupy the same niche. When the usual sigmoid growth curve is plotted for two populations and both curves are steeper when they are separate than when they are interacting, competition is operating. Recall, for example, that *Giardia, Ascaris, Trichinella, Strongyloides, Necator, Hymenolepis* and *Taenia* all occur in the small intestine of man. These parasites do not occupy exactly the same ecological niche because a niche, as we have already stated, is not only the space occupied, but the parasite's place in that space—involving food, period of activity, and other behavior factors. All of these parasites, when crowded in one portion of an intestine, do occupy the same habitat, and this situation is possible because of the absence of enemies and the presence of an abundance of food.

The occupied nest of a bird is an excellent subject for the study of various niches of a small community. Numerous populations of arthropods—some of them parasites of birds, others free-living—are usually to be found in such nests. These populations are not stable because the various species of organisms have different requirements for food, temperature, humidity and light. Obviously, then, the populations change with changes in the seasons. Within the nest there may be levels at which some species are more abundant than are others. Out of a total of 3,469 arthropod inhabitants of a great tit's nest, 490 were found in the inner lining, 2,277 in the middle layers, and 702 in the outer layers. In a flycatcher's nest the relative positions were found to be the reverse, over half of the total of 1,568 arthropods being located in the inner lining. Such differences in nests help to explain the differences among the parasitic arthropods on the bodies of birds.

In 1934 Gause[34] first demonstrated experimentally that the rule of one species to a niche is true in a high proportion of cases. This rule is known as *Gause's principle*. We do not know how great an overlap must exist before one species of parasite, or even of a free-living form, pushes out the other. Schad[71a] has shown that although there are 10 or more species of colon-inhabiting oxyuroid nematodes in the European tortoise, there are striking differences in linear and radial distribution of the worms as well as differences in feeding habits, and, probably, in responses to seasonal changes and age of the host.

When two species compete for the same source of energy, the energy (food) will be distributed between the two according to what has been termed the "differential equation of competition." As the population of each species grows, however, there is a change in the equation, and the available energy becomes unequally distributed because one species always multiplies more rapidly than the other. In the words of Gause, "owing to its advantages, mainly a greater value of the coefficient of multiplication, one of the species in a mixed population drives out the other entirely." This generalization was based on a study of populations of free-living protozoa, but the principle also applies to populations of parasites. When the host competes for the same food as that eaten by its parasites, the problem obviously becomes more complicated.

An *ecotone* is a transition between two or more communities. In this junction area the populations of two communities overlap and the area contains some forms peculiar to it—forms not found elsewhere. Often both the number of species and total numbers of individual animals are greater in the ecotone. This tendency for increased variety and density in the ecotone is called the *edge effect*. Such effects are clearly demonstrated in tidal areas along marine shores. One might predict that if the population of a vertebrate species (A) overlaps that of a closely related species (B), and if (A) and (B) each has a distinct fauna of parasites, the ecotone would contain hosts with more varieties of parasites than typical for either (A) or (B). But such studies on the ecology of parasitism have not attracted the attention of many workers.

Parasitic diseases of man and of animals tend to be more prevalent in unstable areas, in ecotones, frontier areas and marginal areas in general. There tends to be greater change, instability or irregularity in biological communities in such frontier areas. These facts are compatible with the concept of stress as a factor in parasitism (see p. 562). Certainly in marginal communities there is greater stress of many kinds than in well established and smoothly running communities.

LIMITING FACTORS

Limits on growth, development and distribution may be imposed by practically all environmental agencies both inside and outside the bodies of parasites and their hosts. The ecological minimum and maximum (*e.g.* essential chemicals and food) help to establish the character of the niche, and the range between these extremes represents the limits of tolerance. The productivity of a parasitic species, whether measured in terms of the reproductive rate or of energy, may be rich or poor as compared with an adjacent species because of limiting ecological factors. Of particular significance in the molding of such closely knit animal societies as insect colonies and parasite-host associations are accumulations of excretory and secretory products, and the metabolism of food and oxygen.

There is an infinite variety of limiting or controlling factors whose actions depend on the needs of the organism, but these needs themselves vary constantly with the individual and with time and place. Thompson[78] has warned us against too bland an assumption that distribution of an organism is chiefly determined by the action of one or two "limiting factors." "The simple truth is that the natural control of organisms is primarily due, not to any complex cosmic mechanisms or regulatory factors, but rather to the intrinsic limitations of the organisms themselves . . . An excessive reverence for the idea of adaptation and the assumption that organisms are indefinitely plastic and capable of fitting themselves into almost any situation at relatively short notice, has led to some rather inaccurate statements on the subject."

CLIMATE AND TEMPERATURE

Climatic factors are often ignored in a study of parasites unless they are directly related to the control of diseases of economic importance, such as the various plant and animal diseases transmitted by insects. The temperature at which a parasite grows is of major significance. Many species of protozoa and of helminths (e.g. *Hymenolepis nana*) have been maintained experimentally at abnormally high temperatures and they have consequently changed their morphology as well as their physiological reactions to a marked degree. Helminths sometimes go through more than a 60° C. change in temperature from host to host during the normal course of their life cycles.

Temperature affects both the reaction of the host salamander (*Triturus v. viridescens*) to the parasite (*Trypanosoma diemyctyli*) and the response of the parasite to the host. Infections of *T. diemyctyli* occur in adult salamanders, and a critical point of change in the nature of the infection from a pathogen to a non-pathogen is at about 20° C. The infection is pathogenic at lower temperatures only, and at higher temperatures the metabolic rate of the host is great enough to reduce the numbers of trypanosomes, probably through the production of antibodies.[11] Here we have an example of an ecological factor (temperature) exerting a direct influence on the equilibrium that exists between a host and its parasites. The third-stage larva of the cattle stomach nematode,

Haemonchus contortus, is the infective stage for grazing animals which become infected by eating the larvae with grass. The three main factors concerned with the vertical migration of the larvae up the leaves are: temperature, humidity and light intensity. Most larvae are in the grass blades during early morning and evening. The time of morning maximum becomes progressively earlier while passing from winter to summer, and the time of evening maximum becomes progressively later. The reverse is true during the second half of the year. A low humidity, accompanied by either low or high temperature, inhibits vertical migration, and the largest number of climbing larvae are to be found during rainy seasons.[66]

Plerocercoid larvae in the stomach of *Gymnodactylus* (a lizard) migrate well if the host is kept at room temperature, but at 37° C migration does not take place. Relatively few experiments have dealt with the effects of high temperatures on developing parasites, but Voge[85] found that adverse effects on *Hymenolepis diminuta* are greatest when exposure occurs during the sensitive period of maximum larval growth and development (three to five days). Major indicators of sensitivity to high temperature (38.5° to 40° C for twenty-four hours) are failure of scolex-withdrawal, and inhibition of infectivity for the mammalian host. Such exposures to high temperature have little or no effect when applied at other times during development. The nature of the temperature effects is not well understood, but it may be related to dehydration.

A careful study of the ecology of the ciliate, *Urceolaria*, has shown that population changes in the parasite are not influenced by changes in the host population, but that the changes (fluctuations) are largely initiated by fluctuations in the surrounding populations of bacteria, which fluctuations in turn are due to rainfall.[67] Temperature was found to be a secondary factor only. These ciliates are tolerant of marked chemical changes in the water in which they live, and they feed chiefly on bacteria which are on or near the freshwater triclad turbellarian flatworms which serve as hosts.

Many parasites are said to be not only more abundant in the tropics but less "adapted" to colder climates. Such conclusions are often the result of a separate consideration of each facet of information rather than a study of and appreciation of the full complex of ecological and epidemiological implications. Otto[59] has sharpened the focus of parasitologists on ecological problems with relation to amebiasis by stating that "the question of whether amebiasis is better provided for survival and transmission in the tropics or in cooler climates involves the consideration of several different ecological factors. It seems to me that there has been a too easy assumption that the organism is *per se* adapted for the tropics and again that it is commonly transmitted in the water supply. In general, both the infection rate and the prevalence of disease is highest in the tropics. But what does this signify with reference to the ecology of the parasite and the epidemiology of the disease? . . . How do we reconcile the tropical distribution of this infection with the indications that the transfer stage, the cyst, is best equipped for survival and distribution in the colder climates?" The recognized and recorded water-borne epidemics of amebic dysentery that have resulted in the highest percentage of infection have all occurred in northern communities. Quite obviously there are significant gaps in our knowledge of even this well-known parasite, and the gaps involve taxonomic considerations, metabolism of the ameba, as well as environmental requirements and influences.

In addition to the strictly climatic influences, other physical factors which play a role in parasite ecology are *radiation* (relatively not important for internal parasites, but important for hosts), biogenic salts, and atmospheric gases. Oxygen is one of the most common limiting factors. A liter of air contains about 210 ml. of oxygen but a liter of water contains no more than 10 ml., and the solubility of oxygen is increased by low temperatures and decreased by high salinities. Parasites and their hosts do not always vary in the same direction with environmental variations. This fact was demonstrated during an investigation of the relation between the range of snails (*Bithynia tentaculata, Dreissensia polymorpha*) and their ciliate parasites in fresh and in brackish waters.[64] As the salinity of the water increased, the ciliate, *Conchophthirus acuminatus*, decreased in abundance whereas the ciliate, *Hypocomagalma dreissenae*, increased in numbers. Thus the host snail is adapted to live in a wide range of salinities but its ciliate parasites vary markedly as to this ability. Other important physical factors of the environment are *currents* and *pressures* (especially important for hosts, *e.g.* water currents for snails, insects, fish—wind currents for insects, birds, plants—barometric pressure, probably not of direct importance); *soil* (recall that soil is not only a factor of the environment and organism, but is produced by them as well); *transparency* of water and air (important in the penetration of light).

SEASONAL VARIATIONS

The results of a few investigations of seasonal variations of parasites are presented below, but final generalizations on the subject cannot be made at the present time. The winter's accumulation of worm eggs may all hatch at once upon the advent of warm weather in June or July. A period of drought may also be responsible for a sudden massive invasion of worm larvae. On the other hand, adverse conditions such as the drying of ponds or winter ice generally mean fewer or less vigorous parasites.

In considering seasonal variations of ectoparasitic arthropods it is well to remember that flea larvae probably have difficulty in developing in soil that is too moist, but that ticks and mites pass all but the egg stage largely on the host, or, if molting on the ground, are capable of extended locomotion to favorable environments. Hence a very dry ground or a very wet ground would be limiting factors for fleas but not for the other ectoparasites. A cumulative flea index on the California ground squirrel, *Citellus beecheyi beecheyi*, showed that the index reached an annual maximum during August, September and October.[69] These months represent the hot, dry season before the fall rains occur, with an associated decline in the mean temperature. The most abundant species of flea was *Echidnophaga gallinacea*, which, as might be expected, is to be found most commonly in localities where the hot, dry seasons are the longest.

A seasonal variation in the incidence and development of cestodes in fishes of temperate climates has frequently been reported.[42] A study of a seasonal cycle of the tapeworm, *Proteocephalus stizostethi*, disclosed that in the yellow pike-perch, *Stizostedion vitreum*, from Lake Erie, viable embryonated eggs occur only in June.[17] The fish are free from the worm in late summer, and new infections are obtained early in the fall, and the worms mature during the following summer. During a year's survey of the protozoa of some marine fishes at Plymouth, England, we found evidence of seasonal variations of myxosporidia of the dragonette (*Callionymus lyra*), the heavy infections being more abundant in the winter, but in the same hosts the heavy haemogregarine infections were more abundant during the summer.[56]

A seasonal increase of host sexual activity possibly is correlated with a seasonal decrease in the extent of parasitism in some animals, but no clear evidence for this bit of speculation is available. It is possible that unfavorable weather may result in decreased sexual activity of an animal, with resultant increase of parasites. Many snails are more heavily infected with trematodes during the fall than during the remainder of the year. Synchronous development of life cycles between host and parasite are well known among insects, but such relationships have not been observed as frequently among other host-parasite associates. The trematode, *Schistosoma mansoni*, may stop its development in the snail, *Australorbis glabratus*, when these hosts go into estivation in natural habitats which are subjected to annual drought. Thus climatic conditions adverse for the snail induce a resting stage (diapause) during larval development of its trematode parasites.[10]

MOVEMENTS AND HIBERNATION

Dogiel[23] has concluded that hibernation of freshwater fishes causes a number of definite changes in their parasites. "It provides an excellent example of the complexity of factors influencing the dynamics of the parasite fauna. The influence of hibernation can more properly be considered as being the sum of the influence of several factors. Involving cessation of feeding, it bars the path of infestation for intestinal parasites. In effect it brings about a lowering of intensity or even disappearance of some intestinal helminths. The drop in water temperature retards sexual and asexual reproduction and leads to a reduction in numbers of ectoparasites (the ciliates, the monogeneans). The loss of mobility and the overcrowding of fish in its winter hollows exposes it to infestation with other ectoparasites (leeches, carp lice) which are not affected by low temperature. Finally, changes in the physiological conditions of the gut, brought about by inanition, lead to destrobilation of some cestodes. All these factors contribute to the sum total of the influence of hibernation."

Hibernation of experimental hamsters may either prevent or retard the development of *Trichinella spiralis*.[15] "Forty-eight and seventy-two hours of hibernation at 5° C. gave complete protection to 4 hamsters receiving 200 *T. spiralis* larvae when onset of hibernation was within the first thirty-six hours."

The migrations within the host of such parasites as larval nematodes and *Plasmodium* are well known, but they have not often been considered in relation to the ecology of the total parasite-host complex. The effects of dispersal of any kind depend upon the status of growth form of the population, and on the rate of dispersal. If the population is well above or well below the "carrying capacity" of the host, dispersal may have more pronounced effects. The phenomenon of dominance among the several parasites of, for example, the blood of a vertebrate, must occur, but little attention has been given to it. See Chapter XXIV, page 604 for some accounts of parasite migrations in relation to the distribution of their hosts.

HOST SIZE, AGE, AND PARASITE NUMBERS

Host Size. Little attention has been paid to the question of size of parasite in relation to size of its host, although parasitologists generally expect to find bigger parasites in bigger hosts. For example, among the parasitic arthropods, within the species of any genus, the larger species of parasites tend to be found on the larger hosts. Often when, in the literature, one finds the statement that the size of the parasite is greater in a given kind or size of host than it is in another, there is no notation of the *numbers* of parasites present. The average size of large numbers of a given species of parasite crowded in a host organ is generally smaller than the average of a few parasites in the same organ.

The *crowding effect* is a reduction in size of individual parasites inversely proportional to the number of parasites in a given infection. This effect has been noted by a large number of parasitologists, but there is still some question as to its cause. It is easy to say that one or two worms in a host organ have more room in which to grow, but that 100 worms in the same organ are crowded for space and have to compete for limited supplies of food. Another logical answer is that harmful metabolic by-products of the worms retard their growth. But such answers are only generalized speculations without the support of experimental evidence. A study of this problem with *Hymenolepis diminuta* in rats offers a clue to answers with respect to tapeworms.[65] There is evidence that this particular worm is independent of protein in the host diet, and possibly that cestodes in general may have no fat requirements. In any event it seems likely that the limiting factor or factors in the crowding effect is not a food substance obtained from the foodstuffs ingested by the host. *H. diminuta* appears to have a definite, though small, free oxygen requirement, and it is the free oxygen, which presumably enters the gut by diffusion from the surrounding tissues, that may be the limiting factor for these cestodes. This factor is not necessarily the limiting one for other species of parasitic intestinal worms. Crowding of worms may also reduce the number of parasite eggs produced,[48,68] and in the case of mermithid nematodes, it may result in the elimination of the females.[14] Undercrowding as well as overcrowding may be limiting.[2]

Carbohydrate intake may modify the crowding effect. With increasing numbers of cestodes in a host there is a decrease in the size of the tapeworms. A reduction in carbohydrate intake may cause a further reduction in the size of some species of crowded worms but may have no apparent effect on other species of worms (see p. 249).

Host Age. The relations between the age of the host and the kinds and numbers of its parasites vary considerably according to the circumstances and to the host group under consideration. As a broad generalization, however, older animals have larger numbers of parasites than do younger animals of the same species. This statement is not in conflict with the fact that immature laboratory animals are often more susceptible to experimental infection than are adults. Young mice, for example, are much more easily infected with *Trypanosoma cruzi* than are adult mice. But young mice have fewer numbers of normal mice parasites than do adult mice. In addition, parasites successfully introduced into the bodies of young animals are often not permanent in the experimental hosts. Age resistance may be the result simply of an extension and heightening of natural resistance. Immunity factors undoubtedly play a role in susceptibility, and in young hosts the antibody response is slower than in adults.[71] One result of this difference is the presence of many more eggs per gram of feces in young grazing mammals as compared with the feces of more resistant adults.

The relationships between the age of the host and the kinds and numbers of its parasites may be separated into: (a) those factors concerned with the results of parasitism—*i.e.* the changes within the host due to the presence of parasites, and (b) those relationships concerned with the normal conditions of host anatomy and physiology encountered by the parasite upon its first contact with the host. The differences between these two groups of factors, however, are not always clear. If a parasite prefers a younger host we often do not know, for example, whether the preference is due to the absence of immunity on the part of the younger host or to the presence of a mechanical barrier, such as a thick skin, in the older host. The results of a few studies on this problem are presented below, but many more investigations are needed. Chapter XXI dealing with the effects of parasitism on the host contains much information of pertinence to this problem.

Many species of miracidia favor young snails over older hosts. Certain species rarely or never penetrate snails over two or three months old, but in other species the age limitation does not appear to exist. This preference for young snail hosts has been demonstrated with the Schistosomatidae and Spirorchiidae, and with *Paragonimus kellicotti* and *Clinostomum marginatum*. Preference by miracidia for young snails does not necessarily mean that young snails are more heavily infected with trematodes. On the contrary, older snails are generally more heavily infected, and they are often killed by their trematode parasites.

Fish hosts have been used extensively as a basis for the study of the effects of host age on parasitism. The average number of worms per freshwater fish usually shows a regular arithmetic increase with age and size of fish. Such worms as the tapeworm, *Dibothriocephalus*, the nematodes, *Camallanus*, *Raphidascaris*, and the flukes, *Tetraonchus*, *Dactylogyrus*, *Azygia*, increase both in numbers and effects on their fish hosts with the latter's age. A few parasites are apparently not affected by host age; others, such as the myxosporidian, *Henneguya oviperda*, reach their maximum numbers in three-year old fish, then decline in intensity. Studies by Gorbunova,[36] and Dogiel and Petrushevéskii[22] of fishes in Russia confirm the generalization that the numbers of parasitic species in most fishes increase regularly with the age of the host. The pike (*Esox lucius*), the roach (*Leuciscus rutilus*) and the salmon received particular attention during these studies.

The intensity of infection also increases as the fish, *Thymallus vulgaris*, becomes older. Forty-eight worms were found in one fish of two years as compared with 500 worms in a three-year old fish. Two factors are probably responsible for the rise in percentages of *Spiroptera tenuissima* from 22.2 to 82.7 in the two-year old fishes, and from 82.7 to 100 in the three-year old fishes. One factor is the intensive feeding activity of the rapidly growing fish which swallow numerous intermediate hosts of the parasites; and the other factor is the addition of newly acquired parasites to those already present.

No age resistance to *Trichinella spiralis* in mice was noted by Larsh and Hendricks.[50] In young mice, however, a significant majority of adult worms was located in the posterior one-half of the small intestine, whereas the reverse was true in old mice. This difference in localization was attributed to the difference in intestinal emptying time. Ackert *et al.*[1] have suggested that the greater amount of mucus present in older birds is responsible for the heightened resistance encountered in infections with *Ascaridia galli*.

A recent study[52] showed that when mice of different ages were experimentally infected with the pinworm, *Aspiculuris tetraptera*, the female host became resistant to infection at the time of first estrus, whereas the male mice gradually developed resistance as they advanced in age. This sexual difference in age response may be related to the level of gonadal hormones. Older fish eat more intermediate hosts (*e.g.* copepods) than do young fish, but sometimes older fish that have *fewer* parasites than younger fish of the same species, have migrated away from the location of infective larval parasites.

In many fishes the parasite infestations increase up to a certain age of host maturity, then decrease. We have found that when average numbers of parasites (the nematode, *Spirocamallanus*) were used as a criterion of infection in the goby, *Gillichthys mirabilis*, the most heavily infected fish were always the older ones. If, however, the mode or median was used, the numbers of worms in the different age groups of hosts were roughly the same. A study of 100 wild rabbits (in an enclosure in Australia) showed that there was no relation to age and sex as to the level of infection with *Trichostrongylus retortaeformis*, but another nematode, *Graphidium strigosum*, was found in larger numbers in older and female hosts.[27] See page 557 for a discussion of the effects of host hormones on parasites.

Age resistance may be associated with the phenomenon of *Premunition*, which is a state of resistance established against an infection after an acute infection by the same pathogen has become chronic, and which lasts for as long as the infecting organisms remain in the body. This phenomenon is probably related to the normal immune reactions of the host body.

THE DENSITY OF POPULATIONS

The new experimental science of *population dynamics* has kindled the interest and imagination of biologists all over the world. In recognizing that the environment of each individual animal includes the population of which the animal is a part, the following two basic questions arise. How are populations controlled in nature? How can we define the relative *fitness* of an individual or of a species? If the demands of life are met, arguments on definitions of "fitness" and "success" are pointless, but one fact seems clear — an increase in population size does not necessarily mean that the individual or the species is fit; it usually means that the pressure of environmental resistance has decreased. Among the problems to be solved before answering the above questions are calculations of: intrinsic fecundity in relation to rate of natural (actual) increase, dispersive ability, the ability to search. All of these problems involve the numbers of individuals in a given area, hence the focus of population ecology is the density of a population and the processes which control this density.

Population equilibrium (biotic balance) is essential for the existence of a species. As pointed out by Smith,[73] there is in the environmental relations of a species, an inherent tendency toward stability in numbers. The numbers of individuals of a parasite population are modified by reproductive rate, sizes and ages of the parasites and hosts, food supply, predators and disease, migratory behavior of the parasite, competition, and, at least indirectly, by all other physical and chemical factors of the environment. In a stable population of any animal species, the rate of increase is zero, the birth rate and death rate balancing each other. Intrinsic fecundity has no effect on the maintenance of equilibrium, only on the rate at which it is achieved. An increase in density may encourage a higher death rate because of food shortage, predation or disease. This principle is illustrated when there is an increase in numbers of insects without an increase in the food supply. The result is more competition for the food, hence fewer insects.

In a study of demology (= population dynamics) Huffaker[43] has emphasized the unity of environmental action; and in the concept of the balance of nature the unity of environmental action may best be understood by studying separately its two major components. These components are twin constants or parameters, the first of which is the furnishing by the physical environment of all the requisites for life and all living things which influence the lives of other living things. The second parameter is the competitive utilization of those requisites. Competition between a host and its parasites is thus an exceedingly useful symbol of the processes involved in the maintenance of balance. Huffaker stated that "the abundance of an animal is restricted by the capacity of the environment for it. Although a population may possess remarkable powers of compensating for stresses encountered and thus maintain a characteristic level of population in relation to the conditions of the environment, the self-determining action is restricted."

Density Dependence

Much has been written about density-dependent factors in the parasite-host complex, but, unfortunately, the concepts of these factors have been defined in conflicting and confusing ways. Let us assume the existence of a population of wild pheasants infected with *Coccidia*. Let us also assume that this flock of pheasants has remained fairly constant in adult numbers (= density) for several years, and that each year about one-fourth of them have died of coccidiosis. Now suppose that the size of the flock increases because of more favorable weather conditions resulting in more plant food. We would expect that with an increase in numbers of birds (hosts), there would be a corresponding increase in numbers of parasites simply because with more hosts to invade, there is more room for parasite reproduction and growth. We might then argue that because the population density within the flock tends to be constant, the chances of any one bird dying of coccidiosis would be the same, the relative numbers of parasites per host remaining the same. It would seem logical to say that the density of the parasites depends upon the density of the host—more hosts, more parasites. But in this case the relationship is not simply a matter of numbers. The *effects* of the parasite on the host change with changes in numbers of parasites within each host, and the important factor is the effect on each *individual* of the population rather than on the whole host population as a unit. In cases where changing host densities regulate the parasite population there is a significant time lag between the increase in host numbers and increase in their parasites.

The usual concept of density-dependence includes "all density-relationships in which the mean effect per individual of the population is higher at high densities than at low densities".[75] The more pheasants there are in a flock of a given size (area distribution), the less chance any one young bird has of surviving to maturity if the flock is infected with coccidia. The effect of a limited food supply is density-dependent because the limitation operates more severely against a population at high densities than at low densities, *per individual of the population*. To put this principle in the words of Smith,[73] "the relative efficiency of both entomophagous insects and disease is greater when the host insect is abundant than when it is scarce, this being the effect of population density on the host-finding capacity of the parasite." According to Nicholson[55] "the action of the controlling factor must be governed by the density of the population controlled."

De Bach and Smith[18] tested the above principle experimentally by making the parasites (*Mormoniella vitripennis*, a chalcid wasp) search for a density of 40 hosts (puparia of the house fly, *Musca domestica*) through 3 quarts of barley for forty hours. The densities of parasites varied from 1 to 300. One of the factors in the host-parasite complex that acted as an automatic control was the effect of host population densities on the rate of increase of the parasite. Although this rate decreased with increments in host density, the higher the host density in relation to the density of the parasite, the greater was the *total* increase of parasite numbers. As a result, however, of competition and overlapping in searching for the host, causing a reduced fecundity in the parasite, the *next generation* of parasites actually decreased in numbers. Thus increases of parasites above a certain optimum will result in a subsequent actual decrease in total numbers of parasites. "In short, increases in host density act to increase numbers of parasites in the next generation, although not in direct proportion to host density, whereas increases in parasite density, beyond a certain point in relation to host density, result in a decrease in the total numbers of parasites in the next generation." These phenomena were previously observed by Flanders[31] in a similar experiment utilizing the chalcid, *Trichogramma* sp., and the eggs of the moth, *Sitotroga cerealella*. It was then pointed out that the limitations revealed by such experimental conditions do not prevail when multiple generations occur under natural conditions. Population oscillations of both host and parasite can occur in constant climatic conditions.

An overwhelming number of such theoretical considerations of

37

the role of parasites in the natural control of insects have been made. Varley[82] demonstrated that the knapweed gallfly, *Urophora jaceana*, is density-dependent because it kills a much greater percentage as well as a larger total number of its hosts when the population of the host is high. Various workers have demonstrated that the number of eggs deposited increases with host density. The inherent reproductive capacity of a parasite is limited, but there is some dispute as to whether the number of eggs deposited by a parasitic insect ever attains this limitation. While working with chalcid wasps, Varley and Edwards[84] found that when the host population density is high, the calculated area of discovery falls to very low values and the number of hosts attacked by each parasite is independent of host density. If density is to be correctly measured, a determination of the type of distribution, size and permanence of species groups and degree of aggregation must be made.

As numbers of individuals increase, competition for space, food and other essentials obviously intensifies. The pteromalid wasp, *Neocatolaccus mamezophagus*, and the braconid wasp, *Heterospilus prosopidus*, attack full-grown larvae of the azuki bean weevil, *Callosobruchus chinensis*, and thus occur as parasites in the same ecological habitat. In mixed populations of these three species the progeny of both wasps and of the host population increases in numbers rapidly at first and then maintains a nearly constant value. In comparing these findings with those resulting from a study of only single parasite species, Utida[81] concluded that the parasitization efficiency of each species of wasps is lowered when they together attack the same host population. *Neocatolaccus* demonstrated a high efficiency of parasitism at higher host densities, but *Heterospilus* exhibited more efficiency of parasitism at lower host densities. Efficiency in these studies was measured in terms of progeny numbers. Under natural conditions, however, as pointed out by Smith,[72] the combined action of two or more competing parasites may give better control of a host than any one parasite acting alone.

For further details see Allee *et al.*,[3] Burnett,[13] Solomon,[74,76] Thompson,[79] and Varley.[83]

Biological Control

Mechanical, chemical, cultural, legislative and other methods of controlling agricultural pests have been used with varying degrees of success for centuries, but biological control (= the manipulation of biotic balance) offers the most hopeful promise of permanent success. Biological control is applied ecology, and the agricultural entomologist must create an environment unfavorable for the occurrence of the arthropod at pest densities. One of the most unfavorable aspects of the environment for the increase of any animal is the presence of relatively large numbers of predators or parasites. Biological control, then, involves the introduction and encouragement of predators and parasites which destroy insects that are destructive to agriculture. The objective of biological control is to change the biotic equilibrium position from a population level at which the pest insect causes economic loss to a level at which its destructive action is negligible.

As we have already indicated, there is a tendency, in any single species, for its population density to fluctuate near an average level. Among the causes of such fluctuations is the interaction of a species with its natural enemies. One of the most interesting and economically important groups of such natural enemies of insects is the parasitic Hymenoptera sometimes designated as *parasitoids*. Although the terms "parasite" and "parasitoid" are frequently used as synonyms (as we shall do in this book), not every parasite is a parasitoid. The latter is parasitic only as a larva, and it destroys its host so that it functions more like a predator except that it destroys only a single host individual instead of several. It is also of large size in comparison with its host which usually belongs in the same taxonomic group (*i.e.* Insecta).

Wasps and wasp-like insects (Hymenoptera) are commonly employed as agents of biological control. The wasp, *Trichogramma minutum*, a parasite of the European corn borer and of the codling moth, is reared by the millions to help eliminate these insects as pests of important agricultural crops. A common sequence of events in the parasite-host relation is first the selection of a host, then the stinging of the host to render it immobile, then the laying of one or more eggs by means of the ovipositor which is jabbed into the host body so that the eggs can be laid therein. The larvae that hatch within the host body feed on the body juices and tissues, and eventually kill the host. Intensive studies of *Trichogramma* and of other parasites have revealed much important information on the ecology of parasitism, especially on population phenomena. The sugarcane borer (*Diatraea saccharalis*) has been partly controlled first by *T. minutum* in several countries, and later by the fly, *Lixophaga diatraeae*, in Cuba. The California black scale (*Saissetia oleae*) on citrus has been partly controlled in California by the chalcid wasp, *Metaphycus helvolus*, imported from Africa in 1937. The coconut moth (*Levuana iridescens*) in Fiji is controlled with a tachinid fly (*Ptychomyia remota*) with striking results. The oriental moth (*Cnidocampa flavescens*) is controlled with the tachnid fly (*Chaetexorista javana*) in Massachusetts with fine results except during seasons following exceptionally cold winters. For details of these and of many other efforts at biological control of populations of harmful insects see Clausen.[16]

In biological control we are primarily concerned with factors which operate in such a way as to maintain biotic balance, the *probability of survival* of a pest individual becoming less as the density increases, and becoming greater as the density decreases. In a population of insects subject to parasitization by larval wasps (or subject to a contagious disease) the probability of survival of an individual is inversely correlated with the population density. The

rate of increase of the parasitoid depends upon its inherent reproductive capacity and upon the number of hosts it can readily find;
the population level of the host obviously depends not upon the host
density but upon the *searching capacity* of the adult female wasp.
Doutt[24] has described three distinct processes of selection which
operate to restrict the host list of parasitic hymenoptera.   (1) *Ecological selection* which implies that for a host and parasite to meet
they must be geographically, seasonally and ecologically coincident.
A combination of random and non-random searching appears to be
most common.   (2) *Psychological selection* which involves the highly
developed nervous system and responses of the adult female parasite.
The sense of smell has commonly been reported as primarily important in host detection.   Ullyett[80] has found that if a cocoon of
the South African brown-tailed moth (*Euproctis terminalis*) parasitized by the pupa of the ichneumonid, *Pimpla bicolor*, is broken
open in the forest, both the pupa and the hands and arms of the
observer are covered in a few minutes by a swarm of the parasitic
females.   (3) *Physiological selection* which involves the physiological
compatibility of the wasp larva and its host.

The searching capacity of the adult female parasite, therefore,
involves the finding of a host habitat and the finding of a host, but
success depends also upon host acceptance and host suitability.
Many insects, for example, have the ability to discriminate between
parasitized and healthy hosts.[32,70] We know very little about the
chemical factors which are at the basis of the selection of a host by
a parasite.   Few species of parasitoids limit their attack to a single
host species, but normally a parasite will attack only a fraction
of the species on which development is actually possible.   Many
host species never attacked in nature can be demonstrated experimentally to be suitable for parasitoid larval development.

The *Hopkins Host Selection Principle* states that a given insect
species that is capable of breeding in two or more hosts will normally
continue to select for its offspring the particular host species on
which its own life cycle was passed.   This interesting behavior implies, therefore, that the host predetermines the selection by the
ovipositing female of the same nutrient medium for her progeny as
she herself enjoyed during her own development.   The result of
many generations of such selection tendencies is the development of
special physiological strains (see p. 653) of parasites each with its
own host preference.

THE PARASITE-MIX OR PARASITOCOENOSIS

The combined populations of organisms, both flora and fauna, that
live together in a host organ, or in the entire host, or in the host population are known as the *parasitocoenosis*. A less technical appelation
is *parasite-mix*.[57] For example, the intestine of a vertebrate animal
generally may contain large numbers of different kinds of bacteria,
yeasts, protozoa and worms. All of these organisms constitute the

parasitocoenosis of the intestine. When we recall that there is a continual change in the numbers, developmental stages and physiological activity of these populations, we begin to appreciate the influence which one species has upon the other in the same community of parasites. A detailed knowledge of the parasite-mix is essential to the understanding of pathogenesis, clinical symptoms and of non-symptomatic carriers. A heavy infection with one species of pathogenic parasite is usually not accompanied by a heavy infection with another species of pathogenic parasite. This relationship has often been cited for commensal forms.

Young white mice infected with the nematode, *Nippostrongylus brasiliensis*, just prior to infection with *Hymenolepis nana* var. *fraterna* exhibit a marked resistance to the tapeworm.[49] Helminths may be capable of increasing or of decreasing host resistance to microorganisms. Viruses and helminths, and protozoa and helminths are said frequently to be mutually antagonistic. Arguments for such antagonisms, however, are mostly theoretical, and much experimental research is needed to produce actual evidence for the existence of these phenomena. Kilham and Olivier[45] reported that encephalomyocarditis (EMC) virus alone produced only mild pathogenic symptoms in laboratory rats, but when the rodents were given a combined infection with the nematode, *Trichinella spiralis*, the rats "experienced a high incidence of crippling and death while control rats remained free of disease." The cause of this phenomenon is unknown.

One such experiment[39] demonstrated that the fluke, *Diplodiscus*, is partly responsible for the absence of opalinids from the intestine of the Green Frog, *Acris gryllus*. In this host the tadpoles are heavily infected with the protozoa but lightly infected with the worm. The situation is reversed in adult frogs. If flukes are experimentally introduced into the rectum of opalinid-infected frogs, the opalinids either completely disappear or they become reduced in number.

Another study of the influence of a prior infection on a subsequent infection demonstrated that in mice the introduction of the roundworm, *Ancylostoma caninum*, twenty-four to forty-eight hours before an experimental infection with the nematode, *Trichinella spiralis*, caused a significant reduction in the number of adult *Trichinella* normally expected to be found in the small intestine. Of considerable interest is the fact that, if the hookworms were administered 12, 96, 144, or 192 hours prior to the *T. spiralis* infection, no such interference with the trichina occurred. The reduction in numbers of nematodes took place primarily in the anterior portions of the small intestine, and it may have been the result of non-specific inflammation engendered by the hookworms.[37]

Concurrent infections may be of a quite different nature than those examples mentioned above. If larval nematodes (*Toxocara canis*) are given to guinea pigs one week to one month prior to infection with *Entamoeba histolytica*, the presence of the nematode in the liver of the host does not affect development of cecal amoebiasis, but it does apparently *increase* the number of positive amebic cultures (*in vitro*) obtainable from the liver in animals with cecal lesions caused by the ameba.[47] Some parasites of the intestine evidently account for the appearance of exacerbation of some bacterial diseases, and vice versa. "*Hymenolepis diminuta* developing in the presence of *Moniliformis dubius* are lighter, shorter, have a lower average weight: length ratio, and are limited to the posterior part of the intra-intestinal range they occupy in single infections. *M. dubius* in the concurrent infections are lighter, possibly shorter, have a lower average weight: length ratio, and tend to attach further anterior than in single infections." The similarities between these effects of concurrent infections and those of crowding suggest that the former are due to competition, possibly for carbohydrates.[41] If albino rats are experimentally infected with *Balantidium* plus ascarid larvae, the protozoa become much more pathogenic than when the worm larvae are absent.[12]

In spite of the paucity of experimental evidence we can say with assurance that some parasitic species do not tolerate others within the same host organ. A human visitor to the tropics, however, may return to temperate climates to find himself a walking zoo—the delight of any class in parasitology. It is only from extensive ecological studies that the entire influence of the parasite-mix on the health and activities of the host can be ascertained. During such studies the entire life history of each parasitic species should be considered because each species has a biotype (*e.g.* an organ of the host), but the parasite species may pass through and be specific for several markedly different biotypes during the course of its life cycle.

Mutualistic Intestinal Protozoa and Bacteria

1. Insects

A classic example of mutualism is the cooperation between termites and their intestinal protozoan fauna. The hindgut of many termites is so crowded with protozoa (Fig. XXIII–1) that the

---

FIG. XXIII–1.—Representative protozoa from termites. 1 from *Kalotermes occidentis*, Lower California. 2 and 3 from *Termopsis angusticollis*, California. 4 from *Kalotermes perezi*, Costa Rica. 5 from *Kalotermes minor*, California. 6 from *Kalotermes flavicollis*, California. 7 from *Kalotermes marginipennis*, Costa Rica. 8 from *Termopsis angusticollis*, California. 9 from *Kalotermes flavicollis*, Europe. 10 from *Glyptotermes parvulus*, Uganda. 11 from *Kalotermes occidentis*, Lower California. 12 from *Glyptotermes parvulus*, Uganda. 13 from *Mastotermes darwiniensis*, Australia. 14, 15, and 16 from *Amitermes beaumonti*, Canal Zone. 17 from *Kalotermes jeannelanus*, East Africa. 18 from *Termopsis angusticollis*, California. 19 from *Glyptotermes* sp, Uganda. 20 from *Amitermes silvestrianus*, Canal Zone. 21 from *Termopsis angusticollis*, California. 22 from *Kalotermes* (*Neotermes*) *connexus*, Hawaii. 23 from *Kalotermes simplicicornis*, California. 24 from *Amitermes beaumonti*, Canal Zone. (1 and 11 from Lewis; 5 from Cross; 23 from Light; all others from Kirby; 14, 15, 16, 20, 24 courtesy *Parasitology*, Cambridge; all others courtesy Univ. Calif. Pub. Zool.)

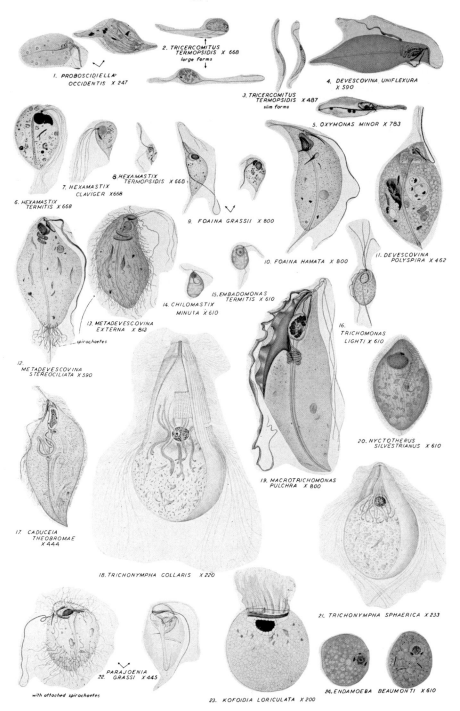

1. PROBOSCIDIELLA⁰ OCCIDENTIS X 247

2. TRICERCOMITUS TERMOPSIDIS X 668 large forms

3. TRICERCOMITUS TERMOPSIDIS X 487 slim forms

4. DEVESCOVINA UNIFLEXURA X 590

5. OXYMONAS MINOR X 783

6. HEXAMASTIX TERMITIS X 668

7. HEXAMASTIX CLAVIGER X 668

8. HEXAMASTIX TERMOPSIDIS X 668

9. FOAINA GRASSII X 800

10. FOAINA HAMATA X 800

11. DEVESCOVINA POLYSPIRA X 462

12. METADEVESCOVINA STEREOCILIATA X 590

13. METADEVESCOVINA EXTERNA X 813

spirochaetes

14. CHILOMASTIX MINUTA X 610

15. EMBADOMONAS TERMITIS X 610

16. TRICHOMONAS LIGHTI X 610

17. CADUCEIA THEOBROMAE X 444

18. TRICHONYMPHA COLLARIS X 220

19. MACROTRICHOMONAS PULCHRA X 800

20. NYCTOTHERUS SILVESTRIANUS X 610

21. TRICHONYMPHA SPHAERICA X 233

22. PARAJOENIA GRASSI X 445

with attached spirochaetes

23. KOFOIDIA LORICULATA X 200

24. ENDAMOEBA BEAUMONTI X 610

FIG. XXIII–1.—(Legend on opposite page)

protozoan bodies are often distorted from being pressed on all sides. The protozoa in nymphs of *Zootermopsis* constitute one-seventh to one-third of the total weight of host and parasites. Most of the larger flagellates in termites belong to the order Hypermastigida (see p. 72). The termite families Mastotermitidae, Kalotermitidae, Hodotermitidae and Rhinotermitidae are normally host to an abundance of flagellates. Significantly, most members of the largest and most specialized of termite families, the Termitidae, do not feed on wood, but the few members that do so feed possess in their intestines bacteria which presumbably elaborate enzymes that digest wood. The first nymphal instar acquires its protozoa by proctodeal feeding at the anus of an infected termite, and during each molting period the protozoa are temporarily lost—to be regained as originally acquired. Only the adult, asexual, non-dividing forms ordinarily occur in termites. Encystment of the protozoa does not take place.

If human beings possessed cellulose-digesting enzymes, we would not have so critical a world food-shortage problem as we have today because people could survive quite well, although perhaps not tastefully, on straw, sawdust, wood shavings, bark and dead branches. In a pinch, we could eat paper and old furniture. Neither do the termites and wood-eating roaches themselves elaborate cellulose-digesting enzymes (cellulases), but their protozoan and, probably, bacterial guests, pay for the intestinal housing facilities by digesting the food eaten by the host.

Termites can be defaunated by incubating them at 36° C. for twenty-four hours or by submitting them to two atmospheres of oxygen pressure for four hours. After the protozoa are dead the insects will continue eating wood and other materials, but they will starve to death because they cannot digest their food. If they are soon refaunated they will survive.

The following account of mutualistic intestinal protozoa of insects is taken largely from Hungate.[44] The insect gut is without free oxygen, so the flagellates within it are obligate anaerobes (indeed, free oxygen is toxic to the protozoa), and, consequently, the protozoa derive their necessary energy through fermentation. Such fermentation reactions may be defined as electron transference in which molecular oxygen is not a participant. For the most part, the carbon compounds, which are both oxidized and reduced, are the reactants in fermentation. In termites and in wood-eating roaches the carbohydrate constituents (cellulose) of wood serve as the substrate for this fermentation. Hence various acids and gases appear as products. A common observation is that, upon acidification of the gut contents of termites, there is a strong odor of acetic or similar acid. The fermentation products are oxidized by the host to the mutual advantage of host and parasite. The way in which the protozoa obtain their nitrogen is still a matter of speculation, but fungi in wood apparently serve as a source of N for *Zootermopsis*. Symbiotic bacteria and yeasts in the insect as well as in the vertebrate gut may be able to assimilate molecular nitrogen of the atmosphere. Hungate has suggested the attractive hypothesis that gut protozoa use the nitrogenous wastes of the termite, and the latter absorb the wastes of the protozoa—mutual benefit carried to an exquisite point! Unfortunately, experimental evidence for this exchange is lacking.

Among the roaches is a wood-eating species, *Cryptocercus punctulatus*, whose hindgut, like that of termites, is crowded with flagellates which comprise twelve genera embracing twenty-five species. All the genera differ from those in termites except *Trichonympha* (Fig. III–27, p. 73) which is to be found both in termites and in this roach. These roaches are probably originally infected by cyst-forming species of flagellates, or by trophozoites having thickened cuticles in pellets formed as the result of molting.

Physiological experiments dealing with *Cryptocercus* and its flagellates have not been so extensive as those with termites, but in all probability the roach is also dependent almost entirely on the fermentation of cellulose by its intestinal protozoa. One marked difference between roach and termite protozoa is the habit of encystment of many of the protozoa in the roach during molting of the insect. The roach retains its infection throughout its life. Another difference is that encystment is accompanied by a sexual process, and the stimulus for the initiation of a sexual cycle in the flagellate is extrinsic, attributable to the molting hormones of the host (see Chapter XXII, p. 560). Molting and the sexual cycles never occur separately. Although the sexual cycles of the flagellates are initiated by host hormones, the follow-up is directly influenced by the rise in pH (7.2 to 7.4) of the gut fluids during the molting period.

The role of extracellular symbiots (bacteria, spirochaetes) on the surfaces of protozoa in termites and in roaches remains obscure. A great diversity in numbers, kinds and distribution of both extracellular and intracellular symbiots occurs in the flagellates of termites,[46] but experimental evidence concerning their nature is lacking. The intracellular bacteria in parasitic flagellates may well play a part in the digestion of cellulose. Indeed, some workers[35] believe that the bacteria are responsible for all cellulose digestion.

2. Ruminants

The placid cud-chewing habit of cattle is directly related to the digestion of cellulose, and to the masses of symbiotic ciliates to be found in the first stomach of these animals. In sheep and goats the holotrich ciliates (superficially resembling such forms as *Paramecium*) occur in numbers between 160,000 and 200,000 per milliliter of rumen content. The three most common species in sheep and goats (also to be found in cattle) are *Isotricha prostoma*, *Isotricha intestinalis* and *Dasytricha ruminantium*. Hungate[44] found an average number of 7000 *Diplodinium* per milliliter of rumen contents in cows fed timothy hay and concentrate, with a range between 800 and 30,000! Considerable differences and fluctuations occur among the various ruminants, but some protozoan species are common to many kinds of hosts, even to those widely separated geographically. The microfauna of ruminants consists principally of holotrichous ciliates belonging to the suborder Trichostomina, and spirotrichous ciliates belonging to the suborder Oligotricha, particularly the family Ophryoscolecidae (Fig. XXIII–2). The young ruminant acquires its infection by ingesting infected saliva.

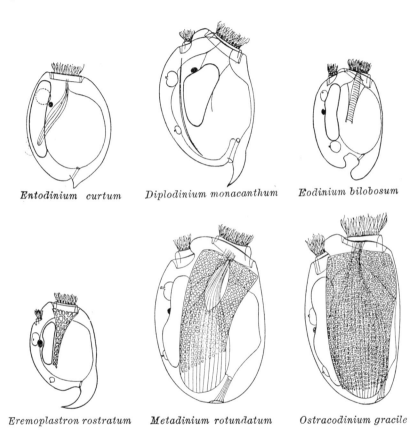

Entodinium curtum   *Diplodinium monacanthum*   *Eodinium bilobosum*

Eremoplastron rostratum   *Metadinium rotundatum*   *Ostracodinium gracile*

Fig. XXIII–2.—Illustrations of ciliates of the family Ophryoscolecidae.
These drawings illustrate sample genera and species from the stomach of a wild bull (*Bos gaurus*) in Mysore, India. (Kofoid, and Christenson, courtesy of Univ. Calif. Pub. Zool.)

The relationships among the bacteria, protozoa and other microorganisms in ruminant stomachs are little understood, but, as with the termites, interest in these relationships centers on the question of cellulose digestion, and on the extent to which the protozoa are used by the host as a source of protein. Cattle ciliates contain a cellulase, but the bacteria of the rumen also possess cellulolytic properties. In addition, the possibility that intracellular symbiotic bacteria are concerned with cellulose and starch digestion should not be overlooked. Hungate has said, "The faculty for an obligately anaerobic existence is so widespread among bacteria and so relatively uncommon in protozoa that utilization of anaerobic intracellular bacteria for synthesis of essential building materials (*e.g.* high-energy phosphate) might account for the ability of the protozoa to survive under anaerobic conditions. According to this viewpoint the fermentation products could well be those of the intracellular bacteria." The existence of intracellular symbiotic bacteria in rumen ciliates, however, has not been conclusively established, although there are bodies in the cytoplasm that *look* like bacteria. There is clear evidence,[38] however, that species of *Entodinium* and other genera actively ingest bacteria. The rumen protozoa are obviously suitable material for experimental investigations of the problem of "mutualism within mutualists."

Three important genera of ciliates in cattle are: *Diplodinium*, *Entodinium* and *Epidinium*. The role played by these organisms is less well understood than that played by termite protozoa. It is more difficult to defaunate cattle than termites, but it can be done by starvation for several days followed by the administration of a copper sulfate solution. When this is done, cellulose and hemicellulose continue to be digested at the same rate as in untreated cattle. *Diplodinium*, however, can digest cellulose. This ciliate is probably mutualistic. Other genera, including *Isotricha*, *Dasytricha* and *Bütschlia*, readily absorb soluble carbohydrates of the host stomach, and convert the carbohydrates into starch, thereby helping to keep the sugars from being immediately fermented by the bacteria.

In addition to cellulose, the ciliates probably feed on bacteria and on other protozoa or various types of organic debris. *Diplodinium* possesses the enzyme *cellulase* or *cellobiase*, and it may store large amounts of glycogen. Both *Entodinium* and *Epidinium* digest starch, and thus they, too, help to level out the fermentation process which occurs rapidly by action of the bacteria.

The question as to the amount of protein supplied the host in the form of protozoa can be answered by using Hungate's estimates for the bovine of 3000 *Diplodinium*, 3000 *Isotricha*, 5000 *Dasytricha* and 5000 *Entodinium* per milliliter. Calculation shows that about 66 grams of protein are supplied the host in the form of protozoa each day. The exact contribution would fluctuate from day to day as numbers and kinds of ciliates vary. Oxford[60] has suggested that if the rumen ciliates excrete ammonia, there may actually be wastage of protein in the rumen through the conversion of plant protein into protozoan protein. If this wastage occurs, the protozoa may be called "food robbers," but more detailed knowledge is needed before this problem can be solved. The reserve starch storage in the protozoa does not appear to be a major mechanism by which carbohydrates are supplied to the host, but the starch is a reserve source of energy for fermentation. In this manner the polysaccharides in the protozoa are indirectly of value to the host. The average contribution to the host of both fermentation products and protein by the protozoa has been estimated to be about one-fifth of the total requirement. We know that the ciliates and the bacteria in a cow stomach synthesize B-complex vitamins, enzymes and proteins. But if the bacteria can do these things alone, are the protozoa really necessary?

Turning now from ciliates to amebas we find clear evidence that bacteria, both pathogenic and non-pathogenic, play a role in the pathogenicity of *Entamoeba histolytica*.[62,63] Amebas from ameba-trypanosome cultures were found to be unable to establish themselves in germ-free guinea pigs without bacteria, but the addition of either of two species of bacteria (*Aerobacter aerogenes* or *Escherichia coli*) not only permitted the ameba to become established, but promoted invasion of the tissues. One may conclude that "bacteria are involved essentially in the etiology of intestinal amebiasis and that synergism of ameba and bacteria is a prerequisite to development of the disease."

Reflect for a moment on the tremendous churn of activity that is housed in an intestine. Bacteria, yeasts, spirochaetes, protozoa and worms may all be struggling for nutrients and space at the same time. By-products of metabolism are being poured into the mass continuously. Physicochemical conditions (such as pH and gases) are constantly being altered. The bacteria synthesize vitamins and other essentials for the protozoa and worms. No wonder that evolutionary processes among intestinal organisms and their hosts have resulted in relationships which bear the character both of coexistence and of antagonism.[77]

FOOD CHAINS

Food chains may be divided conveniently into the following three types. (1) The predator chain which, starting from a plant base, goes from smaller to larger animals. (2) The parasite chain which goes from larger to smaller organisms. (3) The saprophytic or saprozoic chain which goes from dead organic matter into microorganisms and into a few larger forms such as fungi.

Potential energy is lost at each food transfer—that is, at each step in the chain. Photosynthetic plants fix only about 0.2 per cent of the energy of the sunlight which falls upon them, and when these plants are eaten by herbivorous animals, about 10 per cent of the potential energy of the plants is used. When the herbivorous animals are eaten by small carnivores, perhaps 12 or 15 per cent of the potential energy in their bodies is used. A fourth step in the chain would be the devouring of small carnivores by large ones, and the percentage of potential food energy obtained would be slightly more than that at the previous step in the chain.

In distinguishing between a predator and a parasite the matter of size of food is important. Although in the parasite chain organisms at successive levels (steps) are smaller and smaller instead of generally larger and larger as in the predator chain, there is no fundamental difference between the two. A predator usually disposes of its prey all at once, whereas a parasite disposes of its host, or part of its host, a little at a time—usually at a slow enough rate so as not to interfere seriously with the host well-being. Both predator and parasite chains are limited to a few steps or links as shown in figure XXIII–3. One significant feature in the evolution of parasitism is the parasitization of adjacent links in the predator food chain.

The parasite pyramid of food is upside down because most parasites are smaller and more numerous than are their hosts. If, instead of a pyramid of numbers we use a pyramid of mass or

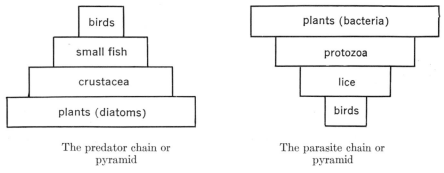

The predator chain or pyramid   The parasite chain or pyramid

FIG. XXIII–3

"biomass" we find that the parasite biomass and the predator biomass are the same because the total *weight* of individuals at successive levels or steps is plotted. The biomass pyramid indicates the over-all effect of food chain relations for the ecological group as a whole. For a detailed discussion of this subject see Elton[29] and Odum.[58] Since the number of organisms that can be supported depends on the number of food organisms being replaced as fast as some are eaten (rather than on the amount of food organisms present at any one time), parasites bathed in a continous supply of nutrients furnished by the host are in a highly favored position. This situation helps to explain the presence of enormous numbers of parasites sometimes to be found in a single host.

THE IMMEDIATE ENVIRONMENT OF THE HOST

A review of much of the discussion on the preceding pages of this chapter can be made in the form of a case history by selecting an ecological study of one kind of host and its parasites, and by noting the interplay of as many environmental factors as possible. Such a study was made by Fischthal over a period of years on parasites of northwestern Wisconsin fishes, and summarized by him in 1953.[30] The following account is taken largely from his paper, and confined to his observations on lake habitats.

Physical Factors

Form of Basin.—High productivity of aquatic organisms tends to favor a high percentage and intensity of parasitism in fishes. Greater biological productivity is favored in a lake where the photosynthetic zone is closely superimposed over the decomposition zone. If the lake basin edge is steep, much of the essential decomposition material is removed to deep water where it is inaccessible, and as one consequence, the mollusks, turbellarians, annelids, insects and crustaceans which may be utilized as intermediate hosts for trematodes or cestodes find living conditions untenable.

Shore Line and Changes in Water Level.—Other factors being equal, the longer the shore line the greater the biological productivity. Hence where there is an irregular shore line with resulting bays, coves and shallow water, there is more superposition of photosynthetic and decomposition zones and a greater diversity of bottom and margin conditions. These features favor an abundance of plankton and larger plants and animals, including parasites in all stages of development.

Water Movements.—Movements of lake water may assist the dissemination of parasites by spreading larval stages to new hosts, or they may have an adverse effect by moving free-living larval parasites or parasitized intermediate hosts out of reach of the next host in the life cycle.

Wave Action.—The action of waves tends to denude exposed shores and to reduce the incidence of parasitism except in those hosts which are capable of burrowing.

Temperature.—Cold, deep water is not conducive to a high productivity. This limiting factor tends to result in a concentration of the fauna in the upper, warm layers, therefore aiding in an increased superposition of hosts and parasites. The metabolic rates of poikilothermic hosts are greatly increased with high temperatures. Fishes generally harbor more parasites in the summer and early fall than in winter and early spring seasons. With a higher metabolic rate more food is required, and with an increase in food intake a fish acquires a higher degree and variety of parasitism.

Light.—Increased light results in increased development of green plants and increased biological productivity in general. The movement of many planktonic organisms is affected by light. Diurnal movements of various aquatic organisms, including fishes, is well known. Light affects the emergence of cercariae from snails, some preferring darkness, others light, and still others favoring the sunrise or sunset periods. When heavy snow blankets ice on a lake, a prolonged shutting-out of light may occur, resulting in a winter-kill which destroys free-swimming larval stages and their hosts.

Chemical Factors

Dissolved Oxygen.—In lakes a stratification of oxygen is closely correlated with a thermal stratification. The deeper waters are deficient in oxygen, thereby limiting the kinds and numbers of animals which can live there. A light winter-kill in lakes, resulting from a depletion of oxygen under ice, decreases the fish population. During summer months in plant-choked lakes and ponds there may be oxygen exhaustion at night and oxygen replacement during the day, resulting in a partial kill of fishes, plankton and associated parasites. Thus parasitism may be increased or decreased by the presence or absence of a sufficient quantity of oxygen.

Carbonates.—Soft waters (*i.e.* with little carbonates) are usually unproductive, whereas hard waters are normally very productive. Mollusks require carbonates as shell building materials. Crustacea are reduced in numbers as the carbonates decrease. When these invertebrates disappear the larvae of trematodes and acanthocephalans cannot find their intermediate hosts, and the fishes experience a freedom from heavy infections. Leeches are generally much more abundant in hard water than in soft water. In contrast with an alkaline humus substrate, an acid humus substrate tends to poison most leeches, thereby reducing the opportunities for transfer of such protozoan parasites as haemogregarines and trypanosomes.

Hydrogen Ion Concentration (pH).—Mollusks are scarce or absent in excessively acid lakes (in part soft water and bog lakes) because the acid either dissolves or corrodes the carbonate shells, thereby reducing the trematode population. Intermediate hosts of cestodes and acanthocephalans are frequently reduced in the plankton of acid waters.

Pollution.—It is common practice in the maintenance of commercial fish ponds to add a small amount of manure or of commercial fertilizer to increase the general biological productivity. The natural drainage of manure into lakes increases the growth of algae, plankton and bottom organisms, thereby favoring the productivity of parasites. Excessive pollution with sewage or with industrial wastes is usually detrimental to all aquatic organisms.

Biological Factors

Plankton.—As we have already noted, plankton plays an essential part in the life cycles of many fish parasites, especially as it provides intermediate hosts. Plankton also serves as food for fish larvae and young.

Benthos.—The bottom fauna includes snails, clams, aquatic insects, annelids, turbellarians and crustacea—all of which may serve as intermediate hosts for various worms of fishes.

Aquatic Plants.—We have already emphasized the importance of a close association between the photosynthetic zone and the decomposition zone for the maintenance of fishes and their parasites. Trematodes in fishes are particularly abundant in weedy bays and shorelines because of the greater superposition, in these habitats, of fish, snails and stages in the life cycles of the parasites.

Food Chain.—Abundant evidence leads to the conclusion that fishes are most heavily parasitized during the seasons when they ingest the largest quantities and kinds of food. The fry of many fishes start to accumulate parasites as soon as they begin feeding on plankton, and if, when they become adults, they change their feeding habits, the nature of their parasitic faunas also changes. Many larval worms in fishes owe their sanctuary to the fact that their fish hosts are eaten by birds in which the larvae reach sexual maturity.

Fish Populations.—Different species of fish as well as individuals of one species are often in competition for food. This food may include invertebrates with larval worms specific to one of the species of fish, but not to others. Overlapping of two fish populations (the ecotone) may enhance parasitism if the parasite involved reaches maturity in both host species, or if one host serves as the intermediate carrier for the parasite that matures in the other host species. The parasitic fauna of a fish species inhabiting inshore, shallow waters may differ considerably from the parasitic fauna in the same species of fish inhabiting offshore, deeper waters. Fishes that migrate from one part of a lake to another tend to acquire more parasites than those fishes that remain all of their lives in one general locality. Lakes with the greatest variety of habitats tend to have the greatest variety and incidence of fishes and parasites.

SYMBIOTIC CLEANING

Many shrimps, small fishes and other organisms regularly move over the willing bodies of such free-swimming animals as fishes and turtles to pick off food particles, damaged and necrotic tissues, copepods, isopods, bacteria, fungi and other bits of material which may become irritating to the "host." Limbaugh[51] and Eibl-Eibesfeldt[23] have described some of these relationships which have been recognized for many years, but have been considered as merely scientific curiosities (Fig. XXIII–4). The widespread occurrence of this phenomenon, especially in the marine environment, and its relation to the biology of ectoparasites and their hosts demands at least a brief consideration in any general treatment of the subject of symbiosis.

The cleaner fishes represent at least eight families (*e.g.* Lebridae) and 26 or more species. Most of them do their cleaning only in the juvenile stages. These fishes, for the most part, are so colored as to contrast with the environment. The cleaner shrimps also are usually brightly colored, often red, and they display themselves to their hosts in a conspicuous manner. The shrimps characteristically wait at the entrance of their dark crevasses or holes with their bright antennae extended into the sunlit water, and they whip the antennae back and forth while the body is swaying. This behavior, plus the color, apparently attracts the fish which need little enticement to seek relief from a burden of ectoparasites. Among the better known cleaner shrimps are: *Periclimenes yucatanicus, Hippolysmata cali-*

fornica, and *Stenopus hispidus* (the common boxer shrimp). At least one crab has been seen to clean fish.

Shrimps are sometimes invited safely to enter the mouths and gill cavities of their hosts. Occasionally the shrimp is allowed by the fish to make minor incisions in order to obtain subcutaneous parasites. Fishes apparently come to particular spots which may be called "cleaning stations," and there they may line up or crowd around waiting their turn to be cleaned. The host fish often opens its mouth, thereby inviting the shrimps to enter and pick its teeth or gills. Parasites are removed rapidly as the shrimp flits over the

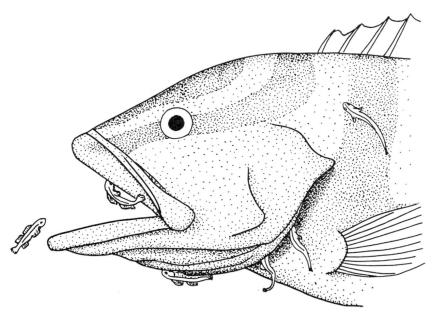

Fig. XXIII 4.—Cleaner fish (*Elacatinus oceanops*) on the head of *Epinepheius*. (Modified from Eibl-Eibensfeldt, courtesy of Zeit. f. Tierpsychologie.)

body of its host. If the shrimp encounters a wound it will spend considerable time in picking away the injured flesh. If all the known cleaners are removed from a given area, such as a portion of a reef in the tropics, the numbers of fishes soon are reduced and those that remain tend to accumulate parasites and skin diseases.

QUESTIONS TO BE ASKED BY ANY INVESTIGATOR OF THE ECOLOGY OF PARASITISM

When a student of parasitology finds a parasite in a host he should ask himself many questions concerning the parasite, concerning other parasites in the same host, concerning the host, and concerning the environment. Some of those questions have been asked in the preceding pages of this chapter, and many of them have been implied. A number of such questions are listed below, and they constitute a summary of important problems encountered in any consideration of the ecology of parasitism.

1. How does the presence of a population of one species of parasite influence the growth and development of another species in the same host organ or in another organ of the same host?

2. Is the host dependent in any manner on its parasites?

3. What effect does a seasonal change have upon the numbers and kinds of parasites for each host?

4. Are the parasites more tolerant or less tolerant than is the host to changes (*e.g.* salinity, temperature) in the environment?

5. Which environmental factors, both inside and outside the host, encourage the maximum degree of pathogenicity?

6. What are the chemical and behavioral aspects of the ecological niche of the parasite and of its host?

7. When two or more species of parasites compete for the same energy (food), what factors operate to favor one over the other?

8. Do the limiting factors of the host environment also directly limit the growth and development of the parasites?

9. How do population changes of the host influence populations of its parasites?

10. What are the size and age relationships between hosts and parasites?

11. What changes in numbers, kinds, and development of parasites are the result of migration of the host?

12. How are populations of parasites controlled in nature?

13. Do the parasites control the populations of their host?

14. What is the relationship between the food of the host and the kinds, number, and development of its parasites?

15. Does the proximity and availability of related host species influence the growth, development and distribution of the parasites?

16. How does the adult parasite differ from its developmental stages in responses to the environment?

17. Is the parasite specific to its host or does it "enjoy" a wide range of host species?

18. How widely is the parasite distributed and what barriers prevent its further distribution?

19. What has been the evolutionary history of the parasite?

20. What is the effect of the sex of the host on the growth and pathogenicity of the parasite?

REFERENCES

1. ACKERT, J. E., EDGAR, S. A., and FRICK, L. P., 1939. Goblet Cells and Age Resistance of Animals to Parasitism. Trans. Amer. Micros. Soc., *58*, 81–89.
2. ALLEE, W. C., 1947. Animal Sociology. Encyclopaedia Britannica, 971*d*–971*r*. pp. 397, 418.
3. ALLEE, W. C., EMERSON, A. E., PARK, O., PARK, T., and SCHMIDT, K. P., 1949. *Principles of Animal Ecology*. W. B. Saunders Co., Philadelphia. 837 pp.
4. ALWAR, V. S. and RAMANUJACHARI, G., 1955. Transmission of *Trypanosoma evansi* Steel, 1885 from Mammals to Fowls. Current Science, *24*, 87.
5. AUDY, J. R., 1954. A Biological Approach to Medical Geography. Brit. Med. J., *1*, 960–962.
6. ————, 1956. Ecological Aspects of Introduced Pests and Diseases. Med. J. Malaya, *11*, 21–32.

7. Audy, J. R., 1958. The Localization of Disease with Special Reference to the Zoonoses. Trans. Roy. Soc. Trop. Med. Hyg., *52*, 308–334.

8. ————, 1960. Parasites as Ecological Labels in Vertebrate Ecology. In: R. D. Purchon, (Ed.) *Proc. Centenary & Bicentenary Congress of Biol.* Singapore, 1958. Univ. Malaya Press, 1960, p. 123–127.

9. Baer, J. G., 1951. *Ecology of Animal Parasites.* Univ. Ill. Press, Urbana. 224 pp.

10. Barbosa, F. S. and Barbosa, I., 1958. Dormancy During the Larval Stages of the Trematode *Schistosoma mansoni* in Snails Estivating on the Soil of Dry Natural Habitats. Ecology, *39*, 763–764.

11. Barrow, J. H., Jr., 1958. The Biology of *Trypanosoma diemyctyli*, Tobey. III. Factors Influencing the Cycle of *Trypanosoma diemyctyli* in the Vertebrate Host. *Triturus v. viridescens.* J. Protozool., *5*, 161–170.

12. Bogdanovich, V. V., 1962. Balantidiaz s Soputstvuyushchei Glistnoi Invaziei (v Usloviyakh Eksperimenta). Med. Parazitol. i Parazitar. Bolezni, *31*, 711–715.

13. Burnett, T., 1959. Experimental Host-Parasite Populations. Ann. Rev. Entomol., *4,* 235–250.

14. Chitwood, M. B., 1957. Intraspecific Variation in Parasitic Nematodes. Systematic Zool., *6*, 19–23.

15. Chute, R. M., 1961. Infections of *Trichinella spiralis* in Hibernating Hamsters. J. Parasitol., *47*, 25–29.

16. Clausen, C. P., 1958. Biological Control of Insect Pests. Ann. Rev. Entomol., *3*, 291–310.

17. Connor, R. S., 1953. A Study of the Seasonal Cycle of a Proteocephalan Cestode, *Proteocephalus stizostethi* Hunter and Bangham, Found in the Yellow Pikeperch, *Stizostedion vitreum vitreum* (Mitchill). J. Parasitol., *39*, 621–624.

18. DeBach, P. and Smith, H. S., 1947. Effects of Parasite Population Density on Rate of Change of Host and Parasite Populations. Ecology, *28*, 290–298.

19. Dogiel, V. A., 1936. (Problems of Ecological Parasitology.) (In Russian.) Annals Leningrad State Univ. No. *7*, 1–194.

20. Dogiel, V. A., 1947. (*Textbook of General Parasitology*) 2nd ed. State Scientific Pedagogical Publishers, Narkompros R.S.F.S.R. Leningrad Department, Leningrad. 372 pp. (In Russian.)

21. Dogiel, V. A., 1958. Ecology of the Parasites of Freshwater Fishes. In: Dogiel, V. A., Petrushevski, G. K. and Polyanski, Yu. I. *Parasitology of Fishes.* Transl. by Z. Kabata, 1961. Oliver and Boyd, Edinburgh and London. p. 1–47.

22. Dogiel, V. A. and Petrushevskii, G. K., 1933. Parazitofauna ryb Nevskoi Guby (Fish Parasites of the Neva Bay). Trudy Lenningradskogo Obshchestva Estestvoispytatelei (Trav. Soc. Naturalistes Lenningrad), *62*, 366–434. (In Russian with German summary.)

23. Dogiel, V. A., Petrushevskii, G. K., and Polyanski, Yu. I., 1958. *Parasitology of Fishes.* Transl. by Z. Kabata, 1961. Oliver & Boyd, Edinburgh and London. 384 pp.

24. Doutt, R. L., 1959. The Biology of Parasitic Hymenoptera. Ann. Rev. Entomol., *4*, 161–182.

25. Dubinin, V. B., 1936. (Investigation of the Parasitic Fauna of *Thymallus vuigaris* in Various Periods of its Life.) In Dogiel, V. A., (Problems of Ecological Parasitology.) Annals Leningrad State Univ. No. *7*, 1–194. (In Russian.)

26. Dubinin, M. N., 1949. (Influence of Hibernation on Parasitic Fauna of Fishes in Volga Delta. [Including Protozoa]). Mag. Parasit., Moscow, *11*, 104–125. (In Russian.)

27. Dudzinski, M. L. and Mykytowycz, R., 1963. Relationship Between Sex and Age of Rabbits, *Oryctolagus cuniculus* (L.) and Infection with Nematodes *Trichostrongylus retortaeformis* and *Graphidium strigosum.* J. Parasitol., *49*, 55–59.

28. Eibl-Eibesfeldt, I., 1955. Über Symbiosen, Parasitismus und andere besondere zwischenartliche Beziehungen tropischer Meeresfische. Zeit. f. Tierpsychologie, *12*, 203–219.

29. Elton, C., 1927. *Animal Ecology.* Sidgwick and Jackson, London. 207 pp.

30. Fischthal, J. H., 1953. Parasites of Northwest Wisconsin Fishes. IV. Summary and Limnological Relationships. Trans. Wisconsin Acad. Sci., Arts & Let., *42*, 83–108.

31. FLANDERS, S. E., 1935.   Effect of Host Density on Parasitism. J. Econ. Ent., *28*, 898–900.
32. FLANDERS, S. E., 1951.   Mass Culture of California Red Scale and its Golden Chalcid Parasites. Hilgardia, *21*, 1–42.
33. FOX, I., 1951.   Relative and Seasonal Abundance of the Common Rat Ectoparasites of San Juan, Puerto Rico. J. Parasitol., *37*, 85–95.
34. GAUSE, G. F., 1934.   *The Struggle for Existence*. Williams & Williams, Baltimore. 163 pp.
35. GHIDINI, G. M., 1940.   Ricerche sull'attività cellulosolitica della flora e fauna intestinale di *Reticulitermes lucifugus* Rossi. Boll. Soc. Ital. Biol. Sper., *15*, 220–221.
36. GORBUNOVA, M., 1936.   (Variations of the Parasitic Fauna of the Pike and the Roach With their Age.) In Dogiel, V. A., (Problems of Ecological Parasitology.) Annals Leningrad State Univ., No. *7*, 1–194. (In Russian.)
37. GOULSON, H. T., 1958.   Studies on the Influence of a Prior Infection with *Ancylostoma caninum* on the Establishment and Maintenance of *Trichinella spiralis* in Mice. J. Elisha Mitchell Sci. Soc., *74*, 14–23.
38. GUTIERREZ, J. and DAVIS, R. E., 1959.   Bacterial Ingestion by the Rumen Ciliates *Entodinium* and *Diplodinium*. J. Protozool., *6*, 222–226.
39. HAZARD, F. O., 1941.   The Absence of Opalinids from the Adult Green Frog, *Rana clamitans*. J. Parasitol., *27*, 513–516.
40. HEISCH, R. B., 1956.   Zoonoses as a Study in Ecology. Brit. Med. J., *22*, 669–673.
41. HOLMES, J. C., 1961.   Effects of Concurrent Infections on *Hymenolepis diminuta* (Cestoda) and *Moniliformis dubius* (Acanthocephala). I. General Effects and Comparison with Crowding. J. Parasitol., *47*, 209–216.
42. HOPKINS, C. A., 1959.   Seasonal Variations in the Incidence and Development of the Cestode *Proteocephalus filicollis* (Rud. 1810) in *Gasterosteus aculeatus* (L. 1766). Parasitol., *49*, 529–542.
43. HUFFAKER, C. B., 1958.   The Concept of Balance in Nature. Proc. Tenth Internat. Congr. Entomol., *2*, 1956 (1958), 625–636.
44. HUNGATE, R. E., 1955.   Mutualistic Intestinal Protozoa. p. 159–199 in: *Biochemistry and Physiology of Protozoa*. Ed. by S. H. Hutner and André Lwoff. Academic Press Inc. N. Y. 388 pp.
45. KILHAM, L. and OLIVIER, L., 1961.   The Promoting Effect of Trichinosis on Encephalomyocarditis (EMC) Virus Infection in Rats. Amer. J. Trop. Med. Hyg., *10*, 879–884.
46. KIRBY, H. JR., 1941.   Relationships Between Certain Protozoa and Other Animals. In: *"Protozoa in Biological Research."* Calkins, G. N., and Summers, F. M. (editors) Columbia Univ. Press, N. Y., Chapt. 19, p. 890–1008.
47. KRUPP, I. M., 1956   Amebic Invasion of the Liver of Guinea Pigs Infected with the Larvae of a Nematode, *Toxocara canis*. Expl. Parasitol., *5*, 421–426.
48. KRUPP, I. M., 1961.   Effects of Crowding and of Superinfection on Habitat Selection and Egg Production in *Ancylostoma caninum*. J. Parasitol., *47*, 957–961.
49. LARSH, J. E., JR. and DONALDSON, A. W., 1944.   The Effect of Concurrent Infection with *Nippostrongylus* on the Development of *Hymenolepis* in Mice. J. Parasitol., *30*, 18–20.
50. LARSH, J. E., Jr. and HENDRICKS, J. R., 1949.   The Probable Explanation for the Difference in the Localization of Adult *Trichinella spiralis* in Young and Old Mice. J. Parasitol., *35*, 101–106.
51. LIMBAUGH, C., 1961.   Cleaning Symbiosis. Sci. Amer., *205*, 42–49.
52. MATHIES, A. W., JR., 1959.   Certain Aspects of the Host-Parasite Relationship of *Aspiculuris tetraptera*, a Mouse Pinworm. I. Host Specificity and Age Resistance. Exper. Parasitol., *8*, 31–38.
53. MAY, J. M., 1958.   The *Ecology of Human Diseases*. MD Publications, N. Y. 327 pp.
54. MAY, J. M. (ed.) 1961.   *Studies in Disease Ecology*. Hafner Publ. Co. N.Y., 613 pp.
55. NICHOLSON, A. J., 1933.   The Balance of Animal Populations. J. Anim. Ecol. (Suppl.), *2*, 132–178.
56. NOBLE, E. R., 1957.   Seasonal Variations in Host-Parasite Relations Between Fish and their Protozoa. J. Mar. Biol. Assoc. U. K., *36*, 143–155.
57. NOBLE, E. R., 1960.   Fishes and their Parasite-Mix as Objects for Ecological Studies Ecology, *41*, 593–596.

58. Odum, E. P., 1953. *Fundamentals of Ecology*. W. B. Saunders Co., 384 pp.

59. Otto, G. F., 1958. Some Reflections on the Ecology of Parasitism. J. Parasitol., *44*, 1–27.

60. Oxford, A. E., 1951. The Conversion of Certain Soluble Sugars to a Glucosan by Holotrich Ciliates in the Rumen of Sheep. J. Gen. Microbiol., *5*, 83–90.

61. Pavlovskii, E. N., 1945. The Ecological Parasitology. J. Gen. Biol., *6*, 65–92 (Moscow). (Russian with English summ.)

62. Phillips, B. P., Wolfe, P. A., and Bartgis, I. L., 1958. Studies on the Ameba-Bacteria Relationship in Amebiasis. II. Some Concepts on the Etiology of the Disease. Amer. J. Trop. Med. & Hyg., *7*, 392–399.

63. Phillips, B. P., Wolfe, P. A., Rees, C. W., Gordon, H. A., Wright, W. H., and Reyniers, J. A., 1955. Studies on the Ameba-Bacteria Relationship in Amebiasis. Comparative Results of the Intracaecal Inoculation of Germfree Monocontaminated, and Conventional Guinea Pigs with *Entamoeba histolytica*. Am. J. Trop. Med. Hyg., *4*, 675–692.

64. Raabe, Z., 1956. Investigations on the Parasitofauna of Freshwater Molluscs in the Brackish Waters. Acta Parasitol. Polonica, *4*, 375–406.

65. Read, C. P., 1951. The "Crowding Effect" in Tapeworm Infections. J. Parasitol., *37*, 174–178.

66. Rees, Gwendolen, 1950. Observations on the Vertical Migrations of the Third-stage Larva of *Haemonchus contortus* (Rud.) on Experimental Plots of *Lolium perenne* S 24, in Relation to Meteorological and Micrometeorological Factors. Parasitol., *40*, 127–143.

67. Reynoldson, T. B., 1955. Factors Influencing Population Fluctuations of *Urceolaria mitra* (Peritricha) Epizoic on Freshwater Triclads. J. Animal Ecology, *24*, 57–83.

68. Roberts, L. S., 1961. The Influence of Population Density on Patterns and Physiology of Growth in *Hymenolepis diminuta* (Cestoda: Cyclophyllidea) in the Definitive Host. Exper. Parasitol., *11*, 332–371.

69. Ryckman, R. E., Lindt, C. C., Ames, C. T., and Lee, R. D., 1954. Seasonal Incidence of Fleas on the California Ground Squirrel in Orange County, California. J. Econ. Ent., *47*, 1070–1074.

70. Salt, G., 1936. Experimental Studies in Insect Parasitism. IV. The Effect of Superparasitism on Populations of *Trichogramma evanescens*. J. Exper. Biol., *13*, 363–375.

71. Sandground, J. H., 1929. A Consideration of the Relation of Host-Specificity of Helminths and Other Metazoan Parasites to the Phenomena of Age Resistance and Acquired Immunity. Parasitol., *21*, 227–255.

71a. Schad, G. A., 1963. Niche Diversification in a Parasitic Species Flock. Nature, *198*, 404–407.

72. Smith, H. S., 1929. Multiple Parasitism: Its Relation to the Biological Control of Insect Pests. Bull. Ent. Res., *20*, 141–149.

73. Smith, H. S., 1935. The Rôle of Biotic Factors in the Determination of Population Densities. J. Econ. Ent., *28*, 873–898.

74. Solomon, M. E., 1949. The Natural Control of Animal Populations. J. Animal Ecol., *18*, 1–35.

75. Solomon, M. E., 1957. Dynamics of Insect Population. Ann. Rev. Entomol., *2*, 121–142.

76. Solomon, M. E, 1958. Meaning of Density-Dependence and Related Terms in Population Dynamics. Nature, *181*, 1778–1781.

77. Stefanski, Vitol'd., 1955. Biotsenoticheskie Otnosheniya Mezhdu Paraziticheskoi Faunoi i Bakterial'noi Floroi Pishchevaritel'nogo Trakta. (Biocoenotic Relations Between Parasitic Fauna and Bacterial Flora of the Digestive Tract.) Zool. Zhur., *34*, 992–999, 1955; Referat. Zhur., Biol., 1956, No. 63975.

78. Thompson, W. R., 1929. On Natural Control. Parasitol., *21*, 269–281.

79. ————, 1956. The Fundamental Theory of Natural and Biological Control. Ann. Rev. Entomol., *1*, 379–402.

80. Ullyett, G. C., 1943. Some Aspects of Parasitism in Field Populations of *Plutella maculipennis* Curt. J. Entomol. Soc. S. Africa, *6*, 65–80.

81. UTIDA, S., 1953. Effect of Host Density Upon the Population Growth of Interacting Two Species of Parasites. Experimental Studies on Synparasitism. Second Report. Oyo-Kontyu, *9*, 102–107. (In Japanese with Eng. summary.)

82. VARLEY, G. C., 1947. The Natural Control of Population Balance in the Knapweed Gall-Fly (*Urophora jaceana*). J. Anim. Ecol., *16*, 139–187.

83. ————, 1958. Meaning of Density-Dependence and Related Terms in Population Dynamics. Nature, *181*, 1778–1781.

84. ———— and EDWARDS, R. L., 1957. The Bearing of Parasite Behaviour on the Dynamics of Insect Host and Parasite Populations. J. Animal Ecol., *26*, 469–475.

85. VOGE, M., 1959. Sensitivity of Developing *Hymenolepis diminuta* Larvae to High Temperature Stress. J. Parasitol., *45*, 175–181.

CHAPTER XXIV

Ecology of Parasitism. II. Distribution and Zoogeography

INTRODUCTION

BIOGEOGRAPHY is a title under which is gathered a vast amount of fact and speculation on problems associated with the distribution of plants and animals in space. This field of inquiry impinges upon many others which are considered in this book, especially host specificity (p. 618) and evolution of parasites (p. 648). Conclusions relating to the biological aspects of geography may invite warm agreement and support, or, conversely, equally warm and entertaining disagreement. Thus, the value of a certain parasitic genus as an indicator of the distribution and evolution of its host may on the one hand be supported by conclusions drawn from biogeography, or on the other hand be exposed to most zealous criticism from the same source. In addition to the obvious practical importance of knowledge about the distribution of parasites, such as that of hookworms or of the insect vectors of trypanosomes, the purely philosophical aspects of biology and geography are not only important, but generally are more interesting. The spread of natural populations of parasites is a specialized aspect of biogeography of particular consequence for the parasitologist.

Present distribution of a species depends on: (1) the age of the species—the older it is the more time it has had in which to disperse; (2) the possibilities it has had for dispersal in the past; (3) the present opportunities it has for dispersal—this factor varies with its ability, if a parasite, to live apart from a host, and with the extent to which the host is bound to a particular habitat. Physical, chemical, mechanical and biological agencies have operated from the remote beginnings of the first parasites to encroach upon the freedom of plants and animals. These factors may produce their effects on adult parasites directly, on larval parasites, on the availability of intermediate hosts, or on definitive hosts. The exact mode of operation, past and present, is often obscure.

Zoological investigations of parasites and their hosts must be based on large numbers of fauna lists or distributional records. Such records for parasites are scanty, but those that exist suffice for a beginning of some generalizations concerning the historical and present relationships among hosts and parasites. When considering the historical record the student should remember that in all sciences built on history, much is hypothesis.

In this chapter we are again concerned with the environmental factors which combine to create the setting that determines the numbers and kinds of parasites to be found associated with one or more hosts. When members of the same species of host become separated in space, do their parasites remain the same? What are the environmental factors outside the host and inside the host that determine the distribution of the parasite? Complete answers to these and related questions must await further ecological studies, but a good start has been made and we shall select examples from the growing literature, and formulate some tentative conclusions.

DISTRIBUTION AND CLIMATE

The distribution of parasites and of their hosts is directly and indirectly governed in a large measure by the climate. Climate varies according to latitude, longitude, altitude and season of the year; and it is the result of infinite and changing combinations of temperature, rain, wind, water currents, land and water masses, mountain ranges and vegetation. Plants which serve as food for animals grow only where there are appropriate conditions of temperature, moisture and soil.

Temperature is the most important single extrinsic factor which influences the existence of parasites. Large areas of water situated around small areas of land tend to equalize temperatures, whereas large areas of land, especially those remote from large bodies of water, tend to retain the sun's heat during the day, and in temperate regions, to lose the heat at night—thereby helping to engender intense cold during the winter months. In warm areas such as North Africa the hot, dry climate is responsible for torrid days and cool nights. In hot, wet climates (tropics) there is relatively constant warm temperature with a high humidity and often with few or no air currents (*i.e.* doldrums). Obviously the chances for survival and dispersal of such parasites as larval hookworms outside the body, free-swimming miracidia and cercariae depend directly upon temperature and moisture. Cysts and spores and invertebrate hosts may also be killed by unsuitable temperature and moisture conditions.

MICRODISTRIBUTION

The phrase "distribution of animals" usually suggests a spread over geographical areas, but it should also connote, for parasites, the spread within or on one host. When one host organ is considered, or even one cell, the term *microdistribution* is particularly appropriate.

The intense pace of competition for space and food forces parasites into almost every kind of available host tissue. Once within the tissue or space, the invader "selects" the best possible location where freedom for feeding and reproduction is at its maximum, within the limits imposed by the metabolism of the parasite, and by the physiological responses of the host. The presence of other pioneer parasites, which have won a head start in the race for host tissue or space, renders even more complex the chemical adjustments which have to be made. At any one time, from a phylogenetic point of view, the several species of parasites together occupying one host appear to have become adjusted to a state of reposed rivalry, each respecting the other's territory, but ever ready to take immediate aggressive advantage of any weakness. This teleological simile suggests some form of communication among the contestants, but, on the contrary, each parasite builds a selfish empire for its own species alone, and blindly pushes the borders of its realm.

Among the most interesting examples of microdistribution are the lice on birds and on man. Most bird groups have 5 or 6 species of lice, often many more.[1a] For example, on the Tinamidae (tinamou group in South America) 12 species of lice belonging to 8 genera and 3 families have been recorded from 1 species of bird host (*Cryplurellus obsoletus*), while 15 species of lice belonging to 12 genera and 3 families were recorded from another host (*Tinamus major*). There is a general correlation between size and shape of the lice and size of feathers. Lice on the smaller feathers of the head and neck, where they are out of reach of the bird bill, tend to be broad, with larger mandibles and head, while lice on the longer, broader feathers of the back and wings are flattened and elongate.

A delicate regulation in the microdistribution of parasites within one host body is constantly operative. Parasites, to be sure, often are adapted to one organ, or to a part of one organ, or to one kind of cell, but the metabolic balance is easily upset and one species of parasite may overrun its usual boundaries. For example, a nematode of the intestine of a vertebrate host may occasionally become so abundant in numbers that it spreads into the stomach, gallbladder, liver and coelom. *Leishmania donovani* normally invades large endothelial cells of blood vessels and lymphatics, as well as a few monocytes of the blood, but it may also parasitize erythrocytes in the liver, bone marrow and spleen, especially in young children in advanced stages of the disease leishmaniasis. In such a situation, this usurpation of space often discourages other kinds of parasites, or even eliminates them altogether.

Distribution of parasites within a host is governed by the same basic forces that control distribution of the hosts. Temperature, moisture, mechanical barriers, chemistry of surrounding medium, food supplies and other ecological factors are always operative, as well as phylogenetic relationships which may determine the degree of host specificity. In the fish called the "mud-sucker" (*Gillichthys mirabilis*) two closely related nematodes live in the mesenteries, but one of these worms is also occasionally found in the intestine.

A physiological difference between the two worms must be the explanation, because both worms appear to possess equal opportunity and equipment for penetrating the bile duct or intestinal wall.

Distribution of many kinds of parasites in a vertebrate body is initially determined by the course of the circulatory system—a natural distributing network for food, oxygen, metabolic products and parasites. Larval hookworms, *Ascaris*, *Wuchereria* and others, are each carried to all parts of the body by the blood and lymph, and each species of parasite is finally delivered to an organ according to its predilection.

No sharp distinction exists between microdistribution and any other kind; hence, before we move to the wider aspects of zoogeographical distribution, we shall consider one group of parasites, the lice, as an illustration of the complex relations between parasites in or on a host, and the distribution of the host. The distribution of lice, in the overwhelming majority of instances, is governed by the phylogeny of the hosts. This situation is in contrast with that of fleas where ecological factors are of paramount importance. On the human body there is a high correlation between the amount of hair and the rate of infestation by lice. Girls generally have more lice than do boys. Evidence for such statements comes from studies of hair from shaven heads among troops, in prisons and orphanages. The more clothing people wear the more lice they tend to possess. Living habits of people affect their lice populations. If men live close together in ships, tents or barracks, the spread of lice is fostered. The temperature and humidity of the space between man's skin and his clothing—that is, the living space for lice, remains remarkably constant in different countries and in different seasons of the year. Since, therefore, man stabilizes the climatic conditions on his surface, a wide geographical distribution of his lice is to be expected. From dry climates in Sahara and Iraq to the constant humid equatorial conditions of Ceylon, Congo and Tahiti, to the temperate lands of Europe and America, man's lice are readily to be found. Local absence of human lice is generally due to social or to hygenic habits of the people.

HOST MIGRATIONS

Migratory animals provide us with unique opportunities for studying the effects of changes in external environments. Few studies have been made on the parasites of mammals and birds in relation to migrations of the hosts, but migratory fishes and their parasites have attracted the attentions of numerous parasitologists.

The circumpolar distribution of *Neoechinorhynchus rutili*, an acanthocephalan parasite, provides incontestable evidence of practically continuous geographical distribution of one species of parasite in freshwater fishes of two continents, North America and Eurasia.[16] The adaptations of *N. rutili* to fish hosts are so flexible that the worms are found in seven families in Europe and eight families in

North America, and in the two continents the following host families are parasitized in common: Salmonidae, Cyprinidae, Esocidae, Gasterosteidae and Percidae. The only obvious way a parasite which occurs so often in fresh waters can become so widely scattered over the world is through the utilization of a great diversity of hosts representing a diversity of habitats. Of the forty or more species of fish which have been listed in the literature as hosts for *N. rutili*, only four (*Esox lucius* the pike, *Gasterosteus aculeatus* the threespine stickleback, *Pungitius pungitius* the ninespine stickleback and *Salvelinus alpinus* the Arctic charr) are common to the two continents. Of particular importance are the wandering hosts such as salmon, trout, stickleback and charr, whose migratory habits often involve passage between salt and fresh water.

Migrations of thousands of miles are common among many fishes (*e.g.* tuna, salmon, eel), but few detailed investigations have been made that tell us whether the fish keep the same parasites during the whole course of migration. The larval eel lives for three years as a marine pelagic fish, and, according to Dogiel,[3] is completely free from parasites during this period. Its feeding habits are a mystery — nothing having been found in the digestive tract at this stage in its life cycle. A post-larval, marine stage of one year's duration is followed by a period of migration up a river where the fish becomes a bottom feeder and gains parasites. The first freshwater parasites in the young eel (about 70 mm. long) are those not requiring an intermediate host (*e.g. Myxidium giardi*, *Trichodina*, *Gyrodactylus*, some trematode larvae and *Acanthocephalus anguillae*). In later life the parasitic fauna of female eels is of a freshwater variety whereas that of the male fish includes both freshwater and marine species. During the last months of their life the eels are said to be free from parasites.

Parasites of salmon change as the fishes migrate from fresh to salt water and back again. Parasites from young freshwater forms show no host specificity and are also to be found in other freshwater fishes in the same locality. The American west coast salmon is parasitized by the fluke-vector (*Nanophyetus*) of the canine salmon poisoning disease. The causative agent is a rickettsia. Fish that are heavily parasitized in fresh water migrate to the sea, and when they return two or three years later to spawn, they are practically free from the flukes. But the salmon again acquire thousands of metacercariae within a few weeks after entering fresh water.

When fishes migrate to a new environment and become isolated there, or when they are introduced by man into new regions, their original parasite faunas become reduced in numbers. To put this conclusion in more general terms, the process of acclimatization leads to impoverishment of an animal's original parasites. A few relics of the past often remain, but, given time, the hosts tend to acquire new species of parasites not to be found in the original habitat. A host generally has a larger variety of parasites, particularly parasites peculiar to it, in the habitat where it has lived the longest. For example, the freshwater fish, *Lota lota*, has numerous parasites characteristic of other freshwater fishes, but *L. lota* is a member of the Gadidae, a family consisting almost exclusively of marine species, and it also has a number of marine parasites which are reminders of its past.

Birds also sometimes migrate for thousands of miles, and carry their parasites with them. The state and extent of parasitism is directly related to the physiology of the host, and the physiology of migrating birds changes during their migrations. For example, some birds spend their summers in Alaska and their winters in the south Pacific. Do these birds possess the same kinds and numbers of parasites at both locations? Probably not, but practically no studies of this nature have been made with birds.

Migratory mammals (except for man) and their parasites offer to the parasitologist an almost untouched field for important basic research. Migratory whales and porpoises may lose their helminth parasites when they reach different environments.[2] One wonders what happens to the parasites of arctic land mammals when the hosts migrate to more temperate climates during the winter time.[1]

Human migrations, especially to and from the tropics, have provided us with a great deal of information on the spread of disease and on the nature of immune reactions. "The migrations of populations have contributed largely to the development of animal parasites in new localities. Evidence favors the view that yellow fever, dengue, estivo-autumnal malaria, broad fish tapeworm infection, the hookworm infection produced by *Necator americanus*, Manson's blood-fluke infection, Bancroft's and other types of filariasisis and dracunculosis were brought to the Western Hemisphere by the white colonists and their slaves imported from Africa, as were typhus fever, leprosy, smallpox, measles, mumps, syphilis, frambesia, and probably influenza. . . . Wherever climate, necessary intermediate hosts, and customs of the population were favorable, these diseases became established in the new soil."[4]

Trypanosomiasis in man and animals has received some intensive study from the point of view of migrating hosts. It is well known that the elimination of an intermediate host leads to the disappearance of a parasite from any given territory. Mammalian trypanosomes of the *Vivax*, *Congolense* and *Brucei* groups are normally restricted to a tropical zone of Africa coinciding with the area of distribution of the tsetse fly, their transport host. *Trypanosoma vivax* is a striking exception to the above rule. This species is found in Africa where it is transmitted to cattle by mechanical contamination of the proboscis of tsetse flies, and it is also found in West Indies, South America and Mauritius where it was introduced in the last century with infected cattle. The non-African strains are morphologically indistinguishable from the African ones, but the former are transmitted by horse flies (Tabanidae) in which the parasites cannot develop, and they are transferred mechanically, as in tsetse flies, by the proboscis. This substitution of one vector for another has enabled the parasite to become widely distributed to distant lands.

The disease known as surra in domestic animals is caused by *Trypanosoma evansi* which is phylogenetically related to *T. brucei*, but it occurs only outside the area of distribution of tsetse flies. Its range includes the Palaearctic, Ethiopian, Madagascar, oriental and neotropical zoogeographical regions. Surra is also transmitted mechanically by the contaminated proboscis of horse flies. There is evidence from laboratory cross infection experiments that *T. evansi* originated from *T. brucei* in Africa. The disease nagana, caused by *T. brucei*, could originally have been contracted by camels which were brought into the "tsetse belt" of Africa; then with a combination of transfer of mode of infection to the mouth parts of horse flies, and migrations of camels, the new disease, surra, could have been extended far beyond the geographic boundaries of its ancestral disease nagana.

There is apparently a direct correlation between relative scarcity of parasites and the ability of the host to adapt itself to widely different environments, as indicated by studies on numbers of parasites in widely dispersed hosts in comparison with parasites in hosts confined to one or two comparatively small areas. A wide geographical distribution of a host may be partly possible because of a relatively high resistance to parasitism. Much more work on this and related problems must be done, however, before convincing evidence and clear conclusions can be obtained.

DISTRIBUTION OF ARTHROPODS BY COMMERCIAL VEHICLES

In prehistoric times when man's means of transportation was confined to his legs, the carriage of food stuffs and other articles and the driving of livestock sufficed slowly to transport insects and other arthropods, as well as other human parasites, from one location to another. The introduction of carts and canoes greatly increased the opportunities for man unwittingly to carry insects away from their natural habitats. Even when dugout canoes afforded the only means of transoceanic transportation, the spread of such insects as mosquitoes among the South Pacific islands by Polynesian voyagers was greatly facilitated. Thus certain mosquitoes of the *scutellaris* group of *Aëdes* commonly breed in beached canoes, and their eggs are resistant to drying. The use of sailing vessels and, later, steamships provided a means for numerous insect introductions to countries all over the world. Flies and cockroaches breed in galleys and quarters, various beetles infest stored foods, and mosquitoes commonly breed in many kinds of containers holding water. As the result of such transportation *Culex p. fatigans* has become cosmopolitan, and *Aëdes aegypti* virtually pantropical.

The development of aviation, however, has been the most alarming and serious encouragement of accidental insect introduction on a global scale. Among the insects most commonly carried by air-craft are: Diptera (mosquitoes and flies), Hemiptera (bugs), Lepidoptera (butterflies and moths), Coleoptera (beetles), and Hymenoptera (ants, bees, wasps). Other insects often to be found in planes are cockroaches, lacewings, earwigs and termites. The hazards associated with air transportation are relatively greater than those with sea transportation, not only because of the much shorter time required for flight, but also because of the character of the international airports which are usually situated in rural or semi-rural districts. The docks for ships, on the other hand, are located most frequently in the heart of heavily built up urban areas — presenting a limited choice of mosquito larval habitats.[6]

The accidental importation of *Anopheles gambiae* into Brazil from West Africa, about forty years ago, led to a disastrous outbreak of malaria, causing intense suffering with more than 300,000 cases of the disease and 16,000 deaths. The same mosquito was introduced into Upper Egypt during World War II, and it initiated a serious malaria epidemic involving 170,000 cases with 11,889 deaths during 1942-44.[18] Vigorously prosecuted campaigns, at great cost, ultimately eradicated *A. gambiae* from both Brazil and Upper Egypt.

A serious threat facing South East Asia today is the possible introduction by international air transportation of yellow fever from Africa or South America. New Zealand and the multitude of tropical Pacific islands south of 20° 12'S and east of 170° E lack anopheline mosquitoes altogether. Hence there is a possibility of the introduction by air lines of these mosquitoes with malaria and yellow fever.

Aspects of insect quarantine were reviewed by Lee[7] who stated, "The concept which lately has been described as insect quarantine simply implies considerations of the prevention of entry of noxious insects into areas where they are not known to occur, whether such areas be geographically or politically limited. Initially of course the emphasis is on the prevention of such entry into countries whether they be continents, major geographical units of continents, or islands large or small. Despite this initial emphasis, problems of prevention of spread of noxious insects within geographically or politically limited areas also arise and are generally considered within the field of insect quarantine."

Most countries now include provisions in their quarantine laws to guard against the special health hazards associated with air trans-portation. The International Sanitary Convention for Aerial Navigation of 1933/44, and the World Health Organization have made recommendations urging recognition of the importance of implementing insect quarantines, and incorporating detailed advice concerning spraying equipment, insecticides and disinsection tech-niques. As yet, however, there is little international uniformity in the interpretation of existing recommendations. Aircraft disinsec-tion is a safe, simple and speedy safeguard, but it should not be regarded as affording complete protection.

DISTRIBUTION WITHIN RESTRICTED AREAS

A comparison of the parasites of the coastal cod and the winter cod (two subspecies) in the White Sea discloses differences in the respective faunas which may be attributed to differences in habits and habitats. The coastal cod feeds on the bottom and is infected with the fluke, *Podocotyle atomon*, obtained from its crustacean food, and with the ciliate, *Trichodina cottidarum*. The fish is heavily infected with intestinal stages of the nematode, *Contracaecum aduncum*, but lightly infected with the trematode, *Hemiurus levinseni*. On the other hand, the winter cod, which feeds primarily on plankton, is only lightly infected with *Contracaecum*, but every fish harbors *Hemiurus*.

The same species of fish in different parts of the White Sea sometimes possesses different parasites, and these differences appear to be related to hydrological factors. On the other hand, the same manner of life in distantly separated (taxonomically) fish may lead to the acquisition of the same parasites. For example, the flounder, *Pleuronectes flessus*, and the wolf fish, *Anarrhichas lupus*, both feed on the sea bottom on the same animals, and they have nine species of parasites in common. But many of these parasites are not specific for these fish.

Infection of the flounder, *Pseudopleuronectes americanus*, with trematodes is heavier in inshore waters than in offshore waters, and close to shore the infection is heavier in fish that are taken in deeper water adjacent to open sea than in fish taken near shoals. Larger flounders have heavier infections than do smaller fish, and there is an absence of marked seasonal variations in the former. In casting about for an explanation for the differences between inshore and offshore fish, one should remember that near the shore there are usually many more kinds of other animals and plants associated with the variety of shoreline habitats (see p. 593). Many of these other animals may serve as intermediate hosts for parasites.

Lake Mogilnoye, situated on the island of Kildin in the Barents Sea, has fresh or brackish water down to a depth of about 5 meters, but below that level the water becomes heavily contaminated with hydrogen sulfide. Codfish are to be found in the lake, and they and other marine animals can live only in the layers between 5 and 12 meters deep. These animals can be considered as descendants from marine forms which lived there at a time when waters of the lake were in communication with the surrounding sea. An examination of the parasites of these relic cod shows that the parasitic fauna becomes impoverished as compared with that of the same species of hosts living under normal marine conditions. Parasites normal to cod include the fluke, *Echinorhynchus gadi*, and the copepods, *Caligus curtus*, *Clavella uncinata*, *C. brevicornis*, and *Lernaeocera brachialis*. These parasites are absent in cod from Lake Mogilnoye. Also absent are several myxosporidia commonly found in marine cod. When intermediate hosts are involved, as with *Lernaeocera*, the absence of the parasite in the lake can easily be explained, but for the others there is no such ready explanation.[3]

CONCOMITANT STUDY OF HOSTS AND PARASITES IN DIFFERENT PARTS OF THE WORLD

A number of writers have contributed to a general principle which may be stated as follows. The systematics and phylogenetic ages of hosts can often be determined directly from the systematics and degrees of organization of their permanent parasites, and, conversely, the systematics and ages of parasites may be determined directly from the phylogenetic and taxonomic relationships of their hosts (see Rules of Affinity, p. 651).

Probably the first scientist to use parasites as indicators of the relationships and geographical distribution of hosts was von Ihering,[18] who based his conclusions upon a study of helminths. A concomitant and comparative study of hosts and parasites in different parts of the world has been labeled as the "von Ihering method." A good many years ago the well-known English helminthologist, H. A. Baylis, pointed out that von Ihering's facts were both inadequate and inaccurate. Von Ihering thought, for example, that the occurrence of the nematode, *Dioctophyme renale*, in wild canidae in Europe and South America necessarily indicated that it had existed in their upper miocene ancestors. Actually this parasite has been recorded from other carnivores and from the horse, pig, organgutan and man. Baylis was doubtful of relying on the von Ihering method when it is applied to helminths because the habits (particularly as regards food) and environment of the hosts have played a far more important part in determining their helminth fauna than have their phylogenetic relationships.

We should remind ourselves that where the relationships of the parasites are confused (*e.g.* the biting lice), and where cases of recent acquisition, divergent evolution, convergent evolution and discontinuous distribution occur, it is impossible to use the parasites as infallible guides to the origins of the hosts. Baylis has aptly warned us that "although the attempt to draw conclusions as to the relationships of animals from their helminth parasites may sometimes yield interesting results, it is fraught with so many pitfalls that it should be made with greatest caution." Mayr[10] has also issued a warning to those who would place too much emphasis on the importance of using parasites as a guide to host phylogeny. He says, "We are dealing here with something very basic, with the whole principle of phylogeny, with the principle of this study of parallel phylogeny and we must be awfully sure of these tools we use, that we do not misuse them, and we must, at all times, allow for an occasional transfer of parasites, and we must allow for different rates of evolution, and we must realize . . . that the comparative anatomy is something more reliable. Two birds can exchange their parasites, nothing prevents this, but I have not yet seen two birds exchanging their heads, their wings or their legs. These have come down from its ancestors and not from another bird that nested in a hole right next to it!"

Keeping the limitations of the von Ihering method in mind, let us now turn to a more detailed consideration of the use of parasites as indicators of the evolutionary relationships of their hosts.

PARASITES AS CLUES TO HOST AFFINITIES AND EVOLUTION

The von Ihering method has been used in the study of the frog family Leptodactylidae which is characteristic of (1) tropical and semi-tropical America (*e.g.* Patagonia), and (2) Australia and Tasmania. These frogs have been reported from nowhere else in the world. This situation can be explained on the basis of the existence of an original land bridge across Antartica, or on the basis of convergent evolution. But all of these frogs have, in their intestines, opalinid parasites of the genus *Zelleriella* composed of very similar species. The presence of similar parasites could also be explained on the basis of convergent or parallel evolution, but for *both* host and parasite so to evolve may be too much to expect. Hence the first explanation above (the existence of a land bridge) has gained questionable support.[11]

A comparison of the trematodes of Australian frogs with their close relatives in frogs of Europe, America and Asia might lead one to support the view that the frogs of Australia originated in a hypothetical Palaearctic center in geological times. But the study of the opalinids of these frogs, as noted above, suggests that the hosts originated in South America.

The entozoa of opossums of America and those of Australian marsupials are quite different. In the Australian marsupials there are fourteen genera of sclerostomes (*e.g.* *Strongylus*) but probably no pinworms. In American opossums there are no sclerostomes, but a peculiar pinworm (*Cruzia*) is common. Both host groups have a primitive tapeworm belonging to a cosmopolitan family, but the South American species is the more primitive. Hence the Australian marsupials appear not to be as closely related to the American opossum as has been supposed. These speculations are not inconsistent with the evidence presented above for the existence of a land bridge over the Antarctic. Fossil records suggest that a bridge connecting Patagonia and the Australian Region must have lasted longer than that between Patagonia and the Palaearctic Region.

Geological studies furnish strong evidence for the existence during the Tertiary period of a wide band of water extending across what is now the Near East, Mediterranean, mid-Atlantic and Gulf of Mexico. This wide band is called the Tethys Sea. Arms of the Sea extended southward to areas now occupied by the Amazon and

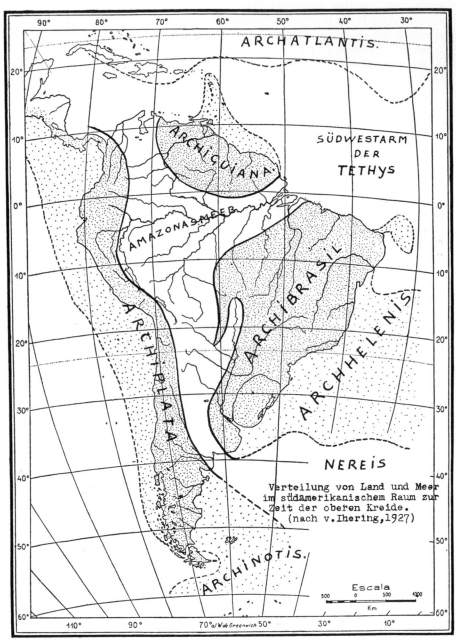

Fig. XXIV–1.—Arms of the ancient Tethys Sea extending over the area now occupied by South America. (Szidat, Proc. XIV Internat. Congress on Zoology. Copenhagen.)

the La Plata-Parana-Paraguay river systems of South America (Fig. XXIV–1). Evidence for the former existence of these arms comes not only from geologic records, but from the flora and fauna of the present-day rivers. Among the animals that furnish this evidence are the trematodes and isopods which parasitize the fishes. Lothar Szidat[13],[14],[15] of Argentina has made a detailed study of the zoogeographical implications of this whole area. Many of the freshwater fish parasites are characteristic of marine waters. Moreover, the nearest relatives of these freshwater parasites are sometimes to be found in the Caribbean and Mediterranean seas rather than in waters adjacent to the outlets of the rivers. Thus it is probable that as the land masses were joined to form what we now call South America, and as the intervening waters changed from salt to fresh, due in part to the rising of the Andes and subsequent melting of snow, the marine organisms either died out or they became adapted to a freshwater habitat. As a result of these changes such fishes as the Characinidae and Siluridae, now strictly freshwater inhabitants, possess parasites which changed more slowly than did their hosts (see p. 649), and which still exhibit marine features transported from their ancestral home. These parasites are relics of the Tethys Sea.

The above considerations offer a ready explanation for the absence of freshwater cymothoid isopods on fishes in the rivers of North America which flow into the Gulf of Mexico and in the rivers of Europe which flow into the Mediterranean — despite the fact that neighboring seas are rich in species of these parasitic isopods. Szidat's theory of evolution of certain digenetic trematodes from Tethys Sea fishes is weakened by the fact that his fish hosts were all members of the family Anostomidae, whereas the Mediterranean hosts are the Mugilidae (mullets).

Many digenetic trematodes of marine fishes are not widely distributed, but some significant geographical comparisons can be made.[8] For example, relatively strong similarities among trematodes occur between (1) the European Atlantic and the Mediterranean; (2) shallow waters at Tortugas, Florida and Bermuda; (3) shallow waters at Tortugas and the tropical American Pacific. Considerable dissimilarity occurs between (1) deeper waters and shallow waters at Tortugas; (2) shallow waters at Tortugas and the North Atlantic; (3) the Mediterranean and the Red Sea.

The nematodes offer poor material for discovering possible host affinities because of the existence of almost all possible gradations from free-living species to obligate parasites, and from strict host specificity to a very wide range of host tolerance, and because of the inadequacy of morphological criteria to distinguish the species. Careful physiological studies of nematode parasites are urgently needed.

Evidence for the phylogenetic relationship between a South American bird, *Cariama cristata*, and the Eurasian bustard has been presented on the basis of an analysis of their helminths. Both birds are parasitized by the nematodes, *Subulura allodapa* and *S. suctoria*. In addition, both birds harbor species of the cestode genera *Chapmania* and *Idiogenes*. Physiological segregation of tapeworms evidently occurred when vertebrates first split into present-day groups, resulting in a phylogenetic specificity. Hence we may conclude (a conclusion corroborated by taxonomic studies on birds) that *Cariama cristata* and the Eurasian bustard are related.

The effects of isolation of ectoparasites are more often reflected in morphological changes than are those of endoparasites. The Mallophaga, or biting lice, exhibit a high degree of host specificity, and they may be used to elicit evidence of parallel evolution of hosts and parasites. Moreover, the lice probably were present on ancestral hosts, and evolved at a slower rate than did the latter. Consequently, phylogenetic relationships of the hosts may be indicated by a comparison of their biting lice.

Distribution is governed largely by geographical factors in most groups of insects, but the biting lice generally spread over an enormous range in area and in climate, and geography is relatively unimportant. These lice thus are ideal parasites with which to estimate relationships among birds because as the hosts have evolved, the lice have evolved, but at a slower rate. For example, there was long disagreement among ornithologists as to the systematic position of flamingos; some authorities placed them in the Ciconiiformes (storks) and others in the Anseriformes (ducks and geese). A study of flamingo Mallophaga shows that the lice correspond very closely to those of ducks and geese. Not one of the parasites suggests any close affinity between flamingos and storks. The Mallophaga of the three North African pelicans are not alike, and the lice of one of them (the Ethiopian pelican) are more like those on the Australian pelican and the South American pelican than those on the other two North African birds. Morphologically the lice of South American pelicans are sufficiently distinct as to be placed in a separate genus, and their hosts are placed in a separate subgenus. We have here a fine example of the effects of ecological segregation of both hosts and their parasites.

A study of the Anopleura, or sucking lice, also presents interesting illustrations of the results of ecological segregation. From information on present-day distribution of these lice we may conclude that they became isolated on their hosts long ago; yet we find that the Australian marsupials do not possess sucking lice—a fact indicating that these hosts had already become isolated before the Anopleura arose as parasites.

Those mammals which are closely related to one another tend to have closely related or identical lice. The ground squirrels (*Citellus*) of North America are related, but they are different from those of Siberia. The lice, however, on these two groups of geographically separated squirrels appear to be identical. Because of the high degree of host specificity exhibited by lice, one can examine an unknown louse and tell, with little risk of error, from what kind of vertebrate it was taken, but unless the range of distribution of the group of hosts is known, one can not tell from what part of the world the louse came. A conspicuous exception to this rule is found among the family Gyropidae which occurs on a wide variety of hosts in South America but is not found elsewhere.

The distribution of parasites within the order Marsupialia conforms almost perfectly with the geographic distribution and antiquity of the hosts. For example, the biting lice of marsupials belong to the most primitive division of the Mallophaga, one family (Boopidae) infesting Australian hosts, and another (Trimenoponidae) infesting South American hosts.

The ostrich and the rhea both have sclerostome nematodes, indicating at least some measure of relationship between the two hosts. But sclerostomes occur in many kinds of grass-eating animals such as horses, elephants, Australian marsupials, rhinoceroses, tapirs, and even in South American tortoises. Ten nematodes have been reported from the rhea, and five from the ostrich, but no species in common. Both birds are parasitized by one genus of louse (*Struthiolipeurus*), but rheas have, in addition, a second louse genus (*Meinertzhageniella*). Both birds have the mite, *Pterolichus bicaudatus*, the only species of parasite in common. The arthropod distribution and similarity support evidence from feather structure and other anatomical features that the two orders of birds are related and not the relics of independent, unrelated stocks.

Space does not permit a review of all groups of mammals, but in general, before clear-cut, detailed lines of phylogenetic relationships can be established, much more research, particularly in the nature of careful comparisons of abundant collections of parasites as well as fossil mammals must be made. The precise classification of parasites must be the basis of comparisons. For details of this problem see especially Hopkins,[5] Vanzolini and Guimarães,[17] and Patterson.[12]

GENERAL RULES AND PRINCIPLES

1. Both the host and its environment determine the distribution of its parasites.

2. Widely separated hosts may have the same species of parasites, but in general the more diverse the environment the more kinds of species of parasites exist in a given host.

3. "Distribution-Pattern" has one meaning for parasites, another for hosts.

4. The classification of the parasite must be known before we presume to offer advice on obscure points about host classification.

5. When unrelated hosts live together and eat the same food they may possess some parasites in common.

6. The size and ecological differentiation of the area in which the host lives is directly correlated with the diversification and distribution of parasites of that host.

7. In all questions concerning distribution of hosts and their parasites the food factor of the host is of primary importance.

8. Parasite-host data may be used to suggest (a) genetic (phylogenetic) relationships among hosts, (b) places of origin and routes of dispersal of both hosts and parasites, and (c) ancient land connections between present and widely separated land masses.

9. Hosts which migrate for long distances tend to lose at least some of their parasites during the course of migration or soon after they arrive at the new location.

10. The process of acclimatization to a new geographical area leads to impoverishment of the host's original parasites, but a few relics of the past often remain.

11. The systematics and phylogenetic ages of hosts can often be determined directly from the systematics and degrees of organization of their permanent parasites, and, conversely, the systematics and ages of parasites may be determined directly from the phylogenetic and taxonomic relationships of their hosts.

12. There are many examples of secondary transfer of parasites (e.g. lice from hawks to owls), and of clearly-related hosts without parasites in common (e.g. penguins and Tubinares). Obviously, then, the role of parasites in studies of distribution adds to the evidence, but should not be used as an unfailing indicator of relationships.

13. When a host is widely distributed (e.g. the clam, Mytilus, or the fish, Gasterosteus aculateus) some of its parasites, such as the protozoa, may accompany the host everywhere it wanders, but when intermediate hosts are involved the distribution of the parasite may be closely restricted simply because the intermediate host has a narrow geographic range.

14. Adult parasitic worms, in contrast with protozoa, do not multiply within the host, although they may produce eggs or larvae. Additional adult worms must enter from outside the host.

15. Never say that a species does not occur someplace simply because it has not (yet) been found there.

BIBLIOGRAPHY

1. CAMERON, T. W. M., 1957. Parasitology and the Arctic. Trans. Roy. Soc. Canada, 51, ser. III: 1–10.
1a.CLAY, T., 1949. Some Problems in the Evolution of a Group of Ectoparasites. Evolution, 3, 279–299.
2. DELYAMURE, S. L., 1955. (The Helminth Fauna of Marine Mammals in the Light of Their Ecology and Phylogeny.) Moscow, Izdatelstvo Akademii Nauk, SSSR. 517 pp. (In Russian.)
3. DOGIEL, V. A., 1936. (Problems of Ecological Parasitology.) (In Russian.) Annals Leningrad State Univ. No. 7, 1–194.
4. FAUST, E. C. and RUSSELL, P. F., 1957. Clinical Parasitology. Lea & Febiger, Philadelphia. 1078 pp.
5. HOPKINS, G. H. E., 1949. The Host-Associations of the Lice of Mammals. Proc. Zool. Soc. London, 119, 387–604.
5a.IHERING, VON H., 1891. On the Ancient Relations Between New Zealand and South America. Trans. Proc. New Z. Inst., 24, 431–445.

6. LAIRD, M., 1956. Insect Introduction Hazards Affecting Singapore and Neighbouring Territories. Med. J. Malaya, *11*, 40–62.

7. LEE, D. J., 1951. The Problems of Insect Quarantine. Proc. Linn. Soc. N.S.W., *76*, 6–19.

8. MANTER, H., 1955. The Zoogeography of Trematodes of Marine Fishes. Exptl. Parasitol., *4*, 62–86.

9. MARKEVICH, A. P., 1944. (Origin and Evolution of Parasitic Fauna of Domestic Animals and Man.) Advances Modern Biol., *18*, 247–262. (Moscow) (In Russian.)

10. MAYR, E., 1957. Evolutionary Aspects of Host Specificity Among Parasites of Vertebrates. pp. 5–14 in: First Symposium on Host Specificity Among Parasites of Vertebrates. Inst. Zool. Univ. Neuchâtel.

11. METCALF, M. M., 1929. Parasites and the Aid they Give in Problems of Taxonomy, Geographical Distribution, and Paleography. Smithsonian Misc. Collections 81, No. 8. 36 pp.

12. PATTERSON, B., 1957. Mammalian Phylogeny. In: First Symposium on Host Specificity Among Parasites of Vertebrates. pp. 15–49. Inst. Zool., Univ. Neuchâtel.

13. SZIDAT, L., 1955. Beiträge zur Kenntnis der Reliktfauna des La Plata-Stromsystems. Arch. f. Hydrobiol., *51*, 209–260.

14. SZIDAT, L., 1956. Über die Parasitenfauna von *Percichthys trucha* (Cuv. & Val.) Girard der Patagonischen Gewässer und die Beziehungen des Wirtsfisches und seiner Parasiten zur Paläarktischen Region. Arch. f. Hydrobiol., *51*, 542–577.

15. SZIDAT, L., 1961. Versuch einer Zoogeographie des Süd-Atlantik mit Hilfe von Leitparasiten der Meeresfische. Parasitol. Schrift. Jena. No. 13, 98 pp. (Spanish summary.)

16. VAN CLEAVE, H. and LYNCH, J. E., 1950. The Circumpolar Distribution of *Neoechinorhynchus rutili*, an Acanthocephalan Parasite of Fresh Water Fishes. Trans. Amer. Micr. Soc., *69*, 156–171.

17. VANZOLINI, P. E. and GUIMARÃES, L. R., 1955. Lice and the History of South American Land Mammals. Rev. Brasil. Ent., *3*, 13–46.

18. W. H. O., 1955. Control of Insect Vectors in International Air Traffic. A Survey of Existing Legislation. Int. Dig. Hlth. Legis., *6*, 377–435.

CHAPTER XXV

Ecology of Parasitism. III. Parasite-Host Specificity

INTRODUCTION

Why are some parasites restricted to one species of host, whereas others flourish in a wide range of unrelated hosts? Why are some kinds of animals burdened with numerous parasites, while other kinds possess few parasites, if any. Seventeen species of fleas are found on swallows or martins and nowhere else, but swifts with similar nesting and feeding habits do not have a single flea restricted to themselves. Although most birds with large nests have many fleas, swan nests are free from these insects. The nematode, *Wuchereria bancrofti*, lives as an adult only in man, but *Trichostrongylus axei*, contrary to nematodes in general, is at home in a wide range and diversity of hosts. This species has been reported from the digestive tracts of the horse, ass, mule, sheep, cattle, goat, several species of wild ruminants, pig, and man, and experimentally in rabbits, hamsters and guinea pigs. Why do these differences exist?

The term *specificity*, when applied to an animal or plant, refers to the things which make it distinct from all others. *Host specificity* refers to the peculiar mutual adaptation which restricts a parasite to its host species. A high degree of host specificity means that the adaptations between host and parasite are so delicate and intermeshed that the parasite is unable successfully to survive in or on the body of another species of host. The central problems in the study of specificity of parasite-host relationships concern mechanisms which limit host selection and which control the ability of the parasite to invade the host and to survive within it.[53]

No parasite lacks host specificity. Obviously there are no parasites which can live in all kinds of vertebrate or invertebrate hosts. The term *monoxenous* indicates limitation to a single host, as occurs with adult *Wuchereria bancrofti*. *Oligoxenous* is used to describe parasites, like adult *Echinococcus granulosus*, which have a small host range. *Polyxenous* refers to the condition involving many suitable hosts, or relatively little host specificity, as occurs with *Fasciola hepatica*.

The problems of host specificity are primarily of a physiological nature, and they can best be solved by the use of experimental methods in life-history studies. "Explanations for specificity must be sought over the whole range of factors which concern the relationship of the parasite to the host throughout its cycle."[51]

Strict host specificity exists between many parasites and their hosts. Numerous flagellates are to be found only in the hindgut of termites. Many species of ciliates occur only in the cecum of horses. Diclidophoroidean trematode parasites on the gills of certain fishes appear to be entirely specific to their particular species of host. Moreover, there is a definite site preference; the trematode, *Diclidophora merlangi*, for example, occurs most frequently on the first gill arch of the cod, *Gadus merlangus*.[30] This exacting topographical relationship between parasite and host is probably an important factor in the mechanism of host specificity, although it may be the result of variations in the flow of water over the different gills rather than of a choice exercised by the parasite.

Since many parasites employ more than one kind of host in their life cycles, the conditions determining the degree of host specificity are often markedly different in the several stages of a cycle. Indeed, the metabolic requirements of a parasite generally vary with its developmental changes within one host. In a study of the action of anti-malarial drugs in mosquitoes infected with *Plasmodium gallinaceum* from chicks, it was found that the first indication of interference with parasite development is usually in the oocyst, but with one of the drugs used the effect was first observed on the sporozoites.[54] The different physiological demands of this parasite at particular stages in its development are demonstrated by marked changes in phosphatases and in nucleic acids in the parasite of the mosquito. Such studies again emphasize the necessity of using biochemical tools to disclose the basic nature of parasite-host specificity.

Whereas two strains of a given parasite might infect a final host with equal facility, they may not be equally infective to a given strain of intermediate host. In other words, a strain endemic in one area might be physiologically distinct from a strain endemic in another area, and this difference might be detected only on the basis of infectivity to an intermediate host.

It is obvious then, that in any consideration of specificity we must not confine our attentions to parasites, but must study their hosts with equal zeal. The host is in many respects equivalent to the surrounding environment of free-living organisms, but the host, as an environment, is constantly developing specific responses and adaptations to its parasites (see Chapter XXI).

ISOLATION OF PARASITE POPULATIONS

Before embarking on a more detailed discussion of the kinds, degrees and significance of host specificity, let us examine briefly some factors which are responsible for the isolation of parasite populations. These factors are basically of a genetic, biochemical, ecological or physical nature.

1. When a species of host is divided into two or more population groups separated geographically in different environments, their respective parasite faunas normally exhibit differences. This fact

is a further indication of the influence of the environment of the host on its parasite-mix.

Given sufficient time, a host population may become divided into non-interbreeding units, thereby forming new species of hosts and, consequently, changing the character of the parasites. Examples may be found in the abundant speciation among mites on isolated groups of lizards, or on bats which occupy very specialized biotopes. Pterygosomid mites (e.g. *Pterygosoma aculeatum* beneath scales of lizards) undoubtedly orginated on ancestral lizards before the hosts became segregated onto different continents.

A puzzling example of an obscure ecological barrier is shown by the intestinal coccidian, *Eimeria mohavensis*, in the kangaroo rat *Dipodomys panamintinus*, and in *D. merriami*.[12] Both rats occupy the same geographical areas, and food contamination between the two seems to be inevitable. The two species of hosts presumably represent non-breeding units originally derived from a common stock. *D. panamintinus* is normally infected with the coccidia, but an examination of 200 *D. merriami* failed to reveal a single infected animal. Yet cross-infection experiments in the laboratory resulted in a 90 per cent infection of *D. merriami* from the other rat. Obviously the ecological barrier in nature, in this case, is not self evident. Numerous experiments of a similar type have demonstrated a laboratory compatibility between certain other protozoan parasites (*e.g.* trypanosomes, amebas, trichomonad flagellates) and "unnatural" hosts. The effect of stress on the host, and its possible relation to lowered resistance needs careful study. The stress factor might help to explain the results noted above.

2. A parasite may become transferred to a "foreign" host living in the same locality as does the original host, and subsequently become isolated due to geographical separation of the two hosts. This type of ecological segregation results from an association between two kinds of hosts close enough to permit their respective parasite populations to mingle before the host groups become isolated. The isolation may, of course, be temporary. After isolation of a parasite upon a host takes place, both morphological and physiological changes may occur—given time and the operation of natural selection. If the separated host populations become reunited, and the parasites have changed, the latter are sympatric species with the orginal ancestral parasites. The hosts may also exhibit secondary infections or infestations acquired during the period of separation.

Fleas from rabbits on Coronados Isles in the Gulf of California have become established on auklets which are burrow-nesting birds. Likewise, puffins and shearwaters from the west coast of Britain have rabbit fleas on their bodies. On the Kerguelen Isles and Antipodes in the southern Atlantic the diving petrel, a gull, and a burrow-nesting parakeet have acquired a species of flea belonging to a group of marsupial fleas common to Australia.

3. The parasite may be unable to develop in any other host.

This kind of isolation may be accomplished by one or more of the following six situations.

(a) *The absence of specific environmental conditions necessary for the growth and development of the parasite within other hosts.* This statement is, of course, vague and unsatisfactory, but it includes such environmental factors as food, oxygen, temperature, osmotic pressure, and water.

(b) *Resistance of the host.* Under this heading are included all activities by which the host defends itself against the presence of the parasite — immune reactions, age resistance, mechanical barriers, and others. Factors conditioning susceptibility and natural immunity of hosts are still partly obscure, but some of these are indicated below. For a discussion of immunity see Chapter XXI.

Ecological aspects of parasitism can be studied effectively by introducing parasites experimentally into foreign hosts and then analyzing the reasons for failure or success in establishing a permanent parasite-host relationship. But the chief difficulty here is to establish adequate criteria for determing "success" of the parasite in the new host. Such criteria as volume of egg production, parasite size and number are extremely variable. The student should remember that a parasite and its host represent a biological system dependent for its maintenance on ecological factors provided by *both* members of the association. If plerocercoid larvae of *Dibothriocephalus latus* are introduced into the stomachs of the lamprey, frog, toad, snake, and lizard, the typical larval migration takes place although none of these animals is a normal host.[41] The experimental hosts are thus potential normal hosts for the fish tapeworm, and the absence of the worm as a natural parasite in these hosts is presumably due simply to the fact that fish are not a part of their natural diet. Uncomplicated morphological features may prevent normal development of a parasite as is shown by the fact that plerocercoids introduced into the adult terrapin cannot migrate because of the rigidity of the stomach wall, whereas in the young turtle the larvae migrate in a normal manner. Temperature alone may prevent or permit infection. Plerocercoids in the stomach of *Gymnodactylus* (a lizard) migrate if the experimental host is kept at room temperature, but not if the temperature rises to 37° C.

(c) *Inability of the parasite to enter the host.* Sometimes larvae are able experimentally to live and grow within a host, but the larvae are not equipped to penetrate the external surface. A lack of suitable means of transmission may also give an erroneous indication of narrow host specificity. *Trypanosoma equiperdum* in horses and mules is transferred normally only by sexual contact, but hypodermic injections of the parasites into the blood of laboratory rats, mice, rabbits and guinea pigs easily produced infections in these "foreign" hosts.

(d) *Presence of other parasites.* Whereas a given host may be infected with many species of parasites, only one or two of these species are found in a host body at the same time. At least 35 kinds of larval trematodes (21 strigeids, 6 plagiorchids, 2 schistosomes, 1 echinostome, 1 monostome, and 4 others) may be found in the freshwater snail, *Stagnicola emarginata*, but usually only 2 kinds (sometimes 3 or 4) occur simultaneously in any one snail. Eleven species of protozoa have been found in the marine fish, *Gadus merlangus*, but only 2 or 3 are generally to be observed in any single host. A related phenomenon is shown by the strigeid trematode cercariae (*Cotylurus flabelliformis*) that encyst in the same snail species as harbor the sporocysts. But if sporocysts of *C. flabelliformis* are already lodged in the snail, the cercariae do not enter. If, however, sporocysts of other trematode species are present their very presence appears to favor the penetration and encystment of cercariae of *C. flabelliformis*. The nature of these phenomena is not clearly understood, but it probably involves the entire immunity mechanism of the host. A previous infection can affect the invasiveness of a parasite. See the discussion of parasitocoenosis, page 582.

(*e*) *Resistance of the parasite.* The above four factors alone might suggest that the parasite would be successful if the host were willing. But the situation may be the reverse. For example, the parasite may simply be too large for the prospective host, or a physiological incompatability may be due to biochemical processes in the parasite rather than in the host. As we have indicated earlier, when one considers the problem of parasite infectivity, one should not forget the problem of host suitability.

(*f*) *Genetic mutations.* Here we are apt to enter highly controversial territory where changes which are claimed by some to be mutational are vigorously explained by others solely on the basis of selective adaptation. Only one example will be mentioned, but others will be found on succeeding pages devoted to comparative host specificity. Probably the most celebrated reputed change in host specificity explainable as a mutation is that of the flagellate, *Trypanosoma rhodesiense*, which appeared rather suddenly in Rhodesia in 1909, supposedly arising from the morphologically identical *T. brucei* of domestic animals. Since then, the parasite has retained this infectivity for man as probably the only difference from *T. brucei* which still stubbornly, and fortunately, refuses to parasitize human beings. One cannot, of course, be sure that this apparently sudden appearance of a new trypanosome of man was not the result of obscure epidemiological factors, rather than of a genetic mutation, for little was known about trypanosome epidemiology in the interior of Rhodesia a half century ago. Nevertheless, regardless of whether *T. rhodesiense* is a recent or an older species, the evidence seems strong that this example is an instance of a change in parasite-host specificity due to a mutation.

KINDS OF PARASITE-HOST SPECIFICITY

Host specificity is a function of physiological specialization and of evolutionary age. These two factors may not, of course, be mutually exclusive, but usually the older (phylogenetically) the parasite the more specialized it becomes, and the more specialized its host becomes. This gradual increase in degree of specialization means that host and parasite become better and better adapted to each other and the parasite is less able to change physiologically (*i.e.* to mutate) enough to survive in a different kind of host. To put this generalization the other way around—if we select genera of parasites which are strictly confined to groups of hosts known to be closely related, we find that not only are the hosts usually specialized, but that the parasites are highly specialized. The student should remember, however, that as more intensive research discloses the existence of larger numbers of parasites, species once considered strictly host specific are often found not to be so.

We may divide parasite-host specificity into two broad categories. The first may be called *ecological specificity*, wherein the parasite is capable of living in a foreign host but normally never reaches one because of an ecological barrier. The second category may be called *physiological specificity* wherein a parasite is physiologically (= genetically) compatible with its "normal" host, and is incapable of surviving in a foreign host because of physiological incompatibility. When physiological specificity involves a pattern of be-behavior, it may be called *ethological specificity*. For examples of the latter see the discussion on page 640 under "The Search for a Partner." Other examples are readily found among the digenetic trematodes. A convincing experiment demonstrating physiological specificity was the one in which two common biting lice from fowl were reared *in vitro*.[9] Both *Lipeurus heterographus* and *Eomenacanthus stramineus* developed successfully under appropraite conditions of moisture and temperature, with chicken feathers and dried blood added for food. When feathers from the little green heron were substituted for chicken feathers, the first mentioned species of lice died. This experiment indicated the presence of some chemical factor in feathers which is characteristic for a given group of birds and to which certain parasites are adversely sensitive. It is possible, however, that the heron feathers *lacked* something essential.

Physiological compatibility often means that the parasite and its host have evolved together. This association over a period of many millions of years results in a *phylogenetic specificity*, which situation is often used to help solve problems of host taxonomy (see Chapter XXVI). Two related hosts, however, may possess closely related or identical parasites not because of the genetic relation between the hosts, but simply because the hosts have been feeding for millions of years on the same food which included larval stages and intermediate hosts of their common parasites. We should be reminded of the usual genetic variations in all species of parasites and hosts. Thus an individual member of host "A" might vary physiologically enough from the average to resist a normal parasite of "A," and this individual variant might be so different from its siblings that it chemically resembles host species "B" enough to tolerate a parasite of host "B." Such an extreme variant is not likely, but its possibility should not be overlooked.

Even when host specificity is phylogenetic, behavior may be important. "Thus the segments of *Taenia saginata* and *Taenia solium* in the faeces of man have a behaviour suited to the feeding habits of their respective hosts. The segments of *Taenia saginata* are active and move onto herbage where they are most likely to be eaten by cattle. On the other hand, the segments of *Taenia solium* are flaccid and remain in the faecal mass where they are more likely to be eaten by a pig."[39]

SPECIFICITY FACTORS RELATED TO INFECTION AND GROWTH

Under this heading we shall present some factors and processes which may affect host specificity, and which occur during each of three major stages, in turn, in the host-parasite association. This material is taken from chapter 10 of W. P. Rogers' book on the Nature of Parasitism (1962).[51] The book contains many useful references.

The First Stage of the Association of the Parasite With the Host. The infective stage (spore, egg, larva) "is a 'resting' stage which requires factors from the host in order to resume development." The nature of these factors and their presence or absence often determine the degree of specificity before resumption of development commences. Those parasites with a direct life cycle (e.g. *Ascaris*) are generally more specific than those that employ intermediate hosts, and ecological factors initially determine the range of hosts. Relatively high concentration of undissociated carbonic acid plus dissolved gaseous carbon dioxide appear to be essential for the exsheathment of larvae of the nematode, *Haemonchus contortus*. These and other requirements occur only in the rumen of ruminants, thus limiting the worm to these hosts (see p. 557 for details on the hatching of *Ascaris* eggs). The initial requirements for infection with other worms, however (e.g. *Ascaris lumbricoides*, *Toxocara mystax*, *Trichostrongylus axei*) may ensure that the early stages of development of the parasitic stages should take place in the appropriate host organ, but they are apparently not specific enough to limit the parasite to one species of host.[50] It has been suggested, without experimental evidence, that infective eggs or molting larvae require substances from the host for the initiation of parasite development.

The hatching factor (eclepic acid) excreted by roots of plants, is essential for further development of the nematode plant parasite, *Heterodera rostochiensis*.[17] When hatching or excystment is induced by direct action of the host (as the action of digestive enzymes on cysts of larval tapeworms, or on metacercariae of *Opisthorchis sinensis*), host specificity is generally low.

Thus "the ecology and behaviour of the infective stage and of the host and the conditions that are necessary in the host for infection to take place affect specificity during the first stage of the association."

The Second Stage of the Association of the Parasite With the Host. The infective stage does not feed or grow, but as soon as infection has occurred the invading organism is truly parasitic, and must find necessary nutrients and be able to withstand any damaging physical or chemical factors in its environment. It is at this stage that the complex parasite-host relationships are often most "crucial in determining the range of hosts." For example, some tapeworms of elasmobranchs require the urea of the host gut fluid to help maintain normal osmotic function.[47] Dietary needs of many parasites (*e.g.* cestodes) are not found in the environments of free-living animals.[45]

Hormones of some hosts also probably influence their susceptibility to parasites (see p. 557). Natural or acquired resistance of a host (Chapter XXI) obviously help to determine its receptiveness for a parasite. Rogers, however, has reminded us that, "as a rule we do not even know if the failure of a parasite to grow *in vivo* is due to lack of nutrients or to unfavorable chemical and physical features of the environment."

Young hosts often are more susceptible than are older hosts, but "in most hosts the development of age resistance, if it occurs, is a gradual process which does not become complete. It is reasonable to suppose, however, that the unfavourable features in the host that give rise to age resistance may often be similar to those which make an organism unsuitable as a host at any period during its life and so affect the range of hosts of parasites."

The Third Stage of the Association of the Parasite With the Host. The period of parasite reproduction is essential not only for maintenance of the species, but also for the production of infective agents. Host specificity during this period may involve natural or acquired resistance, or it may be related to nutritional requirements of the parasite as well as to mechanical factors and changes in temperature. Such requirements may be greater during reproduction. Obviously, the cysts, spores, eggs or larvae of parasites must reach an environment where they can continue their development. The relationships between specificity and parasite reproduction are not well understood.

COMPARATIVE HOST SPECIFICITY

Now let us turn to the various groups of parasites, and inquire into the variations of host specificity which they display. Examples will be selected, more or less at random, to indicate the differences among these groups. Keeping in mind the many exceptions and many pitfalls when making generalizations, we can say that ectoparasites and their mammalian hosts display a rather consistent specificity due to parallel evolution. Such a conclusion is also true for monogenetic trematodes and cestodes of fishes. In birds the problem is more difficult and unsettled, and there is much difference of opinion among ornithologists on bird taxonomy. Parasitological evidence, however, especially from bird lice, is now exciting the interest of the ornithologists. We can also state that parasites with free-swimming stages able to enter the host skin tend to have a narrower range of host species than do those parasites which enter the host through the mouth. Also, in the more plastic groups of parasites, such as the copepods, the aquatic environment appears to be more favorable for the preservation of varieties than does the terrestrial environment. As a generalization, there is less host specificity where there are two intermediate hosts than where only one is employed. For example, the Pseudophyllidea (tapeworms) with two intermediate hosts (crustacea, fish) are less host-specific than are the Cyclophyllidea with a single intermediate host.

Protozoa

One kind of experimental manifestation of host specificity involves biochemical adjustments which favor adaptations to new hosts. If we select a sheep strain of *Trypanosoma vivax* which does not normally infect white rats, a small amount of sheep serum, when added to the trypanosome injection into rats, provides a congenial environment in which the parasites can develop.[11] After a period of adjustment, the parasites become adapted to live in the white rats without the aid of sheep serum, and, in fact, they produce a virulent infection which can be carried indefinitely from rat to rat by mechanical blood injections. If these parasites are transferred back into sheep, they lose their ability to infect white rats, but can regain this ability if again they are injected, with sheep serum, into rats. This evidence indicates an adaptation to a new environment rather than a mutational change.

Genetic changes may affect host specificity not only through the parasite but through its host. Very little is known about the genetics of vertebrate hosts as this factor affects their susceptibility to parasites. In mice the degree of resistance to *Plasmodium berghei* seems to be controlled through the agency of multiple genes. Several workers,[21] however, have been able to change the resistance of mosquito hosts to *Plasmodium* by selective breeding. To cite but one example, the infection rate of *Culex pipiens* for *P. elongatum* has been increased from 5 to 50 per cent in six generations by breeding from infected female mosquitoes.[37]

The genetic complex of a parasite and of its host is obviously the basis for biochemical and physiological patterns which determine the character of parasite-host specificity. The biochemical pattern embraces the production of metabolites which play a decisive role in parasite-host adjustments.

A number of studies have been made in an attempt to discover the role of metabolites in determining the susceptibility of hosts to parasites. Trager and McGhee showed that susceptibility of avian hosts to *Plasmodium* is probably due to a series of changes in which biotin aids in the production of a biotin-like lipoprotein demonstrable in the plasma. When plasma from ducks, which are naturally resistant to *P. lophurae* and in which the concentration of the lipoprotein is high, is injected into normally susceptible ducklings, the latter are at least partly protected from infection. The biotin-like lipoprotein acts by decreasing the rate of reproduction and increasing the rate of death of the parasites.[61,62] Other substances ingested with a host's food may likewise prevent infection with a parasite.

As we have already seen, cross infection experiments in the laboratory may result in the establishment of parasites in hosts never involved in nature. In a series of experiments McGhee[32-36] found that in a suitable red cell environment the avian *Plasmodium lophurae* will invade and carry on at least part of its life cycle in the red cells of mice, rats, pigs, rabbits and man. Obviously, under these experimental conditions, some barriers to infection are removed, but the whole biochemical explanation must await further studies of this nature. In general, however, cells that have the highest potassium content are more susceptible to invasion by the "foreign" *Plasmodium*, and red cells from young mice or young rats are more easily infected than are cells from older animals. Infections may also be established in the reverse direction. Erythrocytes of duck and goose embryos can be infected with *P. berghei* from rodents.

Malarial parasites reach their highest degree of specialization in birds, and they probably originated among the reptiles during the mesozoic period. A single species of bird may harbor a number of kinds of bird malarias, and avian *Plasmodium* possesses a wide latitude of host possibilities. *P. circumflexum*, however, appears to be restricted largely to robins. Among early mammals malarial parasites were able to survive only in that mammalian stem which led to the modern primates. The malarial parasites of man are rather rigidly host-specific, although some of them are infective to anthropoid apes which themselves may harbor species of *Plasmodium* indistinguishable morphologically from those in man. The intracellular sporozoa (e.g. *Plasmodium*, *Eimeria*) tend, in general, to be much more host-specific than are those parasites (*e.g.* blood inhabiting flagellates, bile inhabiting myxosporidia, intestinal amebas) which inhabit the cavities and blood of their hosts.

Each time the woodroach molts most of its flagellates undergo sexual reproduction, then follows the usual long process of fission asexual reproduction) during the growth period of the host, and when it again molts its hormones induce the flagellates to reproduce sexually. On the other hand, the flagellate genera inhabiting the intestine of the termite *Zootermopsis* do not undergo a sexual cycle, and the hosts must refaunate themselves after each molt. All protozoa from both roaches and termites can be removed from the insects without injury to the latter by treating them with oxygen. These conditions provide a prime opportunity to test the host specificity behavior of the parasites. Termite protozoa can live in and support the growth of nymphal and adult roaches until they molt (up to 221 days for nymphs), but roach protozoa can support termites for as long as one year, and can support a colony of *Zootermopsis* indefinitely.[40] The fact that both kinds of insects may be

40

found in nature together in the same logs, and that reciprocal transfer of their flagellates is possible lends evidence to support the belief that the termites and their protozoa are derived from a line of wood-eating roaches. There is a definite resistance to cross infection of the protozoa from one species of termite to another widely different species. The protozoa are thus, in general, both morphologically and physiologically distinct.[13]

Ciliates inhabiting the stomachs of ruminants illustrate some interesting flexibility in host specificity. In general, the sheep and ox families, and to some extent the deer family, tend to harbor similar ciliate faunas as shown by morphological comparisons and by cross infection experiments. But ciliates from horse ceca do not infect cattle stomachs.

Certain types of bacteria can enhance the invasiveness of entamoebae as well, possibly, as their virulence. Recent experiments[25,42,43] have shown that, at least with *Entamoeba histolytica* in guinea pigs, without bacteria the host can not even be infected (see p. 88). The role of the bacteria may be a simple physical one providing a suitable micro-environment for the protozoans, but investigations on the role of bacteria or of other associates in culture with *E. histolytica* indicate that the answer is probably much more complex. The genus *Entamoeba* is widely distributed in vertebrates but its species appear to be fairly host specific. The differences among the species are often not detectable morphologically, but physiological species or at least biological races are common. Much experimental work on cross infection studies needs to be done with the parasitic amebas.

Worms—General

Broadly speaking, the parasitic worms with direct life cycles (*e.g. Ascaris*) are more host-specific than are the worms with an indirect cycle (*e.g.* tapeworms).[2] On the other hand, worms which have an indirect life history generally exhibit more specificity for their intermediate hosts than for their final hosts. Here, again, we may cautiously assume that the parasites are better adapted to their intermediate hosts with which they have been associated for a longer period of time. The only really safe generalization to make is that among worms, as among the protozoa, there are wide ranges of host specificity. The ranges may be exemplified by some studies made on the worm parasites of moles and shrews.[44] One group of worms (*e.g.* the nematode, *Capillaria talpae*, and the tapeworm, *Choanotaenia filamentosa*) exhibits a narrow host specificity and is restricted to one species of mole, whereas another group (*e.g.* the trematode, *Panopistus pricei*, and the tapeworm, *Neoskrjabinolepis singularis* and the nematode, *Longistriata didas*) is less specific and freely invades several genera within the family Soricidae; but the nematode, *Parastrongyloides winchesi*, and other worms are widely distributed among the Talpidae and Soricidae within the order

Insectivora. Finally, a few worms are unhampered with much restrictive host preference, and thereby able to live as parasites in widely differing systematic groups of hosts. An example of the latter is the acanthocephalan worm, *Polymorphus minutus*, which has been reported from freshwater fishes, water birds and water shrews.

Trematodes

Monogenetic trematodes are, as a group, markedly host-specific. This specificity is related to the unusual conditions for isolation which exist in the group, together with the habit of fastening eggs to the surface of the host, and with the several methods of attachment of adult worms (Fig. VII–6, p. 166). When adhesive organs consist of hooks which are adapted to particular areas of the host surface (*e.g.* free edge of gill lamellae), the transfer of the adult worm from one host to another becomes difficult. When the parasites possess suckers, as do the Cyclocotylidae, and are thus able to move about in the gill chamber of a fish host, transfer to other hosts is more likely to take place. Examples of speciation of parasites in fairly close correspondence with speciation of their hosts are probably common throughout the whole group of monogenetic trematodes. *Hexabothrium* and *Erpocotyle* are found exclusively on elasmobranchs; *Dactylogyrus* and *Protogyrodactylus* on freshwater teleosts; *Kuhnia* on members of the herring family; and *Polystomoides coronatum* in the mouth, nostrils and esophagus of turtles.

Host specificity among monogenes is of a physiological or ecological nature, or both, but the specificity is pronounced and is of phylogenetic significance. The more primitive species of worms are generally to be found on the more primitive groups of fishes, and those worms favoring freshwater fish are somewhat less host-specific than those on marine fish.[23] In spite of the high degree of host specificity at the species level, it is rather low at the generic level. When considering a higher taxonomic level, however, we often find a very wide range of host specificity. For example, the gyrodactyloids are distributed throughout teleosts, mollusks and amphibia; and the capsaloids are found in elasmobranchs, holocephalans, Chondrostei and teleosts. Here again, however, much work must be done, especially of an experimental nature, before the limits of host specificity can be ascertained.

One might expect the digenetic trematodes also to be highly host-specific because their parasite-host relationships are the result of a chain of complex adaptations between miracidia and their environment, sporocysts, rediae and snails, cercariae and their hosts; and, finally, between the adult worms and their vertebrate hosts. Too few complete life-history studies of digenetic trematodes have been made to warrant broad generalizations concerning host specificity of entire life cycles. Available evidence points strongly to a different degree of host specificity at each stage or level of the life cycle.

Unfortunately, the possible varieties of intermediate as well as of final hosts have usually not been investigated. For these reasons the comments below, unless otherwise indicated, pertain only to adult trematodes.

Host specificity is not marked in all families of digenetic trematodes, but a study of collection records suggests that specificity prevails to a considerable extent, although closely related species may exhibit great differences in degree of specificity.[31] Thus *Schistosoma mansoni* is restricted to man and monkeys, whereas *S. japonicum* is a successful parasite of man, dogs, cats, pigs, cattle, horses, and others, and of the common laboratory animals. *S. haematobium* lives well in man, albino mice, hamsters, monkeys and baboons. It grows poorly in cats, albino rats, cotton rats, guinea pigs and goats; but rabbits and dogs are refractory to infection. *S. incognitum* occurs in pigs and dogs in India, and it can be established easily in such laboratory animals as cats, sheep, goats, rabbits, guinea pigs, rats and mice. *S. spindale* is successful only in ungulates. Most of the species of blood flukes obviously have no marked host specificity.

When distribution records of trematodes are analyzed, one normally finds that those genera that show a wide host tolerance are none the less limited to hosts which are related ecologically. For instance, all hosts from which about fifty genera of strigeids have been recorded are ecologically associated with water. Among the strigeid trematodes, families have been considered to be restricted to certain kinds of hosts. Members of the Diplostomatinae are parasites of birds,[5] and the Alariinae are found exclusively in mammals.[15] *Fibricola cratera*, a parasite of mammals, can easily be transferred to chicks,[63] but whether avian hosts are infected in nature is not certain. The need for caution in formulating conclusions about host specificity is obvious.

The flukes, *Gorgodera amplicava*, in the frog, *Rana catesbeiana*, and *Gorgoderina attenuata* in *R. pipiens* are adapted to live in the urinary bladders of their hosts. To reach the bladder, larval stages must migrate through the body. It might be presumed that adult stages would be able to live in normal host organs which are compatible with the larval parasites, but experiments[20] in homotransplantion of adult worms showed that they failed to live in the new habitats. Frog bladder flukes implanted into the true urinary bladder of turtles remained normal for seven to ten days, and those transferred to the salamander, *Triturus v. viridescens*, were normal for forty-eight hours. This organ specificity may, therefore, be due to a resistance of the host against excystation of metacercariae or against postmetacercarial migration of juvenile trematodes. But the resistance does not operate against adult flukes artificially implanted into the urinary bladder in normally non-infective hosts.

Fasciola hepatica has become cosmopolitan in distribution and its adults may infect cattle, pigs, rodents, elephants, kangaroos and man. *Echinostoma revolutum* may infect various species of birds and mammals. These and other examples show that many digenetic trematodes tolerate a wide variety of hosts. Furthermore, a comparison of the morphology of one species taken from several different kinds of hosts demonstrates that the range of changes that occur are of the same degree of magnitude which, under other conditions, would justify separation into one or more species. Specimens of *F. hepatica* taken from a cow could hardly be assigned, on the basis of morphology alone, to the same species as *F. hepatica* taken from a guinea pig.

A striking example of speciation related to parallel evolution involving digenetic trematodes and their hosts is the presence of five genera and ten species (all host-specific) of the Accacoeliidae in the intestine of the sunfish, *Mola mola*.

Several genera of invertebrates and vertebrates frequenting a lake district may be infected with the same genus or even species of trematode. Under experimental conditions, however, such unnatural hosts as chickens, ducks, rats, mice, and cats may successfully harbor the adults if fed sufficient numbers of metacercariae. Parasitologists often discover metacercariae or cercariae whose definitive hosts are unknown, but whose entire life cycle can be described because development can take place in a laboratory animal. A recent study of this nature began with metacercariae of *Cryptocotyle concavum* encysted in the skin of the stickleback fish, *Gasterosteus aculeatus*.[65] Rediae and cercariae were obtained from the snail, *Amnicola longinqua*, but the identity of the normal definitive host (probably a bird frequenting the river area) could not be ascertained. Adult stages of this parasite, however, were readily recovered from the intestines of day-old chicks and ducklings twenty-five to forty-eight hours after feeding infected sticklebacks to the birds.

Experimental work with miracidia has often demonstrated a high degree of specificity for snails.[64] The miracidium of *Opisthorchis felineus*, for example, is attracted to the prosobranch snail, *Bithynia leachi*, but not to the closely related *B. tentaculata* that occurs in the same locality. Many such examples could be listed, but little is known about the nature of the attracting agent which is possibly a water soluble skin secretion from the snail. But not all miracidia are host-specific. Snails belonging to the following genera may serve as first intermediate hosts for *Fasciola hepatica*: *Lymnaea*, *Galba*, *Bulinus*, *Physopsis*, *Physa*, *Stagnicola*, *Fossaria*, *Pseudosuccinea* and *Ampullaria*.

As a final generalization, host specificity among digenetic trematodes is greater at the level of the intermediate host, especially the mollusk, than at the adult level. Thus, two distinct species of worms may live together as adults in the intestine of a bird or fish but require different species of snails in which to complete their life cycles. The evolution of trematodes, as exemplified very well by the strigeids, is characterized by a general tendency to replace ecological specificity with phylogenetic specificity.

Cestodes

Tapeworms likewise vary considerably in their range of host specificity, but adults tend to be more specific than do adults of most other groups of worms. Each order of bird and mammal possesses its own characteristic cestodes. Host specificity among these worms attains a high degree of perfection as the hosts become specialized. For instance, the cyclophyllids with a very specialized type of internal anatomy are found only in terrestrial vertebrates. Among the elasmobranchs are tetraphyllid tapeworms which possess extravagant types of scolex structures. The sharks and rays apparently each harbor distinct species of cestodes. Snakes also possess distinct and characteristic species of tapeworms. *Dipylidium* and *Echinococcus* are found only in carnivores; *Moniezia*, *Thysanosoma* and *Stilesia* only in ruminants, and so forth. But host specificity among cestodes reaches its highest development in birds. This relationship is perhaps best illustrated by water birds, such as grebes, loons, herons, ducks, flamingos and cormorants—birds that may occupy the same ponds or lagoons. Each bird possesses its own tapeworm fauna. If we recall the above discussion about ecological segregation, we recognize that among cestodes, contrary to the situation described for trematodes, host specificity is apparently more independent of ecological segregation of their hosts, and more dependent on phylogenetic relationships.

A quotation from Baer[1] summarizes the above statements on cestodes. ". . . it is clear that both larval and adult tapeworms are associated with their hosts in a very intimate fashion. It is obvious that ecological segregation of the hosts originally produced isolation of the parasites in the different vertebrate groups. Yet, on the other hand, cestodes appear to be highly specialized from a physiological standpoint and to have become adapted to their hosts a very long time ago, as is shown by their present-day distribution. It is not possible, even experimentally, to break down this host specificity, as can be done for other parasites (trematodes). The data indicate that ecological specificity has here been replaced by phylogenetic specificity, a much more intimate type of association that arose thousands of centuries ago when cestodes first became parasitic in the ancestors of the species which today serve them as hosts."

Although a given species of adult tapeworm is limited to hosts belonging only to one class of vertebrate, species of worms of the same cestode genus may parasitize hosts belonging to different vertebrate classes. For well-known examples of this general rule we may cite the occasional presence of the dog tapeworm, *Dipylidium caninum*, and the rat tapeworm, *Hymenolepis diminuta*, in man.

Larval stages of cestodes frequently tolerate a much wider range of hosts than do the adults. *Hymenolepis diminuta* larvae have been reported from four different orders of insects and from myriapods. *H. gracilis* occurs in both copepods and ostracods. Larvae of the dwarf dog tapeworm, *Echinococcus*, have been found in many kinds of mammals. A study of these larval stages indicates that larval cestodes are ecologically segregated, but that there exist some forms in which specificity is independent of ecological factors, and has resulted from physiological adaptation. To cite one bit of evidence for this statement—when coracidia larvae of *Dibothriocephalus latus* are fed to several species of freshwater copepods in one dish, some species of the latter are more favored hosts than others.

Opium treated albino mice were experimentally much more readily infected with *Hymenolepis diminuta* than were those not so treated (intraperitoneally).[46] Opium slows the intestinal emptying time, and the effect of this process on the establishment of *H. diminuta* is pronounced. The fact that the parasite only rarely occurs in house mice suggests that the intestinal emptying time should be regarded as a probable explanation of apparent host specificity in this case.

One possible explanation, on a physiological basis, of the high degree of specificity shown by tapeworms is a dependence upon specific nitrogenous compounds secreted by the host intestine. The host specificity of tapeworms is undoubtedly related to specific biochemical characteristics of the worms, and to the chemical and physical properties of the environment within the host.

Nematodes

The study of host specificity among nematodes is particularly perplexing because of the wide variety of kinds of associations between these worms and other organisms, both plant and animal. An almost continuous series of associations from entirely free-living nematodes to highly adapted obligatory parasites exists. There is little evidence of parallel evolution of hosts and their nematode parasites. If parallel evolution did occur, the most primitive genera and species of the parasites of vertebrates would be found in fishes, but they are found, in fact, in mammals. More than two-thirds of the described strongyloids, usually considered as being the most primitive nematodes, are from mammals. There is little evidence of host specificity to support the common belief that nematodes from cavity or tissues of invertebrates are the oldest parasites of this phylum. Although in nematodes we do not find the phylogenetic specificity as exhibited by the cestodes, nor the ethological specificity of trematodes, we do notice a broad host specificity in the more primitive species of hosts, becoming narrow in specialized species of hosts. Numerous plant nematodes vary widely in their tolerance of different kinds of hosts. During the course of evolution a "specificity by affinity of metabolism" becomes more and more pronounced, until the parasite is no longer able to become adapted to a new host.

Brugia malayi can be successfully transmitted from man to forest and domestic animals by direct inoculation of infective larvae.[16] This observation is significant in a consideration of the question of reservoir hosts for this and other filarids. If we can experimentally transmit filarial worms from man to animals in the laboratory, can the parasites be transmitted in nature by mosquitoes or by *Chrysops* from animals to man? Probably so.

Most of the species of parasitic nematodes that are found in birds belong to genera that also occur in mammals, but in many groups of mammals the genera of nematodes are specific. Elephants harbor 6 distinctive genera and 20 or more species of strongyles, while 6 genera and about 18 species may be found in rhinoceroses. Horses and other equines harbor at least 8 genera with more than 50 species of nematodes that are not found in any other group of animals.

Considerable work has been done on speciation of the hookworms, strongyloids and ascarids infecting man, and the results indicate that these parasites in vertebrates often form physiological races (see p. 653). *Ascaris* in man and in pigs are almost identical in their morphology, but physiological differences prevent successful cross-infection under normal circumstances. A biochemical analysis of *A. lumbricoides* and *A. suum* discloses apparently identical constituents, but the carbohydrate fractions composed primarily of glycogen are antigenically distinct. Such studies are needed not only for the separation of *Ascaris* between man and pigs, but also for the separation of other species and races such as the related *Toxocara* in cats and dogs. Specificity of nematodes whose larvae migrate through the body of the vertebrate host may be due primarily to the failure of larvae to complete somatic migration in a "foreign" host rather than to incompatibility between the adult worm and the host. Another kind of specificity in this group of worms is illustrated by the apparent preference by *Ascaridia galli* for male chicks over female chicks.

Sprent (personal communication) has emphasized that among the ascaridoids the larval behavior is a more sensitive indication of specific difference than is the adult morphology. The adult stage is the least likely to reveal specific differences possibly because the environment of the vertebrate host intestine is more uniform than is the internal environment of the intermediate hosts. Thus, the migratory pathway, degree of growth and onset of various molts manifested by these larvae appear to be the most sensitive differentiating features.

Sprent[52] has made some significant observations on the changing specificity patterns during the life history of *Amplicaecum robertsi*, an ascaridoid from the carpet python. We will quote from his summary. "The snake is depicted as the apex of a food pyramid, whose base comprises a variety of animals ranging from earthworms to herbivorous animals. . . . The life history is thus regarded, not as a life cycle, but as a life pyramid; development proceeds according to a pattern of diminishing host-specificity. Host-specificity is wide at the base of the pyramid, so that second-stage larvae occur in a wide variety of paratenic hosts. Host-specificity narrows at the second moult which may occur in birds and mammals. It narrows still further in the third stage because this larva, though it will survive in reptiles, birds and mammals, will not grow to a length at which it is capable of further development in the snake except in certain mammals. At the third moult, host-specificity shifts to certain reptiles but becomes eventually restrictive to the carpet snake, because this host alone appears to provide a suitable environment for maturation of the eggs."

Acanthocephala

The late H. J. Van Cleave has amply demonstrated that adult acanthocephalid worms show a relatively high degree of host specificity. For example, *Gracilisentis* and *Tanarhamphus* are found normally only in the gizzard shad. The Pacific pilotfish, *Kyphosus elegans*, and the closely related Atlantic pilotfish, *K. secatrix*, each harbors a distinct species of the acanthocephalan genus *Filisoma*. Likewise, *Moniliformis moniliformis* (probably a combination of several species) shows a narrow specificity in certain instances. Specificity in these worms is related to the nature of the life cycle in which no free-living stage has been reported, and in which an arthropod transfer host is essential for all species.

Physiological host specificity appears to be highly variable in this group of parasites. Acanthocephalans of carnivorous vertebrates cannot proceed from the arthropod to the final host unless the parasites pass first into an insectivorous host. Collection records indicate that there is little specificity among larval forms of at least some groups of Acanthocephala. A single species of *Centrorhynchus*, for example, has been reported as a larval parasite of lizards, snakes and frogs. Much experimental work on morphological variation and physiological host specificity under controlled conditions is needed. Even morphological criteria are insufficient to establish exact systematics for these worms.[19]

Crustacea

The parasitic copepods are among the most diversified of all parasites, and almost the only ones that are found in the adult stage on both vertebrates and invertebrates. It has been suggested that copepods are probably the oldest parasites actually known, but they may share this position with prosobranch snails which are exclusively parasitic in echinoderms, and with the group of annelids known as myzostomids also exclusively in echinoderm hosts. Both prosobranchs and myzostomids have been recorded as fossils. Ecological segregation of copepods on their hosts has often been accomplished with marked intimacy. Some of the species of blood feeders are restricted to one species of hosts (Fig. XVI–15, p. 402). Although distinct host specificity among copepods occurs, further work of a statistical nature must be done with these crustaceans before we can formulate significant generalizations about them.

One group of parasites which has frequently been considered as strictly host-specific is the parasitic isopods. Apparently each genus of many groups (*e.g.* entoniscids) is found on a particular host or group of hosts that appear characteristic for the parasite. For instance, *Danalia* and *Liriopsis* are found only on decapods. However, *Phryxus abdominalis* has been recovered from at least twenty species of shrimps belonging to two genera. Without a considerable amount of experimental research work on these and other forms, no definite conclusions can be made as to the host specificity of parasitic isopods in general. We can say that parasite-host relationships, including specificity, among the isopods as well as among mites, barnacles and other arthropods, is essentially of an ecological nature.

Hymenoptera

Insects as parasites are generally highly host-specific, but this specificity is predominately ecological, not physiological. Evidence for this conclusion is gained when such activities as searching for the host habitat and for the host are eliminated experimentally, and the parasite is placed directly upon a "foreign" host. In such a situation the parasite very commonly goes ahead and lays its eggs on or in the new host with little or no hesitation.

The entomophagous Hymenoptera (see p. 449) are seldom monophagous (= one kind of food), but they are far from indiscriminate in their attacks upon insect hosts. In nature these parasitic wasps have several potential species of hosts, and in the laboratory many more hosts may be discovered by experimental testing. Why then does the wasp normally select only one or two kinds of hosts in which to deposit its parasitic eggs? Several distinct processes of selection seem to occur, and are discussed under the heading of "Biological Control" on page 580. The hymenopteran insect, *Aphelinus mali*, has been reported in the literature as attacking 6 or 7 species of aphids, but current views suggest that most of these records are erroneous, and that most of the aphids may be synonyms of *Eriosoma lanigerum*, the woolly apple aphid.

The food of an insect host may affect the latter's suitability as a home for a parasite. For example, the hornworm, *Protoparce sexta*, when feeding on tomato is a suitable host for the braconid wasp, *Apanteles congregatus*, but when this host is fed on dark-fired tobacco, the parasite dies before reaching maturity.

A sequence of ecological processes leads to the attainment of host specificity of many Hymenoptera and of other entomophagous insects as well. Searching capacity and host specificity are correlated phenomena. The sequence is as follows: (*a*) the finding of the host habitat, (*b*) the finding (recognition) of the host, (*c*) acceptance by the host, and (*d*) host suitability for parasite reproduction. The quality of the host's environment rather than the qualities of the host itself appears to be the more important controlling factor in restricting the number of host species attacked.

Fleas

The habitat preference of a host may have a distinct effect on its arthropod parasites, and the latter may aid in host identification because of the degree of specificity attained. This relationship has been demonstrated[27] with the fleas of two closely related European wood mice, *Apodemus sylvaticus* which lives in the fields of Normandy, and *A. flavicollis* which lives in adjacent woods or areas of scrub growth. One might question the separation of these mice into two distinct species, and prefer to consider them as representing only two color phases or ecological races of one species. When the mice fleas are scrutinized, however, they are found to belong to two distinct subspecies. *Ctenophthalmus agyrtes agyrtes* is restricted in Normandy to the woods in a district where it overlaps with the northwestern subspecies, *C. a. nobilis*, which lives in open country. Thus we have evidence from the host-preference pattern of fleas for the taxonomic separation of their mice hosts.

Among the most recent reviews of the question of host specificity in fleas is that of Hopkins.[26] "Unlike many parasites, fleas (possibly rare exceptions; see Freeman and Madsen, 1950) pass their entire pre-adult life off the body of the host, their larvae being free-living feeders on organic dust, though the early stages usually take place in the host's dwelling. This means that the early stages of fleas, not being parasitic, are susceptible to the conditions, climatic and others, which govern the distribution of free-living animals to a far greater extent than animals which are parasitic in all their active stages. It also means that it is necessary for the newly-emerged flea to seek out a host, sometimes of one particular species, and that the period of starvation that the flea must undergo during this search can often be reduced and the search be prolonged (with better prospects of a successful conclusion) by the practice of polyhaemophagy (the ability to feed on the blood of hosts other than the one normal to the flea in question). For these reasons it is common to find a flea on a host other than that (or those) to which it is normal, and such occurrences may range from the purely accidental presence of fleas on reptiles (from which they are probably unable to suck blood) through those in which a flea can obtain nourishment from the blood of a host on which it is extremely reluctant to feed, to instances in which a given species of flea has a number of hosts between which it shows little preference and on all of which the species can reproduce indefinitely."

Polyhaemophagy and promiscuity have been of considerable advantage to fleas, yet narrow specificity is indulged in by many species. When considered as a group, it is clear that the ecological conditions in the nest (mammal or bird) are more important than is the host. For example, *Ceratophyllus garei* occurs in the nests of a great variety of birds if the nests are not too dry. *Pulex irritans* of man is sometimes abundant in pig-styes, and it is a true parasite of the badger. Hopkins states that, "The more promiscuous a flea is as regards the source of the blood on which it can mature its eggs, the more probable it becomes that random hopping will eventually result in the deposition of the eggs in an environment suitable for the development of the larvae, while the latter are not affected nearly so much by the question of whether the nest or burrow in which they find themselves was made by a rabbit or a bird, a squirrel or a mouse, as by the environmental conditions within it, particularly the relative humidity and temperature."

Lice

All lice are obligatory and permanent external parasites of birds and mammals. They cannot jump or fly, or even walk very well, and they spend their entire lives on the bodies of their hosts. For these reasons transfer from host to host is normally accomplished only when two host bodies are in close contact as during copulation, feeding of young, or while standing together in herds. Obviously, then, there is no particular disadvantage to the parasite in being narrowly adjusted to one species of host. The death of the host inevitably means the death of the entire community of lice on its body. These limitations explain the intraspecific bounds of distribution, and the relatively extreme specificity in their host associations. It is of interest to note that there are no lice on bats, yet bats are heavily invaded by other parasites. Forty or fifty ectoparasites of several species are not uncommon on one bat. The reasons for the absence of lice on bats are unknown.

Authentic instances of lice distributions not explainable by host-phylogeny are rare, but inter-specific transfers might occur during a struggle between prey and predator, and during the sharing of mud wallows, rubbing trees, roosting or perching spots, and as the result of the usurpation of a nest or burrow by an alien host. Phoresy (p. 12) may also result in inter-specific transfer.

The fact that lice do not have even a resting stage of their life cycle off their host results in a correlation of their phylogeny with that of their hosts almost to the exclusion of other factors (see p. 682). Lice, therefore, almost always occur only on one host or on a small number of closely related hosts. An extreme degree of specificity occurs among lice on the Procaviidae (Order Hyracoidea) where most of the subspecies of the host, *Procava capensis*, have their own species or subspecies of louse (*Procavicola*). The chewing lice appear to be somewhat more host-specific than are the sucking lice. A few instances of incipient speciation of lice have been described; the best known is between *Pediculus humanus corporis*, the human clothing louse, and *P. humanus*, the human head louse.

The lice on primates all belong to the family Pediculidae, and no member of this family occurs on any other host. Both *Pediculus* and *Phthirus* (see p. 430) occur on man and higher apes, but not on monkeys. *Phthirus* includes species from the gorilla and chimpanzee, but since the records are from menagerie material it is not conclusively known that these apes are natural hosts of the crab louse. *Pediculus* has been recorded from the gibbon and from the chimpanzee. Apparently the orang is not infested with lice. Spider monkeys (*Ateles*) of tropical America are far removed anatomically from man and his ancestry, yet, curiously, the monkeys possess a species of *Pediculus* (sometimes separated as an independent genus, *Parapediculus*). It is possible that the lice were transferred from man to spider monkeys, but if such an event occurred it must have taken place in the remote past because considerable differences have been evolved between the parasites of man and of those monkeys.[18] Although straggler lice are of frequent occurrence on birds, the specificity between feather lice and their hosts is relatively marked. For instance, the wing louse, *Lipeurus caponis*, occurs only on the wings, and the shaft louse, *Menopon gallinae*, is adapted to live within the shafts of large feathers.

Many biting lice exhibit an interesting mutualistic association with bacteria which, in nymphs and males, occurs in specialized myelocytes among the fat bodies. In adult females the bacteria accumulate in the ovary from whence they pass into the eggs and so are transmitted congenitally.[49] Lice from which the bacteria have been eliminated soon die. Because the bacteria occur in those lice that feed on blood, it has been suggested that one factor helping to determine host specificity is the inability of the bacteria to survive in a louse feeding on the blood of an abnormal host species.

The causes of host specificity among lice are doubtless related to biochemical differences in the blood, skin, and plumage among the hosts.

Flies

To illustrate some details of the problems of parasite-host specificity among the Diptera we have selected the Family Hippoboscidae of which all members are obligatory, bloodsucking ectoparasites of various orders of mammals and birds. These flies are flattened dorsoventrally, with a strong development of the sternal region of the thorax which forms a smooth plate (Fig. XVIII–20, p. 491). Some species hatch with normal wings which break off on reaching the host, others retain reduced wings and eyes, while one genus is completely without wings. Hippoboscids occur on only 5 orders of mammals and on 18 out of 27 orders of birds. There are no species parasitic on both mammals and birds. Host-preference is more restricted in the flies of mammals than in those of birds, but the parasites show a wide diversity of behavior with all gradations from strict species-specificity to occurrences on host species of different orders. Hippoboscid host-selection patterns are explained chiefly by ecological factors; hence we find that, regardless of taxonomic affinities of the hosts, if they possess similar habits and habitats, they are likely to be burdened with similar parasitic flies. These considerations suggest that when strict specificity exists, it is the result of geographical isolation as in the case of flies on kangaroos. Conclusions similar to those expressed for Hippoboscids have been made for pupiparous Diptera of bats.

During the months of July and August at Fair Isle Observatory near Shetland and Orkney, five species of breeding passerine birds were trapped intensively and hippoboscid flies (*Ornithomyia fringillina*) were removed from each bird. Each fly was marked and then released on any one of the five species of hosts irrespective of the original source of the fly. A few marked flies were released without a host. After the lapse of an appropriate time the flies were again collected and 75 per cent of those recovered were found on the same individual birds on which they had been released, 18.5 per cent had moved to other birds of the same species, and 6.5 per cent had changed to a host species different from that on which they had been released. Of interest is the fact that male flies changed hosts more often than did females.[8] Experiments such as this one give us a better understanding of how parasites behave, but they do not provide answers to the question of *why* the parasites behave the way they do. What is behind the behavior? Is it phylogeny? serology? nutrition? chemotaxis? Or one might ask a negative question—why is there a lack of host specificity?

Although specificity of an insect parasite for a single species of host is rare, *Cryptochaetum iceryae*, a dipterous parasite, is restricted in the United States to the cottony cushion scale, *Icerya purchasi*, but in Australia it has been recorded on other species of the same genus of host. For details of this whole group of flies see Theodor,[55] Bequaert[4] and Guimarães and D'Andretta.[22]

Ticks and Mites

Although a few ticks and mites appear to be confined strictly to one host species, these groups of arachnids follow no hard and fast rule. The tick, *Dermacentor andersoni*, has a wide range of compatible hosts in all of its life stages. The more primitive trombiculid mites exhibit less host specificity than do those species which enjoy a more intimate association with their hosts. The latter group began phylogenetically as nest infesting species which developed first an ecological type of host specificity, then as the intimacy became closer, a degree of physiological host specificity was engendered. Ectoparasites such as mites and chiggers may appear to prefer one host to another, but this "preference" may be largely a matter of difference in the area of host skin exposed or available for infestation, or to differences in extent of host range or other host behavior.[38]

THE SEARCH FOR A PARTNER

A fruitful source of information on the nature of host specificity is a study of commensalism in which the resulting society of two or more individuals depends for its existence on the maintenance of highly specialized and precise "socially-adapted" behavior.[9a] In most of these relationships the commensal makes an active search for its partner, and it is the nature of this search which now concerns us.

Laing[29] stated some principles (based on her work with parasitoidy among insects) which are applicable to all studies of symbiot behavior. She found, by the use of a choice-apparatus, that the chalcid wasp, *Alysia manducator*, is attracted by olfactory means to the environment where its host blow-fly larvae are to be found. This attraction is a result of a chemotaxis to some factor or factors in decomposing meat. The movements of the fly larvae in the meat evoke another stimulus which results in egg-laying by the host. Laing concluded "that some parasites do first seek out a particular environment, in which they afterwards proceed to seek their hosts. The analysis of the process by which the parasite finds its host may be divided into two parts—the finding of the environment and the finding of the host in that environment—is, therefore, not merely a convenient theoretical division, but corresponds to an actual difference in the behavior of the parasite. . . . Not only, then, do some parasites find environments first and hosts later, they often use quite different senses for the perception of the two and make quite different movements to reach them. What those senses and movements are, however, will differ greatly with different parasites, and must be especially determined in each particular case."

Studies on the specificity of recognition of hosts by commensal polynoid annelids have shown that chemical attraction and recognition appear to be the usual mechanisms binding together such partners as the scale-worms, *Arctonoë fragilis*, with the starfish, *Evasterias troschelii*; *A. pulchra* with the sea cucumber, *Stichopus californicus*; *Hesperonoë adventor* with the echiuroid worm, *Urechis caupo*; *Polynoë scolependrina* with the terebellid, *Polymnia nebulosa*; and several others. An experimental technique devised by Davenport[9a] consisted of a choice-apparatus or olfactometer in which "commensal worms were introduced into a Y-tube and were presented with a choice between streams from two aquaria. Material to be tested could be placed in either aquarium at random; similarly, connections with the aquaria were so arranged that streams to be tested could be introduced into either arm of the Y at random, thus making it possible for any consistent behavior resulting from uncontrolled inequalities in pressure or light to appear in the data from a large number of 'runs'. Such apparatus lends itself well to investigation of host specificity in active forms which readily respond to streams of water carrying attractants."

All of the polynoid commensals so far investigated demonstrated strong positive responses to chemical stimulation by their hosts, and with few exceptions, this response was highly specific in spite of frequent close taxonomic affinity among hosts.[24] Davenport and his colleagues have demonstrated that specialized sorts of behavior may be induced by the presence of "host-factor." For example, the frequency of random turning in pinnotherid crabs is directly proportional to the concentration of "host-factor" in the crab's general environment.[10] This response obviously results in keeping the crabs in the vicinity of the clam host, like the ballet dancer who, while performing tight pirouettes, does not move very far. At higher concentrations the same chemical agent from the host has a directive influence on the crab, and induces the animal to move directly toward the clam.

A commensal sometimes is attracted to two unrelated hosts. In such a situation it seems likely that both hosts produce the same "attractant" (probably a metabolite), and that conditioning may not be immediately necessary.

Efforts have been directed toward correlating the *response* specificity of commensal worms on echinoderms with the known *host* specificity. Various categories of response specificity have been demonstrated, ranging from commensal populations which respond to their normal host alone (*e.g.* the polynoid worm, *Arctonoë fragilis* on the seastar, *Evasterias*) to commensals which appear to have no chemical discrimination, and which respond to many host animals. Moreover, all populations of a commensal species do not always behave in the same manner—some being much more specific than others. There are two populations of the polychaete worm, *Podarke pugettensis*, one a facultative commensal on several starfish (*e.g.* the web-star, *Patiria miniata*, and the mud-star, *Luidia foliolata*), the other free-living. The former population shows a strong tendency to respond positively to its host, but the other shows no such tendency. Experiments are needed to determine whether such differences are inherited or are conditioned.

Recent work[28] suggests that smell of a host is a strongly determinative factor for mosquitoes in localizing the blood supplier. Laboratory-bred *Anopheles atroparvus* reacted satisfactorily to airborne stimuli in an air-stream olfactometer, and the experiments pointed to the possibility of adaptation to the smell of a special type of host. Heat and moisture appear to be releasing stimuli for alighting on the host, but heat in addition has a directive influence. This thermotaxis is strongly activated by CO_2, which with other odors probably has an activating value only in the orientation process. Mosquito responses to chemicals are undoubtedly combined with visual responses in seeking and selecting a host. Preliminary experiments in the Belgian Congo suggest that in searching for food, anophelines do not fly above a 60 cm. level.

A problem related to the above is the explanation of preference for one host over another by parasites which may normally infect both. Worth[66] described an example of this problem involving cotton rats, and he said, "It would appear that for some reason the cotton rat is a favored host in the Everglades, being the carrier of more than five times as many individual ectoparasites as rice rats in the same environment despite a similar pattern of host infestations." The answer in this case lies in differences in the quality of host blood, microclimatic variations in the fur, differences in structure and texture of hair and skin, and grooming behavior.   It is often difficult to detect such differences, and, when they are detected, to evaluate their effects upon the parasites.   To cite another example, the ciliate, *Trichodina*, is common on the gills of marine fishes, but it is particularly abundant on sea-bottom fishes.   Hence the preference is presumably associated with sea-bottom life.   The basic principle of variations among species, and variations among individuals within one species lies behind the obvious as well as the obscure patterns of parasite behavior.

Many years ago H. A. Baylis[3] reminded us that although the origin of specificity among the worms appears to offer a striking example of the operation of natural selection, it did not attract the attention of Darwin.   On the other hand, Weismann saw in the life-histories of parasites evidence of adaptations arising through variations in a definite direction which is "determined only by the advantage which it affords to the species with regard to its capacity for existence."   For a discussion of the evolution of parasitism see the next chapter of this book.

GENERAL RULES AND PRINCIPLES

1. Parasite-host specificity may be determined by ecological factors or by physiological factors, or both.

2. Once strict host specificity has been achieved by parasites which spend their entire lives on or in their hosts, variability is no longer advantageous to the parasite.

3. In general, parasites with an indirect life cycle are less specific than those with a direct life cycle.

4. There is less host specificity where there are two intermediate hosts than where only one is employed.

5. Whereas two strains of a given parasite might infect a final host with equal facility, they may not be equally infective to a given strain of intermediate host.

6. The host is in many respects equivalent to the surrounding environment of free-living organisms; but the host, as an environment, is constantly developing specific responses and adaptations to its parasites.

7. Specificity once gained may subsequently be lost.

8. When a species of host is divided into two or more population groups separated geographically in different environments, their respective parasite faunas normally exhibit differences.

9. A parasite may become transferred to a "foreign" host living in the same locality as does the original host, and subsequently become isolated due to geographical separation of the two hosts.

10. After isolation of a parasite upon a host takes place, both morphological and physiological changes may occur — given time and the operation of natural selection.

11. Host specificity is fundamentally a function of physiological specialization and of evolutionary age.

12. In comparing digenetic trematodes with cestodes, host specificity among trematodes is of the ecological nature whereas among cestodes it is more dependent on phylogenetic relationships. Among the trematodes the specificity is more pronounced among the larval stages, but the larval stages of cestodes frequently tolerate a much wider range of hosts than do the adult cestodes.

13. In nematodes, there is usually greater specificity for the intermediate host than for the definitive host.

14. There is probably less host specificity among parasites than is generally assumed because numerous studies are continually disclosing new kinds of compatible hosts for species originally thought to be restricted to only one or a few kinds of hosts.

BIBLIOGRAPHY

1. BAER, J. G., 1951. *Ecology of Animal Parasites.* Univ. Illinois Press. 224 pp.
2. BAYLIS, H. A., 1924. Some Considerations on the Host-Distribution of Parasitic Nematodes. J. Linn. Soc. Zool., *36*, 13–23.
3. BAYLIS, H. A., 1938. *Helminths and Education. In "Evolution: Essays on Aspects of Evolutionary Biology."* Ed. by G. R. de Beer. pp. 249–270. Oxford University Press. 350 pp.
4. BEQUAERT, J., 1953. The Hippoboscidae or Louseflies (Diptera) of Mammals and Birds. Part I: Structure, Physiology and Natural History. Entomologica Americana, *32*, (new ser.): 1–209, *33*, 211–442.
5. BIKHOVSKAYA-PAVLOVSKAYA, I. E., 1957. (The Question of Specificity of Trematodes.) Trudi Leningradskogo Obshchestva Estestvoispitatelei. Otdeleni Zoologii, *73*, 171–177. (In Russian, French summ.)
6. CAMERON, T. W. M., 1952. Parasitism, Evolution, and Phylogeny. Endeavor, *11*, 193–199.
7. CHABAUD, A. G., 1957. Spécificité Parasitaire Chez les Nématodes Parasites de Vertébrés. pp. 230–243. In: First Symposium on Host Specificity Among Parasites of Vertebrates. Inst. Zool. Univ. Neuchâtel.
8. CORBET, G. B., 1956. The Life-History and Host-Relations of a Hippoboscid Fly *Ornithomyia fringillina* Curtis. J. Animal Ecol., *25*, 403–420.
9. CRUTCHFIELD, C. M. and HIXON, H., 1943. Food Habits of Several Species of Poultry Lice with Special Reference to Blood Consumption. Florida Entom., *26*, 63–66.
9a. DAVENPORT, D., 1955. Specificity and Behavior in Symbioses. Quart. Rev. Biol., *30*, 29–46.
10. DAVENPORT, D., CAMOUGIS, G., and HICKOK, J. F., 1960. Analysis of the Behaviour of Commensals in Host-Factor. 1. A Hesioned Polychaete and a Pinnotherid Crab. Anim. Behaviour, *8*, 209–218.
11. DESOWITZ, R. S. and WATSON, J. J. C., 1953. Studies on *Trypanosoma vivax*. IV. The Maintenance of a Strain in White Rats Without Sheep-Serum Supplement. Ann. Trop. Med. and Parasit., *47*, 62–67.
12. DORAN, D. J., 1953. Coccidiosis in the Kangaroo rats of California. Univ. Calif. Publ. Zool., *59*, 31–60.
13. DROPKIN, V. H., 1941. Host Specificity Relations of Termite Protozoa. Ecology, *22*, 200–202.
14. ———., 1946. The Use of Mixed Colonies of Termites in the Study of Host-Symbiont Relations. J. Parasitol., *32*, 247–251.
15. DUBOIS, GEORGES, 1957. La Spécificité de Fait Chez les Strigeida (Trematoda). pp. 213–227. In: First Symposium on Host Specificity Among Parasites of Vertebrates. Inst. Zool. Univ. Neuchâtel.

16. EDESON, J. and WHARTON, R., 1958. The Experimental Transmission of *Wuchereria malayi* From Man to Various Animals in Malaya. Trans. Roy. Soc. Trop. Med. and Hyg., *52*, 25–45.

17. ELLENBY, C. and GILBERT, A. B., 1957. Cardiotonic Activity of the Potato-Root Eelworm Hatching Factor. Nature, London, *180*, 1105–1106.

18. EWING, H. E., 1938. The Sucking Lice of American Monkeys. J. Parasitol., *24*, 13–33.

19. GOLVAN, Y. J., 1957. La Spécificité Parasitaire Chez les Acanthocéphales. pp. 244–254. In: First Symposium on Host Specificity Among Parasites of Vertebrates. Inst. Zool. Univ. Neuchâtel.

20. GOODCHILD, C. G., 1955. Transplantation of Gorgoderine Trematodes Into Challenging Habitats. Exper. Parasitol., *4*, 351–360.

21. GREENBERG, J. and TREMBLEY, H. L., 1954. The Apparent Transfer of Pyrimethamine-Resistance from the BI Strain of *Plasmodium gallinaceum* to the M Strain. J. Parasitol., *40*, 667–672.

22. GUIMARÃES, L. R. and D'ANDRETTA, M. A. V., 1956. Sinopse dos Nycteribiidae (Diptera) do Novo Mundo. Arqu. Zool. Estado Sao Paulo, *9*, 1–184.

23. HARGIS, W. J., Jr., 1957. The Host Specificity of Monogenetic Trematodes. Exper. Parasitol., *6*, 610–625.

24. HICKOK, J. F. and DAVENPORT, D., 1957. Further Studies in the Behavior of Commensal Polychaetes. Biol. Bull., *113*, 397–406.

25. HOARE, C. A. and NEAL, R. A., 1955. Host-Parasite Relations and Pathogenesis in Infections with *Entamoeba histolytica*. In: *5th Symposium Soc. Gen. Microbiol.* Howie and C'Hea, eds. pp. 230–241.

26. HOPKINS, G. H. E., 1957. Host-Associations of Siphonaptera. In: First Symposium on Host Specificity Among Parasites of Vertebrates. pp. 64–87. Inst. Zool., Univ. Neuchâtel.

27. Jordan, K., 1938. Where Subspecies Meet. Novit. Zool., *41*, 103–111.

28. LAARMAN, J. J., 1958 (1959). Host-Seeking Behavior of Malaria Mosquitoes. XVth Internat. Congr. Zool., Proceedings, p. 648–649.

29. LAING, J., 1937. Host-finding by Insect Parasites. 1. Observations on the Finding of Hosts by *Alysia manducator*, *Mormoniella vitripennis* and *Trichogramma evancescens*. J. Anim. Ecol., *6*, 298–317.

30. LLEWELLYN, J., 1956. The Host-Specificity, Micro-Ecology, Adhesive Attitudes, and Comparative Morphology of some Trematode Gill Parasites. J. Mar. Biol. Assn., *35*, 113–127.

31. MANTER, H. W., 1957. Host Specificity and Other Host Relationships Among the Digenetic Trematodes of Marine Fishes. pp. 185–198. In: First Symposium on Host Specificity Among Parasites of Vertebrates. Inst. Zool. Univ. Neuchâtel.

32. McGHEE, R. B., 1950. The Ability of the Avian Malaria Parasite, *Plasmodium lophurae*, to Infect Erythrocytes of Distantly Related Species of Animals. Amer. J. Hyg., *52*, 42–47.

33. ———, 1953a. The Influence of Age of the Animal Upon the Susceptibility of Mammalian Erythrocytes to Infection by the Avian Malaria Parasite *Plasmodium lophurae*. J. Inf. Dis., *92*, 4–9.

34. ———, 1953b. The Infection by *Plasmodium lophurae* of Duck Erythrocytes in the Chicken Embryo. J. Exper. Med., *97*, 773–782.

35. ———, 1954. The Infection of Duck and Goose Erythrocytes by the Mammalian Malaria Parasite, *Plasmodium berghei*. J. Protozool., *1*, 145–148.

36. ———, 1957. Comparative Susceptibility of Various Erythrocytes to Four Species of Avian Plasmodia. J. Inf. Dis., *100*, 92–96.

37. MICKS, D. W., 1949. Investigations on the Mosquito Transmission of *Plasmodium elongatum* Huff, 1930. J. Nat. Malaria Doc., *8*, 206–218.

38. MOHR, C. O., 1961. Relation of Ectoparasite Load to Host Size and Standard Range. J. Parasitol., *47*, 978–984.

39. MÖNNIG, H. O., 1941. Measles in Cattle and Pigs: Ways of Infection. J. S. Afric. Vet. Med. Assoc., *12*, 59–61.

40. NUTTING, W. L., 1956. Reciprocal Protozoan Transfaunations Between the Roach, *Cryptocercus*, and the Termite, *Zootermopsis*. Biol. Bull., *110*, 83–90.

41. Pavlovskii, E., 1946. (Conditions and Factors Affecting the Formation of the Host Organism of a Parasite in the Process of Evolution. [Sketches of Evolutionary Parasitology, I.]) Zool. Zhurnal, *25*, 289–304. (In Russian with Eng. summary.)

42. Phillips, B. P., Wolfe, P. A., and Bartgis, I. L., 1958. Studies on the Ameba-Bacteria Relationship in Amebiasis. II. Some Concepts on the Etiology of the Disease. Amer. J. Trop. Med. and Hyg., *7*, 392–399.

43. Phillips, B. P., Wolfe, P. A., Rees, C. W., Gordon, H. A., Wright, W. H., and Reyniers, J. A., 1955. Studies on the Ameba-Bacteria Relationship in Amebiasis. Comparative Results of the Intracecal Inoculation of Germfree, Monocontaminated, and Conventional Guinea Pigs with *Entamoeba histolytica*. Amer. J. Trop. Med. and Hyg., *4*, 675–692.

44. Prokopič, J., 1957. The Influence of Oecological Factors on the Specificity of Parasitic Worms of Insectivora. Folia Biol. (Prague), *3*, 114–119.

45. Read, C. P., 1958. Status of Behavioral and Physiological "Resistance." Rice Inst. Pamphl., *45*, 36–54.

46. Read, C. P. and Voge, M., 1954. The Size Attained by *Hymenolepis diminuta* in Different Host Species. J. Parasitol., *40*, 88–89.

47. Read, C. P., Douglas, L. T., and Simmons, J. E., 1959. Urea and Osmotic Properties of Tapeworms From Elasmobranchs. Exper. Parasitol., *8*, 58–75.

48. Reynoldson, T. B., 1956. The Population Dynamics of Host Specificity in *Urceolaria mitra* (Peritricha) Epizoic on Fresh-water Triclads. J. Anim. Ecol., *25*, 127–143.

49. Ries, E., 1931. Die Symbiose der Läuse und Federlinge. Z. Morph. Oekol. Tiere, Berlin, *20*, 233–367.

50. Rogers, W. P., 1960. The Physiology of Infective Processes of Nematode Parasites; the Stimulus From the Animal Host. Proc. Roy. Soc. London, B, *152* (948), 367–386.

51. ———, 1962. *The Nature of Parasitism. The Relationship of Some Metazoan Parasites to Their Hosts*. Academic Press, New York and London, 287 pp.

52. Sprent, J. F. A., 1963. The Life History and Development of *Amplicaecum robertsi*, an Ascaridoid Nematode of the Carpet Python (*Morelia spilotes variegatus*). II. Growth and Host Specificity of Larval Stages in Relation to the Food Chain. Parasitol., *53*, 321–337.

53. Stefanski, W., 1962. Quelles Conditions Exige le Parasite Pour s'Etablir dans son Hôte? Ann. Parasitol. Hum. Comp., *37*, 661–672.

54. Terzian, L. A., Stahler, N., and Weathersby, A. B., 1949. The Action of Anti-Malarial Drugs in Mosquitoes Infected with *Plasmodium gallinaceum*. J. Inf. Dis., *84*, 47–55.

55. Theodor, O., 1957. Parasitic Adaptation and Host-Parasite Specificity in the Pupiparous Diptera. In: First Symposium on Host Specificity Among Parasites of Vertebrates. pp. 50–63. Inst. Zool., Univ. Neuchâtel.

56. Trager, W., 1943. The Influence of Biotin Upon Susceptibility to Malaria. J. Exper. Med., *77*, 557–581.

57. ———, 1947a. A Fat-Soluble Material from Plasma Having the Biological Activities of Biotin. Proc. Soc. Exp. Biol. and Med., *64*, 129–134.

58. ———, 1947b. The Relation to the Course of Avian Malaria of Biotin and a Fat-Soluble Material Having the Biological Activities of Biotin. J. Exper. Med., *85*, 663–683.

59. ———, 1948. The Resistance of Egg-Laying Ducks to Infection by the Malaria Parasite *Plasmodium lophurae*. J. Parasitol., *34*, 389–393.

60. ———, 1950. Studies on the Extracellular Cultivation of an Intracellular Parasite (Avian Malaria). I. Development of the Organisms in Erythrocyte Extracts, and the Favoring Effect of Adenosin Triphosphate. J. Exper. Med., *92*, 349–366.

61. Trager, W. and McGhee, R. B., 1949. The Antimalarial Activity of the Plasma of Certain Adult Ducks Against *Plasmodium lophurae*. J. Parasitol., *35*, Sect. 2, p. 24. (Abstract.)

62. ———, 1950. Factors in Plasma Concerned in Natural Resistance to an Avian Malaria Parasite (*Plasmodium lophurae*). J. Exper. Med., *91*, 365–379.

63. Ulmer, M. J., 1955. Notes on the Morphology and Host-Parasite Specificity of *Fibricola cratera* (Barker and Noll, 1915) Dubois 1932 (Trematoda: Diplostomatidae). J. Parasitol., *41*, 460–466.

64. VOGEL, H., 1934.   Der Entwicklungszyklus von *Opisthorchis felineus* (Riv.). Zoologica, *33*, 1–103.
65. WOOTTON, D. M., 1957.   The Life History of *Cryptocotyle concavum* (Creplin, 1825) Fischoeder, 1903 (Trematoda: Heterophyidae). J. Parasitol., *43*, 271–279.
66. WORTH, C. B., 1950.   Observations on Ectoparasites of some Small Mammals in Everglades National Park and Hillsborough County, Florida. J. Parasitol., *36*, 326–335.

CHAPTER XXVI

The Evolution of Parasitism

INTRODUCTION

ALL activities of animals are related, directly or indirectly, to their struggle for food, reproduction and protection. As Schiller long since declared, "the edifice of the world is only sustained by the impulses of hunger and love". From this struggle stems the wonderfully complex pattern of adjustments and changes which we call adaptations. It has been said that adaptations are the chief marvel of the living world, and their method of origin still the greatest problem of biology. Today we can approach only a little closer to the answers.

Current views relating to the nature of evolutionary mechanisms are based chiefly upon studies of highly specialized organisms, and since parasites are specialized, these views are particularly appropriate. Evolution depends primarily upon the occurrence of shifting gene frequencies (see below) in cross fertilizing organisms, followed by reproductive isolation.

Let us examine this statement on specialized evolution, and make sure that the technical terms are clearly understood. To begin with, mutations furnish material (*i.e.* variations) for the kind of natural selection that Charles Darwin described so well. Given, then, a certain frequency of mutations which produce slight, haphazard changes, and given the selective action of the environment which preserves certain mutations and eliminates the others (*e.g.* genetic death), considerable structural and physiological changes are possible within the time available for evolution. The factor of mutation frequencies plus the factor of recombinations of genes as the result of sexual reproduction produces the "shifting gene frequencies" referred to above. Gradual changes (structural and physiological) within a species may proceed so far as to enable the systematist to distinguish a subspecies. Changes among the individuals of the new subspecies may continue further so as to render them incapable of successful reproductive union with the other indivuduals of the species; hence, the changed individuals belong, by common definition, in a new species. These changes result in the development of reproductive isolation.

We must keep in mind that the organic environment is just as important as the inorganic environment in influencing the adaptations of a given species. The organic, or living, environment includes

(648)

all forms of life with which a given individual or species comes into ecological relation. Indeed, it is generally the organic environment which shows the more rapid and important alterations. There is a sharing of the host's body, and of ways of exploiting it, by viruses, bacteria, molds, fungi, protozoa, worms and arthropods. All of these organisms are part of the host's living environment. The dependence of adaptive trends on the organic environment includes, therefore, dependence upon internal and external parasites. This *biological environment* is sometimes not fully appreciated by biologists. The combination of the host plus its parasite-mix evolves as a whole.

THE PACE OF PARASITE EVOLUTION

We have previously pointed out that many parasitic genera are to be found in widely separated groups (even phyla) of hosts, and obviously there is sometimes no correlation between the primitiveness of the host and the primitiveness of its parasites. The evolution of parasites in most instances has not kept pace with the evolution of the hosts.

The mechanism by which parasites evolve more slowly than do their hosts may be explained as follows. Some members of a given species of host were able to survive more easily than others when the environment changed. Those more fortunate hosts were slightly different from those that were less suited (= adapted) to the new environment, but both groups of hosts possessed the same parasites. During the sweep of time in a changing environment all of the hosts gradually changed, but many of these changes involved external features, and the internal parasites were not subjected to the same degree or kinds of environmental influences as were their hosts. The parasite's environment, however, *did* eventually change, but the lag in time between the change of the host environment and of the parasite environment resulted in a difference in rate of evolution. The parasite evolved more slowly than did its host. Evidence for this conclusion is gained from the many examples of highly specialized hosts harboring some generalized parasites. For example, freshwater silurid and characinid fishes of the Amazon and La Plata rivers harbor primitive marine trematodes and isopods. In general, however, the more specialized hosts possess the more specialized parasites (see below under *Rules of Affinity*).

During the evolution of bird lice the birds themselves underwent a rapid period of evolution, and by the end of the Eocene most of the modern families were established. Up to this time the lice must have been subjected to conditions of great evolutionary stimulus, resulting in the division of the louse population into many partially isolated local populations, and by the end of the Eocene most of the present genera were probably also established. After this time the evolutionary pace of birds slowed down (Miocene birds can often be assigned to modern genera), and relatively few morphological changes took place. Concurrently, there was a reduced stimulus for changes in the bird lice, but in addition, the lice enjoyed a more constant environment than did their hosts, and they probably changed less rapidly than did the latter, as indicated by the existence today of many lice genera being restricted to one order of birds.

The complexity of these associations is illustrated further by the following examples. The bedbug, *Cimex lectularius*, that parasitizes man is practically identical morphologically with the bug, *C. columbarius*, that parasitizes pigeons, and the two are fully cross-fertile in captivity. It is not known, however, if the two are reproductively isolated in nature. *Ascaris lumbricoides*, the common intestinal roundworm of man, is morphologically identical with *Ascaris* in pigs and probably in other hosts. But cross infection, although possible, is rare, indicating physiological differences.[37] Similarly, host-races are found with the tapeworm, *Hymenolepis nana*, of man and rodents; and with *Ancylostoma caninum*, the hookworm of dogs. Recall also the discussion of host specificity in Chapter XXV. Without more information about each of these and many other examples it is difficult or impossible to determine whether we are dealing with biological races or with sibling species (closely related species living together in the same environment).

The interbreeding population of a parasite species may be considered as comprising all of the parasites of that species living on or in one host individual, especially if all developmental stages of the parasites occur on the host. The interbreeding population of a parasite species may also be considered to be all those parasites occurring on or in the entire host population which may even be world-wide in distribution. Intermediate hosts have a different, and often wider, geographical range than do the final hosts. When intermediate hosts are involved, therefore, the effective interbreeding population of the parasite may be represented by a geographical distribution considerably wider than that of the final host alone. These considerations become exceedingly important when we study the evolution of parasites because speciation in parasites, as in free-living animals, is the division of a single interbreeding population into two reproductively isolated ones. Thus emphasis should be placed on the different gene pools that must be present if different species are to be maintained.[23a]

When we consider organic change on the basis of genetic factors alone (mutations, random recombinations, random fixation or elimination), we realize that in a group of a very few interbreeding individuals the genetic constitution will change more quickly than it will in a large number of inter-breeding individuals, chiefly because of sampling error. In a large population there are more varieties, so it takes a longer time to achieve a state of homogeneity. Absolutely maximal rates of phylogenetic evolution could occur, therefore, only in very small populations.

RULES OF AFFINITY

Numerous writers have speculated about the value of parasites as clues to the evolution and affinities of hosts. Out of these speculations has come the word *parasitogenesis*, which refers to the evolution of relationships between the parasite and its host. When examining parasites for a clue to the phylogeny and relationships of hosts, one should consider all the parasites in a body, not just one species. The parasite is more conservative than its host; hence where evolutionary relationships have become obscure among hosts a study of their parasites may clear the obscurity.

Several writers have proposed certain rules of affinity between parasites and the phylogeny of hosts. These rules are listed below, but they should be considered only as guides for study, for which *there are many exceptions*. For more details see Janiszewska,[49] and Szidat.[70]

The Fahrenholz Rule. Common ancestors of present-day parasites were themselves parasites of the common ancestors of present-day hosts. Degrees of relationships between modern parasites thus provide clues as to the parentage of modern hosts.

The Szidat Rule. The more specialized the host group, the more specialized are its parasites; and, conversely, the more primitive or more generalized the host, the less specialized are its parasites. Hence among stable parasites the degree of specialization may serve as a clue to the relative phylogenetic ages of the hosts.

The Eichler Rule. When a large taxonomic group (*e.g.* family) of hosts consisting of wide varieties of species is compared with an equivalent taxonomic group consisting of few representatives, the larger group has the greater diversity of parasitic fauna.

ADAPTATIONS AND PRE-ADAPTATIONS

The term "pre-adaptation" as first used by C. B. Davenport[28] suggests that the organism must have originally possessed characters that made it capable of living an altered life. The term refers to the property in an animal or plant of suitability for some change in its habit or habitat. The concept of pre-adaptation has received some resistance from among biologists and psychologists, but the differences of opinion seem to be due to differences in definitions rather than to a general acceptance of the belief that adaptive mutations appear as chance mutations suitable for use in a situation before the situation arises.

Julian Hawes, late of the University of Exeter, England, once found some amebas in the intestine of a snake. The method of pseudopodial formation and the nuclear structure of the "parasites" were similar to the free-living *limax* amebas of the soil. The amebas were tentatively considered as forms picked up with the snake's food, but when they were cultured *in vitro* they grew equally well in anaerobic and in aerobic media. If certain free-living soil amebas are able to grow and develop in a medium without free oxygen, that is, in a medium similar to the intestine of a vertebrate animal, the soil forms must have become pre-adapted to an intraintestinal life at least so far as free oxygen requirements are concerned. If, also, they are pre-adapted to food conditions to be found in the vertebrate intestine, they are pre-adapted to the state of parasitism. These amebas give us a relatively simple picture of the role of pre-adaptations in preparing a free-living species for the parasitic habit. The important changes which fit a free-living form for the parasitic habit are physiological, not the visible structural traits. The physiological changes must, of course, stand the test of selection. Many species of parasites, such as some gregarines and tapeworms, possess hooks by means of which they attach themselves to the host. How did these complicated structures, which presumably were not present in free-living ancestral forms, ever evolve? Are the hooks essential for the parasitic life? The answer to the last question is, apparently, no, because we find that closely related species can get along very well without hooks. These groups of parasites probably were able to enter and live in their first hosts because of at least some physiological compatibility. After they once became established, mutations affecting structural and physiological changes which had adaptational advantages persisted.

The majority of students of evolution believe that whereas both adaptive and non-adaptive traits characterize any taxonomic level, adaptive characters are generally more numerous; but at the low taxonomic levels non-adaptive characters are more common. A classic example of a non-adaptive character is the coccyx of man. Among parasitic insects are many that have appendage modifications that have no *known* use. The difficulty, of course, is to be *sure* that a character is non-adaptive. This assurance we do not have. On the other hand, some of the characters we judge to be useful may not be so.

Any genetic change which decreases the harm or increases the benefit of either parasite or host will be adaptively advantageous and be encouraged by selection. On the other hand, non-adaptive differentiation (= indeterminate change or divergence) in a small population is called *drift*. Hence, a geographical or host divergence may be linked with the non-adaptive divergence due to drift which may result in the fixation or the elimination of genes entirely by chance with no relation to their selective value.

Can we expect a great amount of genetic change among parasites securely housed in the relatively stable environment of the host? Have we not been accustomed to thinking that species change only if the environment changes? But a changing environment *selects* from among genetic varieties *already present* in the gene pool of the population. In the stable environment of an adjusted parasite the gene pool making up the parasite population gradually becomes larger because all of the non-harmful (including the beneficial) mutations tend to persist. Evidence for the truth of this statement may be obtained experimentally by transferring all the parasites from the intestine of one host to the intestine of another, but closely related, host. In the latter animal natural selection operates to reduce the numbers of variations to those which can survive in the new environment.

BIOLOGICAL (=PHYSIOLOGICAL) RACES

Let us assume that a mammal possesses a certain species of ectoparasite, A, that is adapted to live in the dorsal body hair. Let us also assume that during the course of evolution a group of these parasites begins to find the ventral part of the host's head more to its liking. This divergent group we will call B. We find that A and B are morphologically identical, but B becomes better adapted to live on the lower side of the host's head than does A. In other words, A and B are physiologically different, and each belongs to a different biological race. This kind of divergent adaptation of separate groups within one species of parasite may progress to a state of full species differentiation, and all gradations from incipient physiological subspecies to intersterile species are common. During the process of divergence the appearance of visible morphological differences lags behind the appearance of physiological differences, and barriers to intercrossing are quickly established by natural selection. The method by which such differentiation originates is not clear to biologists. Our greatest difficulty arises, of course, in the detection of minor, or even many major, changes of a physiological nature. This whole problem is reviewed by Thorpe[71,74] and discussed by Huxley[47]. Some examples follow.

Trypanosoma gambiense, T. rhodesiense and *T. brucei* are morphologically indistinguishable, but they differ in their host preference and in their effects upon the hosts. These flagellates are probably biological races of one species. We have found that there is no way to distinguish clearly on a morphological basis the forms of *Entamoeba* from sheep, pigs, goats and cattle.[57] These amebas probably belong to one species, but cross infection experiments will have to be made before proof can be established. Possibly, however, each group of amebas represents a true biological species, but since they do not reproduce by sexual union, proof of the latter possibility must be obtained by criteria less satisfactory than the interbreeding test. In the same manner the mange-mites of the species *Sarcoptes scabiei* are probably divided into biological races, each adapted to a single host species—sheep, dogs, goats, camels, horses, rabbits, men, etc.

Hoare[42] has emphasized that "there is no fundamental difference between geographical races of free-living organisms separated spatially and biological races of parasites segregated by differences in hostal environment." There are numerous examples "of the existence among parasitic micro-organisms of intraspecific groups or 'types' in which the chief differential characters are represented by the pathological immunological manifestations produced by them in the host." Pathogenic trypanosomes, for example, can rapidly develop different "strains" which are immune to antibodies of the host.

The ichneumonid insect, *Nemeritis canescens*, normally parasitizes only the larvae of the meal moth, *Ephestia kuhniella*. The ichneumonid was reared experimentally on the larvae of the wax moth, *Achronia grisella*. Whereas all adult females of the ichneumonid species possess a genetically-determined response to the odor of the meal moth, those which were reared on the wax moth, or even brought into close contact with it immediately after emergence from the pupa, demonstrated an additional response (attraction) to the wax moth.[75] Later work showed that this larval conditioning depends on a tendency to be attracted by any olfactory stimulus characteristic of a favorable environment. Thorpe[73] concluded that "the theoretical importance of such a conditioning effect is that it will tend to split a population into groups attached to a particular host or food plant, and thus will of itself tend to prevent cross-breeding. It will, in other words, provide a non-hereditary barrier which may serve as the first stage in evolutionary divergence." As Huxley[47] put it, we have here "a beautiful case of the principle of organic selection . . . according to which modifications repeated for a number of generations may serve as the first step in evolutionary change, not by becoming impressed upon the germ-plasm, but by holding the strain in an environment where mutations tending in the same direction will be selected and incorporated into the constitution. The process simulates Lamarckism but actually consists in the replacement of modifications by mutations".

The causes of biological race production are not clearly understood, as was pointed out above. Let us go back to some considerations presented at the beginning of this chapter. If a species is subject to high mortality through the activities of a predator, we can speak of *predator-pressure*. Likewise we can use the term *competitor-pressure*. With a decrease in predator-pressure and a decrease in competitor-pressure there is a decrease in *selection-pressure*. That is, there are fewer agencies which tend to "kill off" the less favorably adapted individuals of a species. We are using Simpson's definition of the term "selection" as anything tending to produce systematic heritable change in populations between one generation and the next. We should now recall the phenomenon of continuous, more or less random mutations in all species. It follows that decreased selection-pressure is attended by increased variation. Now then, in the preface to this book we stated that parasitism is "a life of large income without work". The parasitic life has greatly reduced the danger from destruction by predators, and from the demand for competition. From the arguments presented above, it follows that one would expect more variation among parasitic species as compared with non-parasitic species. Among the parasitic protozoa we frequently find apparently distinct species with extremely small, or no morphological differences, with over-lapping geographical or host distribution, and with a similarity in ecological preferences—a puzzling situation indeed. Examples are illustrated by *Balantidium*, trypanosomes, *Plasmodium*, Myxo-sporida, *Hexamita*. But probably the state of parasitism favors the persistence and the accumulation of genetic variations which result in preservation of relatively large numbers of biological races. These races are incipient species.

Nature, however, is full of checks and balances, and we must not forget that the parasite, even a mild one, carries on an assault against its host and that the host is a responsive environment. For these reasons selection *does* take place and it limits the numbers of incip-ient species of parasites.

A clue to answers to such problems as raised above lies in more careful studies of environmental changes within a host organ. The intestine, for example, contains a large community of populations forever growing, changing, dying. Fluctuating populations, streams of metabolic by-products, changes in enzyme concentrations, and, in general, the surge of chemical activity coincident with the pro-cesses of ingestion, assimilation, respiration and excretion of thou-sands of organisms crowded together do not support a stable or constant environment.

The student should be cautious when using such terms as "host-races," "biological species" and "ecological races," because of the obvious difficulty of distinguishing morphologically similar sibling species (reproductively isolated) from morphologically similar but physiologically different races or demes (reproductively compatible), and from phenotypically different populations which may or may not be reproductively isolated.

ORIGINS OF PARASITISM

On the preceding pages of this chapter we have dealt with mecha-nisms of speciation, using parasites and their hosts as examples. We could have substituted free-living forms, because whereas parasites often complicate the problem of interpretation, they do not present us with new, basic principles. We now turn to some questions on the origins of the parasitic habit. Assuming that the *first* parasites were derived from free-living species, how did they become parasites?

If we review the several theories on the origin of life, we recall that primitive free-living organisms gradually used up the available sup-ply of complex organic substances and at the same time developed new enzymes that enabled them to synthesize those complex sub-stances from available chemical precursors. Now, if the first virus-like microorganisms failed to develop these enzymes, and if they were dependent upon other primitive forms of life in whose bodies were to be found the only source of complete food, the virus-like or-ganisms would, if they were to survive, become obligate parasites.

When bacteria finally appeared the viruses found a ready supply of hosts. To use the words of Dodson,[30] "The evolution of the bacteria made parasitism possible." On the other hand, the viruses have been called "degenerate" parasites.

Cytoplasmic components of a cell appear to be independent, in varying degrees, of the cell in which they are contained.[52] This independence supports the theory that these cytoplasmic components may have arisen through symbiotic association between microbial forms and colonies of "virus" or higher units. The cell nucleus, according to this view, is the descendent of the original virus colony with its surrounding envelope, and the cytoplasm consists essentially of the descendents of symbiotic organisms, together with products of the nucleus and substances resulting from their interaction. Such speculations on the role of symbiosis in evolution fires the imagination, but they lack experimental evidence to support them. Studies on DNA and RNA molecules may provide some evidence.

We may assume that at the time the first pre-parasite entered a host the guest was either already resistant to host antibodies, that is, it was pre-adapted to life within the host, or it was able to change rapidly so as to become tolerant of the host. The host, on the other hand, had to be, or quickly became, tolerant of the guest. The changes had to be genetic if the relationship was to become permanent. In Chapter XXII of this book we mentioned several important problems which must be solved by any parasite. Problems of obtaining food, of leaving the host alive, and of regaining entrance are as important for continued success in parasitism as is the problem of combating host antibodies.

In many parasite-host relationships the parasite is attracted to the host because of the presence of some kind of chemical compound elaborated by the host. Such compounds are presumably detected by the sensory apparatus of the parasite (see page 641). One way in which a wide range of hosts might be secured by one species of parasite during its evolution is the fortuitous production by a "foreign" animal of a metabolite similar to the "attractant" produced by a host animal. Given sufficient adaptability on the part of the parasite, the foreign animal becomes another host. Davenport[29] feels certain that this kind of behavior takes place.

As we have already seen, the reproductive organs are the most conspicuous and important of all internal structures in parasitic worms. It has often been stated that animals that produce immense numbers of eggs must do so in order to compensate for the tremendous loss of eggs and young sustained by the species. This explanation is teleological, but the *result* of the production of a large number of eggs is the assurance of survival of a few. The egg-producing capacity, with its concurrent complexity of reproductive organs may have been developed from a series of pre-adaptations to parasitism. Caullery[12] rejects this possibility in favor of his proposal that the processes of reproduction in parasites have developed as a result of environmental conditions not essentially related to parasitism or to the need for species preservation. Support for the latter belief is gained from a study of sedentary animals, such as the coelenterates, which characteristically reproduce both sexually and asexually. Asexual reproduction tends to efface individuality. Instead of a single body physiologically and morphologically independent (a condition characteristic of animals reproducing solely by sexual reproduction), the parasite and the sedentary animal have lost their individuality, due to the combined effect of asexual reproduction (*e.g.* polyembryony) and such factors as special nutritional behavior. Caullery tentatively suggested that polyembryony is initiated by osmotic changes in the medium surrounding the parasite. In any case, simple analogy of parasites with sedentary animals cannot explain the facts of sporocyst and rediae development, proglottid formation, etc. in parasitic worms. All the factors of mutations, recombinations of genes, selection, pre-adaptation, adaptation and the "environmental conditions" surrounding each individual combine to mold the evolution of parasites as well as of free-living organisms.

Secondary hosts could have been introduced into a life cycle because of the ability of an embryo stage or larva of the parasite to survive in many kinds of animals. The larva (*e.g.* of a cestode) would have been resistant to the antibodies of the new host, but it might have stimulated more antibody production so that, in order to survive, the larva would have had to protect itself by forming a cyst wall around itself. The new (transfer) host would, of course, have had to be part of the food supply of the original host to be of any value in completing the life cycle of the parasite.[84]

Most biologists agree that the intermediate host, particularly when it is an invertebrate, generally represents the ancestral single host. The assumption is made that at one time the parasite enjoyed the embrace of a single invertebrate host, but that infective stages, through the same evolutionary mechanisms as those which result in any parasitism, gradually became parasites in another host closely associated with the first one. A classic example is that of *Plasmodium*, the malarial parasite. In this case the mosquito is often considered to be the "definitive" host harboring the sexual phases of the life cycle; and the vertebrate is the alternate secondary host. This evolutionary sequence would explain the more compatible adjustment and apparent lack of pathogenicity between *Plasmodium* and the mosquito. The significance of the degree of host reaction, however, is open to question. The mosquito vector is considered by some authors to represent a secondary involvement. Ball[7] has made a survey of instances where the degree of pathogenicity would be a poor guide for determining the evolutionary time relationships between host and parasite. He has emphasized that a high degree of pathogenicity is not "*prima facie* evidence of recent and still imperfect development of the host-parasite relation." We must bear in mind that many factors beyond the mere length of association time play significant roles in determining the incidence and degree of pathogenicity of parasitic infections in new hosts. By and large, however, commensalism may be considered as an evolutionary goal of true parasitism. The former type of association conserves available hosts and thus favors survival of the well-adapted parasite.

The intriguing concept of "adaptation tolerance" has been proposed by Sprent.[65] The general idea is that, whereas new hosts react to the maximum of their potential against a new parasite, as parasites and hosts become adapted to each other, the latter gradually lose the ability of immunological reactivity, so that they become tolerant, in the immunological sense, of their parasites. Sprent suggested that this tolerance might have been achieved in two ways: (1) by the selection of parasites whose antigenic structure tended to approximate those of the hosts, so that the antigens of the parasites came to comprise the same immunological determinants as the "self" components of the host, and thus became immunologically inactive (for example, the loss of those parasite enzymes that differ appreciably from enzymes present in the host); (2) by a tendency towards the obliteration of antibody patterns which correspond to antigens possessed by the parasite.

The adaptation tolerance idea was stimulated by Burnet's[7b] clonal selection hypothesis of acquired immunity. Burnet suggested that antibodies are produced by clones of lymphocytes, each clone representing a particular combining-pattern which corresponds to a particular antigenic determinant. He proposed that all possible antigenic patterns have their counterparts in the lymphocytes produced during the development of an individual. The net result is that instead of the antigen directly influencing the synthesis of globulin, it merely selects an appropriate pattern and instigates the proliferation of a particular clone of cells. If, as a result of selection, parasites become associated with hosts which lack certain patterns, i.e. those which correspond to parasite antigens, then the host is incapable of recognizing the parasite.

"PROGRESSIVE" AND "RETROGRESSIVE" EVOLUTION

Much of our discussion on the preceding pages has implied progressive evolution, that is, changes which in some way improve an organ or enhance a function. But evolution may also be retrogressive. The development of the parasitic habit almost always involves some regression in evolution largely because natural selection does not work against mutations which damage a useless character.

Whereas the loss of such structures as the intestine in the evolution of tapeworms (or at least in the evolution of the turbellarian-like ancestors of tapeworms) is clearly a result of regression in the usual anthropomorphic sense, from the point of view of the worm it is progressive because the animal has progressed to a situation where it no longer needs an intestine, and it can turn its attention to the more important function of producing eggs.

When we say that an animal is highly specialized, we are saying that evolutionary changes during its phylogeny have been extended in complexity beyond those changes characteristic of animals that are less specialized. "Degenerate" changes are essentially a form of specialization, but obviously many structures and habits not of a degenerate nature are also specialized in parasites. Julian Huxley has defined "specialization" as improvement in efficiency of adaptation for a particular mode of life, and "progress" as an improvement in efficiency of living in general; but we are inclined to agree with J. B. S. Haldane who denies the existence of evolutionary *progress*, and calls it a mere anthropomorphism. The terms "degenerate," "regressive" and "retrogressive" are, of course, also anthropomorphic, and perhaps should not be used.

A group of organisms having a high degree of specialization does not give rise to a new type. Only the relatively unspecialized group is able to give rise to new forms. Consequently, parasites as a whole are worthy examples of the inexorable march of evolution into blind alleys.

One category of parasites may be an exception to the generalization that parasitism is a comfortable shortcut to evolutionary blind alleys. Examples of insects which are parasitic as larvae (*e.g.* wasps which lay their eggs in the larvae of other insects) are well known. Recall, for a moment, our earlier discussion about the advantages of being a parasite, and compare the protection, ready food supply and shelter enjoyed by the parasite with the struggle endured by the free-living animal. In other words, the life of parasitism is not as hard on the parasite as the free life is on the free-living animal. Recall also that the more specialized the parasite the more irrevocable the habit. The benefits bestowed by parasitism are more marked in larval forms when growth of the parasite is rapid, but often the larva soon leaves its host and emerges as a free-living organism before there has been time to sacrifice its independence. Some entomologists believe that all the hymenoptera, as well as the Cyclorrhapha flies, which include the house fly, have been descended from ancestors which were parasitic in their larval stages. The French zoologist Giard gave the name "placental parasite" to the mammalian fetus because it lives at the expense of its mother, the "host", and in all essential ways resembles a parasite which has adjusted to its environment with marked success. During the period of rapid growth of the fragile "parasite" it is far better cared for and protected than is its free-living mother. Rothschild and Clay[63] have remarked that "a fundamental distinction can be drawn between the parasitic adult and the parasitic young, the full significance of which has not hitherto been fully appreciated. In the former, parasitism appears to lead to dependence and a loss of evolutionary potential, whereas in the immature stages, it may, on the contrary, prove to be a successful and progressive step". Obviously the

42

parasitic young is not a parasite of the host *species*, but only of the individual.

On the following pages dealing with the origins of the several different groups of parasites, much of the discussion is no more than an intriguing exercise of the imagination. But new facts are daily coming to light and eventually the true pattern of parasite evolution will be revealed.

ORIGINS OF SPECIFIC GROUPS
Protozoa

Entozoic protozoa may have been derived from ectoparasites, as various authors have suggested. It does seem logical to suppose that free-living forms first became associated with hosts as casual commensals loosely attached to the skin or gills, then gradually fortified their position by moving into the mouth, gill chambers, anus, and other openings. But ectozoic forms are mostly primitive ciliates, flagellates and suctoria, and only a few genera such as *Trichodina* and *Hexamita* contain both ectozoic and entozoic species.[62,83]. Another logical guess as to origins of parasitic protozoa is that they were derived from species accidentally ingested by their future hosts. When we consider the large numbers of protozoa that are steadily ingested with the food of larger animals, and when we think of the nutritional benefits and the protection and moisture provided by the intestine, we appreciate the inescapable advantages for survival furnished by lodgings in a gut. Once established in the intestine, the parasite could migrate to all other parts of the body.

Since the parasitic habit among protozoa is not limited to exclusively parasitic groups but is scattered among orders containing free-living species, the parasitic habit probably arose frequently and independently from different groups of free-living ancestors. Sporadic and temporary invasion by free-living species into hosts may be comparable with the initial step in the origin of endoparasitism. For example, species of the Euglenida are sporadically found in tadpoles and in millipedes, and *Tetrahymena* is occasionally found in such sites as the digestive tracts of slugs, the coelom of sea urchins, the hemocoel of insects and the gills of the amphipod, *Gammarus pulex*.

When the complete life cycle of a protozoon is known, a critical examination of the various stages will often lead to information suggesting phylogenetic relationships with neighboring groups. Such a study of the opalinids (parasitic in the large intestine of tailless Amphibia) with particular attention to the infraciliature and mode of fission has led several authorities to the conviction that these parasites are zooflagellates instead of ciliates, but distantly related to other existing groups of Mastigophora.[18,26,39]

In 1935 Wenrich[83] made a comprehensive study of the hypothetical origin of parasitism among protozoa, and we shall begin our review with generous samples taken from his study. A number of investigations have shown that when free-living protozoa first become entozoic they do not necessarily undergo any marked morphological modification. If protozoa intermediate in behavior and habitat between free-living and parasitic can be found, they should present a clue to an answer to the question of origin raised above. Such intermediate forms are common. Wenrich[82] described a holotricious ciliate, *Amphileptus branchiarum*, found on the gills of tadpoles. The ciliate has a free-swimming stage which roams over the gills devouring ectozoic *Trichodina* or *Vorticella*. At other times, and more commonly, the "parasite" attaches itself to the tadpole gills by a thin membrane within which it gently rotates, pausing now and then to indulge its predacious tendencies to engulf masses of gill cells. The ciliate is, perhaps, in the process of changing over from a free-living predacious organism to a parasitic one. Other common species of *Amphileptus* are predacious.

Wenrich discovered some colorless euglenoids, belonging to the genus *Menoidium*, in the gut of the milliped, *Spirobolus marginatus*. He attempted to infect the millipeds by feeding both *Menoidium* sp. and *Euglena gracilis* to them, and he found that both (the former more successfully) were able to survive within the host intestine for a few days, but neither was able to become established as a permanent entozoic flagellate. Wenrich concluded that the *Menoidium* "displayed the facultative capacity of maintaining for a brief time, at least, an entozoic existence."

This situation led Wenrich to conclude that the host, representing a special and limited environment, has not had a marked directive influence on the evolution of its parasites; otherwise there should be more evidence of convergence in evolutionary trends among the parasites. It should be recalled, however, that hosts markedly influence physiological changes in their parasites. Such changes, as we have already indicated, are the first to take place in evolutionary divergence and, indeed, are often the only significant modifications to occur. After all, the protozoa have had a longer time than any other animal phylum in which to evolve. They have invaded almost every possible ecological niche, and some genera, such as *Hexamita*, are to be found in a wide variety of unrelated hosts without the parasites exhibiting significant morphological changes.

Speculations on the evolution of the family Trypanosomatidae have recently been made by Baker.[6] The leptomonad body form (see p. 47) is considered to be the most primitive type of the family, and ancestral flagellates presumably were parasites of the gut of invertebrates. This ancestral leptomonad type probably led on the one hand to the genera *Leptomonas* and *Phytomonas*, and on the other hand to the genera *Trypanosoma*, *Rhynchoidomonas* (including "*Herpetomonas*" as used by Wenyon), *Blastocrithidia* and *Crithidia*.

Methods of transmission offer clues as to the kinds of evolution experienced by the genus *Trypanosoma*. Thus the contaminative type of infection in *Trypanosoma cruzi* is evidently the more primitive. Hoare[43] has suggested that the origin of inoculative transmission and its attendant form of parasite life cycle, as in *T. gambiense*, may be a secondary acquisition which originally developed in the hind-gut of the insect vector. Such trypanosomes may have been taken up by tsetse flies which began to transmit them mechanically to new vertebrate hosts, but when the flagellates adapted themselves to development in the proboscis and/or salivary glands, tsetse flies became their new obligatory transport hosts. Evidence for this hypothesis is presented by *T. vivax* which develops only in the mouth parts of its insect vector, and by *T. congolense* (representing the next step in evolution), which develops in the mid-gut of the insect, and finally by the *Brucei*-group, which utilizes the mid-gut and then the salivary glands of the tsetse fly. A final bit of evidence for the described phylogenetic relations among trypanosomes is provided by the differences in susceptibility of their vectors to infection. Practically 100 per cent of triatomid bugs fed *T. cruzi* become infected, while fewer than 1 per cent of tsetse flies fed *T. brucei* become infected. The obvious conclusion is that *T. cruzi* and its bugs represent a much older and more stable association. Moreover, tsetse-borne trypanosomes easily lose the power to develop in the insect host and they may revert to mechanical trans-

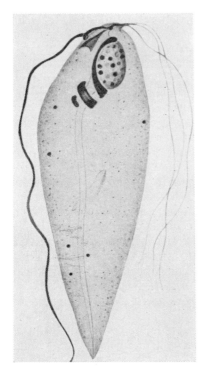

Fig. XXVI–1.—*Devescovina cometoides*, from the termite *Cryptotermes dudleyi*. (Kirby, courtesy of Univ. Calif. Pub. Zool.)

mission. Such a transformation is illustrated by *T. vivax* in cattle of South America, and by *T. evansi* which presumably originated in Africa from *T. brucei* (see page 54). A final step in the evolutionary series is *T. equiperdum* which has become completely emancipated from an insect vector, and is transmitted directly from horse to horse by contact during the sexual act. See also Baker.[6]

The evolution of the large and complex group of flagellates which inhabit the intestines of termites stemmed from the simple *Monocercomonas* or from a *Monocercomonas*-like form. This form (Fig. III–20, p. 65) has an uncomplicated parabasal body and axostyle, three free flagella, and an adherent or free-trailing flagellum. The Trichomonadidae have added a costa and an undulating membrane in place of the recurrent flagellum (see Fig. III–21, p. 66). *Devescovina* (Fig. XXVI–1) is similar to *Monocercomonas*, but it possesses a triangular cresta and its parabasal body is coiled around the axostyle. The Calonymphidae are derived from the Devescovinidae. For a detailed discussion of these relationships see Hollande.[44]

The Sarcodina have arisen from flagellates, and they appear to represent a polyphyletic group. The numerous examples of ameboid flagellates (e.g. *Tetramitus* and *Naegleria*) lend ample support to these conclusions.

Little attention has been given to the evolution of the sporozoa. A group of workers in Russia, headed by Cheissin,[20] has been much interested in the taxonomy and phylogeny of these obligatory parasites. Cheissin has reminded us that the sporozoa possess some structural characteristics suggestive of the flagellates (*e.g.* merozoites similar to leptomonads; flagellated microgametes similar to *Bodo*; sexual processes similar to those of phytomonads). However, an ameboid method of locomotion is common among the sporozoa (page 97). Nevertheless, these protozoa probably arose from flagellates which possessed life cycles similar to those of present-day phytomonads. The sporozoa probably became adapted to parasitism in the intestines of aquatic invertebrates, then moved to terrestrial invertebrates and vertebrates. The gregarines today have retained the ancestral characteristic of inhabiting the intestinal lumen, but the other sporozoa have become adapted exclusively or at least predominately as intracellular parasites or as parasites of such cavities as the gallbladder and coelom.

The most comprehensive works on the phylogeny of the protozoa have been those concerned with the ciliates. The following theories on the evolution of the orders containing numerous parasitic forms will serve to introduce recent conceptions relating to the "new systematics" of the group. These theories were developed chiefly by the French schools of Chatton and of Fauré-Fremiet, and they have been modified and refined by Corliss,[27] whose paper on the evolution and systematics of ciliated protozoa may be consulted for details and for a bibliography.

The new approach to phylogenetic problems of the ciliates utilizes the subpellicularly located basal granules, or kinetosomes, which are intimately and indispensably associated with all external ciliary systems. This *infraciliature*, as it is called, is present even in the absence of external ciliature. The approach also focuses attention on the ontogeny or morphogenetic aspects of ciliate development. From an unknown zooflagellate ancestry the Gymnostomatida, a large order embracing a great variety of forms, is situated at the base of the ciliate evolutionary tree. Two examples of this order are *Amphileptus branchiarum*, common on the skin and gills of frog tadpoles, and *Chilodonella cyprini*, a skin and gill parasite of fishes. The gymnostomes gave rise to the polyphyletic order Trichostomatida in which is placed the well-known *Balantidium*. This genus shows affinities with the Holotrichia.[34,56] From the trichostomes arose the order Hymenostomatida which stands at a major crossroads in ciliate evolution. A primitive member of this order is the highly pathogenic fish skin parasite, *Ichthyophthirius* (Fig. VI–5, p. 149). A probable side branch of the evolutionary tree is the order Astomatida which contains *Haptophyra*, an intestinal parasite of amphibia and of the turbellaria. Another probable side branch is the order Apostomatida containing, among other parasites, *Cyrtocaryum halosydnae* whose host is a marine polychaete. The hymenostomes gave rise to the Heterotrichida, but the former were also ancestors of other orders containing parasitic holotrichs. These orders are Thigmotrichida, in which we find numerous symbiotic ciliates such as *Conchophthirius* in mollusks, and *Boveria*, an ectoparasite on gills of various marine animals; and the order Peritrichida, the largest of all ciliophoran orders in which is placed *Urceolaria* and *Trichodina* (Fig. VI–9, p. 154), both to be found on or in many aquatic animals.

The subclass Spirotricha is characterized by a buccal ciliature composing the adoral zone of membranelles, the prominence of which is accentuated by an increasing loss of simple somatic ciliature. The first order, Heterotrichida, in this subclass contains *Licnophora* and other marine ectocommensals, and it probably gave rise, through the oligotrichs, to the order Entodiniomorphida. It is in the latter order that we find the highly specialized stomach commensals of herbivorous mammals. Examples are: *Cycloposthium*, *Entodinium*, *Epidinium*, *Ophryoscolex*.

Pixell Goodrich[60] has listed a series of ciliates (order Apostomatida) starting with the scarcely modified blue ciliate (*Physophaga*) which is practically free-living—merely feeding on the secretion left in the molts of a freshwater shrimp (*Gammarus pulex*)—and grading into genuine entozoic parasites. Nutrition in the holotrichous ciliates of the family Foettingeriidae appears to be essentially parasitic, although these ciliates are free in the water for a considerable part of their life cycles. *Foettingeria* is a ciliate parasite of the gastric cavity of most species of actinians (sea anemones). Vegetative forms, up to 1 millimeter long, escape into the sea water where they change into cysts, which then produce small, active free-living "tomites." Each tomite forms a resting cyst on a crustacean which, if eaten by a suitable actinian, discharges a parasitic ciliate in the gastric cavity of the host. At the end of the series we find *Chromidina*, an astomatus and sedentary entozoic ciliate parasite of the kidneys of cephalopods. The genus also produces free-living tomites as part of its life cycle. Such series, illustrating a gradual progression from free-living to parasitic species have often been presented to demonstrate a probable, or at least a possible, phylogenetic history. Although such a series introduces a pleasant and reasonable picture, it is generally not accompanied by supporting evidence that evolution actually followed the supposed sequence.

Classification of the protozoa is constantly being changed as more precise information on morphology, life cycles and biochemistry permit more accurate estimates of relationships to be made. The sporozoa, for example, have often been characterized by the absence

of locomotor organelles, but we know now that most of these protozoa possess and use pseudopodia at least during one stage in their
life cycles. This feature of their morphology and activity is the
chief basis for recent recommendations to consider the sporozoa as
of polyphyletic origin, and to place some of their orders with the
Sarcodina. On the other hand, Cleveland[24] has shown that gametogenesis in the flagellates (particularly *Trichonympha*) of the wood-
eating roach does not differ greatly from the same phenomenon in
the life cycle of *Plasmodium*, but it is more simple and direct in the
flagellates. Also, the flagellate cycle is similar to that of *Monocystis*,
a gregarine, although in the latter there are two gametocytes, whereas in the flagellate there is one gametocyte, but cysts occur in both
forms. Thus in the primitive roach is preserved types of protozoan
sexual behavior which are probably older than the sporozoa, and
the mastigophora probably existed with the sporozoa as a single
group in the far distant past.

The Flatworms in General

The first metazoa were almost certainly radially symmetrical
animals, and speculations on the origins of the flatworms always
run into the thorny question of an alteration from radial to bilateral
symmetry. Hyman[48] has reviewed the several theories of origin,
and she has presented convincing arguments to support the view
that an ancestral planuloid form (resembling the ciliated-larva of
coelenterates) gave rise on the one hand to coelenterates and on the
other hand to the flatworms. This planuloid type of ancestor was
probably a radially symmetrical and elongated organism without
mouth or digestive tract, with a ciliated or flagellated epidermis,
and with ingestion and digestion processes of the protozoan type.
It was undoubtedly polarized with definite anterior and posterior
ends. The planuloid theory is based upon the remarkable features
of the primitive flatworms of the order Acoela (class Turbellaria).
These small worms have the coelenterate characters of a ciliated
epidermis, often syncytial, and often with basal muscle fibers.
The interior of the worm is a solid mass of cells as in a planula
larva, but there is a central, ventral mouth leading to a short
pharynx. Sex cells are differentiated from out of the interior cell
mass, and although the animals are hermaphroditic, internal cross-
fertilization is the rule. Obviously there is no difficulty in visualizing
an evolution from planuloid ancestors to an acoeloid form (Fig.
XXVI–2). Perhaps one objection to the hypothesis that all flatworms, including the Mesozoa, have been derived from a group of
hypothetical, generalized, planula-like progenitors, may be based on
the fact that there is no close comparison between the oncosphere
and any known type of planula larva. Contrast, for example the
figure of a pseudophyllidean oncosphere (coracidium) (Fig. X–10,
p. 251) with that of a planula. See also papers by Stunkard.[67,68]
Major differences of opinion exist regarding the origins of the

different groups within the Phylum Platyhelminthes.[59a] The order Rhabdocoelida (class Turbellaria) consists of small worms characterized by a mouth and unbranched digestive tract, protonephridia, oviducts, and nervous system usually with two main trunks. Most of these worms are free-living in salt, brackish, or fresh water, but a few are parasitic in other turbellarians, mollusks, echinoderms and crustaceans. Within this order the suborder Temnocephalida represents one of the few groups of parasitic rhabdocoels. Temnocephalids (Fig. VII–2, p. 161) are leech-like, almost devoid of

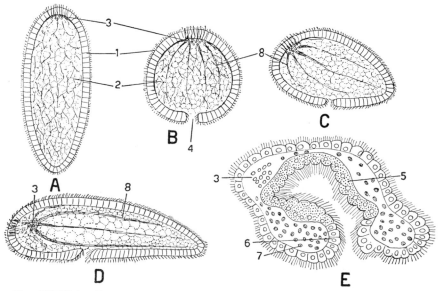

Fig. XXVI–2.—Diagrams illustrating the planuloid-acoeloid theory of the origin of the Bilateria. *A*, Planula larva, mouthless with apical nerve center. *B*, Mouth formed, oral-aboral axis shortening. *C*, Body elongating in a sagittal (originally transverse) plane, nervous center shifting forward. *D*, Acoeloid stage, a bilateral creeping worm with anterior nerve center. *E*, Later stage, archenteron formed; actual embryonic stage of a polyclad (*after Surface, 1907*).

1, ectoderm; *2*, entodermal mass; *3*, nervous center; *4*, mouth; *5*, archenteron; *6*, stomodaeum; *7*, mesoderm; *8*, nerve cords. (Hyman, *The Invertebrates*, Vol. II, courtesy of McGraw-Hill Book Company.)

cilia, and the anterior end is extended into two to twelve tentacles. The posterior end is equipped with one or two adhesive disks, the pharynx is barrel shaped (doliiform), and the gonopore is single (common sex pore). Temnocephalids are ectocommensals on freshwater animals, chiefly crustaceans, but also on turtles and snails, frequently occurring within the branchial chamber. They do not derive nourishment from their hosts, but capture and devour insect larvae, rotifers and other small crustaceans. Another group of rhabdocoelids containing parasitic forms is the Dalyellioida within the suborder Lecithophora. Dalyellioids possess a doliiform type of pharynx, no proboscis, mouth generally at the anterior tip of the

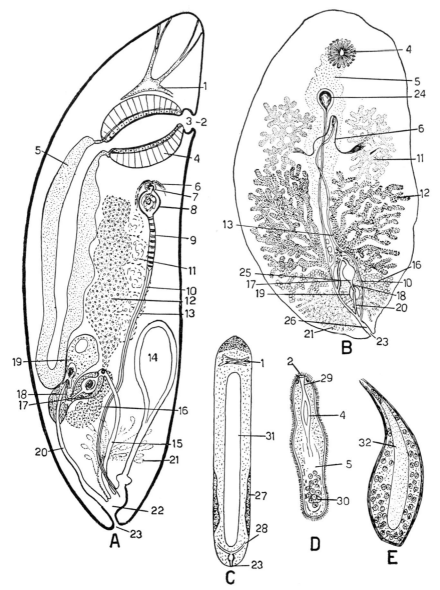

Fig. XXVI–3.—Dalyellioida. Umagillidae, Fecampiidae. *A*, *Anoplodiera voluta* (*after Westblad*, 1930), from the gut of sea cucumbers, sagittal section. *B*, *Syndisyrinx* from the gut of California sea urchins, from life. *C–E*, *Fecampia*, (*after Caullery and Mesnil*, 1903). *C*, Adult without mouth or pharynx. *D*, Juvenile stage with digestive system and eyes. *E*, *Fecampia* secreting the capsule containing many clusters of eggs and yolk cells.

1, brain; *2*, mouth; *3*, pharyngeal cavity; *4*, pharynx; *5*, intestine; *6*, sperm ducts; *7*, spermiducal vesicle; *8*, seminal vesicle; *9*, penis bulb; *10*, penis stylet; *11*, testis (only one shown in *A*); *12* yolk gland (one shown in *A*); *13*, ejaculatory duct; *14*, uterus; *15*, vagina; *16*, ovary; *17*, seminal receptacle; *18*, insemination canal; *19*, copulatory bursa; *20*, bursal canal; *21*, cement glands; *22*, common antrum; *23*, common gonopore; *24*, longstalked capsule in the uterus; *25*, ovovitelline duct; *26*, vagina; *27*, hermaphroditic gonad; *28*, gonoduct; *29*, buccal tube; *30*, yolk in intestine; *31*, space; *32*, worm inside capsule. (Hyman, *The Invertebrates*, courtesy of McGraw-Hill Book Company.)

(667)

body, a single gonopore, and no rhamnite tracts (Fig. XXVI–3). These parasites occur within the bodies of mollusks, echinoderms and other turbellarians.

As was suggested above, all the orders of Platyhelminthes have undoubtedly arisen either from the Acoela or from forms closely resembling them. The parasitic classes of flatworms probably arose from dalyellioid rhabdocoels. As Hyman[48] reminds us, it is noteworthy that these rhabdocoels occur primarily in mollusks and echinoderms. Mollusks are the chief intermediate hosts of flukes, and echinoderms are believed to be situated in the main line of evolution of vertebrates. The redial stage of trematodes resembles a rhabdocoel. Ancestral adult flukes presumably parasitized mollusks, and when vertebrates arrived, the flukes (by elaboration of adhesive organs already present in rhabdocoels, and by modification of the reproductive system in the direction of greater egg production) became adapted to vertebrate hosts, but retained their dependence upon molluskan hosts. Let us, then consider each helminth group in order.

Trematoda
Monogenea

One might imagine that the free-living ancestors of all trematodes began feeding on mucus and dead epithelial cells of their "hosts", particularly the mucus of the gills, and then gradually became adapted to live in deeper gill areas, then in the pharynx and finally in the intestine. Except for *Polystoma* (see below), however, there is no evidence for such an hypothesis for any of the Monogenea.

A better hypothesis is as follows. From a planuloid ancestor a rhabdocoel worm was developed. This worm gave rise to several forms including the nemertians (Rhynchocoela), temnocephalans and dalyellioids. From the latter group a stock form without asexual reproduction, with anterior mouth, paired testes, one or two ovaries, and with a copulatory bursa, gave rise to a form with a paired protonephridial system. This form then led to three orders— the Monogenea, the Aspidobothria, and the Digenea. The large majority of monogenetic trematodes are highly host-specific parasites of fishes, particularly of the ancient group of cyprinoids, which fact suggests that this parasitic group is of great antiquity.[4] The apparent lack of specificity in some genera (*e.g. Benedenia, Polystoma*) does not necessarily indicate recent origins. The genus *Polystoma*, occurring on the gills of tadpoles, in the bladder of amphibians and turtles, and in the mouth or nose of the latter, is of special interest. The larval parasites are found attached to the gills of tadpoles, and when host metamorphosis takes place the worms migrate to the alimentary canal and thence to the urinary bladder where they become adults. This unique life history suggests a method whereby ectoparasitic worms may have evolved into endoparasitic worms, but it does not support a supposition that entozoic

Digenea were derived from ectozoic Monogenea. After all, the Digenea life history almost always involves a molluskan host, and original ancestral forms probably were free-living miracidia-like organisms.

The ancestral monogeneans may have been facultative skin parasites whose most direct descendents are the modern capsaloideans[54]. The early skin parasites gave rise to forms which sought the protection of gills and then acquired the habit of obligatory blood-feeding. The latter mode of nutrition led to symbiosis with bacteria and consequent acquisition of a genito-intestinal tract, and it also required a physiological adaptation to the blood-borne antibodies of the host. These obligatory blood-feeding gill parasites, the ancestral polyopisthocotylineans, then radiated in development in correspondence with the radiation of their hosts. An ancient divergence from the Capsaloidea, characterized by viviparity, appears to have given rise to the Gyrodactyloidea.

Two possible explanations for the persistence of the ectoparasitic nature of the Monogenea have been suggested.[7a] First, their oxygen requirements may have prevented occupancy within the host, and second, being attached exclusively to aquatic hosts, there was no need to migrate inside to avoid desiccation. The latter explanation suggests that "getting inside" is some sort of positive selection pressure—an unnecessary suggestion because present habitats of trematodes may simply reflect the original habitats adopted by ancestral forms.

Trematoda
Aspidobothria

Knowledge of a complete life cycle of an aspidobothrid is lacking, but development is believed to be basically direct; that is, the young worm develops directly into an adult either in the same host or in another individual of the same or different species. The worms definitely do not belong to the monogenetic group because there is no posterior sucking disc or cuticular hooklets or anchors. The excretory pore or pores are posterior rather than anterior in position, and the intestinal tract is always rhabdocoelic in type, as in the turbellarians and in the digenetic gasterostomes. On the other hand, there is no evidence of an alternation of generations. The larva has no trace of ciliated epithelium.

The simplest type of host relationship among the aspidobothrids is that in which either a gastropod or a bivalve mollusk is the sole host, as in *Aspidogaster conchicola*. When such an infected mollusk is eaten by a fish, frog or reptile, the parasites sometimes demonstrate an ability to withstand digestion and to attach themselves to the wall of the vertebrate stomach or gut—suggesting the initiation of a second host as in the Digenea. A more complicated host relationship is that of *Stichocotyle nephropsis* in which encysted larvae are present in crabs and lobsters, while adults occur in

biliary passages of elasmobranchs.   The first-stage larva of the
parasite may develop in a marine mollusk, thence to a crab or
lobster.   Thus we have a suggestion in this group of trematodes of
how alternation of hosts may have evolved.[19]

Trematoda
Digenea

Genetic relationships between the Monogenea and Digenea are
clearly indicated by a similarity in cleavage and in other early
developmental stages of the digenetic miracidia, and the monogenetic ciliated larvae.   These early stages are also very similar to the
planula-like ancestral type described above.

The Digenea, as well as the Monogenea, probably have had
polyphyletic origin, the different groups converging in their evolution to similar-appearing forms today.   Evidence for this supposition is provided from a comparative study of adults and cercariae,
but the Monogenea and Digenea are only very distantly related.
When we recall that the elasmobranchs, an ancient group of fishes,
possess no characteristic genera of digenetic trematodes, and that
American marsupials harbor trematodes belonging to species different from those in Australian marsupials, we must admit the
relatively recent origin of the Digenea as compared with the Monogenea.   But in any speculation of origins of the Digenea we must
take into account the universal use of molluscan hosts, the universal
employment of sexual reproduction, the universal habit of encystment of pre-adults, and the relatively greater host specificity among
the widely diversified larval stages.   Wright[36] has suggested that
speciation occurs most often as a result of parallel evolution between
larval flukes and their molluscan hosts rather than final hosts.

The problem of the origin of the Digenea is made much more
complex than that of the Monogenea because of the introduction,
in the former, of intermediate hosts.   The intermediate hosts probably were originally the final hosts containing the sexually mature
adult parasites.   A study of the germ-cycles in Digenea supports this
theory.   Further support is provided by the fact that sexually
mature stages of Digenea are to be found in vertebrates which are of
relatively recent origin.   Sporocysts and rediae of the Digenea
should, therefore, be regarded as ancestral forms whose mode of
reproduction might originally have been sexual.   Cercariae may
have originally attained maturity in a second host, but subsequently
became modified into intermediate forms during the time the original definitive host was becoming a second intermediate host.[10] This
theory is accepted by the majority of parasitologists.

The evolution of the digenetic trematodes probably began with
a life cycle containing a free-swimming planuloid larva (*i.e.* miracidium) which changed into a tailed pre-adult (*i.e.* cercaria) which,
in turn, became an encysted adult (*i.e.* metacercaria) which then
excysted for a brief free-living stage.   From this type of free-living

life cycle the first host, in the form of a mollusk was introduced. The free-swimming larva (miracidium) was eaten by the mollusk, or it became a commensal in the mantle and subsequently invaded the host tissues, and it evolved an elaborate process of asexual multiplication within its host. The next step in the evolutionary sequence probably came when the encysted cercariae (*i.e.* metacercariae) were ingested by a vertebrate host and matured in its intestine. The tail of the cercaria has been considered as a reverse aquatic adaptation taking the place of cilia. See Baer[3] and Chauhan.[19]

The initial phases of bladder formation are the same in the two major divisions of the Digenea, but the differences in the structure of the two bladder types have been recognized as of fundamental importance, and as representing stages in the evolution of the excretory system of the Digenea. A thin-walled bladder is probably the more primitive.[51]

Cestoidea

Speculation concerning the origins of tapeworms is particularly difficult because of the absence of free-living stages in their life cycles. Add to this deficiency the lack of a gut, presence of ten-hooked and six-hooked embryos, holdfasts, proglottids, tetraradiate symmetry, and progenesis, and the difficulties are compounded indeed. The adult cestodes, as we have seen, are relatively highly host specific, and they illustrate to a striking degree the morphological specialization so typical of the parasitic mode of existence. These facts suggest an ancient origin.

The majority of helminthologists have believed that cestodes as well as trematodes have evolved directly and independently from rhabdocoele turbellarian ancestors. There is little evidence, however, as to the probable structure of this hypothetical common progenitor. There is considerable difference of opinion as to the identity of the present-day cestode which most nearly represents the original ancestral form. On the basis of morphological evidence and host distribution Fuhrmann[35] regarded the Tetraphyllidea (scolex with four flexible, lappet-like suckers, adults mostly in sharks, freshwater fishes, amphibians and reptiles) as the most primitive group of tapeworms. Baer,[5] and others, have argued that the two-bothriate tapeworms are the most primitive of present-day forms, and have been derived from a pro-trematode stock. The two-bothriate worms are basically similar to digenetic trematodes in many respects, and they apparently have given rise to the four-suckered and four-bothriate worms. Supporting evidence for this statement is derived from a study of *Haplobothrium* (see below). Wardle and McLeod[80] have rejected this hypothesis on the grounds that proteocephalan genera (see p. 259), not two-bothriate genera, are the characteristic tapeworm parasites of primitive vertebrates. These authors tentatively suggest that the protocestode gave rise, through a process of delayed autotomy and secondary tetraradial symmetry, to the present tetrafossate forms, and that the two-bothriate tapeworms are neotenic, persistent larval forms of the protocestode stock.

Since the most primitive hosts for adult cestodes are fishes, we may expect to find the most primitive tapeworms in the cyclostomes, chimaerids and elasmobranchs. Cestodes have not been described from cyclostomes or chimaerids, but in the latter archaic fish (*e.g.* the ratfish) is to be found the cestodarian, *Gyrocotyle* (Fig. X–12, p. 256). Other genera inhabit the body cavity of ganoid and teleost fishes and, in one instance, the coelom of a turtle, but their relationships to the true tapeworms are obscure, and they are considered as an isolated, aberrant and progenetic group. The presence of vestiges of a haptor in all stages of amphilinids (see p. 255) suggests that the cestodarians are related to the monogenetic trematodes; but the nature of the excretory system, presence of calcareous bodies, general biology, and other features, are more similar to the cestodes.[32] This group of highly specialized parasites probably represents the remains of a once flourishing assemblage of parasites from freshwater hosts. The original hosts migrated to the sea and became the ancestors of modern elasmobranchs and chimaerids.

The freshwater ancestral hosts that gave rise to elasmobranchs have disappeared, but one freshwater derivation of these hosts has remained as an archaic, relatively unspecialized fish whose parasites should provide a fruitful source of speculation on evolution. This ganoid host is the bowfin, *Amia calva*, and it possesses a tapeworm, *Haplobothrium*, which is found nowhere else. The scolex of the worm (Fig. XXVI–4), suggests affinities with the tetrarhynchid cestodes from elasmobranchs, but the internal anatomy is more similar to that of the pseudophyllids (see page 260). The body of the worm exhibits a curious secondary segmentation, and it often breaks into smaller pieces, the anterior end of each piece becoming differentiated into a secondary pseudophyllidean scolex. The life cycle of this unique tapeworm appears to involve two intermediate hosts, a copepod and a fish. Thus *Haplobothrium* possesses the morphological features which may well have been characteristic of a primitive cestoid ancestor to both pseudophyllids and tetraphyllids.

Once the pseudophyllids were established in fishes, an easy step to birds and mammals was possible because the latter group of hosts often feed abundantly on infected fishes. Thus the bothriocephalids are to be found in teleost fishes, but the related diphyllobothrids occur in birds and mammals.

The great majority of the genera of Cyclophyllidea, which include the common tapeworms of man, are to be found in birds. We have already pointed out that birds evolved very rapidly, and Baer has suggested that the explosive evolution of birds is reflected in the rapid and diversified evolution of bird tapeworms. The evolution of mammals has progressed at a slower pace, and we find comparatively few cestode genera in their intestines.

A common theory states that tapeworms were originally parasites of invertebrates that today are intermediate hosts. This theory is based on the fact that *Archigetes* (Fig. XI–2) is found in an invertebrate (the only such instance among tapeworms), and on such evidence as the use of insect hosts in the life cycle of *Hymenolepis nana*. The dwarf tapeworm, *H. nana fraterna*, sometimes utilizes a flea or beetle as a vector host within which the cysticercoid develops a large caudal appendage not present in the usual larva. The vertebrate host becomes infected through ingestion of infected insects. When we recall that the direct type of life cycle is characteristic for ces-

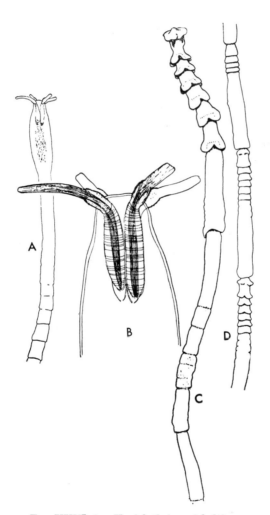

FIG. XXVI–4.—*Haplobothrium globuliforme.*

A, Scolex; *B,* scolex greatly enlarged showing the four retractile tentacles; *C,* Portion of a strobila showing a pseudoscolex that resembles the scolex of pseudophyllidean species; *D,* Strobilia dividing secondarily into identical pieces (*after Fuhrmann*). (Baer, *Ecology of Animal Parasites,* courtesy of University of Illinois Press.)

todes, and is a secondary acquisition, we may consider the unusual use of insect hosts in this life cycle as a reversion to an original mode of life.

The theory presented in the above paragraph has been vigorously opposed by Baer,[5] who maintains that *Archigetes* is probably a neotenic procercoid and not an ancestral type of tapeworm. Moreover, the cestodarians are more closely related to the ancestral stock than are the cestodes, and the former group includes the amphilinids which are coelomic parasites whose adults are possibly free-living.

A recent critical review by Stunkard[69] of the problem of *Archigetes* affinities contained the following statements. "In the Cestodaria there are abbreviated life cycles, in which larval stages become sexually mature. The idea has been suggested, with much support, that the Caryophyllidae are paedogenetic plerocercoids of pseudophyllidean cestodes, in which strobilate stages no longer develop. Indeed, the recent findings of Calentine and Ulmer[11] on the *Archigetes-Biacetabulum* relationship confirms the report of Wisniewski,[85] that species of *Archigetes* from tubificid oligochaetes are progenetic larvae, morphologically indistinguishable from and probably identical with caryophyllaeid worms from fishes. These monozoic forms have sometimes been regarded as primitive, and the progenitors of merozoic cestodes, but the present information supports the idea that they are merely precocious progenetic larvae that have dropped the strobilate stage. It is possible that they represent an earlier phylogenetic stage."

Speciation of cestodes by isolation has probably occurred not only within groups of hosts which are phylogenetically related, but also within specialized hosts. Ancestors of the present-day genera of cestodes parasitic in both birds and mammals must probably be sought among the species that lived in Mesozoic reptiles.

Acanthocephala

In all probability the Acanthocephala originated as parasites of freshwater fishes, with a single, invertebrate intermediate host. Potential transport hosts (*i.e.* paratenic hosts) have become ecological intermediate hosts because immature worms are able to become re-encapsulated in vertebrate hosts that feed on arthropods. An appropriate final host may sometimes also become a potential intermediate host, and because of this adaptability there has been established a flexibility in parasite-host specificity. Acanthocephalans have become adapted to the bodies of reptiles, birds and mammals, and they undoubtedly represent an ancient group of parasitic worms[5]. The short, subglobular proboscis with a relatively small number of hooks seems to be the type, morphologically and phylogentically, from which other modifications have been derived.[76, 77]

Nematoda

Relatively few of the estimated half million species of nematodes are parasitic. The parasitic forms undoubtedly originated from more than one type of free-living ancestor. Parasitic and free-living nematodes are remarkably alike. The chief differences are, in parasitic forms, an increase in complexity of genital organs and rate of reproduction, loss of sense organs, and decrease in production of digestive enzymes. Nevertheless, the interconnections between free-living and parasitic forms are far more evident and complex in the Nematoda than in any other group of worms. For detailed reviews of these relationships see papers by Chabaud,[13,13a,14] Chitwood and Chitwood,[22] Chitwood and Wehr,[23] and Dougherty.[31]

There is evidence[48] for the belief that the nematodes find their nearest free-living relatives among (1) the Kinorhyncha (= Echinodera)—microscopic marine nematode-like worms devoid of cilia, with a circlet of spines; and among (2) the Priapulida, also marine, with cylindrical shape and warty appearance, a superficially segmented trunk and terminal mouth and anus.

The parasitic nematodes in vertebrates form an increasing scale of complexity from those in elasmobranchs to those in mammals[5]. This distribution seems to suggest that these worms became abundant in vertebrates only after the hosts had taken to a terrestrial life, and that the parasites evolved in complexity with the evolution of their hosts. The larvae of these parasites often enter the lungs of their final hosts. It has been suggested that this site preference probably represents the vestige of an ancestral condition when the lungs, with their abundance of oxygen, were the only locations of infection. Hookworms, however, can develop directly in the intestine. A significant experiment has shown that inert particles injected under a frog's skin will follow the same route of migration as that pursued by larvae of *Rhabdias bufonis*, a parasite of the lungs.[36] The migratory habit of nematode larvae, as well as the penetration of host skin might, therefore, be due in part to mechanical causes, but such a conclusion is hazardous without further evidence. When intermediate hosts, usually arthropods, are involved, they almost invariably acquire infection by ingesting the larvae while the latter are still enclosed by the egg shell. One might regard the subsequent transference of the larva to the vertebrate host as simply an elaboration of the direct type of life history.[7a] The origin of larval migration might be related to the habit of ingesting infected secondary hosts— the final host becoming also an intermediate one.

The intermediate host is particularly interesting because it represents a relatively recent acquisition in the life cycles of nematodes, although within certain families (*e.g.* Ascaridae) the use of transport hosts may be a primitive characteristic of that particular group. One can assemble a fine series of larval forms from numerous species representing a gradual transition from entirely free-living to entirely

43

parasitic larvae. Such a series could begin with *Rhabditis* and end with *Ascaris*.

A scheme of the evolutionary relationships of the nematodes is shown in Figure XXVI–5. In this scheme, devised by Dougherty,[31] the group "Phasmidea" has given rise to many more parasitic forms than has the group "Aphasmidea." Free-living phasmids are largely inhabitants of the soil, whereas the free-living aphasmids are more

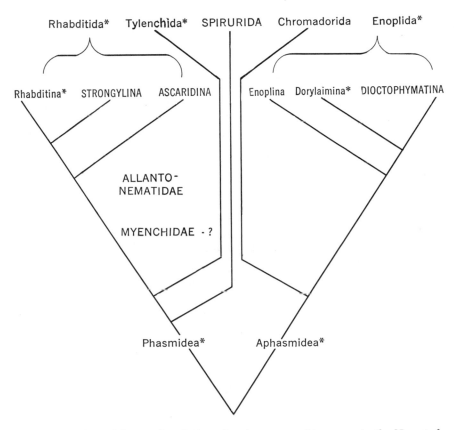

Fig. XXVI–5.—Scheme of evolution of major zooparasitic groups in the Nematoda. Exclusively parasitic groups are printed in capitals; partly parasitic groups are marked with an asterisk. (Dougherty, courtesy of Jour. Parasitology.)

characteristically aquatic, and they include the great bulk of marine species. Life in the soil is peculiarly suited to the development of parasitism because of the opportunity and necessity for a worm to seek the protective moisture of a host's body (plant or animal) when the soil becomes dry. Once a temporary refuge is gained, evolutionary processes resulting in stability of the relationship may occur; then parallel evolution of host and parasite logically follow. A thorough survey and census of all species of nematodes needs to be carried out before we can formulate with assurance definite conclusions on evolutionary relationships, but some trends and tentative generalizations can be expressed.

Class Secernentea (= Phasmidia)

Certain members of all four rhabditoid families (with caudal sensory organs) occur in intimate relationship with soil-dwelling insects, mollusks, crustaceans and vertebrates. Although some of these relationships are no more than accidental, others represent facultative parasitism. In the latter group the infective third stage larva generally becomes parasitic. For example, earthworms and carrion beetles often contain larval stages of free-living rhabditoids.[79] In the earthworm the encysted larva is not set free unless the host dies. These examples of transport hosts appear to be clear instances of incipient stages in the evolution of obligate parasitism. Hence we find in the basically free-living suborder Rhabditina all stages of parasitism. This group, in the words of Dougherty, is "a veritable laboratory of evolutionary parasitism." See also Chabaud and Petter.[17]

The suborder Strongylina apparently arose from rhabditoids similar to the Rhabditidae, and it is almost certainly monophyletic.[61] The more primitive strongylines recapitulate in their early larval stages the development of the rhabditoid stoma and esophagus. These organs (Fig. XXVI-6) have generally been regarded as the most important criteria for the recognition of rhabditoid families. Skin penetration probably was the primary mode of entry of primitive strongylines. Very likely vertebrates were not infected until after the transition from aquatic to semi-terrestrial tetrapods took place, because at that time the soil worms had the opportunity to penetrate the skins of primitive amphibians and thus avoid desiccation. Strongylines have come to flower, so to speak, in mammals, especially in herbivores.

A commonly-accepted view of ascaridoid evolution holds that they arose from a primarily terrestrial stem from the Rhabditoidea through the Oxyuroidea, and that the direct life history (e.g. that of Ascaris) is the primitive type (see Chitwood,[21] Dougherty,[31] Chabaud[14]). A more recent view (see Osche,[58] and especially the review by Sprent[66]) holds that the marine ascaridoids and the indirect life history patterns are the more primitive.

Sprent has based his theory partly on a study of the excretory system, and he suggests that the first marine ascaridoids "arose from a group of free-living marine nematodes, which underwent their sexual maturation in decaying animals. The first stage of parasitism occurred when the larvae of these nematodes were swallowed by living animals, also feeding on the carrion. By mechanical penetration, these larvae gained access to their tissues where they remained unchanged, until the animals died and their development could proceed in its carcass. In this way, marine arthropods, possibly shrimp-

like creatures, could have gained larvae resembling the second-stage
larvae of present-day ascaridoids.

"The infected shrimps would be likely to be swallowed by larger
animals, such as fish, so that instead of the larvae completing their
development in a decaying shrimp on the sea bed, they may have

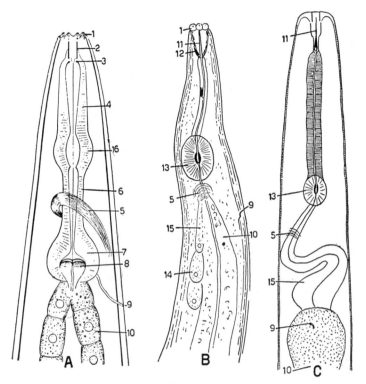

Fig. XXVI–6.—Esophagus of nematodes. *A*, Esophagus of *Rhabditis maupasi*, illustrating rhabditoid type (*after Reiter*, 1928). *B*, Aphelenchoid type of esophagus (*after
Steiner*, 1935). *C*, Tylenchoid type of esophagus (*after Fuchs*, 1915).

1. lips; *2*, protostom; *3*, telostom; *4*, corpus of pharynx; *5*, nerve ring; *6*, isthmus of
esophagus; *7*, end bulb of esophagus; *8*, valve apparatus of end bulb; *9*, excretory pore;
10, intestine; *11*, buccal stylet; *12*, protractor muscles of same; *13*, median bulb of
esophagus; *14*, esophageal glands; *15*, glandular part of esophagus; *16*, median pseudo-
bulb. (Hyman, *The Invertebrates*, courtesy of McGraw-Hill Book Co.)

completed it in a partially digested shrimp in the alimentary tract
of a fish. Thus a two-host life history pattern could have been
established."

Toxocara cati, a nematode of the Felidae (occasionally found in
man and probably not in dogs although easily confused with *T.
canis*) has retained the esophageal ventriculus, a primitive feature
of the subfamily Anisakidae, most of which are parasites of lower
vertebrates. This feature occurs in the second-stage larva, and it
is in contrast with the cervical alae which are probably more super-

ficial characteristics, not being developed until the young adult stage is reached. *T. cati* will hatch and migrate in the tissues of earthworms, cockroaches, birds, mice, lambs, and dogs—thus it tolerates a very wide range of intermediate and paratenic hosts. For all of these reasons the life cycle of *T. cati* probably represents a basic pattern from which the life cycles of other ascarids of terrestrial mammals have originated.[64]

The phylogeny of the Ascaridoidea was described by Osche[58] on the basis of lip formation and on other biological, ecological and metrical considerations. The scheme of relationships presented supports Szidat's rule (see p. 651) which states that the more primitive parasites are to be found in the more primitive hosts.

Ascaridoids range in size from 4 to 400 mm. in length, and they follow *Cope's Rule* that states: the more primitive forms are smallest and the more specialized forms are largest. But the "phylogenetic size" is dominant as is shown by the fact that primitive worms remain small even in large hosts. Also, the more highly developed Ascaridoidea, even in small hosts are relatively small. The large size of ascarids in rodents betrays the large size of the original hosts (ungulates and carnivores). The egg size, however, ranging from 35 to 140 microns in diameter, does not depend on worm size, nor is it related to the host phylogeny or to host ecology.

The order Spirurida is probably the most archaic group of parasitic nematodes. These forms are, as adults, all found in vertebrates and all require an intermediate host, usually an arthropod, to complete the life cycle. The order has presumably lost the morphological features which could suggest affinities with a free-living species.

The primitive subfamily Thelaziinae, of the order Spirurida, has forms with typical spiruroid life cycles (e.g. *Rhabdochona ovifilamenta*), forms with life cycles approaching those of the dipetalonematids (e.g. *Thelazia* spp.), and forms intermediate between these two (e.g. *Oxyspirura*)[1]. Speculations by Anderson[1,2] on spirurid evolution led him to propose the following interrelated rules involving a hierarchy of filarioids, from less specialized to most specialized, and employing important taxonomic features of eggs and larvae.

"1. Species with thick-shelled eggs ('l'oviparité of Chabaud and Choquet, 1953) are more primitive than those with thin-shelled eggs ('la viviparité of Chabaud and Choquet).

"2. Species with fully formed first-stage larvae are more primitive than those which produce microfilariae.

"3. Species whose larvae have spines are more primitive than those without them.

"4. Those species whose eggs reach the external environment are more primitive than those whose larvae accumulate in the tissues of the definitive host.

"5. Species using coprozoic intermediate hosts are more primitive than those associated with haematophagous forms.

"6. Species associated with skin lesions are more primitive than those not associated with them.

"7. Those associated with intermediate hosts that are unable to pierce the skin (e.g. *Musca*) are more primitive than those associated with forms that do so (Culicidae, etc. . . .).

"8. The more primitive species require more time to reach the infective stage in the intermediate host than the more specialized (Chabaud, 1954)."

Clues to the evolution of parasitism among the secernenteal worms may also be found by an analysis of a possible sequence of larval changes which are accompanied by an increase in the restriction of the larvae to an internal environment. Stages in such a sequence[13] are: (1) free-living larvae; (2) larvae which molt inside the egg; (3) larvae which develop in the intermediate host with moderate restriction to an internal environment; (4) larvae which develop within the intermediate host with marked restriction to an internal environment.

Class Adenophorea (=Aphasmidia)

The group Adenophorea (without caudal sensory organs: examples —*Capillaria*, *Trichinella*, *Trichuris*, *Dioctophyma*) possesses a primitive life cycle in which the first larval stage may infect the final host, and in which all four molts may occur within the final host. The free-living forms do not become encysted.

These worms possess the remarkable tendency, among primitive species, to leave the digestive tract of the host and infect other organs. This habit exists also among the Secernentea, but in the latter group of nematodes the habit is manifest in the "higher" members of the group, particularly with the spirurids which migrate during the fourth larval stage. With the Adenophorea, on the other hand, the phenomenon appears at once, and since the eggs are no longer able, in certain cases, to be eliminated to the exterior, a transmission to a new host is accomplished by cannibalism.

Chabaud[13a] distinguished two lines of evolution among the Adenophorea: (1) a cannibalistic cycle leading progressively toward the type of specialized cycle of the trichinas; (2) a multiple-host cycle which, although departing from a type different from that of the Secernentea, has an evolution parallel to them and terminating in a cycle equally complex, as illustrated by *Cystoopsis* which involves sturgeons and aquatic larval insects or amphipods. The phylogenetic relationships of the Adenophorea require much more detailed study.

The Arthropods

Conditions predisposing to parasitism among the arthropods, as well as among other animals, are: wanderlust (mites into cracks), saprophagus nutrition habits, sucking of plant juices, and, especially the preference to live in crowded communities. As Rothschild and Clay[63] have said, the most favorable condition for the dawn and development of dependence is a social environment.

Various species of blood-sucking arthropods (*e.g.* some triatomids) obtain meals by tapping the blood-engorged bodies of other arthropods (*e.g.* bedbugs) which have fed on a vertebrate. It is but a short step from this kind of habit to tapping directly the body of the vertebrate. Pre-parasites were perhaps first attracted to waste food, offal and exudations of certain animals, and when conditions encouraged the pre-parasites to stay with their future host (that is, when the search for food became simplified, or when it became unnecessary to meet competition by seeking other and more distant sources of food), the pre-parasites became mess-mates or scavengers, and from this association they became parasites. Evidence for this sort of speculation may be obtained from parasitic insects where all gradations from free-living to parasitic forms may be traced. Parallel evolution of the host-seeking instinct and somatic characters seems clear, particularly in such groups as the dipterous Tachinidae (see page 484).

Isopods

Relationships among the isopods are suggested by the scheme below.[55] One well-known example of the parasitic members of this group is *Livoneca convexa*, a cymothoid protandrous, hermaphroditic species found on fish. The male isopod is parasitic on the gills of the marine fish, *Chloroscombrus orqueta*, while the female is commensal in the oral cavity of the host. Females are produced from males by a process of metamorphosis, and the relationship between the parasite and host appears to be highly specific.

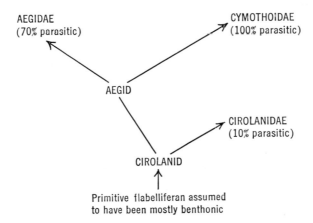

Copepods

Present knowledge of copepods and their ontogeny is only in an initial stage, and a natural scheme of classification, especially for parasitic species can be only tentative, with many gaps. The student should consult Heegaard[41] for an account of the development of various genera and species, with special regard to the phylogeny of the arthropod limb. Since no fossil copepods have been discovered, the question of origins is difficult. The Cyclopoida appear to be the most primitive group, from which the other copepods may have radiated. All parasitic copepods may have a possible origin in the more or less parasitic Ergasilidae,[40] but they possibly exploited this way of life frequently during the course of evolution.

Specialization in parasitic copepods in relation to the distribution of their hosts in time was studied by Leigh-Sharpe[53], who stated that the lowest phylum of animals in the evolutionary series on which parasitic copepods have been found is the Annulata. Among the copepods on annelids are the most highly modified forms known (*e.g.* the Saccopsidae), and they are characterized by a loss of appendages and alimentary tract. A striking feature of intimacy with the host is shown by the hermaphroditic *Xenocoeloma* whose body cavity is continuous with the coelom of its annelid host. Next to this group of highly specialized parasitic copepods on invertebrates, one may find somewhat less specialized species on the more primitive fishes, moderately modified species on less primitive fishes, and slightly modified species of parasitic copepods on the most recent fishes and on ascidians. In spite of many exceptions to the evolutionary trend suggested above, there does seem to be a rough correlation between the degree of parasitic modification of copepods and the primitiveness of the host group.

Lice

Lice presumably have been derived from primitive psocid-like ancestors which probably became parasitic first on birds and later on mammals. The Psocoptera (= Corrodentia) are known as book-lice, and they are not parasitic. They live beneath the bark of trees, and from this habitat ancestral forms could have readily found their way to bird nests and thence to birds themselves. The lice may have passed secondarily from birds to mammals, but the presence of a primitive species of louse on a tree-shrew, a very primitive mammal, suggests a polyphyletic origin for mammal lice. From these beginnings there must have been a considerable amount of parallel evolution. For example, superficially the head and body lice of birds have become adapted to different ecological niches on the host body, and these adaptations have developed on parallel lines in different lice stocks.[50]

Among the chewing lice (Mallophaga) of birds, the group known as Amblycera does not possess a spiracular gland, but the Ischnocera do possess the gland which is similar to the spiracular gland in the sucking lice (Anoplura). The absence of the spiracular gland indicates that the Amblycera were probably well established before the Ischnocera arose. The spiracles of most primitive structures are found in *Eomenacanthus stramineus* of the family Menoponidae.

Thus members of this family are believed to be of more ancient origin than are other Anoplura. The Trichodectidae (Ischnocera) and the Anoplura appear to have arisen from a common ischnoceran parasite which migrated from a bird to a primitive insectivore.[78]

A summary of a chronology of relationships among the lice of mammals has been made by Hopkins[45] as follows.

"Here, again, our deductions are greatly hampered by doubt as to whether certain infestations are primary (and very ancient) or secondary (and relatively recent), but it seems possible to arrive at a few conclusions which are beyond reasonable doubt. Distantly related species of *Pediculus* occur on man and the chimpanzee and the genus is so widely separated from any found on non-Primates that its occurrence on the Primates must be ancient—possibly of Miocene date. Turning to the *Anoplura* as a whole, the most important fact is the universal occurrence of Echinophthiriidae on the seals, because this must certainly have originated before the seals adopted a marine life, because they have not been in contact with other mammals since that event, apart from momentary and fatal encounters with Polar bears; seals are definitely known from the Lower Miocene and probably originated in the late Eocene. Infestation of the ungulate branches of the *Ferungulata* is far too nearly universal to be anything but primary, in my opinion, and the fact that seal-lice and the lice of *Camelidae* and *Tayassuidae* have characters annectent between *Haematopinidae* and *Linognathidae* seems to confirm that even if the infestation of the *Ferungulata* as a whole does not date back (as I believe it does) to before the ancestors of the ungulate and carnivorous branches (the *Condylarthra* and *Creodonata*) diverged during the lowest Paleocene period (or perhaps the late Cretaceous) it must have spread from one group to the other at a not very much later date. At this point we come to a very serious difficulty—the infestation of the *Glires* with *Anoplura* is also practically universal except for certain Nearctic and Neotropical families of *Hystrichomorpha*. I regard the infestation of the *Glires* with *Anoplura* as at least partly primary, and the absence or rarity of these lice on some *Hystrichomorpha* as the effect of the heavy infestation of these groups with *Mallophaga*, while Vanzolini and Guimarães[78] think that the evidence indicates that *Anoplura* were lacking in South America (and probably everywhere) at the beginning of the Tertiary period and that they were brought in by the Pliocene migration of mammals into South America. If Vanzolini and Guimarães are right, then the *Anoplura* probably arose between the Eocene period and the Pliocene migration and perhaps not long before this migration, whereas if I am right they may be very much older."

Flies

Little is known about the evolution of parasitic Diptera, but one family, Tachinidae, has been studied in some detail[33] and it will be used as one example of the problems encountered in exploring the ancestral histories of insects.   The Tachinidae (see page 484) is a very large assemblage of flies whose classification presents imposing difficulties, and about which there is considerable disagreement among entomologists.   They undoubtedly evolved from the family Calliphoridae, a very large group whose larvae are saprophagous or flesh-feeders (e.g. *Sarcophaga*, the fleshfly), or they are parasites of various arthropods.   The closest relatives of tachinids among the calliphorids occur in the subfamilies Sarcophaginae and Rhino-phorinae.   Of these two subfamilies the Sarcophaginae appears to be closer to the ancestral Tachinidae because of both morphological and behavioral similarities.

The most primitive subfamily of tachinids is the Dexiinae, and an evolutionary series of subfamilies can be arranged from this group up to the Goniinae.   The most primitive method of reaching the host (exhibited in all Dexiinae and also to be found in the Sarco-phaginae) is that of active searching by the young larva for its victim. The next step in the evolution of host-feeding is shown by the Macquartiinae whose larvae are deposited near and ingested by the host, or the larvae are deposited on the host.   In the latter method the larvae are sometimes still encased by the egg shell. A third and much more specialized step, shown by the Phasiinae, is the deposi-tion of parasite eggs on particular hosts, or the injection of the eggs into the host body.   The more specialized tachinids are typically parasites of Lepidoptera, whereas the more primitive forms tend more to parasitize a wider range of unrelated hosts.

Fleas

Bird fleas have undoubtedly arisen from mammal fleas.   The genus *Ceratophyllus*, for example, is clearly derived from fleas of squirrels and other tree-dwelling rodents whose nests provide condi-tions not unlike those of bird nests.   Most of the relatively few bird fleas are to be found on birds which return to the same nesting site year after year, or which nest on the ground or in holes.   Such habits obviously favor the difficult transfer of fleas from a mammal to a bird.   *Palaeopsylla*, a genus found on moles and shrews, has been reported from Baltic amber representing the Oligocene.   The origins of mammal fleas remain obscure.

Wasps

A study of the parasitic Hymenoptera shows that species which feed on a few kinds of host foods (oligophagous) have arisen re-peatedly from polyphagous ancestors.   This trend has occurred in spite of the apparent advantages (more available food) of the oligo-phagous forms.   Trends toward specialization seem to be the rule, and toward removing species from competition with one another.

Life histories of wasps and their mites illustrate mutually adaptive modifications, and offer promising subjects for the study of evolution. The eumenine wasp, *Ancistrocerus antilope*, and the larval mite,

Ensliniella trisetosa, live together throughout the whole life of each member of the alliance. "Male wasps must emerge from the nest bearing propodeal loads of deutonymphs. On the other hand, female wasps must emerge from the nest devoid of deutonymphs, even though possessing nearly identically developed acarinaria, and then acquire deutonymphs from the males at mating. Thus the loss of deutonymphs from adult male wasps must in large part take place by transfer to female wasps. In turn, losses of deutonymphs from female wasps must be chiefly (? or only partly) by deposition in the cells of the new nest during its construction or provisioning. Since adult male wasps must emerge from their cells with full deutonymphal loads, and females must emerge without deutonymphs, it would seem that whatever factors determine that a particular egg will be fertilized, hence diploid and giving rise to a daughter, must also decide that normally deutonymphs will not be released to the cell containing a diploid egg."[25]

An adaptative behavioral pattern of this sort is not without parallel among other nest parasites. But the remarkable transfer of parasites from the host male genital chamber to the female genital chamber has no parallel yet described. "Possibly the mite has somehow become as fully necessary to the wasp as the wasp is to the mite", and it is highly probable that "the life cycles of the two organisms have become inextricably interlaced through an exacting evolutionary coadaptation."[25]

Mites and Ticks

Among the Acarina parasitism seems to have developed primarily from a predatory habit, but also from the scavenger habit and from phoresy. Little work has been done on the evolution of mites and ticks, but some recent speculation on the phylogeny of trombiculid mites suggests that from essentially reptile-specific groups four lines of development took place. The larvae (chiggers) of these mites are very small, and instead of preying on smaller arthropods, as do the adult mites, they feed parasitically on large arthropods and on vertebrates "by sampling instead of consuming". The first group to arise from ancestral forms was a small number of species which parasitized arthropods. The second group became adapted to living in the skins of amphibians. The third group managed to isolate itself in the lungs of a sea snake, while the fourth, and by far the largest group, spread out over all the mammals, and they developed many genera. The more primitive species of these mites appear to be distributed over the open home ranges (*e.g.* fields) of their hosts, whereas other, more specialized species are more restricted in their relationships with their hosts. See also, Hughes,[46] and Woolley.[87]

GENERAL RULES AND PRINCIPLES

1. The two basic kinds of changes which normally take place in an organism before it becomes a dependent internal parasite are:

(a) physiological—in which the powers of synthesis of some essential nutritional elements are lost, and (b) morphological—in which superfluous organs are lost. Such changes, of course, also occur in free-living organisms.

2. Parasitism probably arose in different ways in different groups of animals.

3. To become a parasite an organism must undergo physiological adaptations to its host.

4. If a species of parasite is found in a number of different kinds of hosts the parasite probably has recently been introduced to the area. In other words, parasite-host specificity is normally achieved only after long association.

5. Many factors in addition to length of association play significant roles in determining the incidence and degree of pathogenicity of parasitic infections in new hosts.

6. The terms "degenerate", "regressive", and "retrogressive" are anthropocentric, and they should be used with caution, if at all.

7. We may assume that the first pre-parasite that entered a host was either preadapted to life within the host, or it was able to change rapidly so as to become tolerant of the host.

8. Even a "mild" parasite carries on an assault against its host, and the host is a responsive environment. For these reasons natural selection takes place and limits the numbers of successful parasites.

9. Parasites usually evolve more slowly than do their hosts.

10. The advantages of parasitism have tended to preserve large numbers of mutations.

11. Parasites as a whole are worthy examples of the inexorable march of evolution into blind alleys.

BIBILOGRAPHY

1. ANDERSON, R. C., 1957. The Life Cycles of Dipetalonematid Nematodes (Filarioidea, Dipetalonematidae): The Problem of their Evolution. J. Helminthology, 31, 204–224.

2. ———, 1958. On the Classification of the Filarioidea with Special Reference to the Filariidae and the Stephanofilariidae (I). Bull. Soc. Zool. France, 83, 144–157.

3. BAER, J. G., 1931. Etude Monographique du Groupe des Temoncéphales. Bull, Biol. France-Belg., 65, 1–57.

4. ———, 1946. Les Helminthes Parasites des Vertébrés. Relations Phylogénétiques entre leur Évolution et celle de leurs Hôtes. Conséquences Biologiques et Médicales. Ann. Franche-Comté et de l'Université de Besançon, 15 pp.

5. ———, 1951. Ecology of Animal Parasites. Univ. Illinois Press, Urbana. 224 pp.

6. BAKER, J. R., 1963. Speculations on the Evolution of the Family Trypanosomatidae Doflein, 1901. Exper. Parasitol., 13, 219–233.

7. BALL, G. H., 1943. Parasitism and Evolution. Amer. Natur., 77, 345–364.

7a.BAYLIS, H. A., 1938. Helminths and Evolution. In "Evolution: Essays on Aspects of Evolutionary Biology." Ed. by G. R. de Beer. pp. 249–270. Oxford, University Press, 359 pp.

7b.BURNET, F. M., 1958. The Theories of Antibody Production. p. 1–17 In: Immunity and Virus Infection, ed. by V. A. Najjar, 1959, John Wiley & Sons, N. Y. 262 pp.

8. BÜTSCHLI, O., 1876. Studien über die ersten Entwickelungsvorgänge der Eizelle, die Zellteilung, und die Conjugation der Infusorien. Abh. Senck. Ges., 10, 213–464.

9. BYCHOWSKY, B. E., 1957. *Monogenetic Trematodes, Their Systematics and Phylogeny.* Acad. Nauk. SSSR, 509 pp. Eng. editor, W. J. Hargis, Transl. by P. C. Oustinoff. Amer. Inst. Biol. Sci., Wash. D. C., 627 pp.

10. CABLE, R. M., 1934. Studies on the Germ-Cell Cycle of *Cryptocotyle lingua.* II. Germinal Development in the Larval Stages. Quart. J. Microsc. Sci., *76*, 573–614.

11. CALENTINE, R. L. and ULMER, M. J., 1961. Studies on the *Archigetes-Biacetabulum* Relationship. J. Parasitol., *47*, (Suppl.), 27.

12. CAULLERY, M., 1952. *Parasitism and Symbiosis.* Sidgwick and Jackson. London. 340 pp.

13. CHABAUD, A. G., 1954. Sur le Cycle Évolutif des Spirurides et de Nématodes Ayant une Biologie Comparable. Valeur Systematique des Caracteres Biologiques. Ann. Parasit Humaine Comp., *29*, 42–425.

13a.————, 1955a. Essai d'Interprétation Phylétique des Cycles Évolutifs Chez les Nématodes Parasites de Vertébrés, Conclusions Taxonomiques. Ann. Parasit. Humaine Comp., *30*, 83–126.

14. ————, 1955b. Remarques sur la Symétrie Céphalique des Nématodes et Hypothèses Concernant L'Évolution de cette Symétrie chez les Phasmidiens Parasites. Bull. Soc. Zool. France, *80*, 314–323.

15. ————, 1957. Revue Critique des Nematodes du Genre *Quilonia* Lane 1914 et du Genre *Murshidia* Lane 1914. Ann. Parasit. Humaine Comp., *31*, 98–131.

16. CHABAUD, A. and CHOQUET, M. TH., 1953. Allométrie des Variants Sexuels chez les Ixodidae. Arch. Zool. Expl. et Gen., Notes et Rev., *89*, 139–146.

17. CHABAUD, A. G. and PETTER, A., 1961. Evolution et Valeur Systématique des Papilles Cloacales chez les Nématodes Phasmidiens Parasites de Vertébrés. Comptes Rend. Séances l'Acad. Sci., *252*, 1684–1686.

18. CHATTON, E. and BRACHON, M. S., 1936. Sur un Protiste Parasite du Cilié *Fabrea salina* Henneguy. *Gregarella fabrearum,* n. gen., n. sp., et son Evolution. Compt. Rend. Acad. Sci., *203*, 525–527.

19. CHAUHAN, B. S., 1953 (1954). Studies on the Trematode Fauna of India. Part 1. Subclass Monogenea, p. 113–208. Part 2. Subclass Aspidogastrea, p. 209–230. Part 3. Subclass Digenea (Gasterostomata), p. 231–287. Part 4. Subclass Digenea (Prosostomata). (A revision of Hemiuroidea from the Indian Region) p. 289–393. Records of the Indian Mus. *51*, 113–393.

20. CHEISSIN, E. M., 1956. (The Taxonomic System of Sporozoa [Class Sporozoa, Phylum Protozoa].) Zoological J., Acad. Sci. USSR, *35*, 1281–1298. (Zool. Zhurnal, Akad. Nauk SSSR.) (In Russian.)

21. CHITWOOD, B. G., 1950. Nemic Relationships. In: Chitwood, B. G. and Chitwood, M. B., *An Introduction to Nematology.* Section 1. Baltimore, 2nd edition. 213 pp.

22. CHITWOOD, B. G. and CHITWOOD, M. B., 1950. *An Introduction to Nematology,* Sect. I, Anatomy, 145 figs. Baltimore. G. B. Chitwood, Publisher. 213 pp.

23. CHITWOOD, B. G. and WEHR, E. E., 1934. The Value of Cephalic Structures as Characters in Nematode Classification, with Special Reference to the Superfamily Spiruroidea. Zeit. Parasit., *7*, 273–335.

23a. CLAY, THERESA, 1949. Some Problems in the Evolution of a Group of Ectoparasites Evolution, *3*, 279–299.

24. CLEVELAND, L. R., 1949. Hormone-Induced Sexual Cycles of Flagellates. I. Gametogenesis, Fertilization and Meiosis in *Trichonympha.* J. Morph., *85*, 197–295.

25. COOPER, K. W., 1955. Venereal Transmission of Mites by Wasps, and Some Evolutionary Problems Arising from the Remarkable Association of *Ensliniella trisetosa* with the Wasp *Ancistrocerus antilope.* Biology of Eumenine Wasps II. Trans. Amer. Entom. Soc., *80*, 119–174.

26. CORLISS, J. O., 1955. The Opalinid Infusorians: Flagellates or Ciliates? J. Protozool., *2*, 107–114.

27. ————, 1956. On the Evolution and Systematics of Ciliated Protozoa. Systematic Zool., *5*, 68–140.

28. DAVENPORT, C. B., 1903. The Animal Ecology of Cold Spring Sand Spit, with Remarks on the Theory of Adaptation. Univ. Chicago Publ., *10*, 1–22.

29. DAVENPORT, D., 1955. Specificity and Behavior in Symbiosis. Quart. Rev. Biol., *30*, 29–46.

30. Dodson, E. O., 1952. A *Textbook of Evolution*. W. B. Saunders Co., Philadelphia. 419 pp.
31. Dougherty, E. C., 1951. Evolution of Zoöparasitic Groups in the Phylum Nematoda, with Special Reference to Host-Distribution. J. Parasitol., *37*, 353–378.
32. Dubinina, M. N., 1960. The Morphology of Amphilinidae (Cestodaria) in Relation to Their Position in the System of Flatworms. Doklady Biol. Sci. Sect. (Doklady Akademii Nauk SSSR) *135*, 501–504. Translated by the Amer. Inst. Biol. Sci. p. 943–945. 1961.
33. Emden, F. I. van, 1958. Evolution of Tachinidae and their Parasitism (Diptera). Proc. XVth Internat. Congr. Zool., London, p. 664–666.
34. Fauré-Fremiet, E., 1955. La Position Systematique du Genre *Balantitium*. J. Protozool., *2*, 54–58.
35. Fuhrmann, O., 1930–1931. Dritte Klasse des Cladus Plathelminthes. Cestoidea. In Kükenthal, W., and Krumbach, T., *Handbuch der Zoologie*. Berlin & Leipzig. 2, *2*, p. 141 (1930) and p. 257 (1931).
36. Fülleborn, F., 1929. On the Larval Migration of Some Parasitic Nematodes in the Body of the Host and its Biological Significance. J. Helminth., *7*, 15–26.
37. Goodey, T., 1931. Biological Races in Nematodes and their Significance in Evolution. Ann. Appl. Biol., *18*, 414–419.
38. Goodrich, H. P., 1938. Life-Cycles of Certain Infusoria with Observations on Specificity in Parasitic Protozoa. pp. 231–247, in G. R. de Beer. *Evolution, Essays on Aspects of Evolutionary Biology*. Oxford University Press. 350 pp.
39. Grassé, P. P., 1952. *Traité de Zoologie, Anatomie, Systématique, Biologie*. Tome I, Fascicule I. *Phylogénie. Protozoaires: Généralités. Flagellés*. Masson et Cie. Paris. 1071 pp.
40. Gurney, R., 1931–1933. *British Fresh-Water Copepoda*. V. 1, 1931, 238 pp.; V. 2, 1932, 336 pp.; V. 3, 1933, 384 pp. The Ray Society, London.
41. Heegaard, P., 1947. *Contributions to the Phylogeny of the Arthropods. Copepoda*. Bianco Lunos Bogtrykkeri, Copenhagen. 236 pp.
42. Hoare, C. A., 1955. Intraspecific Biological Groups in Pathogenic Protozoa. Refuah Veterinarith (Quart. Israel Vet. Med. Assoc.), *12*, 263–258.
43. ———, 1957. *The Transmission of Trypanosomes and its Evolutionary Significance*. pp. 95–100 in *"Biological Aspects of the Transmission of Disease."* Oliver and Boyd Ltd. London.
44. Hollande, A., 1952. L'évolution des Flagellés Symbiotiques, Hôtes du Cryptocercus et des Termites Inferieurs. Tijdsch. v. Entomol., *95*, 81–110.
45. Hopkins, G. H. E., 1957. Host-Associations of Siphonaptera. In: First Symposium on Host Specificity Among Parasites of Vertebrates. pp. 64–87. Inst. Zool.. Univ. Neuchâtel.
46. Hughes, T. E., 1959. *Mites; or, the Acari*. University of London, The Athlone Press. 225 pp.
47. Huxley, Julian, 1942. *Evolution the Modern Synthesis*. Geog. Allen and Unwin Ltd. London. 645 pp.
48. Hyman, L. H., 1951. *The Invertebrates: Platyhelminthes and Rhynchocoela. The Acoelomate Bilateria*. Vol. II, McGraw-Hill. 550 pp.
49. Janiszewska, J., 1949. Parasitogenetic Rules. Janicki Rule. Zool. Polon., *5*, 31–34.
50. Kéler, S. v., 1957. Über die Deszendenz und die Differenzierung der Mallophagen. Zeit. f. Parasitenk, *18*, 55–160.
51. La Rue, G. R., 1957. The Classification of Digenetic Trematoda: A Review and a New System. Exper. Parasitol., *6*, 306–344.
52. Lederberg, J., 1952. Cell Genetics and Hereditary Symbiosis. Physiol. Rev., *32*, 403–430.
53. Leigh-Sharpe, W. H., 1928. Degeneracy in Parasitic Copepoda in Relation to the Distribution of their Hosts in Time. Parasitol., *20*, 421–426.
54. Llewellyn, J., 1957. The Larvae of Some Monogenetic Trematode Parasites of Plymouth Fishes. J. Mar. Biol. Assoc. U.K., *36*, 243–259.
55. Menzies, R. J., Bowman, T. E., and Alverson, F. G., 1955. Studies of the Biology of the Fish Parasite *Livoneca convexa* Richardson (Crustacea, Isopoda, Cymothoidae). Wasman J Biol., *13*, 277–295.

56. NIE, D., 1950. Morphology and Taxonomy of the Intestinal Protozoa of the Guinea-Pig, *Cavia porcella*. J. Morphol., *86*, 381–493.
57. NOBLE, G. A. and NOBLE, E. R., 1952. Entamoebae in Farm Mammals. J. Parasitol., *38*, 571–595.
58. OSCHE, G., 1958. Beiträge zur Morphologie, Ökologie und Phylogenie der Ascaridoidea (Nematoda). Parallelen in der Evolution von Parasit und Wirt. Zeit. f. Parasitenk., *18*, 479–572.
59. PAVLOVSKIÍ, E. N., 1946. (Conditions and Factors Affecting the Formation of the Host Organism of a Parasite in the Process of Evolution.) (Sketches of Evolutionary Parasitology, I.) (In Russian with Eng. summary.) Zool. Zhurnal, *25*, 289–304.
59a. PIGULEVSKI, S. V.. 1958. (The Phylogeny of Flatworms.) Papers on Helminthology Presented to Academician K. I. Skryabin on his 80th Birthday. Izdatelstve Akad. Nauk SSSR, pp. 263–270. (In Russian.)
60. PIXELL GOODRICH, H., 1938. Life-cycles of Certain Infusoria with Observations on Specificity in Parasitic Protozoa. In *Evolution: Essays on Aspects of Evolutionary Biology*. Ed. G. R. de Beer. Oxford University Press. 350 pp.
61. POPOVA, T. I., 1958. (The Phylogenetic Interrelationships of Nematodes of the Superfamily Strongyloidea Weinland, 1858.) Papers on Helminthol. Presented to Academician K. I. Skryabin on his 80th Birthday. Izdatelstvo Akademii Nauk SSSR, pp. 279–284. (In Russian.)
62. REYNOLDS, B. D., 1930. Ectozoic Protozoa. In: Hegner and Andrews, *Problems and Methods of Research in Protozoology*. Chapter III. Macmillan, N. Y.
63. ROTHSCHILD, M. and CLAY, T. 1952. *Fleas, Flukes & Cuckoos*. London. Collins, 304 pp.
64. SPRENT, J. F. A., 1956. The Life History and Development of *Toxocara cati* (Schrank 1788) in the Domestic Cat. Parasitol., *46*, 54–78.
65. ——, 1959. Parasitism. Immunity and Evolution. pp. 149–165 in: *The Evol. of Living Organisms*, A Symposium of the Roy. Soc. Victoria.
66. ——, 1962. The Evolution of the Ascaridoidea. J. Parasitol., *48*, 818–824.
67. STUNKARD, H. W., 1937. The Physiology, Life Cycles and Phylogeny of the Parasitic Flatworms. Amer. Mus. Nat. Hist. Amer. Mus. Novitates, *908*, 1–27.
68. ——, 1954. The Life-History and Systematic Relations of the Mesozoa. Quart. Rev. Biol., *29*, 230–244.
69. ——, 1962. The Organization, Ontogeny, and Orientation of the Cestoda. Quart. Rev. Biol., *37*, 23–34.
70. SZIDAT, L., 1956. Geschichte Anwendung und finige Folgerungen aus parasitogenetischen Regeln. Zeit. f. Parasitenk., *17*, 237–268.
71. THORPE, W. H., 1930. Biological Races in Insects and Allied Groups. Biol. Rev., *5*, 177–212.
72. ——, 1938. Further Experiments on Olfactory Conditioning in a Parasitic Insect. The Nature of the Conditioning Process. Proc. Roy. Soc. Ser. B., *126* (844) 370–397.
73. ——, 1939. Further Studies on Pre-imaginal Olfactory Conditioning in Insects. Proc. Roy. Soc. Ser. B: Biol. Sci., *127* (848), 424–433.
74. ——, 1940. Ecology and the Future of Systematics. In J. S. Huxley's *The New Systematics*, The Clarendon Press, Oxford. 341–364.
75. THORPE, W. H. and JONES, F. G. W., 1937. Olfactory Conditioning in a Parasitic Insect and its Relation to the Problem of Host Selection. Proc. Roy. Soc., B, *124*, 56–81.
76. VAN CLEAVE, H. J., 1941. Relationships of the Acanthocephala. Amer. Nat., *75*, 31–47.
77. ——, 1952. Some Host-Parasite Relationships of the Acanthocephala, with Special Reference to the Organs of Attachment. Exptl. Parasitol., *1*, 305–330.
78. VANZOLINI, P. E. and GUIMARÃES, L. R., 1955. Lice and the History of South American Land Mammals. Rev. Brasil. Ent., *3*, 13–46.
79. VÖLK, J., 1950. Die Nematoden der Regenwürmer und aasbesuchunden Käfer. Zool. Jahrb. Abt. Syst., *79*, 1–70.
80. WARDLE, R. A. and McLEOD, J. A., 1952. *The Zoology of Tapeworms*. Univ. Minn, Press. Minneapolis. 780 pp.

81. WEBB, J. E., 1946. Spiracle Structure as a Guide to the Phylogenetic Relationships of the Anoplura (Biting and Sucking Lice) with Notes on the Affinities of the Mammalian Host. Proc. Zool. Soc. London, *116*, 49–119.

82. WENRICH, D. H., 1924. A New Protozoan, *Amphileptus branchiarum*, n. sp., on the Gills of Tadpoles. Trans. Amer. Micros. Soc., *43*, 191–199.

83. ————, 1935. Host-Parasite Relations Between Parasitic Protozoa and Their Hosts. Proc. Amer. Philos. Soc., *75*, 605–650.

84. WILSON, M. and HINDLE, E., 1950. Discussion on Heteroecism. Proc. Linn. Soc. London, *162*, 4–8.

85. WISNIEWSKI, L. W., 1930. Das Genus *Archigetes* R. Leuck. Eine Studie zur Anatomie, Histogenese, Systematik und Biologie. Mém. acad. polon. sci., Sér. B., *2*, 160 pp.

86. WRIGHT, C. A., 1960. Relationships Between Trematodes and Molluscs. Ann. Trop. Med. Parasitol., *54*, 1–7.

87. WOOLLEY, T., 1961. A Review of the Phylogeny of Mites. Ann. Rev. Entomol., *6*, 263–284.

Index

A

ABALONE, host of *Echinocephalus*, 350
Ablastin, 56, 541
Acanthamoeba, 78
Acanthatrium jonesi, 223
Acanthella, 292
Acanthocephala, 288
  evolution of, 674
  host specificity, 635
Acanthocephalus, 297
  anguillae, 605
Acanthocheilonema, 351
Acanthocolpidae, 193
Acanthoclinus quadridactylus, host of
  Scyphidia, 154
Acanthocystis, 525
Acanthor, 291, 292
Acanthostomatidae, 193
Acariasis, psoroptic, 507
  sarcoptic, 507
Acaricides, 515
Acaridae, 513
Acarina, 387, 494
  morphology, 495
Accacoeliidae, 631
Acephalina, 39, 99
Acephaline gregarines, 98
Acetabulum, 242, 257
Achronia grisella, 654
Achtheres, 404, 407
Acipenser, 255
Acoela, 665
Acranil for, dibothriocephaliasis, 263
  for *Hymenolepis* infection, 271
Acris gryllus, 583
ACTH, 562, 563
Actinians, 664
Actinomyxida, 40, 139
Actinopodea, 39, 77, 95
Aculeata, 451
Adamsia palliata, 16
Adaptations, 23, 549, 551, 651
  physical, 549
  physiological, 552
  tolerance, 658
Adelea, 104
Adeleidae, 39, 104
Adeleina, 39, 104
Adelina deronis, 104
Adenophorea, 301, 310, 366
  evolution of, 680

Adolescariae, 189
Aëdes, 125, 607
  aegypti, 102, 556, 607
Aega spongiophila, 388
Aerobacter aerogenes, 590
Agaontidae, 455
Agamermis, 310
  decaudata, 366
Age, 552
  resistance, 533, 575
Aggregata eberthi, 107, 108
Aggregatidae, 39, 107
Ala, 299
Alaria arisaemoides, 198
Alariinae, 630
Alasmidonta varicosa, host of *Cercaria*, 188
Albertia, 525
Alcohol, 553
Alcopara, as an anthelminthic, 309
Aldrin, for warble flies, 483
Aleochara, 461
Alepas, 414
Aleyrodidae, 434
Algae, 15
Allantosoma brevicorniger, 155
  dicorniger, 155
  intestinalis, 155
Allocreadiidae, 193, 225
Allocreadium alloneotenicum, 188
Allopatric species, 20
Alteration of generations, 89
Alveolar cyst, 285
Alysia manductor, 641
Ambloplites rupestris, host of
  Leptorhynchoides, 292
Amblycera, 387, 422, 423, 682
Amblyomma, maculatum, 500, 506
Amebiasis, 88, 89, 571
Amebic cysts, 29, 86, 87, 90
Ameiurus nebulosus, 262
American spotted fever, 506
Amia calva, 262, 272
Amino acid, 125
Ammodytidae, 12
Amnicola longinqua, 631
Amodiaquine, 63
Amoeba proteus, 77
Amoebida, 39, 77
Amoebidae, 77
Amphibia, host of, Cyclophyllidea, 266
  Dicrocoeliidae, 219
  Lankesterella, 107

44

Amphibia, host of, *Lintoniella*, 260
  Lucilia, 486
  mites, 685
  nematodes, 311
  opalinids, 144, 146, 611
  Opisthorchiidae, 231
  Plagiorchiidae, 223
  Polystoma, 668
  Proteocephalidea, 259
  Tetraphyllidea, 671
Amphids, 302
Amphileptus branchiarum, 661, 663
Amphilina foliacea, 255
Amphilinidea, 255
Amphipod, host of, Acanthocephala, 292
  Allocreadiidae, 225
  Cystoopsis, 680
  mite, 507
  Polymorphus, 296
  Spirachona, 155
Amphipoda, 387, 409
Amphiprion, 11
Amphistomidae, 215
Amplicaecum robertsi, 634
Ampullacula, 148
Ampullaria, 631
Anaerobic parasites, 552, 586, 589
Anal struts, 446
Analgesidae, 507
Anaplasma, 140
  marginale, 18
Anarrhichas lupus, 609
Anceus, 390
Anchoring systems, 550
Ancistrocerus antilope, 684
Ancistrocoma myae, 150
Ancistrocomidae, 40, 149
Ancylostoma, 310
  braziliense, 308, 319
  caninum, 308, 319, 322, 544, 583, 650
  duodenale, 319
  tubaeforme, 319
Ancylostomidae, 318
Andrena, 461
Anelasma squalicola, 414
Anemia, 534
Anemone, 11
Anepitheliocystidia, 195
Angitia, 19
Anguina tritici, 378
Anisakidae, 335, 678
Anisogamete, 35
Annelid, attraction to host, 641
  host of Actinomyxida, 139
    Adelina, 104
    Archigetes, 263
    barnacles, 414
    copepods, 682
    Eupomatus, 188
    Liriopsis, 536

Anobiidae, 16
Anodonta, host of mite, 507
Anopheles, 117, 125
  atroparvus, 642
  freeborni, 121
  gambiae, 608
  quadrimaculatus, 121
Anopheles and *Culex* larvae compared, 476
Anophrys, 148
Anopleura, 387, 419, 426
Anoplocephalidae, 244, 255, 285
Anoplodiera voluta, 667
Anoplodium, 159
Anoplophrya orchestii, 36
Anoplura, 682, 683
Anostomidae, 613
Anseriformes, 614
Ant, host of *Dicrocoelium*, 219
Antelope, host of Schistosomatidae, 200
Anterior station, 51, 53
Anthophora, 463
Anthrax bacilli, 17
Anthropomorphism, 659
Anthropozoonoses, 17
Antibodies, 539, 541, 544, 545
Antienzymes, 544, 556
Antigens, 541
Antimony compounds for, leishmaniasis, 60
  schistosomiasis, 206
Antiphen, for *Taenia* infection, 277
Ants, 13, 449
  host of *Dicrocoelium*, 219
Aonidiella aurantii, 437
Apanteles, 19
  congregatus, 636
  glomeratus, 454
Ape, 91, 94
  host of lice, 638
  plasmodia, 627
Aphaniptera, 441
Aphanurus, 238
Aphasmidia, 301, 310, 366, 680
Aphelenchoides, 380
  besseyi, 37, 378
  parietinus, 299
  ritzema-bosi, 378
Aphelinidae, 456
Aphelinus jucundus, 457
  mali, 636
Aphid, 13, 434
  host of *Aphelinus*, 636
Aphididae, 434
Aphis fabae, 435
  mellifica, 80
Apocrita, 451
Apodemus flavicollis, 637
Apoidea, 387, 461
Apomorphine, anthelminthic, 231
Aponomma, 386

Aporidea, 254
Aporocotyle simplex, 199
Aporocotylidae, 199
Apostomatida, 40, 150, 664
Appendiculate flukes, 235
Arabellidae, 526
Arachnida, 387, 494
Arachnoidea, 387, 494
Aralen, for malaria, 120
Archianthocephala, 297
Archigetes, 263, 264, 673, 674
Arctonoë fragilis, 641, 642
    pulchra, 641
Arecoline, for *Multiceps* infection, 279
Argas americanus, 500
    persicus, 503
Argasidae, 387, 496
Arginine phosphate, 552
Argulus, 409, 550
Arilus cristatus, 438
Armigeres, 125
Armillifer, 517
    annulatus, 515
Aromatic diamidines, 60
Arrow worm, 60
Arsphenamide, for elephantiasis, 358
Arthropoda, 13, 384, 387, 469, 494
    distribution, 607
    evolution of, 680
Ascariasis, 341
    treatment for, 341
Ascaridae, 675
Ascaridia, 310, 335
    galli, 347, 555, 557, 559, 576, 634
Ascaridine, 28
Ascaridoid, 634
    evolution of, 677
Ascaridoidea, 304, 310, 335, 679
Ascaris, 19, 310, 531, 533, 551, 557, 568, 624, 628, 676, 677
    eggs of, 29
    lumbricoides, 24, 28, 337, 624, 634, 650
    suum, 337, 634
    vitulorum, 214
Ascaron, 531
Ascaroside, 339
Ascidian, host of ameba, 79
    copepods, 12, 682
    gregarine, 102
Ascidians, and symbiotic organisms, 403
Asellus aquaticus, host of, *Filicollis*, 296
Aspiculuris tetraptera, 558, 562, 576
Aspidobothria, 159, 170, 668
    evolution of, 669
Aspidocotylea, 171
Aspidogaster conchicola, 170, 669
Aspidogastrea, 171
Aspidogastridae, 171
Ass, host of *Trichostrongylus*, 618
Assassin bugs, 437, 438

Asterias rubens, 536
Astomatida, 40, 664, 151
Astomatous protozoa, 144
Atabrine for, dibothriocephaliasis, 263
    for *Giardia* infection, 63
    for *Hymenolepis* infection, 271
Ateles, 639
Atoxoplasma, 107
Auchmeromyia luteola, 492
Australorbis glabratus, 573
Austrobilharzia variglandis, 208
Autoinfection, 313
    hookworm, 325
    Strongyloides, 313
Avitaminosis, 531
Avitellina, 285
Avium group, 51
Axinoides raphidoma, 168
    truncatus, 168
Axolotl, 42, 64
Axostyle, 66
Azygia, 576
Azygiidae, 192, 237

B

Babesia, 128, 535, 541
    argentina, 130
    bigemina, 36, 128, 504
    bovis, 130
    canis, 130
    moshkovskii, 130
Babesiasis, 128, 130
Babesiidae, 39, 128
Bacillus necrophorus, 17
Bacteria, 16, 17, 545, 571, 587, 589, 590, 628, 656
    in insects, 16
    in lice, 639
    in ruminant stomach, 588
    intracellular, 421
    mutualistic, 584
    symbiotic, 586
Bacterial infections, 16
Bacteriostatic action, 214, 546
Badger, host of *Opisthorchis*, 231
    Paragonimus, 225
Bairamlia fuscipes, 449
Balance hypothesis, 538
Balantidiasis, 18, 151
Balantidiidae, 40, 151
Balantidium, 151, 584, 655, 663
    caviae, 151
    coli, 151, 152
    duodeni, 151
    praenucleatum, 151
Barbulanympha, 561
    ufalula, 72
Barium antimony tartrate, for *Syngamus* infection, 318

Barley itch, 513
Barnacle, 11, 12, 19, 411, 536
  host of, *Pennella*, 19
Baryodma, 461
Bass, host of *Leptorhynchoides*, 292
Bat, 638
  host of bedbug, 439
    flies, 640
    Plagiorchiidae, 223
Batfly, 489
Bdellobrillus, 526
Bdellonyssus, 513
Bee, 80
BHC in acariasis, 515
  in lice control, 432
Bedbug, 16, 438
  disease, 440
Beef tapeworm, 278
Beetle, 461
  host of *Macrachanthorhynchus*, 293
    Moniliformis, 296
Behavior of host, 562
Benedenia, 668
Benthos, 593
Benzol, in: screw worm control, 487
Benzyl benzoate in acariasis, 515
Bephenium hydroxynaphthoate, anthel-
    minthic, 309
  in hookworm infection, 324
Besnoitia, 132
Beta-naphthol, for *Fasciolopsis* infection,
    214
Biyyaria, 148
Bilateria, origin of, 666
Bilharziasis, 200
Bilharziella, 200
Bilharziidae, 200
Biocenose, 10, 20, 566
Biochemistry, 18
Biogeography, 601
Biological control, 580
  races, 653
Biomass, 591
Biotic balance, 577
Biotin, 626
Biotype, 584
Bird, migration, 18, 606
  nest, 568
Birds, host of ameba, 82
    Ascaridia, 347
    Brachylaimus, 209
    coccidia, 111
    Cyclophyllidea, 672
    Dicrocoeliidae, 219
    Dioctophymatoidea, 374
    diphyllobothrids, 672
    Echinostoma, 212
    flies, 639
    Haemoproteus, 114
    Hexamita, 63

Birds, host of *Isospora*, 113
    Lankesterella, 107
    Leucochloridium, 209
    Leucocytozoon, 114
    Microphallidae, 220
    Plasmodium, 125, 126, 542, 627
    Plagiorchiidae, 223
    tapeworms, 632
Bison, host of *Cooperia*, 328
    Ostertagia, 327
Bithynia fuchiana, 204
    leachi, 631
      tentaculata, 572, 631
      as host of *Opisthorchis*, 231
Biting lice, 419
Bivalves, host of Allocreadiidae, 225
Bivesiculidae, 192
Black blowfly, 488
    scours, 329
Blackfly, 114, 116, 479
Blackhead, 42, 43, 95, 341
Bladderworm, 252, 277
Blaps gigas, 296
    mortisaga, host of *Stylocephalus*, 99
Blastocrithidia, 47, 661
Blastodinium, 41
Blastophaga psenes, 455
Blastothrix, 456
Blatella germanica, 531
Blatta germanica, 296
    orientalis, 99, 151, 296
Blepharoconus, 148
Blepharoplast, 44, 47
Blepharoprosthium, 148
Blepharosphaera, 148
Blood capsule, 283
    changes, 534
    predator, 15
Bloodsucking mites, 512
Blowflies, 486
Bluebird, host of *Plasmodium*, 125
Bluebottle fly, 486
Bodo, 663
Body louse, 428
Bolbosoma, 298
Boll weevil, as host of mite, 512
Bonellia, 526
Boophilis annulatus, 128, 498
Boopidae, 615
Bopyridium, 392
Bopyrids, 535
Bopyrina, 391
Bopyrus squillarum, 393, 535
Bostrychidae, 16
Botfly, 483, 551
  life history of, 485
Bothria, 262, 242
Bothridia, 259
Bothriocephalids, 672
Boveria, 664

Bovicola, 424
Branchiura, 387
Brachycoelium, 219
Brachylaimidae, 192, 208
Brachylaimus, 209
Bracon hebetor, 452
Braconid wasp, 19, 453
Branchiobdella, 526
Branchiura, 409
Brevipalpus, 512
Brittle stars, hosts of mollusks, 529
Broad tapeworm, 262
Brotea, host of *Paragonimus*, 228
Brotia libertina, 204
Brucei-group, 51, 662
Brugia, 310, 351
　malayi, 358, 633
Brumptidae, 193
Bubonic plague, 448
Bucephalidae, 188, 192, 209
Bucephalus, 209
Budding, 77
Bufo valliceps, host of *Zelleriella*, 147
Bugs, 432
Bulimus, 200, 631
　contortus, 204
　tentaculata, host of *Opisthorchis*, 231
Bundleia, 148
Bursa, 290, 304
　Fabricii, 220
Bustard, 613
Bütschlia, 148, 589
Bütschliidae, 40, 147
Butterflies, 440

C

CADDIS fly, as host of *Allocreadium*,
　188, 189
Calandra orizae, 296
Calanus, parasites of, 19
Calcareous corpuscles, 249
Caligidae, 399
Caligus, 399, 400, 550, 609
　host of *Udonella*, 166
Caligoida, 399, 403
Caliperia brevipes, 153, 154
Calliatis parasitica, 11
Callionymus lyra, 573
Calliphora, 47, 486
　erythrocephala, 492
Calliphoridae, 387, 486, 684
Callitroga, 493
　macellaria, 488
Callosobruchus chinensis, 580
Calonymphidae, 64, 663
Camallanida, 310, 335, 362
Camallanus, 576
Cambarus, host of *Paragonimus*, 229

Camel, host of ciliates, 148
　Dicrocoelium, 219
　Echinococcus, 281
　Sarcoptes, 653
　Taenia, 274
　Trypanosoma, 54
Camelidae, 683
Camouflage, 16
Canary, host of *Plasmodium*, 125
　lung mite, 513
　malaria in, 554
Capillaria, 310
　annulata, 367
　hepatica, 368
　talpae, 628
Caprellids, 410
Capsaloids, 629, 669
Capybara, 55
Carabao, host of *Schistosoma*, 200, 201
Carbarsone, 68, 89
Carbohydrates, 555, 557
　and crowding effect, 575
　metabolism, 23
Carbonates, 593
Carbon bisulfide in, hyostrongyliasis, 330
　dioxide, 557
　tetrachloride in dibothriocephaliasis, 263
　　Paramphistomum infection, 219
　　trichostrongyliasis, 330
Carbonic acid, 557
Carcinonemertes, 525
Cardium edule, host of *Gymnophallus*, 221
Cariama cristata, 613
Carp, 60
　lice, 409
Caryophyllidae, 255, 263, 674
Castration, parasitic, 536, 537, 553, 559
Cat, host of, *Alaria*, 198
　Dipylidium, 268
　Eimeria, 111
　Entamoeba, 82
　fleas, 442
　Heterophyidae, 235
　hookworm, 319
　Isospora, 112, 113
　Moniliformis, 296
　Opisthorchis, 231
　Paragonimus, 225
　Schistosoma, 201
　Strongyloides, 311
Catarrhal enteritis, 63
Catbird, host of *Plasmodium*, 125
Catenotaenia dentritica, 536
Cathaemasiidae, 193
Cattle, host of, Ciliates, 587, 148, 628
　Cooperia, 328
　Dicrocoelium, 219
　Eimeria, 111
　Echinococcus, 281
　Entamoeba, 82, 653

Cattle, host of, Entodinimorphida, 158
  Fasciola, 189, 212, 214
  Fascioloides, 214
  Haemonchus, 326
  Multiceps, 279
  Nematodirus, 328
  Ostertagia, 327
  Paramphistomum, 219
  Piroplasma, 128
  Schistosoma, 200, 201
  Trichomonas, 71
  Trichostrongylus, 618
  trypanosomes, 56
  Trypanosoma, 662
Cattle tick fever, 128
Caudal alae, 299
Caularchus meandricus, host of *Helico-metrina*, 225
Cebas fatuellus, 53
Ceca, 165
Cellobiase, 589
Cellulase, 588, 589
  digestion, 587
Cement glands, in Acanthocephala, 290
Centipede, host of *Eimeria*, 109
Centriole, 78
Centrorhynchus, 635
Cepedia, 146
  cantabrigensis, 147
  lanceolata, 145
Cephalina, 39, 99
Cephaline gregarines, 98
Cephalobium microbivorum, 311
Cephalobothriidae, 259
Cephalopod, host of *Chromidina*, 664
Cerambycidae, 16
Ceratomyxa, 136
  blennius, 135
Ceratophyllus, *arei*, 445
  borealis, 445
  columbae, 445
  fasciatus, 56
  gallinae, 444
  styx, 448
Ceratopogonidae, 114
Cercaria, 29, 30, 183, 185, 558, 670
  catatonki, 188
  diplostomi phoxini, 186
  hartmanae, 188
  loossi, 188
  milfordensis, 188
Cercocystis, 252
Cercomere, 252
Cercommonas, 37
Cervical alae, 299
Cestoda, 255, 259
  host specificity, 632
  in fish, 573
Cestodaria, 242, 255, 672, 674

Cestoidea, 255
  evolution of, 671
Ceratophyllus, 684
Cetonia aurata, 293
Chaetexorista javana, 581
Chagas' disease, 54, 55, 437
Chagasella, 104
Chalcid wasps, 455
Chalcidoidea, 387, 455
Chalimus, 401
Chapmania, 614
Characinidae, 613
Chelonibia, 414
Chemical attraction, 641
  factors, 592
Chemotaxis, 641
Cheyletidae, 507
Chicken, host of mite, 512
  Plasmodium, 125, 561
Chiclero's ulcer, 58
Chiggers, 509, 685
Chilodochona, 155
Chilodonella cyprini, 663
Chilomastix mesnili, 60, 540
Chimaeroid fish, as host of *Gyrocotyle*, 257, 627
Chimpanzee, host of lice, 638
  Plasmodium, 127
  Strongyloides, 311
Chinese liver fluke, 231
Chiniofon, for dibothriocephaliasis, 263
  for trichomoniasis, 68
Chironomid, containing cercariae, 224
Chlordane for lice control, 432
Chloroform, for screw worm control, 487
Chloroquine, 63, 120
  for opisthorchiasis, 231
  for paragonimiasis, 230
Chloroscombrus orqueta, 681
Choanotaenia filamentosa, 628
Choerostrongylus pudendotectus, 331
Cholesterol, 128
Chondracanthidae, 399, 406
Chondracanthus gibbosus, 401
  merluccii, 398, 400
Chondrostei, host of capsaloids, 629
Chonotrichida, 11, 40, 154
Choricotyle louisianensis, 169, 170
Chromatin, 77
Chromatoid bodies, 32, 77, 87
Chromidina, 664
  elegans, 151
Chromosome, 27
Chronic form of sleeping sickness, 53
Chrysomphalus ficus, 437
Chrysomyia, 493
  bezziana, 486
Chrysops, 534, 634
  centurionis, 481
  dimidiata, 481

Chrysops, langi, 481
  silacea, 481
Chytriodinium parasiticum, 41
Ciconiiformes, 614
Ciliatea, 40, 143
Ciliates, 143–158
  in ruminants, 628
  phylogeny of, 663
  symbiotic, 587
Ciliophora, 40
Cimex, columbarius, 650
  hemipterus, 439
  lectularius, 421, 439, 650
  pilosellus, 439
Cimicidae, 438
Ciona intestinalis, 139
Cionella lubrica, host of *Dicrocoelium,* 219
Cirolano borealis, 388
Cirripedia, 387, 411
Cirrus, 173
Citellus, 573, 614
Clam, host of, *Allocreadium,* 188
  Ancistrocoma, 150
  aspidogastrids, 171
  cercaria, 188
  crab, 13
  Paravortex, 159
Classification of, arthropods, 387
  digenetic trematodes, 192
  Cestoidea, 255
  nematodes, 309
  protozoa, 39
Clavella brevicornis, 609
  uncinata, 609
Clavellina lepadiformis, 79
Claws, 551
Cleaner fish, 594
Cleg, 480
Cleptoparasite, 456
Climate, 570, 602
Clinical periodicity, 30
Clinostomatidae, 192
Clinostomum marginatum, 576
Cliona celata, 521
Clonal selection hypothesis, 658
Clonorchis sinensis, 231
Clusterfly, 487
Cnidocampa flavescens, 581
Cnidospora, 39, 134
Cnidosporidea, 39, 134
Coccidia, 39, 103, 535
Coccodinium, 41
Coccidiosis, 109, 112, 113, 542, 543
  treatment for, 112
Coccoidea, 436, 455
Cochliomyia macellaria, 492
Cockchafer beetle, host of *Macracanthor-hynchus,* 293
Cockroach, 608
  host of *Balantidium,* 151

Cockroach, host of *Gregarina,* 99
  Hymenolepis, 274
  Moniliformis, 296
  Nyctotherus, 157
Codfish, 609
Coelenterates, 12, 16, 80, 521
Coenurus cerebralis, 279
Coitus, 51
Coleoptera, 16, 387, 461, 608
Collastoma, 159, 161
Colpidium, 148
Colpoda, 148
Columba livia, 114
Columbicola columbae, 420
Comenteroxenos, 529
Commensalism, 10, 640
Community, biotic, 567
Competition, 569, 578
  for space, 580
Competitor-pressure, 654
Complement fixation, 540, 542
Conchoderma virgatum, 19
Conchophthirius, 664
  acuminatus, 572
Concurrent infections, 545, 583, 621
Condylarthra, 683
Conenose bug, 438
Congolense group, 51
Conocyema, 525
Conjugation, 35
Contracaecum, 335
  aduncum, 305, 609
Control of malaria, 124
Cooperia, 310
  bisonis, 328
  curticei, 328
  oncophora, 328
  pectinata, 328
  punctata, 327
Copepod, 12, 19, 387, 395, 536, 551, 635, 672
  evolution of, 681
  host of, *Dibothriocephalus,* 252
    Halipegus, 238
    Hymenolepis, 632
    procercoid, 263
    Udonella, 166
  parasite of codfish, 609
Cope's rule, 679
Copidosoma, 386
Copper sulfate, for *Haemonchus* infection, 327
Copra itch, 513
Coprochara, 461
Copromonas, 37, 38
Coprophilic protozoa, 36
Coprozoic protozoa, 36
Coptotermes formosanus, 73
Copulatory bursa, 304
Coracidium, 252

Coral polyps, 15
Cordylobia anthropophaga, 488
Coronula, 414
Corrodentia, 682
Cortisone, 562
  for onchocerciasis, 360
Corycella armata, 98
Corynosoma, 292, 288, 298
Costia, 66, 74
Cotton rat, 642
Cottonseed itch, 513
Cotyl, 162
Cotylaspis, 170
Cotylogaster, 170
Cotylophoron microbothriodes, 219
Cotylurus flabelliformis, 183, 197, 622
Crab, 13, 16
  host of *Aggregata*, 107
    Paragonimus, 229
    Stichocotyle, 669
  louse, 430
Crambactis, host of *Amphiprion*, 11
Crane fly, 80
Crataerhina, 491
Crayfish, host of Allocreadiidae, 225
    annelids, 526
    oligochaetes, 11
    Paragonimus, 229
    Plagiorchiidae, 223
Creeping eruption, 319, 323
Creodonata, 683
Cricket, host of *Cephalobium*, 311
Crinoids, hosts of annelids, 526
Crithidia, 45, 47, 661
  euryophthalmi, 35
  fasciculata, 47
  leptocoridis, 47
Cropworm, 367
Crowding effect, 249, 574
Crustacea, 384, 387
  host of, *Echinobothrium*, 260
    rhabdocoels, 159
    Temnocephalida, 161, 666
  host specificity, 635
Cruzia, 611
Cryptobia borreli, 60
  cyprini, 60
  helicis, 60
Cryptocercus, 561, 587
Cryptobiidae, 60
Cryptochaetum, 385, 640
Cryptococcus fagi, 437
Cryptocotyle, concavum, 631
  lingua, 235, 532
Cryptogonimidae, 193
Cryptolepas, 414
Cryptoniscina, 391
Cryptoniscus, 391
Cryptozoite, 117
Crypturellus obsoletus, 603

Ctenocephalides, canis, 442
  felis, 441, 442
Ctenophora, 521
Ctenophthalmus, 637
Ctenophyllus garei, 637
Cuclotogaster, 427
  heterographus, 426
Cucumaricola notabilis, 396, 405
Culex, 125, 137
  fatigans, 607
  pipiens, 607
  tarsalis, 437
Culicidae, 387, 471
Culicoides adersi, 128
Currents, 572
Cutaneous larva migrans, 308
  leishmaniasis, 58
Cuterebra emasculator, 536
Cuticle, 556
Cuttlefish, host of *Aggregata*, 107
Cyamidae, 410
Cyamus, 12
  ceti, 410
Cyathocotylidae, 192
Cyclocoelidae, 192
Cyclocotyla, 162
Cyclocotylidae, 629
Cyclophyllidea, 255, 265, 672
  as parasites of mites, 509
Cyclophyllids, 632
Cyclopoida, 395, 401, 682
Cycloposthiidae, 158
Cycloposthium, 664
Cyclops, 395, 396, 525
  host of *Dracunculus*, 363
    Gnathostoma, 350
    Haplobothrium, 262
    Lintoniella, 260
  fuscus, host of *Nosema*, 138
Cyclorrhapha, 489, 659
Cyclotorna, 441
Cyclotornidae, 441
Cymothoa, 389
Cymothoidae, 388
Cynipoidea, 387, 454
Cyprinoids, 668
Cypris, 411
Cyrtocaryum halosydnae, 664
Cystacanth, 292
Cysticercoid, 252, 557
Cysticercosis, 276, 277, 278
Cysticercus, 252, 276
  cellulosae, 276, 277
  fasciolaris, 249, 279
  ovis, 277
  tenuicollis, 277
Cytochrome, 24
Cystoopsis, 680
Cytopyge, 147

D

Dactylogyrus, 576, 629
Dalyellioida, 666, 667, 668
Damalinia bovis, 424
Danalia, 636
Daphnia, 525
Daraprim, for malaria, 120
  for toxoplasmosis, 134
Dasyhelea obscura, host of Helicosporidium,
  139
Dasytricha, 148, 587, 589
Davainea meleagridis, 267, 268
Davaineidae, 255, 267
DDT for acariasis, 515
  for lice control, 432
Decacanth, 257
Decapod, host of isopod, 636
Deerfly, 480
Deer, host of Echinococcus, 281
    Fasciola, 189
    Fascioloides, 214
    Schistosoma, 201
Deer mouse, 558
Definitions, 7
Degenerate changes, 659
Deltotrichonympha, 73
Demes, 655
Demodex, canis, 514
  folliculorum, 514
Demology, 578
Dennyus, 423
Density dependence, 578
  of populations, 577
Dentex argyrozona, 60
Deoxyribonucleic acid, 121. See DNA.
Dermacentor andersoni, 24, 498, 506, 640
  variabilis, 498, 506
  venustus, 498
Dermanyssus gallinae, 512
Dermatobia hominis, 483, 492
Dermodicoidea, 514
Deroceras reticulatum, 148
Derogenes, 238
Derolinnosa, host of Adelina, 104
Derris, in lice control, 432
Deutomerite, 98
Devescovina, 662
Devescovinidae, 64, 663
Dexiinae, 684
Diamidine for trypanosomiasis, 53
Diaptomus, 252
Diatraea saccharalis, 581
Dibothriocephalus, 576
  erinacei, 263
  latus, 243, 250, 251, 262, 531, 535, 621
  mansoni, 263
Dichlidophora merlangi, 619
Dicrocoeliidae, 193, 219

Dicrocoelium dendriticum, 219, 221
  lanceolatum, 219
Dictyocaulus, 310
  filaria, 331
  viviparus, 331
Dicyema sullivani, 524
Dicyemennea, 525
Dicyemida, 522, 524
Didelphic, 304
Didesmis, 148
Didymocystis, 238
Didymozoidae, 193, 238
Dieldrin, for warble flies, 483
Dientamoeba fragilis, 17, 84, 94
Diet, 533, 554, 555
Diethylcarbamizine citrate, for
  strongyloidiasis, 314
Digenea, 172, 195, 668
  evolution of, 670
Digestion by host, 172
Dilepididae, 255, 268
Diloxanide furoate, for amebiasis, 89
Dimastigamoebidae, 77
Dinematura producta, 399
Dinoflagellate, 536
Dinoflagellida, 39, 41
Dinuridae, 193
Diococestus, 266
Dioctophymatida, 366, 374
Dioctophymatoidea, 310, 374
Dioctophyme, 310
  renale, 374, 610
Diodoquin, 68
Dioecious, 27
Diorchitrema, 235
Dipetalonema, 351
Dipetalonematids, 679
Diphenthane for, Dipylidium infection,
  270
  for Multiceps infection, 279
Diphona, 489
Diphosphopyridine nucleotide, 127
Diphyllidea, 255, 260
Diphyllobothrids, 672
Diphyllobothriidae, 255, 262
Diphyllobothrium latus, 262. See
  Dibothriocephalus latus.
Diplectanum melanesiensis, 164
Diplocardia, host of Metastrongylus, 331
Diplodinium, 158, 587, 588, 589
Diplodiscidae, 193
Diplodiscus, 583
Diplolepis rosae, 454
Diplomastix, 60
Diplomonadida, 62
Diplophyrus jordani, 535
Diplostomatidae, 192
Diplostomatinae, 630
Diplostomulum, 197
  phixini, 186

Diplostomum pelmatoides, 179
Diplozoon ghanense, 167
Dipodomys merriami, 620
  panamintinus, 620
Diptera, 16, 387, 469, 608
  host specificity, 639
Dipylidium caninum, 268, 632
Dirofilaria, 310
  conjunctivae, 362
  immitis, 362, 560
Discoceohalidae, 259
Disculicepitidea, 254
Distome, 172
Distomum megastomum, 536
Distribution of parasites, 571, 601, 602
Dithiazanine, for ascariasis, 341
  for enterobiasis, 349
  for hookworm infection, 324
  for strongylodiasis, 314
  for trichuriasis, 374
Ditrichomonas, 66
Ditylenchus, 380
  destructor, 378
  dipsaci, 378
DNA, 121, 127, 656
Dog, and salmon poisoning fluke, 17, 230
Dog, host of *Alaria*, 198
  Dicrocoelium, 219
  Dipylidium, 268
  Echinococcus, 280
  Eimeria, 111
  Fasciola, 212
  fleas, 442
  Heterophyidae, 235
  hookworm, 319
  Isopora, 112, 113
  Leishmania, 58
  Moniliformis, 296
  Opisthorchis, 231
  Paragonimus, 225
  Sarcoptes, 653
  Schistosoma, 201
  Strongyloides, 311
  Taenia, 274
  tick, 506
  Trypanosoma, 54–56
Domestic ducks, 114
  turkeys, 114
Donax truncatus, host of *Gymnophallus*, 223
Donkey, 54
Dorylaimida, 310, 366
Dourine, 56, 541
Dracunculoidea, 310, 362
Dracunculus, 310
  medinensis, 362
Dreissensia polymorpha, 572
Drift, 652
Drilonereis benedicti, 526
Drosophila confusa, 47

Drought, 573
Dry sores, 58
Duboscqella tintinnicola, 41
Duck, host of *Entamoeba*, 82
  Haemoproteus, 114
  Leucocytozoon, 114
  Levinseniella, 223
  Plasmodium, 125
  Schistosoma cercariae, 208
Dum dum fever, 58
Dung beetle, host of *Hymenolepis*, 274
Duodenum, 557
Dwarf tapeworm, 270
Dypetalogastea, 54

E

EARTHWORM (*See also*, Annelid, and
  Oligochaetes)
  host of *Heterakis*, 342
  maggots, 487
  Metastrongylus, 331
  Monocystis, 99, 102
  Plagiotoma, 158
  Syngamus, 317
Earwigs, 608
  host of *Hymenolepis*, 274
Ecdysone, 561
Echeneis remora, 11
Echidnophaga gallinacea, 442, 573
Echinobothrium, 260
  affine, 260
  benedeni, 260
  longicolle, 260
  typus, 260
Echinocephalus pseudouncinatus, 350
Echinochasmus, 212
Echinococcus, 252, 632
  granulosus, 280, 281, 618
  multilocularis, 285
  sibiricensis, 285
Echinodera, 675
Echinoderms, hosts of Dalyellioida, 668
  mollusks, 529
  myzostomids, 635
  prosobranch snails, 635
Echinoparyphium, 212
Echinophthiriidae, 683
Echinorhynchidae, 298
Echinorhynchus, 297, 609
Echinostoma ilocanum, 211
  revolutum, 536, 630
Echinostomatidae, 172, 193, 209
Echinostomida, 193, 209
Echinus, host of ciliates, 148
Ecological approach, 20
  labels, 567
  niche, 568
  segregation, 620
  selection, 582

Ecology, 566
  applied, 580
  chemical factors, 592
  physical factors, 592
Ecotone, 569
Ecsoma, 235
Edge effects, 569
Edwardsia, 521
Eel grass, 95
Eel, parasites of, 605
Eggs, 656
  of *Ascaris*, 28, 29
    lice, 420
    nematodes, 303
    Parascaris, 29
    schistosomes, 203
    worms, 177
Egg shell, 28
  formation, 245
  nematode, 304
Eichler rule, 651
Eimeria, 109, 627
  acervulina, 111
  adenoeides, 111
  arloingi, 111
  bovis, 111
  brunetti, 111
  canis, 111
  caviae, 543
  deblieki, 111
  dispersa, 111
  ellipsoidalis, 111
  faurei, 111
  felina, 111
  gallopavonis, 111
  hagani, 111
  innocua, 111
  maxima, 111
  meleagridis, 111
  meleagrimitis, 111
  mitis, 111
  miyairii, 543
  mohavensis, 620
  necatrix, 111, 553
  ninae-kohl-yakimova, 111
  parva, 111
  perforans, 543
  praecox, 111
  scabra, 111
  schubergi, 109
  stiedae, 111
  subrotunda, 111
  tenella, 111
  zurnii, 111
Eimeriidae, 39, 107
Eimeriina, 107
Elacatinus oceanops, 595
Elasmobranchs, 629
  host of capsaloids, 629
    cestodes, 632

Elasmobranchs, host of *Stichocotyle*, 670
    tapeworms, 259
    trematodes, 670
Elephants, 55
  hosts of strongyles, 634
Elephantiasis, 30, 357, 358
  symptoms of, 358
  treatment for, 358
Eliocharis, 214
Elk, host of *Dicrocoelium*, 219
Ellobiophrya donacis, 154
Embadomonas gryllotalpae, 62
Embryology, 27
Embryophore, 29, 244, 245
EMC, 583
Emetine for, fascioliasis, 214
  for paragonimiasis, 230
Emetine bismuth iodide, for amebiasis, 89
Emys orbicularis, 105
Encephalitozoon, 132
Encyritidae, 456
Endamoeba, 79
  apis, 80
  blattae, 79
  javanica, 80
  minchini, 80
Endolimax clevelandi, 81
  cynomolgi, 84
  gregariniformis, 82
  janisae, 82
  nana, 83, 84, 91, 540
  sp., 83
Endophoresis, definition, 13
Energy production, in tapeworms, 249
English sparrow, host of *Plasmodium*, 125
Enheptin T, 44
Ensliniella trisetosa, 685
Entamide, 89
Entamoeba, 146, 653
  anatis, 82
  aulastomi, 80
  bovis, 82
  canibuccalis, 83
  caprae, 83
  caudata, 83
  caviae, 83
  chattoni, 84
  cobayae, 83
  coli, 29, 83, 84, 89, 540
  cuniculi, 83
  debliecki, 83
  dilimani, 83
  dispar, 85
  duboscqi, 84
  dysenteriae, 85
  equi, 83
  equibuccalis, 83
  gallinarum, 82
  gedoelsti, 83
  gingivalis, 83, 84, 91

Entamoeba, hartmanni, 85
  histolytica, 20, 29, 83, 84, 539, 540,
    583, 590, 628
  intestinalis, 83
  invadens, 80, 530
  lagopodis, 82
  legeri, 84
  moshkovskii, 84
  muris, 83, 84
  nuttalli, 84
  ovis, 82
  phallusae, 79
  polecki, 83
  ranarum, 80
  suis, 83
  venaticum, 83
  wenyoni, 83
Entamoebidae, 78
Enterobiasis, treatment of, 349
Enterobius, 95, 310
  hominis, 74
  host of *Dientamoeba,* 17
  vermicularis, 17, 348
Entocolax, 528
Entodiniomorphida, 40, 158, 664
Entodinium, 158, 588, 589, 664
Entodiscus borealis, 147, 148
Entoniscidae, 393, 506
Entorhipidiidae, 40, 148
Environment, 20
  biological, 649
  organic, 649
Enzymes, 7, 556
  glycolytic, 552
Eoacanthocephala, 298
Eodinium, 588
Eomenacanthus, 423
  stramineus, 682
Ephestia kuhniella, 654
Epicaridea, 387, 391
Epicaridae, 536
Epicaridium, 391
Epicauta pennsylvanica, 463
Epidemiology, 566
Epidinium, 589, 664
Epimerites, 98, 551
Epinephelus, 595
Epipyropidae, 440
Epitheliocystida, 193, 219
Epizooites, 11
Eratyrus, 54
Eremoplastron, 588
Eretmocerus serius, 458
Ergasilidae, 682
Eriocheir, 229
  japonicus, as host of barnacle, 415
Eriosoma lanigerum, 636
Eristalis tenax, 492
Erpocotyle, 629
Erysipelas, 17

Erythrocytic phase, 118
Erythromycin, 89
Escherichia coli, 590
Esox lucius, 576, 605
Espundia, 58
Eucoccidiida, 39, 103
Eucomonympha imla, 33, 73
Eucotylidae, 193
Euglena, 34, 661
Euglenida, 660
Eugregarinida, 39, 99
Eulima, 529
Eulophidae, 457
Eumenacanthus stramineus, 623
Eunicea, 526
Eunicidae, 526
Eupagurus bernhardus, 13
  prideauxi, 16
Euparyphium, 212
Euplectrus, 457
Euplotes, 148
Eupomatus dianthus, 188
Euproctis terminalis, 582
Euryhelmis, 172
Euryophthalmus convivus, 35
Eurytrema pancreaticum, 219, 220
Euryxenous, 34
Euspora, 39, 79
Eustrongylides, 310, 553
Eutriatoma, 54
Eutrichomastix, 66
Evansi subgroup, 51
Evasterias, 641, 642
Evolution of parasites, 648
  pace of, 649
  progressive, 658
  retrogressive, 658
Exconjugant, 35
Excretion, 34, 173, 192, 247, 248, 290, 302
Excretory system of flukes, 192
Excystation, 87
Excystment, of tapeworm, 252
Exoerythrocytic stage, 117
Eyeworm, 351, 361

                        F

FAHRENHOLZ rule, 651
False spider mite, 512
Fannia scalaris, 492
Fasciola gigantica, 214
  hepatica, 212, 618, 630, 631
Fascioliasis hepatica, 18
Fasciolidae, 193, 212
Fascioloides magna, 214
Fasciolopsis buski, 214
Fats, 557
Feather lice, 423
  mites, 506

Fecampia, 161, 667
Fecampiidae, 667
Fellodistomatidae, 192
Fermentation, 586, 589
Fertilization, 27
Ferungulata, 683
Fibricola cratera, 630
Fierasfer, 12
  in sea cucumber, 11
Fig insects, 455
Filarial worms, 351
Filarioidea, 310, 351
Filicollis, 288, 298
  anatis, 296
  sphaerocephalus, 296
Filisoma, 635
Fish, host of, Allocreadiidae, 225
  aspidogastrids, 171
  Caryophyllidae, 263
  cestodorians, 672
  Contracaecum, 305
  copepods, 682
  Corynosoma, 292
  Cryptobia, 60
  Didymozoidae, 238
  Dioctophymatoidea, 374
  Diplozoon, 167
  Filicollis, 296
  Gyrodactylus, 166
  haemogregarines, 107
  Hepatozoon, 107
  Hysterolecitha, 238
  Lintoniella, 260
  Livoneca, 390
  opalinids, 144
  Monocercomonas, 66
  myxosporidia, 139
  Opisthorchiidae, 231
  Proteocephalidea, 259
  Raphidascaris, 335
  Strigeidae, 196
  trematodes, 162
Fish lice, 409
  population, 594
  tapeworm, 251
Flabellifera, 387, 388
Flame bulb, 173, 290
  cell, 172, 173
Flamingos, 614
Flatworms, evolution of, 665
Fleas, 441, 604
  disease, 448
  evolution, 684
  host specificity, 637
  larvae, 572
  life history, 447
  morphology, 442
  host of *Dipylidium*, 270
    Hymenolepis, 274
Fleshflies, 488, 546

Flies, 88, 469
  evolution of, 683
  host specificity, 639
Fly, 88
Foettingeria actiniarum, 150
Foettingeriidae, 40, 150, 664
Follicular mites, 514
Food chains, 590
  mites, 513
Formica fusca, host of *Dicrocoelium*, 219
Fossaria, 631
Fouadin, for schistosomiasis, 206
Fox, host of *Alaria*, 198
  Echinococcus, 280
  hookworm, 317
  Opisthorchis, 231
  Paragonimus, 225
Frenzelina conformis, 138
Friderica parasitica, 526
Fringed tapeworm, 285
Frog, host of *Alaria*, 198
  ameba, 79, 80
  Gyrodactylus, 166
  Haematoloechus, 225
  Halipegus, 238
  opalinids, 611
  Plagiorchiidae, 223
  pleurocercoid, 263
  Polystoma, 166
Fucus scabra, 17
Fungi, 16
Fur seal pup, host of hookworm, 319
Furamide, 89

G

GADFLY, 483
Gadidae, 606
Gadus merlangus, 619, 622
Galba, 631
Gall midge, 386
  wasp, 454
Galumna longipluma, host of *Moniezia*, 285
Gametogenesis, 26
Gammaridea, 410
Gammarus, host of *Acanthocephala*, 292
  Tetrahymena, 660
Gammexane, in lice control, 432
Gaper clam, host of *Pinnixa*, 12
Garter snake, host of *Strigea*, 197
Gasterophilus intestinalis, 483
Gasterosiphon deimatis, 529
Gasterosteus aculeatus, 605, 631
Gasterostomidae, 209
Gastrodes parasiticum, 521, 522
Gastrodiscidae, 193
Gastrodiscus, 215
  hominis, 218
Gastrothylacidae, 193

Gause's principle, 569
Genarchella genarchella, 558
Gene frequencies, 648
  pool, 650, 652
Genetic changes, 626
  factors, 650
Gentian violet, for ascariasis, 341
  for enterobiasis, 349
  for strongylodiasis, 313
Gerda acanthoclini, 154
Giardia, 20, 550, 557, 568
  lamblia, 62
  muris, 34, 536
Gibbon, host of lice, 639
Gid worm, 279
Giganthorhynchidae, 297
Gigantobilharzia acotyles, 200
Gigantocotyle explanatum, 215
Gill maggot, 401
Gillichthys mirabilis, 577, 603
  host of Hysterolecitha, 238
Gizzard shad, host of acanthocephala, 635
Gladorchiidae, 193
Glaucoma, 148
Glires, 683
Glochidia, 527
Glossina, 51
  longipennis, 490
  morsitans, 54
  pallidipes, 54
  palpalis, 53
Glycolytic enzymes, 207, 552
Glycyphagidae, 513
Glypththelminis, 225
Gnathia maxillaris, 391
Gnathiidae, 390
Gnathostoma, 310
  spinigerum, 350
Goat, host of ameba, 54, 653
  ciliates, 587
  Cooperia, 328
  Dicrocoelium, 219
  Eimeria, 111
  Fasciola, 212
  Haemonchus, 326
  Oesophagostomum, 317
  Ostertagia, 327
  Paragonimus, 225
  Sarcoptes, 653
  Schistosoma, 200, 201
  Trichostrongylus, 618
  Trypanosoma, 54
Godwit, host of Microphallidae, 220
Golden nematode, 381
Goldfish, host of Cryptobia, 60
Gongylonema, 310
  pulchrum, 350
Goniinae, 684
Goniobasis silicula, host of Nanophyetus, 230

Goniocotes, 421
Gononemertes parasitica, 525
Gonopore, 288, 291
Gonotyl, 235
Gordiacea, 375
Gordius, 310
  aquaticus, 375
  robustus, 375
Gorgodera amplicava, 630
Gorgoderidae, 193
Gorgoderina attenuata, 630
Gorgonocephalus, 526
Gorgorhynchidae, 297
Gorgorhynchus, 297
Gracilisentis, 635
Grain beetle, host of Hymenolepis, 274
  itch mite, 512
Graphidium strigosum, 577
Grasshopper, host of Agamermis, 366
  tachinids, 484
Green blowfly, 486
Greenbottle fly, 486, 488
Gregarina blattarum, 99
  garnhami, 99, 101
Gregarine, host of Nosema, 138
  Perezia, 139
Gregarines, 663
Gregarinia, 97
Grocer's itch, 513
Ground itch, 323
Ground squirrels, 58, 614
  host of Trichomonas, 563
Growth, 559
  relation to specificity, 624
Gubernaculum, 304, 321
Guinea pig, 83
  host of Balantidium, 151
Guinea worm, 362
Gymnodactylus, 571, 621
Gymnophallinae, 188
Gymnophallus, 220
Gymnostomatida, 147, 663
Gynecophoral canal, 201
Gyraulus, host of Echinostoma, 211
  prashadi, 204
Gyrocotyle, 257
  fimbriata, 256, 257
  urna, 257
Gyrocotylidea, 255, 257
Gyrodactyloidea, 669
Gyrodactyloids, 629
Gyrodactylus, 166, 605
Gyropidae, 615

H

HABITAT, 568
Habrocytus, 457
Haemaphysalis leporispalustris, 504
Haematobia, 489
Haematocleptes terebelloides, 526

Haematoloechus, 225
Haematopinidae, 428, 683
Haematopinus suis, 428, 431
Haematosiphon modorus, 439
Haemocera danae, 408
Haemogregarina stepanowi, 105, 106
Haemogregarine, 573
Haemogregarinidae, 39, 105
Haemonchus, 310
   contortus, 302, 326, 571, 624
   placei, 327
Haemoproteus, 114, 115
   columbae, 114
Haemopsis sanguisugae, 80
Haemosporina, 39, 113
Hair lungworm, 331
Halictophagus curtisii, 466
Halipegidae, 193
Halipegus, 237, 238
   ovocaudatus, 239
Halteridium, 114
Hamanniella, 297
Hamsters, 537
Haplobothrium, 671, 672
   globuliforme, 262, 673
Haplometridae, 193
Haplorchis yokogawai, 235
Haplorhynchus, 199
Haplosplanchnidae, 193
Haplosporidia, 139
Haplosyllis cephalata, 526
Haptophyra, 664
Haptor, 162, 257, 550
Hard ticks, 498
Harposporium anguillulae, 309
Harpyrynchus, 506
Hartmanella, 78
Harvest mites, 509
Hatching, fluid, 557
   of flukes, 203, 207
   of nematodes, 340
Head louse, 428
Heelfly, 482
Helea, host of *Schizocystis*, 99
Helicometrina elongata, 225, 226
Helicosporida, 40, 139
Helicosporidium parasiticum, 139
Helicotylenchus, 378
   nannus, 379
Heliochona, 155
Helix, 60
Helminths, 544
   transmission of disease, 16
Helodrilus, host of *Metastrongylus*, 331
Hemasthla, 212
Hemiptera, 387, 432, 608
Hemiurata, 193
Hemiuridae, 193, 235, 237
Hemiurus, 238
   levinseni, 609

Henneguya, 136
   oviperda, 576
Hepatocystis, 127
Hepatozoidae, 39, 107
Hepatozoon, 105, 107
Heptocystis kochi, 128
Herbivores, hosts of ciliates, 148
Hermaphroditism, 25, 386
Hermit crab, 13, 536
   host of *Nereilepas*, 13
Heronimidae, 193
Herpetomonas, 47, 661
   muscae-domesticae, 47
   muscarum, 47
Hesperoctenes, 386
Hesperonoë adventor, 641
Hesthesis immortua, 299
Heterakis, 310
   gallinae, 43, 302, 341, 557
      as host of *Histomonas*, 17
   meleagridis, 341
   spumosa, 544
Heterocyemida, 525
Heterodera, 380, 382
   gottingiana, 381
   major, 381
   rostochiensis, 381, 382, 624
   schachtii, 381
Heteroderidae, 380
Heterodoxus, 423
Heterogenetic, 35
Heteromita, 60
Heterophyes brevicaeca, 235
   heterophyes, 235
   karasuradai, 235
Heterophyidae, 193, 235
Heteroptera, 387, 437
Heterospilus prosopidus, 580
Heterotrichida, 40, 157, 664
Heterotylenchus pavlovskii, 537
Heteroxenous, 34
Hetrazan, for ascariasis, 341
   for elephantiasis, 358
   for onchocerciasis, 360
   for trichinosis, 372
Hexabothrium, 629
Hexacanth embryo, 252, 550
Hexamita, 655, 660, 661
   meleagridis, 63
   salmonis, 63
Hexamitiasis, 63
Hexamitidae, 62
Hexylresorcinol, for ascariasis, 341
   for enterobiasis, 349
   for *Fasciolopsis* infection, 214
   for hookworm infection, 324
   for *Hymenolepis* infection, 271
   for strongyloidiasis, 314
   for trichuriasis, 374
Hiatella arctica, host of *Gymnophallus*, 221

Lanicides vayssierei, as host of *Cercaria*, 188
Lankesterella, 107
Lankesterellidae, 107
Lankesteria, 102
  ascidiae, 139
  culicis, 102
Larva migrans, 308, 336
Laurer's canal, 175
Leander serratus, 537
  serrifer, 535
Lecanicephalidea, 255, 259
Lêche de higuéron, in ascariasis, 341
  trichuriasis, 374
Lecithochirium, 238
Lecithodendriidae, 193
Lecithophora, 666
Leech, 14, 527
  as host of *Haemogregarina*, 105
  as host of Strigeidae, 196
Leiperia, 519
  gracilis, 515
Leishmania, 48, 49, 57
  brasiliensis, 58
  denticis, 60
  donovani, 10, 57, 58, 603
  mexicana, 57
  tropica, 58, 541
Leishmaniasis, 58, 60
Lemnisci, 290
Lepeophtheirus, 399
Lepidoptera, 387, 440, 608
  hosts of tachinids, 684
    wasps, 454
Lepidosaphes ulmi, 436
Lepocreadiidae, 193
Leptocimes boueti, 439
Leptocoris, 47
Leptodactylidae, 611
Leptomonas, 47, 661
  bütschlii, 47
  ctenocephali, 47
Lepton, 527
Leptorhynchoides, 297
  thecatus, 292
Leptotheca, 136
Lernaeocera, *branchialis*, 403, 609
Lernaeopodidae, 399, 403
Lernea carassii, 551
Leuciscus rutilus, 576
Leucochloridium macrostomum, 209
Leucocytozoon, 114
  simondi, 114
  smithi, 114
Levinseniella, 220
  minuta, 222, 223
Levuana iridescens, 581
Lewisi group, *Trypanosoma cruzi*, 49
  duttoni, 49
  lewisi, 49

Lewisi group, *Trypanosoma melophagium*, 49
  nabiasi, 49
  rangeli, 49
  theileri, 49
Lice, 419, 614
  distribution, 614
  ecological segregation of, 614
  evolution of, 682
  flies, 489
  host specificity, 638
  human, 428
  microdistribution of, 603, 604
Licnophora, 664
Life cycles, 23, 24
  of flukes, 180
  of nematodes, 305
  of protozoa, 34
  of tapeworms, 251
Ligament sacs, 290
  strand, 290
Light, 592
Limax, host of *Leucochloridium*, 209
Limiting factors, 509
Limnephilus, host of *Allocreadium*, 188, 189
Lindane, for acariasis, 515
  for warblefly, 483
Linguatula, *rhinaria*, 519
  serrata, 516, 517, 518
Linognathidae, 428, 683
Linstowiidae, 255, 286
Lintoniella adhaerens, 260
Lipeurus caponis, 426
  heterographus, 623
Lipid, 128
Liriopsis, 636
  pygmaea, 536
Lissorchiidae, 193
Lithobius forficatus, 109
Litomastix, 386
Litomosoides carinii, 553
Littoridina australis, 558
Littorina saxtilis, as host of Gymnophallinae, 188
Liver impairment in man, 534
Livoneca, 681
  convexa, 389
  symmetrica, 390
Lixophaga diatraeae, 581
Lizard, host of opalinids, 144
  Eumeces, 343
  Pharyngodon, 343
  Plagiorchiidae, 223
  Plasmodium, 127
  plerocercoid, 571
Loa loa, 310, 361, 534
Lobster, host of *Stichocotyle*, 669
Locust, host of *Gregarina*, 99
Longistriata didas, 628

Lota lota, 606
Lousefly, 489
Lucanthione hydrochloride, for
  schistosomiasis, 206
Lucilia, 47
  bufonivora, 486
  sericata, 486, 492
Luidia foliolata, 642
Lung mites, 513
Lungworm, 330, 331
Lycophore, 257
Lymexylidae, 16
Lymnaea, 200, 204, 631
  host of *Fasciola*, 213
Lynchia, 114
Lyperosia irritans, 489
Lysiphebus testaceipes, 453

M

MACAQUE monkey, 84
Macoma balthca, host of, *Gymnophallus*,
  221
Macracanthorhynchus hirudinaceus, 293,
  294, 297, 550
Macroderoididae, 193
Macrogamete, 35, 103
Macrogametocyte, 35, 118
Macronyssidae, 512
Macrophages, 553
Macrosaigon flabellatum, 462
Maggots, to clean wounds, 486
Mal de Caderas, 55
Malacosoma, 454
Malaria, 30, 116
Malarial parasite, 553, 534, 541, 608.
  See also *Plasmodium*.
  treatment, 120
Male fern. *See* oleoresin of aspidium.
Mallophaga, 387, 419, 421, 682
Malnutrition, 533, 554
Mammal, as host of *Brachylaimus*, 209
  Dicrocoeliidae, 219
  Dioctophymatoidea, 374
  flies, 639
  migration of, 606
Mange mite, 507
Mansonella, 351
Mansonia, 125
Mantibaria manticida, 459
Marietta carnesi, 458
Maritae, 189
Maritrema, 220
Marsupials, 611, 615
  trematodes of, 670
Mastigophora, 32, 39, 40
Mastina hylae, 42
Mastotermitidae, 586
Mayfly, host of Allocreadiidae, 225
Mealy bugs, 436, 437

Measles in sheep, 277
Measly pork, 276
Mediorhynchus, 297
Mediterranean, 59
Medusae, hosts of barnacle, 414
Mega condition, 55
Megadenus, 529
Megadrepanoides, 516
Megaperidae, 193
Mehlis' gland, 174, 262
Meinertzhageniella, 615
Melania, host of *Paragonimus*, 228
Melanoides, host of a blood fluke, 188
Melanolestes picipes, 438
Meleagris gallopavo, 268
Meloidae, 463
Meloidodera, 381
Meloidogyne, 380
Melolontha vulgaris, 293
Melophagus ovinus, 56, 491
Membranelles, 143
Menacanthus biseriatum, 423
  stramineus, 423, 425
Menoidium, 661
Menopon, gallinae, 423, 639
  pallidium, 422, 423
Menoponidae, 682
Mermithoidea, 310, 366
Merogony, 98
Merozoite, 98, 103, 117
Mesocercaria, 188, 197
Mesocestoides, 27, 29
Mesocestoididae, 244, 255, 287
Mesostigmata, 387
Mesozoa, 522, 665
Metabelba papillipes, 510
Metacercariae, 29, 196, 184, 631, 670
Metacryptozoites, 117
Metacyclic stage, 54
Metacystic stage, 87
Metadinium, 588
Metagonimus yokogawai, 235, 236
Metaphycus helvolus, 581
Metastrongyloidea, 310, 330
Metastrongylus, 310, 330
  apri, 331
  elongatus, 331
  pudendotectus, 331
  salmi, 331
Methionine, 127
Metoecus paradoxus, 463
Metopiidae, 488
Metopus circumlabens, 157, 158
Miastor, 386
Mice, host of, *Alaria*, 198
  Moniliformis, 296
  Plasmodium, 125
Microcotylidae, 169
Microcyemi, 525
Microdistribution, 602

45a

Microfilariae, 30, 31, 351, 353
Microgamete, 35
Microgametocyte, 36, 118
Microlynchia, 114
Micromalthus debilis, 386
Microniscus, 391
Microphallidae, 193, 220
Micropredator, 14, 24
Microsporidia, 39, 138, 536
　hosts of, 139
Microthrix, 249
Microtriches, 249
Midges, 114
　larvae, host of fluke, 224
Miescher's sacs, 132
Migration, in host, 574
　of birds, 606
　of hosts, 605
　of man, 606
　of porpoise, 606
　of whales, 606
Milk, 555
Miller's itch, 513
Millipeds, hosts of euglenids, 660
　　Menoidium, 661
　　Nyctotherus, 157
Mink, host of, *Alaria*, 198
　Opisthorchis, 231
　Paragonimus, 225
Miracidia, 29, 181, 576
　specificity for snails, 631
Miracil hydrochloride, as treatment for
　schistosomiasis, 206
Mites, 494, 496, 506, 572, 620
　diseases, 507
　evolution of, 685
　host of tapeworm, 509
　host specificity, 640
　parasites of wasps, 684
　typhus, 511
Mitochondria, 32
Mixotricha, 73
Mnestra, 521
Modiolaria, 527
Modiolus, host of *Paravortex*, 159
Moist sores, 58
Mola mola host of Accacoeliidae, 631
　Didymozoidae, 240
Mole cricket, host of oxyurids, 346–347
　　Retortamonas, 62
Moles, 628
　hosts of *Palaeopsylla*, 684
Mollusca, 527
　hosts of, dalyellioids, 668
　　Echinobothrium, 260
　　Gymnophallinae, 188
Molt, 561
Molting, in nematodes, 307
Molting hormones, 587
Monas communis, 37

Moniezia, 20, 632
　benedeni, 285
　expansa, 285, 536
Moniliformidae, 297
Moniliformis, 297
　dubius, 296, 584
　moniliformis, 296, 635
Monkey, host of *Entamoeba*, 91
　Iodamoeba, 94
　lice, 639
　Plasmodium, 127
　Schistosoma, 206
　Strongyloides, 314
　Taenia, 274
　Trypanosoma, 57
　Watsonius, 218
Monocercomonas, 662
Monocercomonidae, 64
Monocystis, 99, 665
　lumbrici, 102
Monodelphic, 304
Monoecious, 34
Monogenea, 159, 162
　evolution of, 668
Monogenetic, 35
Monomorphic form, 51
Monopisthocotylea, 165
Monopsyllus sciurorum, 445
Monorchiidae, 193
Monostomes, 172
Monoxenous, 34, 618
Monozoic, 255, 262
Morula, 29
Mosquito, 472–477, 556, 657
　destruction of, 475
　host of *Brugia*, 358
　　Lankesteria, 102
　　Microsporidia, 138
　　Plasmodium, 117, 118, 125
　　Wuchereria, 356
　localization of host, 642
Monstrillidae, 406
Monstrilloida, 406
Montacuta, 527
Moose, as host of, *Echinococcus*, 281
　　Fascioloides, 214
Mormoniella vitripennis, 579
Morphology of Acarina, 495
Moth, 16, 440
　as host of *Angitia*, 19
　as host of *Apanteles*, 19
Movements, 573
Mucopolysaccharide, 28, 172
Mucoprotein, 556
Mucron, 98
Mugilidae, 613
Mule, host of *Trichostrongylus*, 618
　　Trypanosoma, 54
Mullerius capillaris, 331
Multiceps multiceps, 279

Multiglandularis megalorchis, 190, 191
Multiparasitism, 19
Multiple cysts, 252
Multiocular cyst, 285
Musca domestica, 489, 492, 579
Musca, host of *Herpetomonas*, 47
Muscidae, 387, 489
Mussel, host of cercaria, 188
    mite, 507
Mutations, 648
Mutualism, 8, 15
Mya arenaria, 150
Myiasis, 486, 491, 492
Myocoptes musculinus, 509, 510
Myriapods, hosts of *Hymenolepis*, 632
Mytilus edulis, host of, *Cercaria*, 188
        Gymnophallus, 221
        Pinnotheres, 394
Myxidium, 136
    giardi, 605
Myxobolus, 136
Myxosoma squamilis, 136
Myxosporida, 35, 39, 134–137, 573, 655
Myzostomids, 526, 635
Myzostomum pulvinar, 526

N

Naegleria, 77, 663
Nagana, 54, 607
Nanophyetus salmonicola, 17, 230, 605
Narvesus carolinensis, 438
Nasalfly, 483
Nasal mites, 513
Nassarius obsoletus, 208
Natural resistance, 575
Nauplius, 415
Neascus, 197
Nebalia, 525
Necator, 319, 568
Nematobothrium, 238
Nematodes, 299, 548
    eggs of, 303
    esophagus of, 678
    evolution of, 675
    host specificity, 633
    in plants, 376
    infections, treatment for, 309
Nematodirus helvetianus, 328
    spathiger, 328
Nematogens, 524
Nematomorpha, 310, 366, 375
Nematospiroides dubius, 559
Nemeritis canescens, 654
Nemertea, 525
Nemertians, 668
Nemertopsis actinophila, 525
Nemural, for *Multiceps* infection, 279
Neocatolaccus mamezophagus, 580
Neodiplodistomum paraspathula, 195

Neoechinorhynchidae, 298
Neoechinorhynchus, 296, 298, 605
Neolinognathidae, 428
Neolinognathus, 428
Neorickettsia helmintheca, 17, 230
Neoskrjabinolepsis singularis, 628
Neostam, for oriental sore, 58
Neotenic, 167
    procercoid, 287
Nereid worm, 13
Nereilepas fucata, 13
Nerocila, 389
    orbignyi, 390
Niche, 568
Nicotine sulfate for, acariasis, 515
        Haemonchus infection, 327
Nidality, doctrine of, 566
Nippostrongylus, 310, 583
    brasiliensis, 17, 328, 537
    muris, 328
Nippotaenidea, 254
Nitrothiazole, 44
Nodular worm of swine, 316
Nomada, 461
Nomeus gronovii, 11
Nosema, 530
    apis, 138
    bombycis, 138
    cyclopi, 138
    frenzelinae, 138
    helminthorum, 20, 536
    notabilis, 139
    stegomyiae, 138
Nosopsyllus fasciatus, 449
Notemigonus crysoleucas auratus host of,
        Pliovitellaria, 263
Notocotyllidae, 193
Notodelphyidae, 401
Nucleogony, 35
Nudibranchs, 14
Nutrition, 533
    holophytic, 34
    holozoic, 34
    saprozoic, 32
Nutrition-inhibition hypothesis, 538
Nycteribia biarticulata, 491
Nyctotherus, 157
    cordiformis, 36, 156, 158
    faba, 157
    ovalis, 158
    parvus, 158
    velox, 157
Nymph, 497

O

OCHETOSOMATIDAE, 193
Ochridanus ocellatus, 151
Octomitus salmonis, 63
Octopus bimaculatus, 522, 524, 525
    vulgaris, 525

Octospinifer, 298
Octospiniferoides, 298
  chandleri, 289
  macilentis, 289
Odostomia eulimoides, 528
  scalaris, 528
Oeciacus hirundinis, 439
Oekiocolax plagiostomorum, 159
Oesophagostomum, 310
  columbianum, 317
  dentatum, 316
Oestradiol, 560
Oestridae, 387, 482
Oestris ovis, 483, 484
Oil of chenopodium, for ascariasis, 341
  for hookworm infection, 326
  for trichuriasis, 374
Oleoresin of aspidium for dibothrio-
    cephaliasis, 263
  for *Dipylidium* infection, 270
  for echinostomiasis, 212
  for helminthiasis, 231
  for *Hymenolepis* infection, 274
  for *Taenia* infection, 277
Oligacanthorhynchidae, 297
Oligarces, 386
Oligochaetes, 11, 526
  host of *Archigetes*, 674
    Astomatida, 151
    Dioctophyme, 375
    Heterakis, 342
    Temnocephala, 161
Oligognathus parasiticus, 526
Oligotricha, 588
Oligoxenous, 618
Onchobothriidae, 259
Onchocerca, 310
  volvulus, 358, 479, 534
Onchophanes lanceolator, 451
Oncomelania, 203
  hupensis, 204
  host of *Paragonimus*, 228
Oncomiracidia, 165
Oncosphere, 28, 29, 244, 252, 544, 665
Onicola, 297
Onuphidae, 526
Onuphis magna, 526
Oochoristica symmetrica, 252
Oocyst, 103, 117
Oogenesis, 26
Ookinete, 117
Ootype, 174
Opalina, 146
  hylaxena, 146
  oregonensis, 145
  ranarum, 144, 146
  spiralis, 146
Opalinida, 40, 143
Opalinids, 583, 660

Opecoelidae, 193
Ophidascaris, 335
Ophionyssus natricis, 506
Ophryoglenidae, 40, 149
Ophryoscolecidae, 19, 588
Ophryoscolex, 158, 664
Opisthaptor, 162
Opisthoglyphe, 225
Opisthorchiidae, 193, 231, 234
Opisthorchis felineus, 231, 235, 631
  sinensis, 25, 231, 232, 550, 624
  tenuicollis, 231
Opossums, 53, 611
Opsanus beta, 139
  tau, 139
Orang, host of lice, 639
Orcheobius, 104
Orchestia agilis, host of *Anoplophrya*, 36
Organogenesis, 29
Oribatid mites, 509
  host of *Moniezia*, 285
Oriental sore, 541
Ornithobilharzia, 200
Ornithodoros, 55
  moubata, 497, 501
  salahi, 502
Ornithofilaria, 310
  fallisensis, 351
Ornithomyia fringillina, 640
Ornithonyssus bacoti, 512, 513
Orthonectida, 522
Ostertagia, 310
  bisonis, 327
  circumcincta, 327
  lyrata, 327
  ostertagi, 327
  trifurcata, 327
Ostracodinium, 588
Ostracods, hosts of Acanthocephala, 292
    Hymenolepis, 632
Ostrich, 615
Otobius megnini, 500
Otodectes cynotis, 509
Otodistomum, 237
Ova. See Eggs.
Ovarian balls, 291
Oviparous, 385
Owl, host of *Plasmodium*, 125
Oxhead cercariae, 209
Oxygen, 552, 553, 572, 575, 592
  reduction potential, 87, 557
  tension, 34
Oxyspirura, 679
Oxytetracycline, for trichomoniasis, 68, 89
Oxyuris, 310
  equi, 343
Oxyuroidea, 304, 310, 342, 677
Oyster shell, 521

P

PACHYSENTIDAE, 297
Paedogenesis, 26, 386
Paguritherium alatum, 536
Pagurus longicarpus, 536
Palaeocanthocephala, 297
Palaeopsylla, 684
Pallisentis, 298
Panagrellus, 309
Panesthia javanica, 80
    panopistus pricei, 628
Pansporoblast, 135
Pansporocyst, 139
Papain bromelin, 172
Papillae, on *Ascaris*, 339
Parabasal body, 64
Parachaenia myae, 150
Paracyamus, 411
Paradesmose, 35, 94
Paradexodes epilachnae, 453
Paradinium poucheti, 41
Parafossarulus striatulus, 204
Paragonimiasis, treatment for, 230
Paragonimus compactus, 225
    edwardsei, 225
    iloktsuensis, 225
    kellicotti, 225, 576
    ringeri, 225
    westermani, 180, 225, 227
Paragordius varius, 375
Parallel evolution, lice and hosts, 614
Paramphistomata, 193, 215
Paramphistomatidae, 193, 215
Paramphistomum microbothriodes, 219
Parapediculus, 639
Parascaris, 27, 28, 338
    eggs of, 29
Parasite, definition, 7
    intracellular, 561
    numbers, 574
    resistance of, 622
    versus predators, 590
Parasite-host specificity, 618
    kinds of, 622
Parasite-mix, 20, 582
Parasitic castration, 535, 536, 537
    zoonoses, 17
Parasitica, 451
Parasitism, 8, 9, 14
    definition, 8, 14
    intermittent, 14
    origins, 655
    prosperous, 549
Parasitocoenosis, 582
Parasitogenesis, 651
Parasitoid, 581, 582
    mites, 512
Parasitoidea, 512

Parasitoidism, 15
Parasitoidy, 641
Parasitosyllis, 526
Parastrongyloides winchesi, 628
Paratenic hosts, 674, 679
Parathelphusa, 229
Paratractis hystrix, 301
Paratrioza cockerelli, 434
Paravortex gamellipara, 159
Parenchyma, 164
Paromomycin, 89
Parorchis, 212
    acanthus, 26
Parthemita, 188
Parthenitae, 189
Parthenogenesis, 26, 189, 386
Partnerships, examples, 10
Pasteur effect, 552
Patagifer, 212
Patasiger, 212
Patiria miniata, 642
Pea crab, 12
Peachia, 521
Pediculidae, 428, 638
Pediculoides ventricosus, 512
Pediculoididae, 512
Pediculus, 428, 429, 638, 683
    humanus, 421, 430, 638
        corporis, 430, 638
Pelicans, 614
    hosts of *Metagonimus*, 235
Pelmatodrilus planariformis, 526
Pelta, 66
Peltogaster curvatus, 536
Pennella filosa, 19
Penetration of *Schistosoma* cercaria, 205
Pentamidine, for sleeping sickness, 53
Pentastomida, 387, 494, 515
Pentastomum, solaris, 518
Pentatrichomonas, 66
    hominis, 5, 67, 68, 540
Pepsin, 172
Perezia lankesteriae, 139
Periclimenes yucatanicus, 594
Periodicity, 29, 31
    clinical, 30
Periplaneticola periplaneticola, 346
Peritrichida, 40, 154, 664
Perivitelline fluid, 28
Peromyscus, host of *Trypanosoma*, 534
Petalostoma minutum, 139
pH, 557, 593
Phaenicia sericata, 488
Phagocytosis, 542
Phagotroph, 127
Phallusia mamillata, 79
Pharyngodon mamillatus, 343
Pharyngora, 225
Phasiinae, 684

Phasmidia, 299, 301, 309, 677
Phasmids, 301
Phenothiazine for enterobiasis, 349
    Heterakis infection, 44
    for Heterakis infection, 44
    for lice control, 432
    for Oesophagostomum infection, 317
    for Ostertagia infection, 327
    for trichostrongyliasis, 330
Philophthalmidae, 193
Phlebotominae, 481
Phlebotomus, argentipes, 481
    chinensis, 482
    intermedius, 482
    longipalpis, 482
    papatasii, 58, 481
    perniciosus, 482
    sergenti, 482
Phoresy, 12, 638
Phormia, 47, 493
    regina, 488
Phoronte, 150
Phronima sedentaria, 410
Phronimidae, 410
Phryxus abdominalis, 636
Phthirus, 638
    pubis, 430
Phygadeuon subfuscus, 453
Phyllidia, 242, 259
Phyllirhoe, 521
Phyllobothriidae, 259
Phyllodistomum simile, 181
Physa, 631
Physalia, host of Nomeus, 11
Physaloptera hispida, 531
Physiological races, 653
Physiology and Biochemistry, 18
Physophaga, 664
Physopsis, 204, 631
Phytomonas, 47, 661, 663
Phytoptipalpidae, 512
Phytozoon, 15
Piagetiella, 422
Pian-bois, 58
Pig, host of, Ascaris, 337
    chilomastix, 60
    Dicrocoelium, 219
    Echinococcus, 281
    Euritrema, 219
    Entamoeba, 83, 91, 653
    Fasciola, 189, 212, 214
    Fasciolopsis, 214
    Hyostrongylus, 330
    Iodamoeba, 94
    Macracanthorhynchus, 293
    Paragonimus, 225
    Schistosoma, 200, 201
    Stephanurus, 315
    Taenia, 274
    Trichostrongylus, 618

Pigeon, 57, 70, 114
    host of Plasmodium, 125
Pillbugs, 388
Pimpla bicolor, 582
Pimply gut, 317
Pinnixa faba, 12
Pinnotheres pisum, 394
Pinnotherion vermiforme, 394
Pinworm, 342, 343, 348, 611
Piperazine for ascariasis, 341
    for enterobiasis, 349
    for trichinosis, 372
Piroplasma, 128
Piroplasmea, 39, 128
Piroplasmida, 39, 128
Piroplasmosis, 128, 130, 535
Piscicola, 57
Pisidium abditum, host of Allocreadium, 188
Placental parasites, 659
Placobdella catenigera, 105
Plagioporus, 225
Plagiorchiida, 193, 219
Plagiorchiidae, 193, 223
Plagiorchis, 176, 225
    megalorchis, 190, 191
    vespertilionis, 223
Plagiostomum, 159
Plagiotoma lumbrici, 158
Plagiotomidae, 40, 157
Planaria, host of Lankesteria, 102
Plankton, 593
Planorbidae, host of, Schistosoma, 207
Planorbis, 200
    boissyi, 204
Plant lice, 433, 434
    parasites, 16
Plants, aquatic, 593
    hosts of nematodes, 376
Planula larvae, 522, 665
Planuloid, 665, 668, 670
Planuloid-acoeloid theory, 665
Plasmodiidae, 39, 114
Plasmodium, 10, 35, 116, 535, 549, 554, 657, 665
    berghei, 18, 125, 553, 626
    cathermerium, 125, 561, 626
    circumflexum, 125
    cynomolgi, 127
    durae, 125
    elongatum, 125, 626
    falciparum, 20, 117
    fallax, 561
    floridense, 127
    gallinaceum, 30, 125, 127, 556, 561, 619
    hexamerium, 125
    inui, 127
    juxtanucleare, 125
    knowlesi, 127
    kochi, 128

Plasmodium lophurae, 125, 126, 561, 626
  lygosomae, 127
  malariae, 117, 127
  mexicanum, 127
  nucleophilum, 125
  oti, 125
  ovale, 117
  polare, 125
  reichenowi, 127
  relictum, 125, 540, 554
  rhadinurum, 127
  rouxi, 125
  vaughani, 125
  vivax, 30, 117, 118, 127
Plasmodium, life cycle diagram, 119
  migration, 574
Plasmotomy, 35, 77
Plastin cells, 29
Platycyamus, 411
Platygaster dryomyiae, 459
Platyhelminthes, 159, 255
Platylepas, 414
Plerocercoid, 252, 253, 571, 621
Plerocercus, 252
Pleuronectes flessus, 609
Pleurotrocha, 525
Pliovitellaria wisconsinesis, 263
Plistophora culicis, 137
Plover, host of Microphallidae, 220
Plutella, 19
Pneumocystis, 140
Pneumoneces, 225
Pneumonyssidae, 506
Podarke pugettensis, 642
Podocnemis dumeriliana, host of
  Paratractis, 301
Podocotyle atomon, 609
Pollenia rudis, 487
Pollution, 593
Pollystomoidella oblongum, 163
Polydelphic, 304
Polyembryony, 29, 183, 386, 451, 459
Polymnia nebulosa, 641
Polymorphic forms, 51
Polymorphidae, 296, 298
Polymorphus, 288, 298
  minutus, 296, 629
Polynoë scolependrina, 641
Polyopisthocotylea, 166
Polyopisthocotylineans, 669
Polyphenol, 172
Polyphenol quinone tanning, 300
Polyplax spinulosa, 431
Polystoma, 668
  integerrimum, 166
Polystomoides coronatum, 629
  polyxenous, 618
Polyzoic, 255, 262
Pomatiopsis, 228
Pomphorhynchidae, 297

Pomphorhynchus, 297
  bulbocolli, 288
Pond fish, 74
Population, 567
  density, 577
  dynamics, 577
  equilibrium, 577
  interbreeding, 650
  isolation of, 619
Porifera, 521
Pork tapeworm, 274
Porocephalus, 516
Porpoises, migration, 606
Porrocaecum, 335
Portunus depurator, 107, 536
Post kala-azar leishmaniasis, 59
Posterior station, 54
Potassium antimony tartrate, for
  schistosomiasis, 206
Potomon, as host of *Paragonimus*, 229
Poultry, host of, bedbug, 439
  bloodsucking mites, 512
  coccidia, 111
  Flicollis, 296
  Heterakis, 342
  Polymorphus, 296
  Raillietina, 267
  Syngamus, 317
  Trichomonas, 68, 70
Praniza, 390
Pratylenchus penetrans, 379
  vulvus, 377
Prawn, host of *Bopyrus*, 393
Pre-adaptations, 651
Predaceous mites, 512
Predator, 14, 580, 590
Predator-pressure, 654
Prednisone, for oncocerciasis, 360
Premunition, 20, 577
Pressure effects, 531
Priapulida, 675
Primaquine, for malaria, 120
Primates, hosts of lice, 638, 683
Pritionchus aerivora, 311
Proales, 525
Proboscis sac, 290
Procava capensis, 638
Procavicola, 638
Procaviidae, 638
Procercoid, 252
Proctotrupoidea, 387, 459
Progenesis, 29, 189
Progenetic larvae, 257
Progesterone, 559
Proglottid, 242
Prohaptor, 162
Pronotal comb and ctenidium, 443
Pronocephalidae, 193
Prontosil, for paragonimiasis, 230
Prosorhyncus, 209

Prosthogonimus, 225
Protamidine, for sleeping sickness, 53
Protandrous hermaphroditism, 390
Protease, 172
Protein deficiency, 534
  supplied by ungulate ciliates, 589
Protelean parasitism, 386
Proteocephalidea, 244, 255, 259
Proteocephalans, evolution of, 671
Proteocephalus stizostethi, 573
Proteomyxida, 39, 95
Protista, 34
Protogyrodactylus, 629
Protomerite, 98
Protomonte, 150
Protomyzostomum polynephris, 526
Protonephridia, 290
Protoopalina intestinalis, 145
  mitotica, 145
  saturnalis, 145
Protoparce sexta, 636
Protostrongylus rufescens, 332
Protozoa, 32 to 158
  evolution, 660
  host specificity, 626
  mutualistic, 584
Pseudaliidae, 331
Pseudemys floridana mobilensis, 81
Pseudobilharziella, 200
Pseudococcus, 436
Pseudocoel, 288
Pseudodicyema, 524
Pseudolynchia, 114
Pseudolynchia maura, 491
Pseudophyllidea, 244, 255, 260, 672
Pseudopleuronectes americanus, 609
Pseudopodia, 77
Pseudosporidae, 39, 95
Pseudosuccinea, 631
Pseudotrichonympha grassii, 73
Psilostomatidae, 193
Psocoptera, 682
Psoroptic mites, 507
Psychodidae, 481
Psychological selection, 582
Psylla, mali, 434
  pyricola, 434
Psyllidae, 433
Pterolichus bicaudatus, 615
Pteromalidae, 457
Pterygosoma aculeatum, 620
Ptychomyia remota, 581
Pulex irritans, 442, 446, 639
  host of *Dipylidium*, 270
Pungitius pungitius, 605
Puparium, host of staphylinids, 461
Pupiparia, 489
Pycnogonids, 14
Pygidium, 444
Pyramidellidae, 528

Pyrimethamine, for malaria, 120
Pyrimithamine, for toxoplasmosis, 134
Pyruvic acid, 24
Pyrvinium pamoate, in enterobiasis, 349
Python, host of *Amplicaecum*, 634

Q

Quadraspidiotus perniciosus, 437
Quadrigyridae, 298
Quarantine laws, 608
Qudrigyrus, 298
Quinacrine, for *Dipylidium* infection, 270
  for *Giardia* infection, 63
  for *Hymenolepis* infection, 274
  for *Taenia* infection, 277
Quinone-tanned proteins, 29, 304
Quinone-tanning, 178

R

RABBIT, host of ameba, 83
  Dicrocoelium, 299
  Echinococcus, 281
  Eimeria, 111
  Fasciola, 189, 212
  Sarcoptes, 653
Rachis, 27
Raccoon, host of *Alaria*, 198
  Trypanosoma, 55
Radiophrya ochridana, 151
Race, biological, 653
  physiological, 653
Radiation, 572
Radiolaria, 15
Radopholus, 378
Raillietiella, 516
  mabuiae, 515
Raillietina cesticillus, 244, 266, 267
  tetragona, 267
Rainey's corpuscles, 132
Rana, host of fluke, 630
  Nyctotherus, 156
Raphidascaris, 335
Rat, host of, *Alaria*, 198
  ameba, 84
  flea, 56
  Heterakis, 544
  lice, 431
  Moniliformis, 296
  Nippostrongylus, 328
  Paragonimus, 225
  Trypanosoma, 56
Ratfish, host of *Gyrocotyle*, 257, 672
Rattus alexandrinus, host of
  Moniliformis, 296
Receptaculum, 175
Red caltrop, 214
  lungworm, 332
  mite, 512

Red scale, 437
stomach worm, 330
Rediae, 29, 182, 670
Reduviidae, 437
Remora, 11
Renicolida, 193
Renicolidae, 193
Renifer, 225
Reproduction in insects, 385
Reptile, host of ameba, 80
Cyclophyllidea, 266
Dicrocoeliidae, 219
Haemoproteus, 114
Lintoniella, 260
Plasmodium, 127
Schellackia, 107
Tetraphyllidea, 671
Reproduction, 25
and life cycles, 34
Reservoir hosts, 59
of infection, 58
Resochin, for malaria, 120
Respiration in insects, 384
in protozoa, 34
Response specificity, 642
Retortamonadida, 60
Retortamonadidae, 60
Retortamonas intestinalis, 61
Rhabdias bufonis, 311, 675
Rhabdiasidae, 311
Rhadinorhynchidae, 297
Rhadinorhynchus, 297
Rhabditida, 299, 309
Rhabditina, 677
Rhabditis, 309, 676
coarctata, 311
nigrovenosa, 311
ocypodis, 311
Rhabditoidea, 309, 677
Rhabdochona ovifilamenta, 679
Rhabdocoel, 159
Rhabdocoelida, 666, 668, 671
Rhaphidascaris, 576
Rhea, 615
Rhinoceross, hosts of strongyles, 634
Rhinotermitidae, 586
Rhipicephalus appendiculatus, 131
evertsi, 131
sanguineus, 130, 505, 506
Rhipidocotyle, 209
Rhizocephala, 414, 415, 535
Rhizolepas annellidicola, 414
Rhizomastigida, 38, 41
Rhizomastix gracilis, 42
Rhizopodea, 39, 77
Rhodnius prolixus, 53, 54, 437
Rhombogens, 524
Rhopalura, 524, 525
Rhynchobdellids, 527
Rhynchocoela, 525

Rhynchoidomonas, 661
Rhynchonympha, 72
Rhynchophthirina, 423
Rickettsia, 140, 230
in lice, 431
tsutsugamushi, 511
Riela, 459
Riggia paranensis, 389
Ripidius, 464
denisi, 462
Ripiphoridae, 461
RNA, 121, 127, 656
Roach, 80
wood-feeding, 561
Robin, host of *Plasmodium*, 125
Robins, 627
Rocky Mountain spotted fever, 506
Rodents, hosts of ascaridoids, 679
fleas, 684
Schistosoma, 201, 207
Rogas, 454
Roost mite, 512
Rostellum, 242, 265, 268
Rotenone for, lice control, 432
Rotifera, 525
Rules of affinity, 651
Ruminants, 587

S

SACCOPSIDAE, 682
Sacculina, 412, 415, 532, 535, 551
Sagitta, 49, 60
Sailfish, host of *Pennella*, 19
Saissetia oleae, 581
Salamander, host of *Entamoeba*, 80
Halipegus, 238
Strigeidae, 196
Trypanosoma, 570
Salmincola salmonea, 403
Salminus maxillosus, 558
Salmon, gill-maggot, 403
host of *Costia*, 74
migration, 605
poisoning fluke, 17, 230
Salmo trutta, host of *Phyllodistomum*, 181
Salpa fusiformis, 521
Salvelinus alpinus, 605
Sambonia, 516
Sampling error, 650
Sandfleas, 410
Sand flounder, 57
Sandfly, 58, 481
Sandpiper, host of Microphallidae, 220
Santonin, for enterobiasis, 349
Sappinia diploidea, 37, 78
Saprozoites, 15
Sarcophagidae, 387, 488
Sarcocystidae, 39, 131

Sarcocystis, 131
  blanchardi, 132
  darlingi, 132
  harvathi, 132
  lindemanni, 131, 132
  muris, 132
Sarcodina, 77
Sarcophaga, 47, 492, 684
  hemorrhoidalis, 489
Sarcoptes scabiei, 25, 507, 508, 653
Sarcoptiformes, 387
Sarcoptoidea, 507
Scab mites, 507
Scale insects, 436
Sceloporus, host of *Plasmodium*, 127
Schellackia, 107
Schistocephalus solidus, 245
Schistocerca gregaria, 99
Schistosoma bovis, 200
  hematobium, 201, 207
  incognitum, 200, 630
  intercalatum, 200
  japonicum, 201, 630
  mansoni, 201, 207, 560, 573, 630
  mattheei, 200
  nasale, 200
  spindale, 200, 630
Schistosomatidae, 200, 576
Schistosomatium douthitti, 26
Schistosomiasis, 200, 534
  treatment of, 206
Schizocystis gregarinoides, 99
Schizogony, 30, 98, 103, 117
Schizogregarinida, 39, 98
Schizont, 98
Schizothaerus nuttalii, host of *Pinnixa*, 12
Schizotrypanum, 54
Schmardaella lutzi, 526
Sclerostomes, 615
Scolex, 242
Scolioidea, 387, 459
Scoloplos, 525
Screw worm, 487
Scrobicula tenuis, host of *Gymnophallus*, 221
Scrub typhus, 511
Scyphidia acanthoclini, 154
Scyphidiidae, 40, 154
Sea anemones, 521
  host of *Foettingeria*, 664
Sea cucumbers, hosts of, *Anoplodiera*, 667
  Fierasfer, 12
  rhabdocoels, 159
  Thyonicola, 551
Sea gull, host of Microphallidae, 220
Sea lily, host of rhabdocoels, 159
Seals, hosts of lice, 683
Search for a partner, 640
Searching capacity, 582
Seasonal variations, 572

Sea stars, hosts of mollusks, 529
  rhabdocoels, 159
Seatworm, 348
Sea urchin, host of Entorhipidiidae, 148
  ciliates, 148
  Metopus, 158
  mollusks, 529
  rhabdocoels, 159
  Syndesmis, 159
  Syndisyrinx, 667
  Tetrahymena, 660
Sebekia, 519
Secernentea, 299, 309, 677
Secondary screwworm, 488
Seed ticks, 497
Segmenter, 118
Segmentina schmackeri, 204
Seison, 525
Selection, 654
  ecological, 582
  psychological, 582
Selection-pressure, 654
Semisulcospira, 228
Sensilium, 444, 445
Sepia, 524, 525
  officinalis, 107
Sepsis, 492
Serological reactions, 542, 543
Serphoidea, 459
Serrasentis, 297
Sesarma, 229
Sex, 560
  cycles, 560, 587
  hormones, 558, 559, 560
  processes of host, 535
  reversal, 535, 536
  seasonal, host activity, 573
Shark, effects of tapeworms in, 555
  host of barnacles, 414
    Lintoniella, 260
    Tetraphyllidea, 671
Sheep, ked, 56, 491
  maggotfly, 486
  scab mite, 507
  tick, 491
Sheep, host of ciliates, 148, 587
  Cooperia, 328
  Dicrocoelium, 219
  Eimeria, 111
  Entamoeba, 82, 653
  Fasciola, 189
  Fascioloides, 214
  Haemonchus, 326
  Multiceps, 279
  Nematodirus, 328
  Oesophagostomum, 317
  Ostertagia, 327
  Scarcoptes, 653
  Schistosomatidae, 200
  Trichostrongylus, 618

Sheep, host of *Trypanosoma*, 54, 55
Shell, formation, 178
  gland, 174
  globules, 178
Shiner, host of *Pliovitellaria*, 263
Shore birds, hosts of Microphallidae, 220
Shore line, 592
Shrews, 628
  hosts of *Palaeopsylla*, 684
Shrimps, cleaner, 595
  hosts of *Phryxus*, 636
Sibling species, 20, 650, 655
Siedleckiella, 139
Signet ring, 118
Silkworm, host of *Nosema*, 138
Siluridae, 613
Silver fish, 60
Simuliidae, 114, 387, 477
Simulium, 354, 479, 534
  nigroparvum, 480
  occidentale, 480
  venustum, 480
Siphonaptera, 387, 441
Siphunculata, 426
Sipunculid, host of Actinomyxida, 139
  rhabdocoels, 159
Sitaris muralis, 463
Sitotroga cerealella, 579
Size, 548, 552
Skate, host of *Caliperia*, 154
  Stichocotyle, 171
Skrjabinia tetragona, 267
Slime ball, 219
Slug, host of, *Leucochloridium*, 209
  Syngamus, 317
  Tetrahymena, 148, 660
Snails, 578, 635
  as hosts of aspidogastrids, 171
    hair lungworm, 332
    maggots, 493
    Schistosomatidae, 199
    Spirorchiidae, 199
    Strigea, 197
    Syngamus, 317
    Temnocephalida, 666
  as intermediate hosts, 631
  as parasites, 528
Snake, host of amebas, 651
    barnacle, 414
    mites, 506, 685
    opalinids, 144
    pentastomid, 516
    Plagiorchiidae, 223
    plerocercoids, 263
    Strigeidae, 196
    tapeworms, 632
Snowy owl, host of Strigea, 197
Social behavior in fish, 542
Sodium antimony tartrate, for
  schistosomiasis, 206

Sodium fluorosilicate, for lice control, 432
Sodium stibogluconate, for leishmaniasis,
  60
Soft ticks, 498
Soma, 235
Spargana, 252, 263
  in mice, 530
Spathebothridea, 255, 285
Specificity, 618
  ecological, 623
  ethological, 623
  phylogenetic, 623
  physiological, 623
Spelophallus, 220
Spelotrema, 220
Spermatheca, 444, 445
Spermatogenesis, 26
Sphaerita, 79, 140
Sphaerospora polymorpha, 139
Spinose ear tick, 500
Spirachona gemmipara, 154
Spiracles, 682
Spiracular gland, 682
Spirobolus marginatus, 158, 661
Spirocamallanus, 577
Spirochaetes, 587
Spirometra, 263
Spironoura, 302
Spirophrya subparasitica, 151
Spiroptera tenuissima, 576
Spirorchiidae, 199, 576
Spirorchis, 199
Spirotrichia, 40, 157, 664
Spirurida, 310, 335, 349, 679, 680
Spiruroidea, 310, 349
Sponge, 521
Sporadin, 99
Spore, 103
Sporoblasts, 102, 135
Sporocyst, 29, 103, 182, 670
Sporogony, 103, 117
Sporoplasm, 135
Sporozoa, 97
  evolution of, 663
Sporozoite, 103, 117
Squid, host of *Chromidina*, 151
  Isancistrum, 166
Squirrel, host of *Fasciola*, 212
  fleas, 684
Stablefly, 489
Stagnicola, 622, 631
Staphylinidae, 461
Staphylococcus aureus, 17
Starfish. *See also*, Seastar.
  as host of *Fierasfer*, 12
Starling, host of *Plasmodium*, 125
Starvation, 555
Stegophryxus hyptius, 392, 536
Stenopteryx, 491
Stenopus hispidus, 595

Stenoxenous, 34
Stephanofilaria, 351
Stephanurus dentatus, 310, 315
Sternites, 443
Sternostoma tracheacolum, 513
Sterrhurus, 238
Stibophen, for oriental sore, 58
  for schistosomiasis, 206
Stichocotyle, 171, 669
Stichocotylidae, 171
Stichocytes, 367
Stichopus californicus, 641
Stichosome, 367
Sticklebacks, 631
Stilbazium iodide as anthelminthic, 309
Stilesia, 632
Stizostedion vitreum, 573
Stoecharthrum, 525
Stomoxys, 55, 492
  calcitrans, 489
Stratiodrilus, 526
Strepsiptera, 387, 464, 537
Streptococcus pyogenes, 17
Stress, 562, 563, 578, 620
Strigea elegans, 197
Strigeatoidea, 195
Strigeidae, 195
Strigeids, 630, 631
Strobila, 242
Strongylida, 299, 310, 314
Strongylina, 677
Strongylocentrotus, host of ciliates, 148
    Syndesmis, 159
Strongyloidea, 304, 310, 314
Strongyloides, 568
  cebus, 314
  fülleborni, 314
  papillosus, 17
  ratti, 562
  simiae, 314
  stercoralis, 24, 167, 307, 311
Strongyloids, 633
Strongylus, 611
Strophitus, host of bucephalids, 188
Struthiolipeurus, 615
Sturgeons, hosts of *Amphilina*, 257
    Cystoopsis, 680
Stylets, 526
Stylifer, 529
Stylocephalus longicollis, 99, 100
Stylochona, 155
Stylodrilus leukocephalus, 151
Stylopids, 464
Stylops, melittae, 466
  shannoni, 465
Subulura allodapa, 614
  suctoria, 614
Suctorida, 40, 155
Sucking lice, 419
Suis subgroup, 51

Sulfadiazine, for toxoplasmosis, 134
Sulfonamides, for paragonimiasis, 230
  for toxoplasmosis, 134
Superinfection, 20
Superparasitism, 19
Suramin, 53
Surra, 55, 480, 607
Surrounding fluids, 556
Swallows, hosts of *Plasmodium*, 125
Swimmer's itch, 27, 208
Syllidae, 526
Symbiosis, 8, 9, 403
Symbiote, 14
Symbiotic cleaning, 594
Sympatric species, 20
Sympetrum, 225
Symphilism, 13
Symphyta, 450
Syncyamus pseudorcae, 411
Syncytium, 35
Syndesmis, 159
Syndisyrinx, 667
Syngamus, 310
  trachea, 317
Syngamy, 35
Synoecy, 10
Syphacia, arctica, 345
  citelli, 345
  eutamii, 345
  muris, 344
  obvelata, 344
  thompsoni, 345
Systropus conopoides, 388
Syzygy, 98
Szidat's rule, 651, 679

T

TABANIDAE, 361, 387, 480, 606
Tabanus, 55, 56, 480
Tachinidae, 387, 484, 681
  evolution of, 683
Tadpole, host of, *Alaria*, 198
    Amphileptus, 661
    euglenids, 660
    Nyctotherus, 158
    opalinids, 145
    Plagiorchiidae, 223
    Polystoma, 166, 668
    Strigeidae, 196
Taenia, 20, 28, 252, 568
  crassicollis, 279
  hydatigena, 277
  listeri, 536
  mustelae, 531
  pisiformis, 243, 278
  saginata, 275, 278, 623
    egg, 246
  solium, 274, 275, 623
  taeniaeformis, 249, 562

Taeniidae, 255, 274
Tanarhamphus, 635
Tao, 89
Tapeworm, 159, 242
  evolution of, 672
  host specificity, 632
  intestine, 658
  larvae in mites, 509
Tarsonemoidea, 512
Tartar emetic, for Schistosomiasis, 206
Tegeticula yuccasella, 16
Telosentis, 297
Telosporea, 39
Temnocephala brevicornis, 161
Temnocephalida, 161, 666, 668
Temperature, 570, 571, 592
  and distribution, 602
Tenebrio molitar, 296
Tentacularia megabothridia, 261
  musculara, 261
Tenuipalpidae, 512
Terebellidae, 526
Terebellides stroemi, 526
Termites, 72, 562, 608, 627
  protozoa in, 585
Termitidae, 586
Termitostroma, 386
Tern, host of Microphallidae, 220
Terramycin, for enterobiasis, 349
Testosterone, 559
Tetactinomyxon intermedium, 139
Tethys Sea, 611
Tetrabothrius affinis, 247, 248
Tetrachlorethylene for ascariasis, 341
  for echinostomiasis, 212
  for enterobiasis, 349
  for helminthiasis, 309
  for hookworm infection, 324, 326
  for *Ostertagia* infection, 327
  for trichostrongyliasis, 330
  for trichuriasis, 374
Tetracotyle, 196, 197
Tetractinomyxidae, 139
Tetrahymena, 148, 660
  corlissi, 148
  limacis, 148
Tetrahymenidae, 148
Tetramitus, 663
Tetraonchus, 576
Tetraphyllidea, 255, 259, 632, 671, 672
Tetrarhynchidea, 244, 255, 260
Tetrastemma, 525
Texas cattle fever, 504, 541
Thalessa, 453
Theileria parva, 131
Theileriidae, 39, 130
Thelazia, 310, 679
  californiensis, 351
  callipaeda, 351
Thelaziinae, 679

Thelazioidea, 310, 351
Thelohania californica, 138
Theobaldia, 125
Thiara, 228
Thigmotrichida, 40, 149, 664
Thompsonia, 415
Thread lungworm, 331
Threadworm, 307
Thyassuidae, 683
Thyca, 529
Thymallus vulgaris, 576
Thyonicola, 529
  serrata, 551
Thyroxin, 557
Thysanosoma, 632
  actinioides, 285
Ticks, 55, 494, 496, 562, 572
  diseases, 500
  evolution, 685
  host specificity, 640
  key to genera, 499
Tickfly, 489
Tiger, host of *Opisthorchis*, 231
Tinamus major, 603
Tiphia, 451
  popilliavora, 460
  transversa, 460
Tiphiidae, 460
Tipula, 492
Tissue invasion, 88
  reactions, 285, 531
Toad, 79
  host of *Cepedia*, 147
Tomite, 151, 664
Tomonte, 150
Tongue worms, 515
  infections, 18
Tortoise, host of nematodes, 569
Toxaphene, for acariasis, 515
  for lice control, 432
Toxascaris, 310
Toxocara, 310, 634
  canis, 308, 335, 678
  cati, 335, 583, 678, 679
  leonina, 336
  mystax, 624
Toxoplasma gondii, 132, 541
  hosts, 133
Toxoplasmatidae, 39, 132
Toxoplasmea, 39, 131
Toxoplasmidia, 39, 131
Toxoplasmosis, 133
  treatment of, 134
Toxopneutes, host of ciliates, 148
Trachichthys, 11
Transmission of microbe-caused diseases, 16
Transversotrematidae, 192
Trapa, 214

Trematoda, 159, 161, 172, 195, 549
    evolution of, 668, 669, 670
    specificity, 628
Triacetyloleandomycin, for amebiasis, 89
Triactinomyxidae, 139
Triactinomyxon legeri, 139
Triatoma, 437
    sanguisuga, 438
Triatomids, 53, 662, 681
Triatominae, 437
Trialeurodes vaporariorum, 435
Triangulus munidae, 415
Tribolium, 530
    confusum, with *Hymenolepis*, 274
Tricarboxylic acid, 24
Trichina worm, 368
Trichinella, 17, 310, 568
    spiralis, 368, 532, 576, 583
        hibernation of, 574
        life cycle, 371
Trichinellidae, 368
Trichinelloidea, 310, 367
Trichinosis, 532
Trichobilharzia, 200
Trichochona, 155
Trichodectes bovis, 424
    canis, 423
    mustilae, 426
Trichodectidae, 683
Trichodina, 11, 148, 154, 605, 643, 660, 664
    cottidarum, 609
    pediculus, 154
    urinicola, 154
Trichodorus, 310, 378
Trichogramma, 552, 554, 579
    minutum, 457, 581
Trichogrammatidae, 456
Trichomastix, 66
Trichomonadida, 64
Trichomonadidae, 66
Trichomonas augusta, 35, 66, 563
    buccalis, 68
    gallinae, 68, 70
    gallinarum, 68
    tenax, 68
    vaginalis, 68
Trichomoniasis, treatment for, 70, 71
Trichonympha, 73, 561, 587, 665
    corbula, 72
Trichonymphidae, 72
Trichosomoides crassicauda, 302
Trichostomatida, 40, 151, 663
Trichostomina, 588
Trichostrongyloidea, 310, 326
Trichostrongylus, 557
    axei, 618, 624
    retortaeformis, 577
Trichuris, 95, 310
    trichiura, 306, 372

Tricocephalus trichiura, 306
Tricrania sanguinipennis, 463
Trilobus gracilis, 47
Trimastigamoeba, 77
Trimenoponidae, 615
Triton palmatus, 80
    taeniatus, 80
Tritrichomonas, 66
    batrachorum, 65
    foetus, 70, 71
Triturus v. viridescens, 570, 630
Troglotrematidae, 193, 225
Trombicula alfreddugesi, 511
Trombiculidae, 509
    evolution of, 685
Trombidiformes, 387
Trombidiidae, 509
Trombidoidea, 509
Trophamnion, 451
Trophont, 150
Trophozoite, 78, 118
Tropical rat mite, 512
Tropics, 571
Trout, 63, 74
    host of, *Phyllodistomum*, 181
Trypanodinium ovicola, 41
Trypanophis sagittae, 49
Trypanoplasma, 60
Trypanorhyncha, 255, 260
Trypanosoma, 47, 49, 51, 535, 655, 661
    ariarii, 53
    avium, 51, 57
    brucei, 54 55, 541, 607, 622, 653
    calmettei, 51
    caulopsettae, 57
    congolense, 49, 57, 662
    cruzi, 49, 55, 534, 541, 575, 662
    diemyctyli, 570
    duttoni, 530, 563
    equinum, 51, 55
    equiperdum, 51, 55, 541, 621, 622
    evansi, 51, 55, 480, 607
    gallinarum, 51, 57
    gambiense, 49, 51, 53, 653, 662
    giganteum, 57
    hannai, 51, 57
    in domestic animals, 51, 55
    lewisi, 49, 56, 530
    melophagium, 56
    numidae, 51
    percae, 57
    rangeli, 49, 53
    rhodesiense, 49, 51, 54, 622, 653
    simiae, 57
    suis, 54
    theileri, 56
    theodori, 56
    vivax, 56, 606, 626, 662
Trypanosomatidae, 45
    evolution of, 661

Trypanosomiasis, 606
  treatment for, 53, 54
Tryparsamide, 53
Trypsin, 172
Tsetse fly, 489, 662
Tubicinella, 414
Tubifex, host of Actinomyxida, 139
  Archigetes, 265
Tubifex ochridanus, 151
  oligosetosus, 151
Tularemia, 504
Tumbufly, 488
Tunicate, host of *Perezia*, 139
Turbellaria, 159, 665
Turbellarians, 159
  hosts of dalyellioids, 668
Turtles, hosts of aspidogastrids, 171
  barnacles, 414
  cestodarians, 672
  Endolimax, 81
  Entamoeba, 83
  Filicollis, 296
  Haemogregarina, 105
  Haemoproteus, 114
  Hexamita, 63
  Plasmodium, 125
  Polystoma, 668
  Polystomoides, 629
  Spirorchiidae, 199
  Temnocephalida, 161, 666
Twisted-winged parasites, 464
Tylenchida, 309
Tyroglyphoidea, 513
Tyrophagus lintneri, 513

U

Udonella, 166
Umagillidae, 668
Unarmed tapeworm, 278
Uncinaria lucasi, 319
  stegocephala, 319
Undulating membrane, 64, 66
Ungulate, host of ciliates, 148
  lice, 683
Unilocular cyst, 283
Unionicola, 507
Unionidae, 528
Urceolaria, 11, 571, 664
  urechi, 154
Urceolariidae, 40, 154
Urechis caupo, 154, 641
Urinympha, 72
Uronema, 148
Urophora jaceana, 580
Urosporidium charletyi, 536
Uta, 58
Uterine bell, 291

V

Vahlkampfia, 37
Vahlkampfia patuxent, 78
Vampire bat, 55
Vampyrellidae, 95
Varanus, host of opalinids, 144
Vasotrema, 199
Vaucheria, 525
Vector, 10
Venom, of Hymenoptera, 451
Vespoid wasps, 459
Viofon, 68
Virgula, 550
Virulence, 553
Virus, 16, 17, 543, 583, 656
  EMC, 583
Vitamins, 16, 531, 555
  B_{12}, 531
Vitellaria, 174, 244
Vitelline glands, 174, 244
  globules, 178
  membrane, 28
Vivax group, *Trypanosoma uniforme*, 51
  vivax, 51
Viviparous, 385
Vole, 558
Volvox, 525
Von Ihering method, 610
Vorticellids, 11, 525

W

Warble fly, 482
Wasps, 449, 554, 580, 581
  evolution of, 684
Water chestnuts, 214
  flea, 395
    host of vorticellids, 11
  movements, 592
Watsonius, 215, 218
Wave action, 592
Weasel, host of, *Alaria*, 198
  Paragonimus, 225
Weight, 555
  increase, 530
Wet sores, 58
Whale, host of barnacles, 414
  migration, 606
Whale louse, 12, 410
Wheel bug, 438
Whipworm, 306, 372
Whiteflies, 434
Wild boar, host of *Paragonimus*, 225
Witch, 57
Wohlfahrtia magnifica, 489
Wolf, host of, *Echinococcus*, 280
  hookworm, 319
Wood lice, 388

Woodroach, 72, 627
  host of Hoplonymphidae, 72
Wuchereria, 310
  bancrofti, 30, 31, 354, 618

X

Xenobalanus, 414
Xenocoeloma, 403, 682
  brumpti, 404
Xenopsylla cheops, 448, 449
  fasciatus, 449
Xenos vesparum, 464, 466
Xiphidiocercariae, 550
Xiphinema, 310, 378

Y

YEAST, 16, 140
  symbiotic, 586

Yellow fever, air transport, 608
Yolk cells, 29
Yucca, 16

Z

Zahropalus inquisitor, 457
Zelleriella, 79, 144, 146, 147, 611
  elliptica, 147
  opisthocarya, 147
Zoochlorellae, 15
Zoogeography, 601
Zoogonidae, 193
Zooids, 242
Zoonoses, 17
Zootermopsis, 586, 627
Zooxanthellae, 15
Zostera marina, 95